KU-265-348

A-Level
Geography
Exam Board: AQA

A-Level Geography is like a day-trip to a British seaside town — one minute you're concerned with the nature and distribution of cold environments, the next you're seriously questioning the importance of place in human life and experience.

Unfortunately, you have to take exams at the end instead of going to the chip shop. That's where this fantastic book comes in — it has everything you need to make sure you're 100% prepared for anything the examiners might throw at you.

And since it's made by CGP, you can be sure it's going to be a whole lot more entertaining than anybody else's dreary Geography guide...

A-Level revision? It has to be CGP!

Contents

Exam Structure 1

Topic One — Water and Carbon Cycles

Natural Systems..2
The Water Cycle 4
Drainage Basins..6
Variations in Runoff and the Water Cycle 8
The Carbon Cycle 10
Water, Carbon and Climate 14
The Amazon Rainforest — Case Study 16
The Eden Basin — Case Study 18

Topic Two — Hot Desert Systems and Landscapes

Desert Systems 20
Deserts — Distribution and Characteristics....22
Processes in Hot Desert Environments 25
Landforms in Hot Desert Environments.........28
Hot Desert Environment — Case Study........31
Desertification 33
Desertification — Case Study 36

Topic Three — Coastal Systems and Landscapes

The Coastal System...................................38
Coastal Processes 40
Coastal Landforms 42
Sea Level Changes....................................45
Coastal Management 48
Coastal Environment — Case Study 50
Humans at the Coast — Case Study............52

Topic Four — Glacial Systems and Landscapes

Cold Environments 54
Glacial Systems 56
Glacial Processes......................................58
Glacial Landforms 60
Fluvioglacial Processes and Landforms.........62
Periglacial Processes and Landforms............64
Glacial Landscapes — Case Study 66
Human Impacts on Cold Environments.........68
Humans in Glacial Landscapes — Case Study............70

Topic Five — Hazards

Natural Hazards 72
Plate Tectonics...74
Types of Plate Margin 76
Volcanic Hazards 78
Volcanic Hazards — Impacts and Responses....80
Seismic Hazards 82
Seismic Hazards — Impacts and Responses....84
Storm Hazards 86
Storm Hazards — Case Studies....................88
Wildfires..90
Multi-Hazard Environment — Case Study 92
Hazardous Setting — Case Study................93

Topic Six — Ecosystems Under Stress

Ecosystems 94
Biodiversity 97
Biomes 99
Tropical Rainforests 100
Savanna Grasslands 103
Ecological Change — Case Study 106
Coral Reefs 108
Great Barrier Reef — Case Study 110
Succession..112
Succession in the British Isles 114
Local Ecosystems....................................116
Local Ecosystems — Case Study 119

Topic Seven — Global Systems and Global Governance

Globalisation..122
Factors Affecting Globalisation 124
Global Systems.......................................126
International Trade....................................129
The Global Coffee Trade 132
Transnational Corporations (TNCs) 134
Global Governance 137
The Global Commons...............................139
Global Commons — Antarctica 140
Impacts of Globalisation..........................143

Topic Eight — Changing Places

The Concept of Place....................................144
The Character of Places 146
Changing Places — Shifting Flows..............148
Changing Places...150
Meanings and Representations of Place.....152
Place Studies 154

Topic Nine — Contemporary Urban Environments

Urbanisation...158
Urban Change..160
Urban Forms...162
Urban Issues...164
Urban Climate..166
Urban Air Quality...168
Urban Drainage..170
Urban Waste 172
Urban Environmental Issues 174
Sustainable Urban Development 176
Mumbai — Case Study 178
Birmingham — Case Study 180

Topic Ten — Population and the Environment

People and the Environment.........................182
Food Production and Consumption 184
People and Climate 186
People and Soils 188
Increasing Food Security..............................191
Global Patterns of Health, Disease and Death 192
The Geography of Disease............................194
Health in Knowsley — Case Study................198
Natural Population Change...........................200
International Migration 204
Population and Resources.............................206
Global Population Futures 209
Population Change in Bangladesh
    — Case Study...212

Topic Eleven — Resource Security

Resource Development 214
Water Supply and Demand 217
Increasing Water Security 220
Water Conflicts...223
Jordan Basin Water Resources — Case Study 224
Resource Futures — Water 226
Energy Supply and Demand 227
Energy Supply and Globalisation 230
Energy Supply — Environmental Impacts..................231
Increasing Energy Security 232
Energy in the Netherlands — Case Study 234
Resource Futures — Energy 236
Ore Mineral Supply and Demand..................237
Ore Mineral Security 238
Resource Futures — Ore Minerals 241

Fieldwork Investigation

Fieldwork Investigation................................242

Exam Skills

Answering Questions.....................................244
Answering Case Study Questions...............245
Answering Resource Interpretation
    Questions..246
Graph and Map Skills...................................249
Statistical Skills...252

Answers..255
Acknowledgements 277
Index...279

This book covers all the core and optional topics for **AS** and **A-Level** Geography. Exam-style questions throughout the book are matched to the **A-Level exams** — if you're studying AS, they'll be a bit different to the ones you'll get in the exam, but they're still excellent practice.

Published by CGP

Based on the classic CGP style created by Richard Parsons.

Editors:
Claire Boulter, Joe Brazier, Ellen Burton, Chris McGarry, Jack Perry, Claire Plowman.

Contributors:
Paddy Gannon, Leanne Parr, Helena Richards, Sophie Watkins, Dennis Watts.

ISBN: 978 1 78294 648 9

With thanks to Krystyna Pasek-Corsar, Nicholas Robinson, David Sefton, Glenn Rogers and Karen Wells for the proofreading.
With thanks to Jan Greenway for the copyright research.

Clipart from Corel®
Printed by Elanders Ltd, Newcastle upon Tyne.

Text, design, layout and original illustrations © Coordination Group Publications Ltd. (CGP) 2017
All rights reserved.

Every effort has been made to locate copyright holders and obtain permission to reproduce sources.
For those sources where it has been difficult to trace the copyright holder of the work, we would be grateful for information.
If any copyright holder would like us to make an amendment to the acknowledgements, please notify us and we will gladly
update the book at the next reprint.

Photocopying more than one chapter of this book is not permitted. Extra copies are available from CGP.
0800 1712 712 • www.cgpbooks.co.uk

Exam Structure

The road is long... with many a winding meander... so just to make sure you don't get lost along the way, here's a page that tells you all about how your A-Level Geography course will be assessed.

You'll Have to do **Two Exams** and Some **Fieldwork**

If you're doing AS Geography, the structure of your assessment will be different — ask your teacher for more information.

Component 1 Exam — Physical Geography

1) It's **2 hrs 30 mins** long and there are **120 marks** up for grabs (worth 40% of your A-Level grade).

2) It tests six physical geography topics, but you only have to answer questions on **THREE** of them.

3) There are **three sections** in the paper — **A**, **B** and **C**:

SECTION A

You have to **answer** the **multiple-part question** on Water and Carbon Cycles. The question is worth **36 marks**.

SECTION B

You have to **answer ONE multiple-part question** from a choice of three:
- Hot Desert Systems and Landscapes **OR**
- Coastal Systems and Landscapes **OR**
- Glacial Systems and Landscapes.

Each question is worth **36 marks**.

SECTION C

You have to **answer ONE multiple-part question** from a choice of two:
- Hazards **OR**
- Ecosystems Under Stress.

Each question is worth **48 marks**.

Exams — who needs them, don't you know who my father is?

Component 2 Exam — Human Geography

1) It's **2 hours 30 mins** long and there are **120 marks** up for grabs (worth 40% of your A-Level grade).

2) It tests five human geography topics, but you only have to answer questions on **THREE** of them.

3) There are **three sections** in the paper — **A**, **B** and **C**:

SECTION A

You have to **answer** the **multiple-part question** on Global Systems and Governance. The question is worth **36 marks**.

SECTION B

You have to **answer** the **multiple-part question** on Changing Places. The question is worth **36 marks**.

SECTION C

You have to **answer ONE multiple-part question** from a choice of three:
- Contemporary Urban Environments **OR**
- Population and the Environment **OR**
- Resource Security.

Each question is worth **48 marks**.

For both of the exams you have just over 1 minute per mark — so if a question's worth 4 marks you should spend about 4 minutes answering it.

Component 3 — Geography Fieldwork Investigation

The final **20%** of your A-Level grade will come from your **Geography fieldwork investigation** (worth **60 marks**). You have to complete your **own investigation**, which will be marked by your teacher — there is **no exam** for this component. See pages 242-243 for more about completing your fieldwork investigation.

There are Different **Question Types** That May Come Up in the Exam

Each question is made up of **several parts**, each with a slightly **different format** and worth a different number of **marks**:

1) There will be some **multiple-choice** questions where you'll need to shade your chosen option.

2) Some questions come with **figures** (e.g. maps and tables) that you'll need to **refer to** when you write your answers. You may need to use your **understanding** of a topic to **interpret** these **figures**.

3) Some questions are worth **9** or **20 marks** — you'll need to write a longer, **'essay-style' answer** for these.

4) Sometimes you'll need to use **case study content** in your answers — see page 245 for more.

Natural Systems

Nature is complicated... really complicated. So sometimes it's useful to cheat a little bit and imagine all those natural processes as a nice, well-ordered system. It's a simplification, but it makes things so much easier to understand...

Systems are Made Up of **Stores**, **Flows**, **Boundaries**, **Inputs** and **Outputs**

1) You need to **learn** what these **parts** of a **system** are:
   - **Inputs** — when matter or energy (e.g. solar energy) is **added** to the system.
   - **Outputs** — when matter or energy **leaves** the system.
   - **Stores** (or components) — where matter or energy **builds up**.
   - **Flows** (or transfers) — when matter or energy **moves** from one store to another.
   - **Boundaries** — the **limits** of the system.

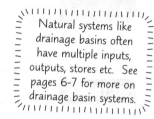
Matter is any physical substance involved in a system, e.g. water or carbon.

> **Example**
>
> In a **drainage basin system**, water enters as rain (**input**). The system's watershed is the **boundary**. Some water is **stored** in the soil and in vegetation. Water travels from the drainage basin to the river and then down the river (**flows**). It leaves the system where the river meets the sea (**output**).

Natural systems like drainage basins often have multiple inputs, outputs, stores etc. See pages 6-7 for more on drainage basin systems.

2) Systems can be **open** or **closed**:

Open Systems

- Both **energy** and **matter CAN enter** and **leave** an open system — there are inputs and outputs of both.
- Example: **drainage basins** (see p.6) are **open systems** — energy from the Sun enters and leaves the system. Water is input as precipitation, and output as river discharge into the sea.

Systems can also be isolated (neither matter nor energy can enter or leave) but these aren't found in nature.

Closed Systems

- **Matter CAN'T enter** or **leave** a closed system — it can only cycle between stores.
- **Energy CAN enter** and **leave** a closed system — it can be input or output.
- Example: the **carbon cycle** (see p.10) is a **closed system** — energy is input (e.g. from the sun by photosynthesis) and output (e.g. by respiration), but the **amount** of carbon on Earth stays the **same** because there are **no inputs** or **outputs** of matter.

Systems are Affected by **Feedbacks**

1) If the inputs and outputs of a system are **balanced**, the system is in **equilibrium** — flows and processes continue to happen, but in the same way at all times, so there are no overall changes to the system.

2) However, in reality there are lots of small **variations** in the inputs and outputs of a system (e.g. the amount of precipitation entering a drainage basin system constantly varies). These variations are usually small, so the inputs and outputs remain about **balanced** on average. The system is said to be in **dynamic equilibrium**.

3) **Large**, **long-term** changes to the balance of inputs and outputs can cause a system to change and establish a **new** dynamic equilibrium.

4) Changes can trigger **positive** or **negative** feedback:

① Positive Feedback

- **Positive feedback** mechanisms **amplify** the change in the inputs or outputs.
- This means the system responds by **increasing** the effects of the change, moving the system even **further** from its **previous state**.
- **Example:**

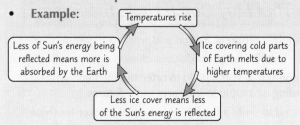

② Negative Feedback

- **Negative feedback** mechanisms **counteract** the change in the inputs or outputs.
- This means that the system responds by **decreasing** the effects of the change, keeping the system **closer** to its **previous state**.
- **Example:**

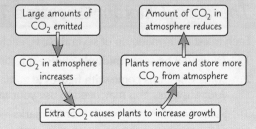

Natural Systems

The **Earth** Can be Seen as **One System** Made Up of **Lots** of **Subsystems**

1) The Earth can be seen as a **closed system** — **energy** is **input** from the **Sun** and **output** to **space**, but **matter** is **not input or output** to space (except for the odd space probe).

2) The whole Earth system can be **broken down** into **smaller** parts called **subsystems**:

"No outputs of matter to space?" scoffed Sam. "We'll see about that."

1 Cryosphere

The cryosphere includes all the parts of the Earth system where it's **cold** enough for water to **freeze**, e.g. **glacial landscapes** (see pages 54-55).

2 Lithosphere

The lithosphere is the **outermost** part of the Earth. It includes the **crust** and the **upper parts** of the **mantle** (see p.74).

3 Biosphere

The biosphere is the part of the Earth's systems where **living** things are found. It includes **all** the living parts of the Earth — plants, animals, birds, fungi, insects, bacteria etc.

4 Hydrosphere

The hydrosphere includes all of the **water** on Earth. It may be in **liquid** form (e.g. in lakes and rivers), **solid** form (ice stored in the cryosphere) or **gas** form (e.g. water vapour stored in the atmosphere). It can also be **saline** (salty) or **fresh**.

5 Atmosphere

The atmosphere is the layer of **gas** between the **Earth's surface** and **space**, held in place by **gravity**.

3) These subsystems are all **interlinked** (connected together) by the cycles and processes that keep the Earth system as a whole running as **normal** (e.g. the water cycle and carbon cycle).

4) **Matter** (e.g. water and carbon) and **energy move between** the subsystems — the output of one cycle is the input of the next, then the output of that cycle is the input of the next, and so on...

See pages 4-5 for how water moves through the subsystems and pages 10-11 for how carbon moves through the subsystems.

5) Because of the way that matter and energy move from one subsystem to the next, the Earth system is said to be a **cascading system**.

6) **Changes** that occur in one subsystem can **affect** what happens in the **others**.

Practice Questions

Q1 What is meant by the term 'store' in a system?
Q2 What is meant by the term 'boundary' in a system?
Q3 What does it mean when a system is said to be in 'dynamic equilibrium'?
Q4 What is 'negative feedback'?
Q5 Name the five subsystems of the Earth.

Exam Questions

Q1 Outline the differences between open and closed systems. [4 marks]

Q2 Explain how positive feedback can alter a natural system. [4 marks]

And lastly, there's the examosphere...

...which is where knowing about all those other -spheres might come in useful. Not to be confused with the examofear, which is that feeling you get as you walk into the exam hall if you haven't revised as well as you could have. Luckily, you have a book in your hands right now (put that comic down and pick this book up) that can help avoid that. You just have get on with it.

The Water Cycle

Okay, I know you'll have studied the water cycle umpteen times before... but you can't have too much of a good thing.

Water is Stored in **Solid**, **Liquid** and **Gas** Forms

The hydrosphere contains 1.4 sextillion litres of water (that's 1, 4, then twenty 0s).

1) Most of this is **saline** water in the **oceans**. **Less than 3%** is **freshwater** (which most species, including humans, need to survive).

2) Of the Earth's **fresh water**:

- **69%** is frozen in the **cryosphere**.
- **30%** is **groundwater** (water stored underground in the lithosphere).
- **0.3%** is **liquid freshwater** on the Earth's surface in lakes, rivers etc.
- **0.04%** is stored as **water vapour** in the **atmosphere**.

3) Water must be **physically** and **economically accessible** for humans to be able to use it (e.g. groundwater is hard to access, so it may not be cost effective to extract it). As a result, only a **small** amount of water on the planet can be used by humans.

4) Water can change between solid, liquid and gaseous forms. For water to boil or melt, it has to gain **energy** (e.g. from the Sun). For water to **condense** or **freeze**, it has to lose energy.

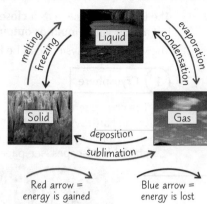

Red arrow = energy is gained

Blue arrow = energy is lost

Water is **Constantly Cycling** Between **Stores**

1) Water is continuously **cycled** between **different stores**. This is known as the **global hydrological cycle**.

2) The global hydrological cycle is a **closed system** — there are no **inputs** or **outputs** of water.

There's more on the processes shown here below and on the next page.

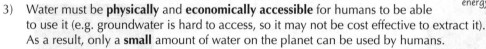

INPUT Solar energy

OUTPUT Energy lost to space

STORE Atmosphere

Water vapour — condensation — Clouds — precipitation

deposition

sublimation

precipitation

STORE Cryosphere (Glaciers, ice caps)

evaporation

melting

STORE Liquid water (Oceans, lakes, rivers)

STORE Groundwater & lithosphere

infiltration

baseflow

The **Magnitude** of the Stores Varies Over **Time** and in **Space**

1) The **amount** of water present in each store varies over a range of scales from **local** (e.g. an individual hillslope) to **global**.

2) The **magnitude** of each store depends on the **amount** of water **flowing between** them.

3) Different flows occur at a range of **spatial** and **temporal** (time) scales:

Evaporation

- Evaporation occurs when **liquid** water changes state into a **gas**, becoming **water vapour** — it **gains** energy, normally from **solar radiation**. Evaporation **increases** the amount of water stored in the **atmosphere**.

  Long-term changes in the climate can also affect the magnitude of evaporation. E.g. during the last glacial period, temperatures were lower, so evaporation was lower.

- The **magnitude** of the evaporation flow varies by **location** and **season**. If there is lots of **solar radiation**, a large supply of **water** and **warm, dry air**, the amount of evaporation will be **high**.

- If there is **not much** solar radiation, little available liquid water and **cool** air that is already **nearly saturated** (unable to absorb any more water vapour), evaporation will be **low**.

The Water Cycle

Condensation

1) Condensation occurs when **water vapour** changes state to become a **liquid** — it **loses** energy to the **surroundings**. It happens when air containing water vapour **cools** to its **dew point** (the temperature at which it will change from a gas to a liquid), e.g. when temperatures fall at **night** due to heat being **lost** to **space**.

2) Water droplets can stay in the atmosphere or **flow** to other subsystems, e.g. when water vapour condenses, it can form **dew** on leaves and other surfaces — this **decreases** the amount of water **stored** in the atmosphere.

3) The **magnitude** of the condensation flow depends on the **amount** of water vapour in the atmosphere and the **temperature**. For example, if there is **lots** of water vapour in the air and there's a **large or rapid drop** in temperature, **condensation** will be **high**.

Cloud Formation and Precipitation

1) Cloud formation and precipitation are **essential** parts of the water cycle — precipitation is the **main flow** of water from the atmosphere to the ground.

2) Clouds form when **warm air cools down**, causing the **water vapour** in it to **condense** into **water droplets**, which gather as **clouds**. When the droplets get **big** enough, they fall as **precipitation**.

3) There are several things that can cause **warm air** to **cool**, leading to **precipitation**:

- **Other air masses** — warm air is **less dense** than cool air. As a result, when warm air meets cool air, the warm air is forced up **above** the cool air. It cools down as it rises. This results in **frontal precipitation**.
- **Topography** — when warm air meets **mountains**, it's forced to **rise**, causing it to cool. This results in **orographic precipitation**.
- **Convection** — when the sun **heats up** the **ground**, moisture on the ground **evaporates** and rises up in a column of warm air. As it gets higher, it cools. This results in **convective precipitation**.

4) Water droplets caused by condensation are **too small** to form clouds **on their own**. For clouds to form, there have to be **tiny particles** of other substances (e.g. dust or soot) to act as **cloud condensation nuclei**. They give water a **surface** to **condense** on. This encourages clouds to form, rather than allowing the moist air to **disperse**.

5) Cloud formation and precipitation can vary **seasonally** (e.g. in the UK there's normally more rainfall in winter than in summer) and by **location** (e.g. precipitation is generally higher in the tropics than at the poles).

Cryospheric Processes

1) Cryospheric processes such as **accumulation** and **ablation** (see p. 56) change the **amount** of water **stored** as ice in the **cryosphere**. The **balance** of accumulation and ablation varies with **temperature**.

2) During periods of global cold, **inputs** into the cryosphere are **greater** than **outputs** — water is transferred to it as snow, and less water is transferred away due to melting. During periods of warmer global temperatures, the magnitude of the cryosphere store **reduces** as losses due to melting are **larger** than the inputs of snow.

3) The Earth is **emerging** from a **glacial period** that reached its maximum **21 000 years ago**. There are still extensive stores of ice on **land** in Antarctica and Greenland, as well as numerous alpine glaciers. There is also a large volume of **sea ice** in the Arctic and Antarctic.

4) **Variations** in cryospheric processes happen over **different timescales**. As well as the changes in global temperature that occur over **thousands** of years, variations can also occur over shorter timescales. For example, **annual** temperature fluctuations mean that more snow falls in the winter than in summer.

Practice Questions

Q1 What percentage of Earth's water is freshwater?

Q2 Describe one change that can cause water vapour to condense.

Exam Question

Q1 Outline the impact of long-term global temperature changes on the water cycle. [4 marks]

With all this cycling, water could win gold at the Olympics...

There's plenty to learn here. At least it's all exciting stuff. Oh no, wait... Anyway, you've got to know it all, so you'd best crack on with safely storing it in your noggin. There are quite a lot of technical words in this section and it's well worth making sure you understand them all — examiners love it when you use the right technical terms in your answers.

Drainage Basins

And now, bandage raisins. Sorry, got my letters in the wrong order there — I meant drainage basins...

Drainage Basins are Natural Systems

Drainage basins can be viewed as **open**, **local** hydrological cycles:

1) A river's **drainage basin** is the area **surrounding** the river where the rain falling on the land **flows** into that river. This area is also called the river's **catchment**.

2) The **boundary** of a drainage basin is the **watershed** — any precipitation falling **beyond** the watershed enters a **different drainage basin**.

3) Drainage basins are **open systems** with **inputs** and **outputs**.

4) Water comes **into** the system as **precipitation** and **leaves** via **evaporation**, **transpiration** and **river discharge**.

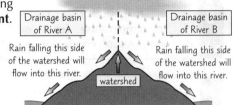

A Typical Drainage Basin System

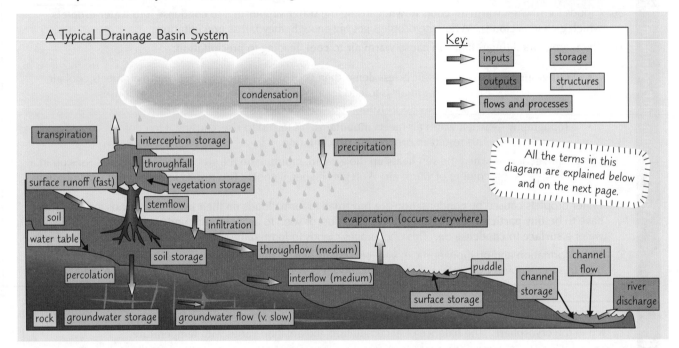

Drainage Basins Have Inputs, Stores, Flows and Outputs

Inputs — Water Coming into the System

Precipitation includes **all** the ways moisture **comes out** of the atmosphere.
Precipitation is mainly **rain**, but it also includes other types like **snow**, **hail**, **dew** and **frost**.

Stacey seemed surprisingly upbeat about atmospheric moisture inputs.

Storage — Water Stored in the System

1) **Interception** is when some precipitation **lands on vegetation** or other structures, like **buildings** and **concrete** or **tarmac** surfaces, before it reaches the soil. Interception creates a **significant store** of water in **wooded areas**. **Interception storage** is only **temporary** because the collected water may **evaporate** quickly, or fall from the leaves as throughfall (see next page).

2) **Vegetation storage** is water that's been **taken up** by **plants**. It's all the water **contained** in plants at any one time.

3) **Surface storage** includes water in **puddles** (**depression storage**), **ponds** and **lakes**.

4) **Soil storage** includes **moisture** in the **soil**.

5) **Groundwater storage** is water stored in the ground, either in the **soil** (**soil moisture**) or in **rocks**. The **water table** is the top surface of the **zone of saturation** — the zone of **soil** or **rock** where **all** the **pores** in the soil or rock are **full of water**. **Porous rocks** (rocks with lots of **holes** in them) that hold water are called **aquifers**.

6) **Channel storage** is so obvious that it's often overlooked — it's the **water** held in a **river** or **stream channel**.

Drainage Basins

Flows — Water Moving from One Place to Another

1) **Infiltration** is water **soaking** into the soil. **Infiltration rates** are influenced by **soil type**, **soil structure** and how much water's **already in** the soil.

2) **Overland flow** (also known as **runoff**) is water **flowing over** the land. It can flow over the **whole surface** or in **little channels**. It happens because rain is falling on the ground **faster** than infiltration can occur.

3) **Throughfall** is water **dripping** from one **leaf** (or other plant part) to **another**.

4) **Stemflow** is water running down a plant **stem** or a **tree trunk**.

5) **Throughflow** is water moving slowly **downhill** through the **soil**. Throughflow is **faster** through "**pipes**" — things like **cracks** in the **soil** or **animal burrows**.

6) **Percolation** is water **seeping down** through soil **into the water table**.

7) **Groundwater flow** is water flowing **slowly below** the **water table** through **permeable rock**. Water flows **slowly** through most rocks, but rocks that are **highly permeable** with lots of **joints** (**gaps** that water can get through) can have **faster** groundwater flow, e.g. limestone.

8) **Baseflow** is groundwater flow that **feeds** into rivers through river **banks** and river **beds**.

9) **Interflow** is water flowing **downhill** through **permeable rock above** the water table.

10) **Channel flow** is the water flowing in the **river** or **stream** itself. This is also called the **river's discharge**.

Outputs — Water Leaving the System

1) **Evaporation** is water turning into **water vapour** (see p.4).

2) **Transpiration** is **evaporation** from within **leaves** — plants and trees **take up** water through their roots and **transport** it to their **leaves** where it evaporates into the atmosphere.

3) **Evapotranspiration** is the process of evaporation and transpiration **together**.

4) **River discharge**, or **river flow**, is another **output**.

> **Potential evapotranspiration** (**PET**) is the amount of water that **could** be lost by evapotranspiration. **Actual evapotranspiration** is what **actually** happens. For example, in a **desert** potential evapotranspiration is **high** (because **heat increases evaporation**) but actual transpiration is **low** (because there **isn't** much moisture).

The **Water Balance** Shows the Balance Between **Inputs** and **Outputs**

Water balance is worked out from **inputs** (precipitation) and **outputs** (channel discharge and evapotranspiration). The water balance affects how much water is **stored** in the basin. The general water balance in the **UK** shows **seasonal patterns**:

1) In **wet seasons**, precipitation **exceeds** evapotranspiration. This creates a **water surplus**. The **ground stores fill** with water so there's **more surface runoff** and **higher discharge**, so **river levels rise**.

2) In **drier seasons**, precipitation is **lower than** evapotranspiration. **Ground stores** are **depleted** as some water is **used** (e.g. by plants and humans) and some flows into the **river channel**, but **isn't** replaced by precipitation.

3) So, at the **end** of a dry season, there's a **deficit** (**shortage**) of water in the ground. The ground stores are **recharged** in the next **wet season** (i.e. autumn).

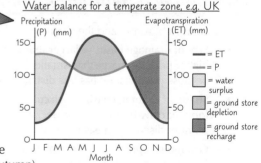

Water balance for a temperate zone, e.g. UK

Practice Questions

Q1 List three stores of water in drainage basin systems.

Q2 Water vapour evaporates from the leaves of plants. What is this process called?

Exam Question

Q1 Outline seasonal changes in the water balance. [4 marks]

If your basin takes an age to drain, you'll probably want to get a plumber in...

There are loads of words to remember on these pages. It might seem like a pain, but if you learn them all now it'll mean the rest of the section will make a lot more sense. And you thought geography was just about colouring in maps...

Variations in Runoff and the Water Cycle

If you like runoff, the water cycle and variation (and who doesn't), these pages are going to blow your mind.

Hydrographs Show River Discharge Over a Period of Time

1) **River discharge** is the **volume** of water (in cubic metres, **m³**) that **flows** in a river **per second**. Unsurprisingly, it's measured in **cubic metres per second (m³/s)** — this is a bit of a mouthful, so it's usually just shortened to **cumecs**.

2) High levels of **runoff** (water flowing on the surface of the land) **increase** the discharge of a river because more water makes it into the river, increasing its volume.

3) **Hydrographs** are graphs of river **discharge** over **time**. They show how the **volume of water** flowing at a certain point in a river **changes** over a **period of time**. **Flood hydrographs** (also called storm hydrographs) show river discharge around the time of a **storm event**. They only cover a relatively **short time period** (hours or days, rather than weeks or months).

① **Peak discharge** — this is the **highest** point on the graph, when the **river discharge** is at its **greatest**.

② **Lag time** — this is the delay between **peak rainfall** and **peak discharge**. This delay happens because it takes **time** for the rainwater to **flow** into the river. A **shorter** lag time can **increase peak discharge** because more water reaches the river during a **shorter period of time**.

③ **Rising limb** — this is the part of the graph **up to** peak discharge. The river discharge **increases** as rainwater flows into the river.

④ **Falling limb** — this is the part of the graph **after** peak discharge. **Discharge is decreasing** because **less water** is flowing into the river. A **shallow** falling limb shows water is flowing in from **stores** long after it's **stopped raining**.

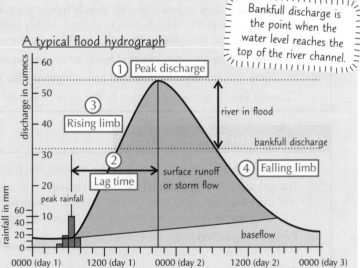

Bankfull discharge is the point when the water level reaches the top of the river channel.

A typical flood hydrograph

4) A basin with **rapid runoff** and not much **storage** capacity gives a hydrograph with a **short lag time** and **high peak discharge**. This is called a "**flashy**" hydrograph — the graph has **steep**, roughly **symmetrical** rising and falling limbs.

Runoff and Hydrograph Shape Are Affected by Numerous Factors

The **amount** of runoff and the **shape** of the hydrograph depends on various factors, e.g.:

Runoff is also affected by precipitation, seasonal changes and human activity (see below and next page).

- **Size of drainage basin** — **larger drainage basins** catch **more precipitation**, so they have a **higher peak discharge** than smaller basins. **Smaller basins** generally have **shorter lag times** because precipitation has **less distance** to travel, so it reaches the main channel more **quickly**.

- **Shape of drainage basin** — **circular** basins are more likely to have a **flashy** hydrograph than **long**, narrow basins. This is because all points on the **watershed** are roughly the **same distance** from the point of discharge **measurement**. This means lots of water will reach the measuring point at the **same time**.

- **Ground steepness** — water flows **more quickly** downhill in **steep-sided** drainage basins, shortening **lag time**. This also means that water has **less time** to **infiltrate** the soil, so runoff is higher.

- **Rock and soil type** — **impermeable** rocks and soils don't **store** water or let water **infiltrate**. This **increases surface runoff**. Peak discharge also **increases** as **more water** reaches the river in a shorter period.

The Water Cycle Varies Due to Physical Factors...

Hydrographs, runoff and the water cycle in general are affected by **natural processes**, e.g. storms and seasonal changes:

Storms and Precipitation

- **Intense storms** generate **more precipitation** and **greater peak discharges** than **light rain showers**.
- The **larger input** of water causes flows, e.g. runoff, and stores, e.g. groundwater, to **increase** in size.
- Some flows, e.g. infiltration, may not be able to occur **rapidly enough** for the size of the input, increasing **runoff**.

Topic One — Water and Carbon Cycles

Variations in Runoff and the Water Cycle

Seasonal Changes and Vegetation

- The **size** of inputs, flows and stores in the water cycle varies with the **seasons** — e.g. in the UK, summer is normally drier than winter.
- During the winter, temperatures may drop **below 0 °C**, causing water to **freeze**. This can **reduce** the size of flows **through** drainage basins, while the **store** of **frozen water** grows. When temperatures **increase** again, flows through drainage basins (and outputs) can be **much larger** as the ice **melts**.
- Most plants show **seasonal variation** (e.g. vegetation usually dies back in winter). Vegetation **intercepts** precipitation and **slows its movement** to the river channel. Interception is **highest** when there's **lots** of vegetation and **deciduous trees** have their **leaves**.
- The **more vegetation** there is in a drainage basin, the **more water** is **lost** (through **transpiration** and **evaporation** directly from the vegetation) before it reaches the river channel, **reducing runoff** and **peak discharge**.

...and Due To **Human Activities**

Human activities also **affect** the size of stores in the water cycle, and the size and speed of flows:

Farming Practices

Infiltration is a key part of the water cycle. When rain hits the surface, what can't infiltrate **runs off** instead. Farming practices can affect infiltration in several ways:

- **Ploughing** breaks up the surface so that **more** water can **infiltrate**, **reducing** the amount of **runoff**.
- **Crops** increase **infiltration** and **interception** compared to bare ground, reducing runoff. **Evapotranspiration** also **increases**, which can **increase rainfall**.
- **Livestock**, such as cattle, trample and compact the soil, **decreasing infiltration** and **increasing runoff**.
- **Irrigation** (artificially watering the land) can **increase runoff** if some of the water can't infiltrate. **Groundwater** or **river levels** can **fall** if water is extracted for irrigation.

Land Use Change

- **Deforestation reduces** the amount of water that is **intercepted** by vegetation, increasing the amount that reaches the **surface**. In forested areas, dead plant material on the forest floor helps to **hold** the water, allowing it to **infiltrate** the soil rather than **run off**. When forest cover (and dead material) is **removed**, the amount of **infiltration** that can take place **decreases**.
- Construction of new **buildings** and **roads** creates an **impermeable** layer over the land, **preventing** infiltration. This massively **increases runoff**, resulting in water passing through the system much more **rapidly** and making **flooding** more likely (see page 170).

Water Abstraction

- More water is **abstracted** (taken from stores) to meet **demand** in areas where **population density** is **high**. This **reduces** the amount of water in **stores** such as lakes, rivers, reservoirs and groundwater.
- During **dry seasons**, even more water is abstracted from stores (especially groundwater and reservoirs) for **consumption** and **irrigation**, so stores are **depleted** further.

Practice Questions

Q1 What is river discharge?

Q2 What is the unit of measurement for river discharge?

Q3 Give three factors that can affect the amount of runoff in a drainage basin.

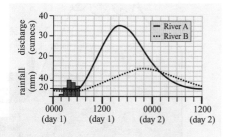

Exam Questions

Q1 The hydrograph on the right shows data for two rivers in the same area. Analyse the possible reasons for the differences between the two rivers. [6 marks]

Q2 Assess the relative importance of physical factors and human activities in driving changes in the water cycle at a drainage basin scale. [20 marks]

I ain't saying we like a bit of bling, but we love our flashy hydrographs...

Flood hydrographs can look quite confusing, but they're not so bad once you've got your head round them. And remember, at the end of the day, they're just fancy graphs — there's no need to runoff in the other direction whenever you see one...

The Carbon Cycle

It's not all about the water cycle you know (although water great cycle that is) — you also need to be clued up on the ins and outs, flows and stores of the carbon cycle. If only all this cycling counted as exercise — you'd be as fit as a fiddle.

Carbon is Found in **All** Earth's Systems

1) Carbon is an **element**, and a really **important** one at that.

2) It's found in both **organic** stores (living things) and **inorganic** stores (e.g. rocks, gases and fossil fuels).

3) Carbon can be found in **each** of the **Earth's systems** in some form or another:

Lithosphere
- Over **99.9%** of the carbon on Earth is stored in **sedimentary rocks** such as limestone.
- About **0.004%** of the carbon on Earth is stored in **fossil fuels**, such as coal and oil, in the lithosphere.

Atmosphere
- Carbon is stored as carbon dioxide (CO_2) and in smaller quantities as **methane** (CH_4) in the atmosphere.
- The atmosphere contains about **0.001%** of the Earth's carbon.

Hydrosphere
- **Carbon dioxide (CO_2)** is **dissolved** in **rivers**, **lakes** and **oceans**.
- The oceans are the **second-largest** carbon store on Earth, containing approximately **0.04%** of the Earth's carbon. The majority of carbon here is found **deep** in the ocean in the form of **dissolved inorganic carbon**.
- A small amount is found at the ocean **surface** where it is **exchanged** with the **atmosphere**.

Biosphere
- Carbon is stored in the tissues of **living organisms**. It is transferred to the **soil** when living organisms **die** and **decay**.
- The biosphere contains approximately **0.004%** of the Earth's total carbon.

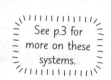
See p.3 for more on these systems.

Cryosphere
- The cryosphere contains **less than 0.01%** of Earth's carbon.
- Most of the carbon in the cryosphere is in the **soil** in areas of **permafrost** (permanently frozen ground) where **decomposing plants** and **animals** have **frozen** into the ground.

Carbon is **Transferred** Between **Different Stores**

1) The **carbon cycle** is the process by which carbon is **stored** and **transferred**.

2) The carbon cycle is a **closed system** (see p.2) — there are **inputs** and **outputs** of energy, but the **amount** of carbon in the system remains the **same**. However, some carbon is **locked away** (sequestered — see next page) in **long-term stores**, e.g. **rock** and **fossil fuels** deep underground. If these are **released** by e.g. burning fossil fuels, they are effectively **inputs**.

3) Make sure you know the major **stores** and **flows** in the carbon cycle:

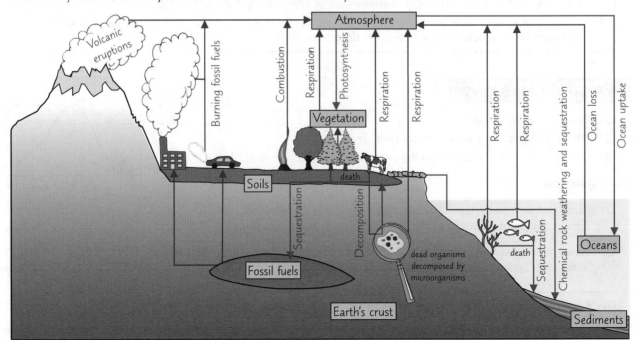

Topic One — Water and Carbon Cycles

The Carbon Cycle

Carbon Stores *Change* in *Size* Over *Time* Because of *Carbon Flows*

There are lots of **flows** of carbon between stores:

Photosynthesis
- Photosynthesis transfers carbon stored in the **atmosphere** to **biomass**.
- Plants and phytoplankton use energy from the Sun to change **carbon dioxide** and **water** into **glucose** and oxygen. This enables plants to **grow**.
- Carbon is passed through the **food chain** and released through **respiration** and **decomposition**.

Respiration
- Respiration transfers carbon from **living organisms** to the **atmosphere**.
- Plants and animals **break down glucose** for energy, releasing **carbon dioxide** and **methane** (a gas containing carbon) in the process.

Combustion
- Combustion transfers carbon stored in **living**, **dead** or **decomposed biomass** (including peaty soils) to the **atmosphere** by **burning**.
- **Wildfires** (see pages 90-91) cause carbon flow.

Decomposition
- Decomposition transfers carbon from dead **biomass** to the **atmosphere** and the **soil**.
- After **death**, bacteria and fungi **break** organisms down. CO_2 and **methane** are released.
- Some carbon is transferred to the **soil** in the form of **humus**.

Ocean uptake and loss
- CO_2 is directly **dissolved** from the **atmosphere** into the **ocean**. It is also transferred to the oceans when it is **taken up** by **organisms** that live in them (e.g. plankton).
- Carbon is also transferred from the **ocean** to the **atmosphere** when **carbon-rich water** from deep in the oceans **rises** to the surface and releases CO_2.

Weathering
- Chemical weathering transfers carbon from the **atmosphere** to the **hydrosphere** and **biosphere**.
- Atmospheric carbon reacts with water vapour to form **acid rain**. When this acid rain falls onto **rocks**, a chemical reaction occurs which **dissolves** the rocks. The molecules resulting from this reaction may be washed into the **sea**. Here, they **react** with CO_2 dissolved in the water to form **calcium carbonate**, which is used by **sea creatures**, e.g. to make shells.

Sequestration
- Carbon from the atmosphere can be **sequestered** (captured and held) in **sedimentary rocks** or as **fossil fuels**. Rocks and fossil fuels form over millions of years when **dead animal** and **plant** material in the ocean falls to the floor and is **compacted**.
- Carbon in fossil fuels is **sequestered** until we **burn** them (**combustion** — see page 12).

Sid the Herring's plans for a quiet burial had been scuppered.

Carbon Flows Happen Over Different *Time* and *Spatial Scales*

1) **Fast** carbon flows quickly **transfer** carbon between sources. It only takes a matter of minutes, hours or days. **Photosynthesis**, **respiration**, **combustion** and **decomposition** are examples of fast carbon flows.

2) **Sequestration** is a **slow** carbon flow. It takes millions of years for carbon to be sequestered in sedimentary rocks.

3) The carbon flows taking place also depend on spatial **scale**. For example, at a **plant** scale, respiration and photosynthesis are the main flows. At an **ecosystem** scale, carbon flows such as combustion and decomposition also occur. At a **continental** scale, all of the carbon flows including sequestration occur.

Practice Questions

Q1 Draw a diagram showing the key processes within the carbon cycle.

Q2 What is carbon sequestration?

Exam Question

Q1 Outline the role of living organisms in the carbon cycle. [4 marks]

The world goes 'cos carbon flows...

You've probably gathered that the carbon cycle is really important. Make sure you know everything here before you move on.

The Carbon Cycle

The carbon cycle can be affected by lots of things. Some of them are natural, but surprise surprise, humans can play a big role too. There's lots to learn here, so get cracking or you'll never get to bed. Although this stuff might put you to sleep...

Natural Processes Can Change the Carbon Cycle

Natural events like **wildfires** and **volcanic eruptions** can alter the **magnitude** of the **carbon stores**:

Wildfires

- Wildfires rapidly transfer large quantities of carbon from **biomass** (or soil) to the **atmosphere**. Loss of vegetation decreases photosynthesis, so **less** carbon is **removed** from the atmosphere.
- In the longer term, however, fires can **encourage** the **growth** of new plants, which take in carbon from the atmosphere for photosynthesis. Depending on the **amount** and **type** of regrowth, fires can have a **neutral** effect on the amount of atmospheric carbon.

Volcanic Activity

- Carbon stored within the Earth in magma is released during **volcanic eruptions**. The majority enters the atmosphere as CO_2.
- Recent volcanic eruptions have released much less CO_2 than human activities. However, there is the **potential** for a very large eruption to disrupt the carbon cycle **significantly**.

Humans Can Also Impact the Carbon Cycle

1) Since the **industrial revolution**, the impact that humans have on the carbon cycle has increased hugely. We're currently causing **carbon flows** from the lithosphere and biosphere to the atmosphere to happen **much faster** than they would naturally.

2) The main **human causes** of change are:

Hydrocarbon (fossil fuel) extraction and use

- **Extracting** and **burning** (**combustion**) of fossil fuels releases CO_2 into the atmosphere.
- Without human intervention, the carbon would remain **sequestered** in the lithosphere for **thousands** or **millions** of years to come.

Deforestation

- Forests may be cleared for **agriculture**, **logging**, or to make way for **developments**.
- Clearance **reduces** the size of the **carbon store** and, if the cleared forest is **burned**, there is a **rapid flow** of carbon from the biosphere to the atmosphere.

Farming practices

Agricultural activities release carbon into the atmosphere:
- Animals release CO_2 and methane when they **respire** and **digest** food.
- **Ploughing** can release CO_2 stored in **soil**.
- Growing **rice** in rice paddies releases a lot of **methane**.

As the world's population has **risen**, so has food production. As a result, carbon emissions from **farming practices** have increased. **Mechanisation** of farming has also increased CO_2 emissions.

Land use changes

As well as deforestation (see above), the change of land use from natural or agricultural to **urban** is a major source of carbon:
- **Vegetation** is **removed** to make way for buildings — this reduces carbon storage in the biosphere.
- **Concrete production** releases lots of CO_2, and lots of concrete is used when urban areas expand.

The Carbon Budget is the Balance Between Carbon Inputs and Outputs

1) The **carbon budget** is the difference between the **inputs** of carbon into a subsystem and **outputs** of carbon from it.

2) For example, in the **atmosphere**, **inputs** of carbon come from **volcanic eruptions**, **burning fossil fuels**, **respiration** and **ocean loss**, and **outputs** occur through **photosynthesis**, **sequestration**, **decomposition**, **chemical weathering** and **ocean uptake**.

3) The **balance** of the inputs and outputs of a subsystem determines whether it acts as a **carbon source** (the outputs of carbon outweigh the inputs, so it **releases more carbon** than it **absorbs**) or a **carbon sink** (the **inputs** of carbon **outweigh** the **outputs**, so it **absorbs more carbon** than it **releases**).

The Carbon Cycle

The Carbon Cycle Affects the **Atmosphere**, **Land** and **Oceans**

The carbon cycle is **fundamental** to life on Earth. When there is a **change** to the carbon cycle, it can have a **significant impacts** on the atmosphere, land and oceans.

> Some impacts of carbon cycle change are linked — e.g. an impact on the atmosphere can have knock-on effects on the land and ocean.

Atmosphere and Climate

- The carbon cycle affects the **amount** of gases containing carbon (e.g. CO_2 and methane) in the atmosphere. These are **greenhouse gases** — they trap some of the Sun's energy, keeping some of the heat in and keeping the planet warm (see p.14).
- As the concentrations of greenhouse gases in the atmosphere **increase** (e.g. due to **changes** in the carbon cycle caused by human activities such as deforestation and the burning of fossil fuels) **temperatures** are **expected to rise**. This is **global warming**.
- Changes in temperature across the globe will affect **other aspects** of the **climate**, e.g. **more intense storms** are predicted.

Though they made gardening unpleasant, Marjorie's increasing greenhouse gas emissions sure deterred Bruce from meddling with the cabbages.

Land

- The carbon cycle allows **plants** to **grow** — if there was no carbon in the atmosphere, plants could not **photosynthesise**. If there was no **decomposition**, dead plants would remain where they fell and their nutrients would **never be recycled**.
- Changes in the carbon cycle can **reduce** the amount of carbon stored in the land, e.g. warmer temperatures caused by global warming are causing **permafrost** to melt. This **releases** carbon previously stored in the permafrost into the atmosphere.
- An increase in global temperatures could also **increase** the frequency of **wildfires** (see previous page).

Oceans

- As part of the carbon cycle, **carbon dioxide** is dissolved **directly** into the oceans from the **atmosphere**.
- CO_2 in oceans is used by organisms such as **phytoplankton** and **seaweed** during **photosynthesis** and by other marine organisms to form **calcium carbonate shells** and **skeletons**.
- Increased levels of CO_2 in the atmosphere can increase the **acidity** of the oceans because the oceans initially absorb more CO_2 (see p.11). This can have adverse effects on **marine life**.
- **Global warming** can also affect oceans. For example, organisms that are **sensitive** to temperature, e.g. phytoplankton, may **not** be able to **survive** at higher temperatures, so their numbers **decrease**. This means that **less** CO_2 is used by them for **photosynthesis**, so less carbon is removed from the atmosphere.
- Warmer water is also **less able** to **absorb** CO_2, so as temperatures rise the amount of CO_2 that could potentially be **dissolved** in the sea **decreases**.

Practice Questions

Q1 How does deforestation cause a change in the carbon cycle?

Q2 What is the carbon budget?

Q3 Give one effect of changes in the carbon cycle on the land.

Exam Question

Q1 Outline how changes to the carbon cycle can affect the oceans. [4 marks]

Carbon, carboff, carbon... my yo-yo dieting's got me stuck in quite a cycle...

Hooray — two more pages on the carbon cycle for you to learn. Make sure you have a crack at the practice questions to help you cement your new-found knowledge. Then just for good measure, go over the pages again until you remember it all.

Water, Carbon and Climate

The water and carbon cycles are a bit like Ant and Dec — sure, you can separate them, but to get the full effect you just have to put them together. The difference is, rather than adding life to Saturday night telly, these two add life to Earth...

The *Water* and *Carbon Stores* and *Cycles* are *Essential* for *Life*

1) Carbon is a **fundamental building block** of life — **all living things** contain carbon. **Water** is also **essential** for life — all living things need water to survive.

2) Plants form the **base** of most **food chains** — when photosynthesis occurs, they use energy from sunlight to convert CO_2 and water into biomass that gets **passed up** the food chain. Photosynthesis requires **inputs** of both **water** and **carbon**.

3) Water is present in the **atmosphere** as **water vapour** (and water droplets), and carbon exists as **carbon dioxide** and **methane**. These are **greenhouse gases** — they cause a **natural greenhouse effect** that prevents some energy from **escaping** into **space** and **reflects** it back to **Earth**. This causes temperatures on Earth to be **higher** than they would otherwise be — without the natural greenhouse effect the Earth would be **frozen** and **uninhabitable**.

4) Human activities are increasing the **concentration** of greenhouse gases in the atmosphere. Most scientists agree that this is causing an **enhanced greenhouse effect**. This is where the **additional** greenhouse gases reflect **more** energy back to the Earth than in the natural greenhouse effect, so **temperature increases** even further. This is thought to be causing **global warming** and other changes to the climate (see next page).

There are *Feedbacks Within* the Two Cycles...

The effects of a change to a system may be **amplified** by a **positive** feedback or **dampened** by a **negative** feedback (see page 2). Sometimes, the **same change** can cause **either** a positive or negative feedback, for example:

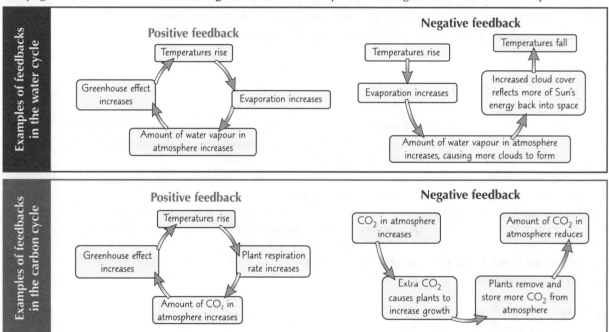

Examples of feedbacks in the water cycle

Positive feedback
- Temperatures rise
- Evaporation increases
- Amount of water vapour in atmosphere increases
- Greenhouse effect increases

Negative feedback
- Temperatures rise
- Evaporation increases
- Amount of water vapour in atmosphere increases, causing more clouds to form
- Increased cloud cover reflects more of Sun's energy back into space
- Temperatures fall

Examples of feedbacks in the carbon cycle

Positive feedback
- Temperatures rise
- Plant respiration rate increases
- Amount of CO_2 in atmosphere increases
- Greenhouse effect increases

Negative feedback
- CO_2 in atmosphere increases
- Extra CO_2 causes plants to increase growth
- Plants remove and store more CO_2 from atmosphere
- Amount of CO_2 in atmosphere reduces

In these examples, the **positive** feedbacks would **increase** global warming because they're **amplifying** the temperature rise. The **negative** feedbacks would **cancel out** the temperature increase, so global warming wouldn't increase.

...as well as *Interactions* Between Them

The carbon and water cycles **depend** on each other. For example:

- **Carbon combines** with **water** in the atmosphere. This allows **chemical weathering**, which **removes** carbon from the atmosphere (see p.11).
- **Water** is needed for **photosynthesis**, which **removes** carbon from the atmosphere.
- The amount of CO_2 in the atmosphere affects **global temperatures**, which affect the amount of **evaporation** that can take place, which affects the amount of **precipitation**.

Nick loved interacting with the water cycle on the way to work.

Water, Carbon and Climate

Climate Change Affects Life on Earth

Climate change is predicted to have major impacts on plants, animals and people, for example:

1) The **pattern** of **precipitation** is expected to **change** — wet areas are expected to get wetter and dry areas are expected to get drier. This could cause **water shortages** in some areas, which could lead to **conflicts** in the future.

2) **Extreme weather events** (e.g. storms, floods and droughts) are expected to get **more frequent**. **Less developed** countries will probably be **worst** affected as they are **less able** to deal with the impacts.

3) **Agricultural productivity** will **decrease** in some areas, which could lead to **food shortages**.

4) **Sea levels** are expected to **rise** further. This will **flood** coastal and low-lying areas.

5) The geographical **range** of some species will change as climate changes. The arrival of new species in an area may **damage** the ecosystem, and some species may become **extinct**.

6) **Plankton** numbers may **decline** if temperatures increase, which will have a knock-on effect on **marine food chains**.

Humans are Trying to Influence the Carbon Cycle

1) Humans have **influenced** the carbon cycle for centuries, particularly by **extracting** and **burning fossil fuels**. There is now **40% more CO_2** in the atmosphere than there was in **1750**.

2) The **Intergovernmental Panel on Climate Change** (IPCC) is an international organisation set up by the UN to share knowledge about climate change. The IPCC states that countries need to **reduce** the amount of CO_2 emitted by **human activities** in order to prevent **large temperature rises**.

3) People are trying to mitigate the impacts of climate change by reducing transfers of **carbon** to the **atmosphere**. These measures can be at a range of **scales**, for example:

Individual
- People can choose to use their **cars less** and buy more **fuel efficient** cars.
- They can also make their **homes** more **energy efficient**, e.g. with double glazing, insulation and more efficient appliances.

Regional and National
- Governments can reduce **reliance** on **fossil fuels** for **heating** and **powering homes** by increasing the availability and reducing the cost of **renewable energy** sources such as **wind**, **tidal** and **solar**.
- **Afforestation** and **restoring degraded forests** can increase carbon uptake by the biosphere.
- Planners can **increase** the **sustainability** of developments by **improving public transport** (to reduce car use) and creating **more green spaces** (see p.177).
- Governments can invest in **carbon capture and storage** (CCS). CO_2 emitted from burning fossil fuels is captured and stored **underground**, e.g. in depleted oil and gas reservoirs.

Global
- Countries can work together to reduce emissions. For example, the **Kyoto Protocol** (1997) and the **Paris Agreement** (2015) are **international treaties** to control the total amount of greenhouse gases released. Participating countries agree to keep their emissions **within** set **limits**.
- There are also international **carbon trading schemes**. Countries and businesses are given a **limit** on the emissions they can produce — if they produce **less** they can **sell** the extra credits, if they produce **more** they need to **buy** more credits.

Practice Questions

Q1 Give an example of a negative feedback in the water cycle.

Q2 What is carbon capture and storage?

Exam Question

Q1 Assess the extent to which feedbacks in the carbon and water cycles may affect life on Earth. [20 marks]

How to influence the carbon cycle — everyone hold your breath...

There's a sure-fire way to influence your marks for questions on interactions between the water cycle, carbon cycle and climate, and it starts with you learning everything on these two pages, then having a crack at those practice questions...

The Amazon Rainforest — Case Study

Now, I know you probably studied the Amazon rainforest at GCSE and Key Stage 3, and quite possibly at least twice at primary school. But don't get too complacent — this time it's all about the water and carbon cycles within the Amazon...

The *Amazon* is a *Rainforest* in *South America*

1) The Amazon is the world's **largest** tropical rainforest and covers 40% of the South American landmass.

2) It has a **hot**, very **wet** climate and the **vegetation** is very **dense**.

3) Many groups of **indigenous people** live in the Amazon rainforest.

4) It's home to up to **1 million plant** species, over **500** species of **mammals** and over **2000** species of **fish**. The Amazon is also home to many **endangered species**, including the Amazonian manatee (an aquatic mammal), black caiman (a reptile) and the pirarucu (a fish).

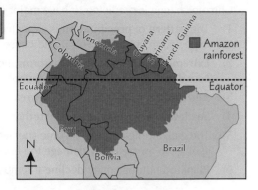

The *Water* and *Carbon Cycles* are *Important* to the *Amazon Environment*

The **water** and **carbon** cycles **affect** the **Amazon rainforest**, and the **Amazon rainforest affects** the **water** and **carbon** cycles:

Water Cycle

1) The water cycle causes the Amazon to be very **wet** — there is a lot of **evaporation** over the Atlantic Ocean, and the wet air is blown **towards** the Amazon. This contributes to the Amazon's very high rainfall.

2) **Warm temperatures** mean that **evaporation** is high in the rainforest itself, which increases the amount of precipitation.

3) The rainforest has a **dense canopy** — this means that **interception** is **high**. As a result, **less** water flows into rivers than might otherwise be expected, and it does so **more slowly**.

4) The water cycle affects the Amazon environment — it is populated by species that are **adapted** to **high humidity** and **frequent rainfall**.

Carbon Cycle

1) The Amazon rainforest **stores** lots of **carbon** in its **vegetation** and **soil**, so it's a **carbon sink** (see p.12).

2) The increasing concentration of CO_2 in the atmosphere has led to **increased productivity** in the Amazon rainforest because the vegetation is able to access more CO_2 for photosynthesis — the amount of **biomass** has been **increasing**.

3) As a result, the amount of CO_2 **sequestered** (see p.11) by the Amazon rainforest has **increased**, making it an even more important carbon store.

4) However, it has been suggested that although trees are **growing** more **quickly**, they're also **dying younger**.

5) As a result, we may **not** be able to **rely** on the Amazon rainforest to **continue** to be such an effective **carbon sink** in the **future**.

Human Activities in the Amazon are *Affecting* the *Water* and *Carbon Cycles*

The activities of people are **changing** the Amazon rainforest environment in various ways:

Deforestation

Lots of deforestation takes place in the Amazon, e.g. to exploit the **timber** or to use the land for **farming**.

Effects on the water cycle:

1) In **deforested areas** there is no tree canopy to intercept rainfall, so more water reaches the ground surface. There is too much **water** to soak into the soil. Instead the **water** moves to rivers as **surface runoff**, which increases the risk of **flooding**.

2) Deforestation reduces the **rate** of **evapotranspiration** (see p. 7) — this means less water vapour reaches the atmosphere, **fewer clouds form** and **rainfall** is **reduced**. This increases the risk of **drought**.

Effects on the carbon cycle:

1) Without **roots** to **hold the soil** together, heavy rain **washes away** the **nutrient-rich** top layer of soil, **transferring** carbon stored in the soil to the hydrosphere.

2) Deforestation means that there is **less leaf litter**, so humus isn't formed. The soil cannot support much new growth, which **limits** the amount of carbon that is **absorbed**.

3) Trees **remove** CO_2 from the atmosphere and store it, so fewer trees means more atmospheric CO_2, which enhances the greenhouse effect and global warming (see p. 14).

> Many of these effects limit vegetation growth, which can amplify changes to the water and carbon cycles. This is an example of positive feedback (see p. 2).

The Amazon Rainforest — Case Study

Climate Change

1) Climate change can severely impact tropical rainforests. In some areas **temperature** is increasing and **rainfall** is decreasing, which leads to **drought**. The **Amazon** had **severe droughts** in **2005** and **2010**.

2) **Plants** and **animals** living in tropical rainforests are adapted to **moist conditions**, so many species die in dry weather. **Frequent** or **long periods** of drought could lead to **extinction** of some species. **Drought** can also lead to **forest fires**, which can **destroy** large areas of forest, **releasing** lots of CO_2 into the atmosphere.

3) Scientists predict that a **4 °C** temperature rise could **kill 85%** of the Amazon rainforest. This would result in lots of **carbon** being **released** into the atmosphere as the dead material **decomposed**, and less carbon dioxide being taken in from the air by trees for **photosynthesis**.

There are Attempts to *Limit Human Impacts* on the Amazon

Selective Logging

1) Only **some trees** (e.g. just the oldest ones) are **felled** — most are left standing.

2) This is **less damaging** to the forest than felling **all the trees** in an area. If only a **few trees** are taken from each area the **forest structure** is kept — the canopy is still there and the soil isn't exposed. This means the forest is able to **regenerate**, so the impact on the carbon and water cycle is small.

Replanting

1) **New trees** are planted to replace the ones that are **cut down**. For example, **Peru** plans to restore **3.2 million hectares** of forest by 2020.

2) It's important that the **same types of tree** are planted that were cut down, so that the **variety of trees** is kept for the future and the local carbon and water cycles return to their initial state.

Environmental Law

Environmental laws can help **protect rainforests**. For example:

- Laws that **ban** the use of wood from forests that are not managed **sustainably**.
- Laws that **ban excessive logging**.
- Laws that control **land use**, e.g. the **Brazilian Forest Code** says that landowners have to keep 50-80% of their land as forest.

'Just keep smiling and back away slowly,' Stu told himself as he met the new head of environmental law for the first time.

Protection

1) Many countries have set up **national parks** and **nature reserves** to protect rainforests. For example, the **Central Amazon Conservation Complex** in Brazil was set up in 2003 and protects **biodiversity** in an area of 49 000 km² while allowing **local people** to use the forest in a **sustainable** way.

2) Within national parks and nature reserves, **damaging activities** such as logging can be monitored and prevented.

Practice Questions

Q1 How does the water cycle affect the environment of tropical rainforests?

Q2 Give an example of how human activities have affected the carbon cycle in tropical rainforests.

Q3 Give one way that people are attempting to limit human impacts on the water or carbon cycles in the Amazon.

Exam Question

Q1 To what extent is human activity affecting the water cycle and the carbon cycle in tropical rainforests? [20 marks]

Learn this lot and you're done*...

*with the first case study of the first section of the book, that is.

(The small print always has the bad news.) This Amazon case study is prime reading material, but you won't wake up to an exciting little package of knowledge on the doormat of your mind tomorrow unless you put the time into learning it (or the case study you did in class). Make sure you give the information a good review and you're sure to deliver the goods on schedule in the exam.

The Eden Basin — Case Study

Pack your bags, we're off to a lovely spot in Cumbria. Unfortunately the water cycle likes to chuck a <u>LOT</u> of water at it from time to time — I'm sure the water cycle means well and just wants to make sure it stays hydrated, but it does cause issues...

The **River Eden** Flows Through **Cumbria**

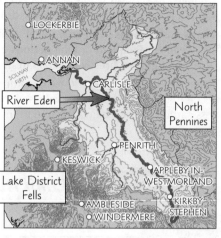

Drainage basin ▬ River — Contour Line — County Boundary

1) The **Eden drainage basin** is in north-west England, between the **mountains** of the Lake District and the Pennines. The river drains the north-east Lake District fells and the north-west Pennines.

2) The River Eden's **source** is in the Pennine hills in south Cumbria. It flows north-west through **Appleby-in-Westmorland** and **Carlisle**. Its mouth is in the **Solway Firth** at the **Scottish border**.

3) The river basin is largely **rural**, although the River Eden does flow through the city of Carlisle.

4) The upland areas that drain into the River Eden experience **extreme weather** that can cause **flooding** downstream — Carlisle is particularly vulnerable as it's at the **confluence** of the **Eden**, **Petteril** and **Caldew** rivers, and is **fairly low-lying**.

The **Characteristics** of the **Eden Basin** Affect the **Water Cycle**

1) **Rainfall** is **higher** than the national average in the Eden Basin, because of the **relief** of the area — the **mountainous** terrain encourages **orographic** rainfall (see p.5). High rainfall means that lots of water enters the river channels.

2) The Eden Basin is **long** and relatively **narrow**, which increases lag time (see p.8).

3) The **slopes** within the basin are **steep**. This reduces lag time and increases peak discharge.

4) The basin is made up of a number of different types of **rock**:

   - The highest ground, to the west of the basin, is made of **igneous rocks**, which are **impermeable** (water won't soak into them). **Infiltration** is very **slow** and **surface runoff** is **high** in these areas, **reducing lag time**.

   - Much of the basin, however, is made up of **limestone** and **sandstone**, which are **permeable**. When precipitation falls in these areas, **infiltration** is **quick** and there is **little surface run off**, **increasing lag time**. The amount of water in **ground stores** increases.

Changes in the Water Cycle have **Affected** the **Risk** of Flooding

Land use changes in the Eden Basin have affected the drainage basin's water cycle and **increased flood risk**:

Farming

1) More **intense** farming has caused soils to become **compacted**, e.g. by **heavy machinery** or **trampling** by **livestock**. Between 2000 and 2009, there was a 30% **increase** in the number of cattle in the Eden Valley, meaning that much more land is likely to have been trampled.

2) Compaction of soils reduces **infiltration**, so surface runoff is higher. This means water levels in rivers **rise quickly** during heavy rainfall, increasing the risk of **flooding**.

3) **Grazing** in upland areas, e.g. hill farming of sheep, has also reduced the **amount of vegetation** that can **intercept** rainfall, resulting in more water reaching rivers.

Construction

1) Although the majority of the Eden Basin is rural, built-up areas have **increased**. Many new **housing estates** have been built in and around Carlisle in recent years, e.g. the Eden Gate development to the north of the city, and there are plans to develop a huge 'garden village' to the south of the city, including up to 10 000 new homes.

2) Surfaces in built-up areas tend to be **impermeable**, which reduces the size of infiltration flows and greatly increases the **size** and **speed** of **surface runoff flows** (see page 170).

3) Some new developments, particularly near Carlisle, have been built on floodplains. This has created a **flood risk** to **property** and has required the construction of **flood defences** to protect homes. Building on floodplains can cause **flooding downstream** as water that would naturally infiltrate on the floodplains flows downstream instead.

The Eden Basin — Case Study

Deforestation

1) Deforestation has taken place in the basin for **thousands** of years, e.g. to provide timber, and land for farming. Much of the original forest cover in the Eden Basin has now been **removed**, giving way to large areas of open grassland and heathland.

2) Trees **increase infiltration** and **decrease runoff** (see page 9), so **fewer** trees means **more** runoff, **flashier** flood hydrographs and a **greater risk of flooding**.

Climate change is predicted to **change rainfall patterns** in the UK. For example, parts of the western UK could get up to 35% more winter rainfall by 2080. **Increased winter rainfall** in the Eden Basin would **increase runoff** and **flood risk**.

Storm Desmond *Caused* Severe Flooding *in the* Eden Basin

1) In **December 2015**, Storm Desmond caused devastating **flooding** in Cumbria. Some of the worst flooding occurred in the Eden Basin.

2) In some areas of Cumbria, there was **record rainfall**. In **Shap**, a village in the Eden Basin, **262.6 mm** of rain fell in **48 hours** between the 4th and 6th December. That's nearly **50 mm more** than the average rainfall for the **whole** of December.

3) **Appleby-in-Westmorland** and **Carlisle** were particularly badly affected. More than **2000** properties were flooded in Carlisle alone, leaving many people homeless.

4) The hydrograph shows the River Eden's response to **Storm Desmond**. The gauging station that recorded this information is located at **Linstock**, just upstream of Carlisle.

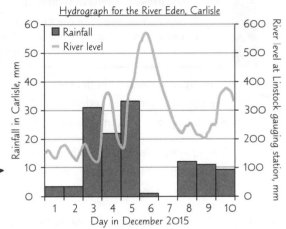

There are Fieldwork Opportunities in River Basins

There are loads of different things you could **investigate** in a convenient drainage basin. For example, you could look at **factors** affecting **flows** and **stores** in the water cycle:

- You could investigate how **rock type** and **land use** affect flows within a drainage basin.
- You might do this by measuring **soil saturation** in different parts of your drainage basin with different land uses or rock types.
- You could also measure the **response** of a river to precipitation. You could use **primary** or **secondary data** for this. In England, the **Environment Agency** regularly publishes **river flow** readings from its gauges on its website.

Dan and Kate hadn't expected fieldwork to be so enjoyable.

Practice Questions

Q1 Give an example of how the water cycle has changed over time in a drainage basin you have studied.

Q2 Give an example of a fieldwork investigation topic you could carry out in a local drainage basin.

Exam Question

Q1 Assess the extent to which changes in the water cycle have affected flood risk or sustainable water supply in a drainage basin that you have studied. [20 marks]

Too much water for the Eden basin? If only we'd had the Eden bath...

You might well have learnt about a different example instead. If you have, don't go thinking it gets you out of doing those practice questions. Oh no siree, you'd better give them a go — but please feel free to answer with a different example.

Desert Systems

In the second part of your physical geography exam, you'll have to answer questions about hot deserts, coasts or glaciers. If you're doing the deserts option, don't bury your head in the sand — get stuck into this section instead.

Deserts are Natural Systems

1) Hot deserts have **inputs**, **outputs**, **flows** and **stores** of **sediment**, **water** and **energy**.

See p.2 for more on systems.

Inputs
- **Water** enters the system through infrequent **rainstorms**.
- **Sediment** can be carried into a desert system by **wind** or **water**.
- **Energy** can come from the **Sun**, **wind** or **rain** (see below).

Flows/transfers
Sediment is **moved** within the system by:
- **Weathering**
- **Erosion**
- **Transportation**
- **Deposition**

Pages 25-27 explain these desert processes.

Stores
- **Landforms** are stores of **sediment**.
- Water may be stored in the **ground** or in **rivers** and other bodies of water (although some of these only store water **intermittently**).

Outputs
- Water **evaporates** rapidly or may leave the system as **runoff**.
- Sediment may be **carried out** of the system by wind or water.

2) Deserts are **open systems** — both energy and matter can enter and leave.

3) Desert systems are generally in dynamic equilibrium — inputs and outputs are balanced.

4) A **change** to an input or output can cause a **negative feedback** that **restores** the balance. For example:

- If temperature increases, evaporation will increase around bodies of water and the ground will be drier.
- Drier sediment is more easily eroded, so dust clouds are more likely to form.
- Dust clouds block some solar radiation, so temperature decreases.

5) Deserts also experience **positive feedbacks** — when a **change** to the system results in **further changes** with a similar effect. For example:

- When wind hits an obstacle (e.g. a stone), it **slows down** and **drops** its load. This dropped sediment forms the start of a **dune**.
- The young (embryo) dune creates a **larger obstacle**, which slows wind speed **further** and causes it to deposit **more** sediment.
- This means that dune growth **encourages further** dune growth.

Sand dunes are covered in more detail on p.29.

6) Positive feedbacks can **change** the system's equilibrium. For example, in the positive feedback loop above, **wind flow** may be changed by the growing dune until it can **no longer** carry sediment to the top and deposit it. This means the dune will **stop growing** — it has reached a new **dynamic equilibrium**.

There are Different Sources of Energy in Deserts

In a desert system, energy comes from the **Sun**, the **wind** and the **rain**:

Insolation

- **Insolation** is the **solar radiation** that reaches Earth — it's **strong** in hot deserts because:
  1) There aren't usually any **clouds** to block it.
  2) In deserts that are at the **mid to low latitudes** (see p.22), the Sun's rays hit the Earth at **high angles**. The higher the Sun is in the sky, the **more radiation** is transferred to the ground.
- High levels of insolation cause **high daytime** temperatures, while cloudless skies mean that **nights are cold**. Rapid temperature **changes** can cause **steep pressure gradients** that drive **strong winds** (see next page).
- High inputs of energy from insolation cause water to **evaporate** quickly, leaving the ground very **dry**. This makes sediment more **mobile**.

Becky and Tara's main energy source was their radioactive costumes.

Desert Systems

Runoff

- **Precipitation** is **infrequent** and **unpredictable** in desert regions. When it does rain, it's often in the form of **intense storms** — these cause high inputs of energy into localised areas.
- There are few **plants** to **intercept** rainfall, so there's a lot of **surface runoff**.
- The ground surface has been **baked hard** by the Sun in some areas, and there's often **exposed rock** because soil is easily eroded. These factors **decrease infiltration** and **increase runoff**.

Winds

- **Winds** are created by air moving from areas of **high** pressure to areas of **low** pressure. Where the pressure gradient is **high** (there's a big difference between high and low pressure), winds can be **very strong**.
- In some areas, wind consistently blows from the **same** direction (this is called a **prevailing wind**) — this causes **more** sediment **erosion** and **transport** than winds that change direction frequently.
- **Lack of vegetation** in deserts means wind can blow long distances without **obstruction**, increasing its power.

Inputs of **energy** from wind and water, combined with **mobile sediment**, means deserts are often very **active** landscapes.

There are Several **Sources** of **Sediment** in Deserts

1) A lot of the **sediment** in deserts comes from **ancient processes**:

- Before they became deserts, many areas used to have a completely different **climate** — **wet** enough for there to be **rivers** and **lakes**.
- Sediment was **transported** into the system in rivers and **deposited** on the beds of lakes. When they dried up, the sediment became available for building dunes and other depositional landforms.
- Other areas were **underwater**, so they still have **marine deposits** from millions of years ago.

2) Sediment is **still** being brought into desert systems today:

- Some comes from **underlying parent material** that's been **weathered**.
- Rivers also bring sediment into deserts — many only flow **occasionally**, so when they **dry up**, the sediment they were **carrying** is **left behind** on the riverbed or, if they **flood**, on the surrounding desert surface (see p.27).
- **Wind** also **transports** sediment into deserts and **deposits** it there (see pages 26-27).

3) Deserts aren't just **recipients** of sediment — they can also be **sources**. **Dust clouds** form when strong **winds** blow fine particles out of the desert — these are sometimes transported thousands of miles.

4) The **difference** between the amount of sediment being brought **into** an area and the amount **leaving** is the **sediment budget**. If sediment inputs are **higher** than outputs, the sediment budget is **positive**. If sediment inputs are **lower** than outputs, the sediment budget is **negative**.

5) Sediment budgets determine what type of **landscapes** form. Where the sediment budget is **positive** (more deposition than erosion), landscapes are dominated by **depositional landforms**, e.g. sand dunes. Where the sediment budget is **negative** (more erosion than deposition), landscapes are dominated by **erosional landforms**, e.g. inselbergs (see p.28).

Practice Questions

Q1 What are the main inputs, outputs, stores and flows in a desert system?

Q2 Name three sources of energy in a desert.

Q3 What is a sediment budget?

Exam Question

Q1 Explain the role of feedback in the development of hot desert landscapes. [4 marks]

Don't desert your revision now, we're only just getting started...

These might not be the most exciting first pages of a topic you've ever seen in your life, but they're certainly worth learning. Examiners absolutely love this systems concepts stuff — if you can stick some of these ideas into an exam answer, you're sure to impress. Remember — desert systems have inputs, outputs, stores and flows, and there are sources of energy and sediment.

Topic Two — Hot Desert Systems and Landscapes

Deserts — Distribution and Characteristics

In my mind, deserts are full of towering sand dunes and camels, but in reality they're a bit different to that...

The **Aridity Index** is Used to **Classify** Deserts

1) **Water balance** is the relationship between **mean annual precipitation** (**P**) and **potential evapotranspiration** (**PET**). If P is **higher** than PET, there is a water **surplus**. If P is **lower** than PET, there is a water **deficit**.

2) In **deserts**, P is **lower** than PET — there is a water **deficit**. The **size** of the deficit (i.e. the difference between P and PET) gives the **aridity index** — this is used to **classify** deserts by their level of aridity.

3) A **low** value means aridity is **high** — a value **below 0.2** means an environment is classed as a **desert**. **Desert margins** (land at the **edges** of a desert) are **semi-arid** environments — they have an aridity index value of **0.2-0.5**.

> Evapotranspiration is evaporation and transpiration (evaporation from plants). Potential evapotranspiration is the amount of water that would be lost if there was an unlimited supply.

	Aridity Index
Hyper-arid	<0.03
Arid	0.03-0.2
Semi-arid	0.2-0.5

Most **Deserts** and **Desert Margins** are **Found...**

1 **Around 30° North and South of the Equator**

1) Air moves in **circular patterns** between the **equator** and about **30° north** and **south** of it. These **circular air patterns** are called **Hadley cells**.

2) In a Hadley cell **air rises** at the **equator**. The air cools as it rises, and moisture **condenses** and falls as **rain**, leaving the air **dry**.

3) The **dry air descends** around **30° north** and **south** of the equator.

4) In areas where the **air descends** a zone of **high pressure** is created.

5) **Winds** blow **outwards** from high pressure areas — so **no moisture** can be **brought in** by the **wind**.

6) This means that the area has **very low precipitation**, which means desert margins and deserts are found there, e.g. the **Sahara**.

30° north
equator
30° south

2 **In the Middle of Continents**

1) The **central** parts of **continents** are usually **more arid** than coastal areas.

2) **Moist wind** from the sea **moves inland** and the **moisture** held is **dropped** as precipitation.

3) So when the **wind reaches** the **centre** of a large **continent** it's carrying **very little moisture**, so **very little rain** falls.

4) For example, the **Turkestan** desert exists because it's in the **central** part of **Asia**.

Tropic of Cancer — 23°
Equator
Tropic of Capricorn — 23°

☐ Desert (arid or hyper-arid)
■ Desert margin (semi-arid)

3 **Next to Mountain Ranges**

1) Tall mountain ranges **force winds upwards**.

2) As air rises it **cools** and is less able to hold water.

3) Any moisture held is dropped as **precipitation** over the mountains, so the wind that moves inland has **very little moisture**, which means that **very little rain falls** there.

4) This is called the **rain shadow effect**.

5) For example, the **Atacama** desert in South America exists because of the rain shadow effect of the **Andes** mountains.

4 **Near Cold Ocean Currents**

1) In some places **cold ocean currents** run along the coast.

2) Wind is cooled as it travels over the cold water and its **ability to hold moisture** is **reduced**.

3) **Moisture** that's stored in the atmosphere is **released** as precipitation over the ocean **before** reaching **land**.

4) So when the wind **reaches** the **land** there's **very little moisture** left, so **very little rain falls**.

5) For example, the **Namib** desert in **Africa** exists because of the **Benguela Current** (a cold ocean current) that runs up the **west coast** of Africa.

Deserts — Distribution and Characteristics

Hot Deserts are Hot and Have Large Variations in Temperature

1) The **mean annual temperature** of most hot deserts is **high** — usually between **20** and **30** °C.

2) There are large **seasonal variations** in **temperature** — up to **50** °C in summer and **below 0** °C in winter.

3) There are also large **daily variations** in **temperature** — up to **50** °C in the day and **below 0** °C at night. Large variations are due to the dry desert air, which can't **block sunlight** during the day or **trap heat** at night.

The temperature in **desert margins** is a bit lower:

1) The **mean annual temperature** of most **desert margins** is **lower** than in deserts — between **10** and **20** °C.

2) The **temperature variations** in **desert margins** are usually **less extreme** (between **10** and **35** °C).

Extreme sports? Pah! Fran and Ed were all about the extreme temperature variations.

There's Little Vegetation in Hot Deserts

1) The **biomass** (total amount of living matter) in a desert is **low** because the **lack of water** makes it **difficult** for things **to grow**.

2) The amount of vegetation within a desert **varies** — there can be **none** where there are sand dunes, and a **variety** of small **shrubs**, **grasses** and **cacti species** in other areas.

3) Plants are **specialised** to **survive** in the hot and arid conditions, e.g. cacti have special ways to **collect**, **store** and **conserve** water.

The vegetation in **desert margins** is a little different:

1) There's **more** vegetation in desert margins than in deserts.

2) Vegetation includes **shrubs**, **grasses** and **trees**.

3) The **amount** of vegetation generally **increases** the **further away** from the **desert** you go, because there's **more water**.

Adaptations of cacti

The enlarged stem stores water.

The thick waxy coating reduces transpiration and protects from strong winds.

Small spiny leaves reduce transpiration, and protect them from being eaten by herbivores.

Long, shallow roots absorb water from a large area, whilst longer taproots reach deeper water.

The Soil in Hot Deserts is Very Dry and Not Very Fertile

1) You usually think of deserts as just being made from **sand**, but there are areas of **bare soil** and also **soil underneath** the sand.

2) Desert soils **aren't very fertile** because they don't contain very much organic matter. This is because **few plants grow** there.

3) The soils are often **sandy** (in areas with sand dunes) or **stony** (in rocky areas).

4) The soils are **very dry** due to the **low rainfall** and **high temperatures**.

Stony soil in Death Valley, California

The soil in **desert margins** is a bit better:

1) The soil in desert margins is **more fertile** than the soil in deserts, because there's more vegetation.

2) The soil contains **more water** than desert soil.

3) The soil is **less sandy** and **stony** than in deserts because there's **more weathering**.

Desert margin in Almeria, Spain

Topic Two — Hot Desert Systems and Landscapes

Deserts — Distribution and Characteristics

There are **Interactions** Between the **Climate**, **Soils** and **Vegetation**

The **components** of hot desert systems all **influence** each other. For example:

1 Climate affects soil

- **Infrequent rain** and high evapotranspiration (caused by **high temperatures**) mean that soil is **dry**.
- Evaporation draws **salt** to the surface — salt can't evaporate, so it's left behind in the **soil**.

2 Climate affects vegetation

The **lack of precipitation** means that vegetation cover is **sparse**. Only species **adapted** to the hot, dry conditions can grow.

4 Vegetation affects soil

- Lack of plant cover and low rates of decomposition mean the soil is **low in nutrients**.
- Sparse vegetation cover increases the risk of **soil erosion**. This is because, without plant roots to **stabilise** the soil, fine particles can be **blown** or **washed away**.

3 Soil affects climate

Soil erosion can lead to **clouds of dust** in the atmosphere. Dust particles can **prevent** water droplets forming in clouds, which **reduces rainfall**.

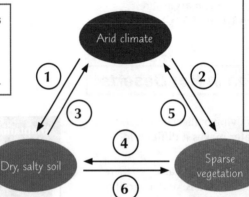

5 Vegetation affects climate

- The **lack of plant cover** means there is little uptake and **transpiration** of water — this inhibits **cloud formation** and reduces **rainfall**.
- With few plants, there is little **evaporative cooling** — this is when air near the ground surface is **cooled** by evapotranspiration. This contributes to the **high temperatures**.
- **Wind speeds** are often **high** in hot deserts because there's little vegetation to **disrupt** air movement.

6 Soil affects vegetation

- Desert **soils** are **dry**, **salty** and **low in nutrients**, so few plants **grow**. Those that do grow have to have a high **tolerance** to salinity and lack of moisture.
- Soils are also **thin**, **nutrient-poor** and prone to **erosion**, so **seeds** that are transported into the area, e.g. by wind, can't start growing. Plants are unable to **colonise** the area, so it remains free of vegetation.

Changes to one component can have **knock-on effects** on the whole system. For example, if **rainfall increased**, more **plants** would grow — as these decomposed it would make **soils** more **nutrient-rich**. Increased plant cover would also **decrease wind speed** and **temperature** and further **increase rainfall**.

Practice Questions

Q1 What does the aridity index show?

Q2 Explain how the rain shadow effect causes aridity.

Q3 Why do deserts have large daily temperature variations?

Exam Question

Q1 The graph on the right shows the climate in Riyadh, Saudi Arabia, which is located 25° north of the equator. Using the graph and your own knowledge, explain the patterns of temperature and rainfall in Riyadh. [6 marks]

WLTM hot desert — must have a dry sense of humour...

You need to know all about where deserts are, why they formed there and what they're like. So get learnin'. Now, with all this talk of deserts I can't stop thinking about chocolate chip cheesecake. Which reminds me — don't forget it's spelt with one 's'.

Topic Two — Hot Desert Systems and Landscapes

Processes in Hot Desert Environments

It's a hard life being a rock in the desert — wind and water erode you and weathering makes bits fall off willy-nilly...

Rocks are Broken Down by Weathering

1) There are several different types of **weathering** that **break down rocks** in hot deserts. They include **mechanical** weathering processes, such as:

Thermal fracture and salt weathering cause the most weathering in hot deserts.

THERMAL FRACTURE

1) There are **daily extreme temperature variations** in deserts.

2) During the **day** (when it's **hot**) rocks **expand**, and at **night** (when it's **cold**) they **contract**.

3) **Thermal expansion** and **contraction** may occur at **different rates** on different parts of the rock, which leads to **fractures**.

rock expands   rock contracts

SALT WEATHERING

1) **Salt weathering** is caused by **saline (salty) water**, which comes from **rainfall** or from **groundwater** that's **drawn up** to the desert **surface** by **evaporation**.

2) This saline water **enters pores** or **cracks** in desert rocks.

3) The **high temperature** in hot deserts causes the **water to evaporate**, forming **salt crystals**. As the salt crystals **form** they **expand**, exerting **pressure** on the rocks.

4) As **more** evaporation occurs the salt crystals **expand** even **more**. This increases **pressure** in the rocks, causing **pieces** to **fall off**.

Rainwater can be slightly salty

FROST SHATTERING

1) **Frost shattering (freeze-thaw** weathering) occurs in areas where there's **moisture** and **temperatures** that fluctuate **above** and **below freezing**.

2) Water from rainfall **enters the joints** and **crevices** in desert rocks.

3) At night, if the temperature **drops below 0 °C**, the water in the cracks **freezes** and **expands**.

4) Over time, **repeated** freeze-thaw action **weakens** the rocks and causes pieces to **fall off**.

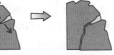

ice expands   rock breaks off

2) **Chemical weathering** processes also operate in hot deserts:

CHEMICAL WEATHERING

Although rainfall is low, there is enough **moisture** in hot deserts (e.g. from occasional rain, dew and fog) to bring about **chemical changes** to the rocks that cause them to **break down**:

1) The main form of chemical weathering in deserts is **hydration**. This is when moisture **combines** with minerals in rocks, especially rocks containing **salt**, and causes them to **swell**. This puts **pressure** on the rock that can cause it to **crack**.

2) **Oxidation** may also occur in deserts — this happens when rocks containing iron are exposed to **oxygen** in air or water. The **iron** can **react** with oxygen to form iron oxide, which is quite **weak** — this makes the rock **crumble** more easily.

Oxidation is why some desert soils are a rusty red colour.

3) **Carbonation** occurs when **carbon dioxide** in the atmosphere dissolves in rainwater, forming a **weak carbonic acid**. This acid **reacts** with rock that contains **calcium carbonate**, e.g. carboniferous limestone, so the rocks are gradually **dissolved**.

3) Desert rocks that have been **weakened** by any of these weathering processes may **break apart** in a number of ways:

- **exfoliation** — the **peeling off** of the **outer layers** of a rock, because of cracks that have formed **parallel** to the surface.
- **granular disintegration** — the breaking off of **individual grains** of sand.
- **block disintegration** — the breaking off of **larger chunks** of rock.

Processes in Hot Desert Environments

Wind Erodes Desert Surfaces and Transports Particles

1) Wind can **erode** desert surfaces in **two** ways:

> (1) **Deflation** — the **removal of fine, loose particles** from the ground surface.
> (2) **Abrasion** — **small particles** being **carried** by the wind **scrape off** particles from the rock surface.

2) It then **transports** the eroded material by **three** processes:

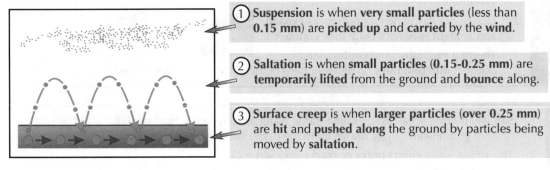

> (1) **Suspension** is when **very small particles** (less than **0.15 mm**) are **picked up** and **carried** by the **wind**.
>
> (2) **Saltation** is when **small particles (0.15-0.25 mm)** are **temporarily lifted** from the ground and **bounce** along.
>
> (3) **Surface creep** is when **larger particles (over 0.25 mm)** are **hit** and **pushed along** the ground by particles being moved by **saltation**.

3) **More particles** are **transported** when the wind is **strong** and comes from a **constant direction**.

There are Three Types of River in Hot Deserts

Like wind, **water** also **erodes** and **transports** sediment in hot deserts.
There are three different kinds of river that can occur:

> 1) **Exogenous** rivers have a **source outside** the **desert margin**. They flow **throughout the year** despite **evaporation** reducing their volume. For example, the source of the **Colorado River** in the USA is in the **Rocky Mountains**. It flows through the **Sonoran Desert** and the **Grand Canyon** to the sea.
>
> 2) **Endoreic** rivers **terminate inland** in the form of an **inland sea** or **delta**. For example, the **River Jordan** terminates in the **Dead Sea** — an inland sea in the **Middle East**.
>
> 3) **Ephemeral** rivers flow **intermittently** or **seasonally** after **rainstorms**. For example, the **Todd River** in the **Simpson Desert** (**Australia**) only flows a few days a year and remains a **dry river bed** for the rest of the year.

Derek promised that an ephemeral river was coming soon...

Flooding Erodes the Desert

Most **rainfall** in hot deserts is **light** and **infrequent**. However, **sometimes** there may be a **sudden**, **high intensity rainstorm** that lasts for a **short period** of time. This can cause **two types** of **flood** in a desert — **channel flash floods** and **sheet floods**.

Channel Flash Flooding

1) A **flash flood** is a **sudden**, **strong** and **rapid** flow of water through a **channel**.
2) They occur because **heavy** rainfall **can't** be **absorbed** by the **dry, hard desert soil** — so the **runoff** collects in **channels** and **flows rapidly downhill**.
3) Flash floods have **enough energy** to transport **large pieces** of desert rock by **traction** (when **very large** particles, e.g. boulders, are **pushed** along the river bed by the force of the water). They also transport **pebbles, gravel** and **sand** by **suspension** and **saltation**. The rocks in the water are **eroded** into **smaller fragments** by **attrition** (rocks smashing into each other).
4) The material carried by flash floods **erodes** the channels by **abrasion**, making them **deeper**.
5) At the **mouth** of a channel, the flash flood waters **spread out, slow down** and **soak into** the **ground** (unless they meet another body of water).

Topic Two — Hot Desert Systems and Landscapes

Processes in Hot Desert Environments

Sheet Flooding

1) A **sheet flood** is a **slow-moving**, **even flow** of water **over land** (i.e. it **isn't** confined to a **channel**).

2) Like flash floods, sheet floods occur **after** a period of **intense rainfall**, where water **collects** across the **dry, impermeable desert floor** and flows down **gentle slopes** as a **sheet** of water.

3) Sheet floods have **less energy** than flash floods, but can still **transport pebbles**, **gravel** and **sand** by **suspension** or **saltation**.

4) The **material** carried by sheet floods **erodes** the **desert surface** by **abrasion**.

Deposition is the Process of Dropping Material

1) Desert material that is **transported** by **wind** or **water** is eventually **deposited**. Deposition occurs when **sediment load** exceeds the ability of the wind or water to **carry** it.

2) This could be because there's a **reduction** in the **speed** of the wind or water flow:

- **Wind** and **water** slow down when they hit an **obstacle**, e.g. a sand dune, or if the roughness of the ground surface increases — this increases **friction** between the air/water and the ground surface.

- **Water** also slows down as the flow **reduces**, if it leaves a channel and **spreads out** (e.g. to form a sheet flood), or if the **gradient** of the ground **decreases**.

3) When wind or water slows down, it **loses energy**. This means it can't carry as much material, so some gets **dropped**.

> *Deposition creates landforms such as sand dunes and bahadas (see pages 28-29).*

Mass Movement Also Occurs in Deserts

1) Mass movement is the **movement** of material **down** a slope due to **gravity**. It is most common on landforms with **steep slopes**, including **inselbergs** and the side walls of **wadis** (see p.28).

2) **Rockfalls** are when material breaks up and moves **rapidly** down a **steep slope** — it is more likely if material is heavily **jointed**, especially if it has lots of **vertical** joints.

3) **Debris flows** occur when material 'flows' downslope — usually during or after **rainfall**. Water increases the **weight** of material and decreases the **friction** between particles, making the material more likely to **collapse**.

> *Rock in deserts can be weakened by weathering, which makes it more vulnerable to mass movement.*

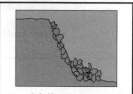

Rockfalls — material **breaks up** and **falls**

Debris flows — material flows downslope

The end of the Geography exam triggered a mass movement of students towards the party poppers.

Practice Questions

Q1 Name two types of weathering that occur in hot deserts.

Q2 Describe two ways in which wind can erode desert landscapes.

Q3 What is an endoreic river?

Q4 Briefly describe how sediment is deposited in a desert.

Exam Question

Q1 Explain the effect of particle size on sediment transport processes in hot deserts. [4 marks]

Surface Creep — Grandad's new disco dance move...

There are tons of technical terms on these three pages — saltation, exogenous, ephemeral... It's tricky enough to get the spelling right, let alone what they mean. But if you shut the book and test yourself a few times you'll soon have 'em sussed.

Landforms in Hot Desert Environments

Wind and water in the desert do really neat things, like sculpting crazy landforms. Ooooooh, aaaaaaaahh.

Water Erosion *Creates Many Different* Desert Landforms

The **fast-moving water currents** that follow **torrential rainfall** in the **desert** can create many different **landforms**:

1 Pediments

Pediments are **desert plains** — **gently sloping** areas of **rock** (usually covered in a thin **layer** of **debris**). They're formed by the **erosion** of rock by **sediment** carried in **sheet floods** or **small streams**.

2 Playas

Playas are **shallow**, extremely **flat depressions** at the **low** point of a **pediment**. Temporary **lakes** periodically form in them when water drains into them after rain. The water quickly **evaporates** because of the high temperatures, and leaves behind layers of **salt**, **silt** or **clay**.

3 Inselbergs

Inselbergs (e.g. **Ayers Rock**) are **steep-sided hills** that rise up from pediments. They're made of **hard rock** that's more **resistant** to **erosion** than the **surrounding rock**. The surrounding rock is **eroded** by **water**, leaving the harder rock **standing out**. Inselbergs can also be formed by **wind erosion**.

Ayers Rock

4 Wadis

A **wadi** is a **gully** or **ravine** that's been eroded by **seasonal rivers**, or by rivers in the **past**, when the **climate** was wetter. Depending on the **strength** of the river, a wadi can have **shallow** or very **steep** valley sides. It can **fill up** with rainwater very **quickly**.

5 Alluvial fans and bahadas

If there's a flat desert plain at the **mouth of a wadi**, the water in a channel flash flood **spreads out** on to the plain. This leads to **sediment** being **deposited** as **energy** is **dissipated**, forming an **alluvial fan**. If there are **several** wadis whose mouths are **close** to one another, a **bahada** might form — this is where several **alluvial fans** have **spread out** and **joined** together, creating a uniform **slope** of **sediment**.

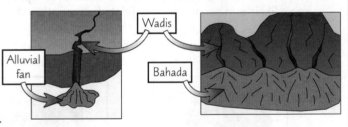

Wadis

Alluvial fan

Bahada

Deflation *Forms* Deflation Hollows *and* Desert Pavements

Deflation — the **removal of fine material** by **wind** (see p.26) creates landforms in hot deserts. These include:

Deflation hollows

Deflation hollows are **depressions** in the ground. They form when **deflation** removes a lot of material from **one** place — they often occur where the material was particularly **fine**. If a hollow is **deep** enough, it will reach the **water table** — this **prevents** deflation from deepening it any further. Deflation hollows can be any size — some are just a **few metres** across, whereas others are **huge**, e.g. the **Qattara Depression** in Egypt covers **18 100 km²**.

Desert pavements

Desert pavements are surfaces of **interlocking stones**. They form when the wind **blows away** the **silt** and **sand** from the desert surface, **leaving behind** the **gravel**, **rocks** and **pebbles** that are too **heavy** to be removed by deflation.

'Aeolian' landforms are created by the action of wind.

Landforms in Hot Desert Environments

Wind Forms Yardangs, Zeugen and Ventifacts by Abrasion

Abrasion also creates landforms in hot deserts. These include:

Yardangs are **narrow, streamlined ridges** that are usually **three to four** times **longer** than they are **wide**. **Strong winds** (blowing in **one direction**) carry sand in **suspension**, which **erodes rocks** by abrasion. **Softer** rock is **eroded faster** than **harder** rock, so **ridges** of hard rock are created (yardangs). The ridges **aren't** always **continuous**.

Zeugen! — That wind is capable of some nifty sculpting.

Zeugen are **long, block-shaped ridges** of rock (a **single ridge** is called a **zeuge**). They're formed in areas where a layer of hard rock sits **above** a layer of softer rock. If **cracks** form in the **hard rock** due to **weathering** processes (see p.25), the **wind** can **erode** through the **cracks** and into the softer rock beneath by **abrasion**. Again, the **softer rock** is eroded **more** than the **hard rock**, and ridges (zeugen) are formed.

Ventifacts are **individual stones** with one or more **smooth sides** that have been **abraded**. The side of the rock that faces the **prevailing** (most common) wind is abraded most, leaving a **flattened face**. The rock may **move**, or the **direction** of the prevailing wind may change, so a different part of the rock is abraded. This gives the rock a **combination** of **smooth faces** and **sharp edges**.

Sand Dunes Form When the Wind Deposits Sand

1) **Sand dunes** form when **sand grains** carried by **suspension** are **deposited** as the wind **slows down**.
2) **Vegetation**, **rocks** and **other dunes** slow wind down, causing it to **drop** its load.
3) The **shape** and **layout** of dunes is affected by several factors:
   - The **speed**, **direction** and **consistency** of the **wind**.
   - The **amount of sand** being transported — the **more** sand, the **larger** the dune.
   - The nature of the **ground surface** — e.g. **rocky outcrops** or **uneven ground** slow wind down.
   - The **amount** and **type of vegetation** — **deposition** occurs **downwind** from vegetation and **around its base**, **deforming** the shape of dunes. Also, **plant root networks** help to **stabilise sand** and **hold** dunes in place.
4) There are lots of **different types** of sand dune, including:

See page 26 for more on how wind transports sand.

Barchan dunes (crescent-shaped)

1) These are **isolated** dunes that develop from mounds of sand. They form in the **direction** of the **prevailing wind** as sand is **deposited**.
2) When the slope of the dune becomes **too steep**, **sand avalanches** occur, depositing sand at the **base** (downwind).
3) **Swirling wind currents** (**eddies**) help to keep the slope **steep**.
4) The dune **slowly moves forward** in the direction of the wind.
5) If there's a **lot of sand** being deposited, many barchan dunes **connect** with each other to form a **barchanoid ridge**.

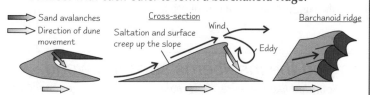

Seif dunes (long wiggly lines)

1) **Seif dunes** are **long, wiggly ridges** of sand.
2) They form **from barchan dunes** if a **change** of **wind direction** occurs.
3) When wind blows from **alternate sides** the 'arms' of barchan dunes are **elongated** and form a wiggly **line**.

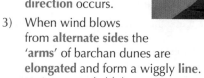

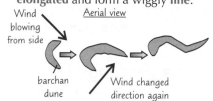

Landforms in Hot Desert Environments

Landforms Make Up Landscapes

1) Individual **landforms combine** to form **landscapes**.

2) Some **desert landscapes** can be dominated by a particular type of landform, e.g. dune fields or desert pavements. Others are made up of a **combination** of landforms.

3) Hot desert landscapes can be dominated by **erosional** landforms, such as pediments and inselbergs, or **depositional** landforms, such as sand dunes and bahadas.

4) They can also be dominated by **aeolian** landforms (those formed by **wind**) or fluvial landforms (those formed by **water**). This may depend on how **frequent** rainfall is in the area.

Monument Valley in the USA contains many different landforms, including dunes, inselbergs and pediments.

Processes Operate Over Time to Alter Landscapes

1) Processes operating in desert systems can **create new landforms** or **change existing landforms**. This means that desert landscapes **change** over time. For example:

- A change in **inputs** can change the landscape, e.g. an increase in **sediment** input may increase **deposition**. Over time, a landscape may change from one dominated by **erosional** landforms to one dominated by **depositional** landforms.

- Landforms that were made by **past** processes can still experience change, e.g. a **wadi** formed by a **river** flowing thousands of years ago might be **eroded** further every time it's flooded during a **rainfall** event.

Processes operate over time; Mark operates over a nice bottle of red.

2) Hot desert landscapes are therefore often made up of a **mixture** of landforms that reflect **different periods** of **change**. E.g. there may be landforms that were formed when the region had a more **humid climate** and landforms formed during **current** climatic conditions.

3) Changes occur over a **range** of **spatial** and **temporal** (time) **scales**. For example, changes can vary from **short** and **episodic** (e.g. short, intense rainstorms transporting material in channels) to **long** and **gradual** (e.g. wind eroding rock over thousands of years to form zeugen).

4) Landscapes in hot deserts often change much more **slowly** than landscapes in other climatic regions, because many **weathering** and **erosional** processes require **water**. Some deserts can go for several years without rain, so these processes operate **slowly** and **episodically**.

Practice Questions

Q1 What are pediments?

Q2 How are desert pavements formed?

Q3 What are ventifacts?

Q3 Give three factors that affect the shape and layout of sand dunes.

Exam Question

Q1 The figure shows Death Valley in the USA. Using the figure, analyse the role of water in shaping this hot desert landscape.

[6 marks]

So, the yardangs fight the zeugen and the inselbergs save the world...

...what's that... we're not talking about Star Trek... Oh. Sounded like we were. Best make sure then that you really do know your yardangs from your zeugen, your pediments from your inselbergs — I suggest you get into gear and sha-wadi-wadi.

Topic Two — Hot Desert Systems and Landscapes

Hot Desert Environment — Case Study

Now you know the general characteristics of hot deserts, let's have a look at a specific example.
You might have studied a different desert in class, but here we're going with the biggest of the bunch.

The **Sahara Desert** is the **Largest** Hot Desert in the World

1) The Sahara Desert covers about **8.6 million km²** — it takes up most of **northern Africa**, partially or fully covering **10 countries**.

2) The desert formed there because of the **air circulation** patterns at this latitude (see p.22). Air that rises at the equator usually **loses** its moisture before it reaches the **Tropic of Cancer**, so rainfall is low.

3) The Sahara is in an area of **high pressure** — air **descends** there, which **prevents cloud formation** and limits rainfall.

The Sahara is **Hot** and **Arid**

1) The majority of the Sahara receives **less than 100 mm** of **rain** per year on average, with some eastern areas receiving **less than 20 mm**. Rain mainly falls during **thunderstorms** — these often come after many years of **no rain** at all.

2) The average annual temperature is **over 30° C** — in the summer it can reach **over 50° C** in the south. **Daily variations** in temperature are often **huge** — a range from –0.5° C to 37.5° C in a single day has been recorded.

3) **Strong winds** that carry **dust** are common. The **prevailing** wind blows from the **northeast**.

4) The climate affects the **soil** and **vegetation**:

> • **Soils** in the Sahara are **dry** and contain **little organic matter**. The soils in **playas** and **deflation hollows** are often quite **saline**.
>
> • Vegetation is **sparse** and the **diversity** of plant life is **low**. Some concentrations of **plants** grow along wadis and in depressions, where more water is found — e.g. date palms and acacia. Vegetation cover **increases temporarily** after rainfall — plants grow and produce seeds very **quickly** to take advantage of the moisture.

Vegetation grows around water sources, such as this oasis in Libya.

The **Climate** Affects the **Processes** that Operate in the Sahara

1) The large temperature range in the Sahara means that rocks are vulnerable to **thermal fracture** and **frost weathering** (see p.25).

2) **Infrequent intense rainstorms** mean that **fluvial processes** (caused by water) operate **intermittently** but are **powerful** when they occur.

3) High temperatures and low rainfall mean that sediment is very mobile. It can easily be eroded and transported by the **strong winds** of the Sahara, so **aeolian processes** (caused by wind) are also important.

There are Lots of **Desert Landforms** in the **Sahara**

The Sahara desert is made up of many different **landscapes**. **Desert pavements** make up about **70%** of the Sahara, and around a **quarter** of the desert is covered by **sandy plains** and **dunes**. Most desert landforms can be found in the Sahara — for example:

Deflation hollows

• The **Qattara Depression** in northwestern Egypt is the **biggest** deflation hollow in the world.

• It covers **18 100 km²** and is **133 m below sea level** at its deepest point.

• It might have begun as a **stream valley** when the climate was wetter, which dried up and got **deeper** and **wider** through **deflation** (when fine particles are **blown away** by the wind).

• **Salt weathering** may have played an important role in the formation of the Qattara Depression, by breaking up the ground surface into **particles small** enough for deflation.

There was a more humid period in Africa from about 11 000 to 5000 years ago.

Hot Desert Environment — Case Study

Wadis

- When rain falls in the Sahara, there is rapid **runoff**, and the water runs into **ephemeral** streams and **wadis** (see p.28). There are often concentrations of **vegetation** along wadi floors.
- Many wadis were formed when the Sahara had a **wetter** climate.
- For example, the **Yellow Nile** was the main **tributary** flowing from the Sahara into the Nile from about 9500 years ago until 4500 years ago — the valley it left behind when it dried up is known as **Wadi Howar**. It's over 1100 km long, and runs through **Chad** and **Sudan**. Its bed has more **moisture** than the surrounding ground, so it can support **vegetation** — a line of **trees** grows along its course.

A wadi in Libya.

Yardangs

- **Yardangs (linear rock ridges)** have formed in some parts of the Sahara. They form where **wind**, mainly coming from **one direction**, erodes rock by **abrasion** (see p.26).
- E.g. the yardangs around the Aorounga Impact Crater in Chad are formed by the prevailing wind from the **northeast**:

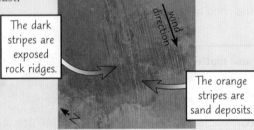
The dark stripes are exposed rock ridges. | wind direction | The orange stripes are sand deposits.

Dunes

- The **Great Sand Sea** is an area of dune fields covering **72 000 km²** of western Egypt and eastern Libya.
- Two thirds of the dunes here are **seif dunes** (see p.29) — they form **parallel lines** running roughly north to south because of the **prevailing winds**.

Some Processes and Landforms Can be Studied Through Fieldwork

The kind of **aeolian** (wind) processes that operate in the Sahara could be **investigated** a little closer to home. **Coastal sand dune** landscapes have **sand dunes** and **deflation hollows** caused by aeolian processes. Studying these coastal landforms and processes could give you information about desert systems, for example:

- You could investigate the **relationship** between **wind** and **dune morphology** (shape).
- You might do this by surveying the **profile** of dunes (e.g. with a clinometer and ranging poles) and the **wind speed** and **direction** in different locations.
- You could also measure the **size** of **deflation hollows** over time, to establish whether they're **growing**, and, if so, the **rate** at which sand is being eroded from them.

Practice Questions

Q1 Why is the Sahara desert arid?
Q2 Describe two landforms in the Sahara desert.

Exam Question

Q1 Assess the extent to which climate affects the processes that operate in hot deserts. [20 marks]

So it's a sand sea, and it's pretty great — what shall we call it?

It's always good to throw some real examples into an exam answer, so make sure you know your hot desert case study really well. Now that you're pretty much an expert on deserts, it's time to head to the next page and learn about problems in places that are becoming more desert-like — you didn't think I'd let you get through a geography topic without any bad news, did you?

Desertification

Desertification isn't the cheeriest topic around, but it's definitely important.

The **Distribution** of Hot Deserts has Been **Changing** for **Thousands of Years**

1) Hot deserts haven't always been where they are today — **changing climates** change their extent and distribution.

2) After the **last glacial period** ended, about **11 500 years ago**, the climate in many parts of the world became **wetter**, which reduced the amount of land covered by deserts.

3) About 9000 years ago, the only **hot deserts** in the world were narrow strips on the west coasts of **Africa** and **South America**, and this is how it remained until about **5000 years ago**.

4) Since then, these areas have remained as desert, but the extent of hot deserts has **increased** significantly.

5) For example:

   - The Sahara region wasn't a desert from about **11 000** to **5000** years ago.

   - This period is known as the '**Green Sahara**' — there were numerous **lakes**, and much more **vegetation**. Animals native to the **savanna** biome (see p. 103-105) were present, such as **giraffes** and **elephants**.

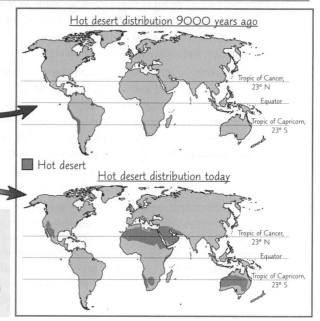

6) Changes to hot deserts thousands of years ago were down to **natural** climatic variations, but in more **recent** times, **humans** have also started to influence the extent and distribution of deserts.

Desertification is a Form of **Land Degradation**

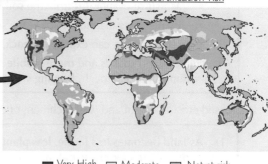

World map of desertification risk

Desertification is the **degradation** of **semi-arid** land by **human activities** and **changes in climate**. It leaves land **unproductive**. **Africa** and **Asia** are the **worst affected areas** but desertification is a problem across the globe.

1) A **third** of land worldwide is **at risk** of **desertification**. 110 countries have regions that are threatened, with those likely to be worst affected in **Africa**, **Asia** and **Latin America**.

2) **250 million people** across the globe are already affected by desertification, the **largest proportion** of which are in **Asia**.

3) **46%** of **Africa** is **at risk** of desertification (**25%** is at **high** or **very high risk**).

Very High   Moderate   Not at risk
High   Low   Dry

Climate Change is a **Physical Cause** of Desertification

Climate change is causing desertification by **reducing rainfall** and **increasing** the **temperature** in some areas:

Lower rainfall	**Higher temperatures**
1) Climate change will probably **reduce rainfall** in **sub-tropical regions** (where most semi-arid environments are).	1) From 1900 to 2016, **global surface temperature** rose by **1.08 °C**, and it's predicted to **continue rising**.
2) If there's **less rain** then **surface water** and **groundwater** will be **reduced** (as it's used up or evaporates but isn't replenished).	2) As **temperatures increase** the **rate of evapotranspiration** also **increases**.
3) This means that the volume of **water** available for **vegetation growth** is **reduced**, which leads to the **death** of vegetation.	3) This **dries out soils** and **lowers surface water levels**, leading to soil erosion and death of vegetation.
4) The **roots** of **plants** and **trees bind the soil together**. **Fewer plants** and **trees** mean **fewer roots**, leading to **soil erosion**.	

Topic Two — Hot Desert Systems and Landscapes

Desertification

Human Activity is the Main Cause of Desertification

There are lots of ways that **humans** are increasing **desertification**, e.g.:

1) **Overgrazing** — **reduces vegetation**, so leads to **soil erosion** (due to lack of **plant roots**). Trampling by large numbers of animals **compresses** and **breaks down** the **structure of soil**, which also makes **erosion more likely**.

2) **Overcultivation** — **reduces soil productivity** as the over-exploitation of the soil leaves it **without** enough **nutrients** to support plants. Without plants (and plant roots) the soil is **easily eroded**.

3) **Deforestation** — removing **trees** and therefore **tree roots** means that (once again) soil is more **vulnerable to erosion**. Forests are cleared to provide **land** for **farming** as well as **wood** for **fuel** and **building materials**.

4) **Irrigation** — can cause desertification in a number of ways:

> • Irrigation **depletes surface water** and may involve **unsustainable pumping** of **aquifers**. As **water levels** are **lowered**, **water availability** for plants **decreases**, leading to **soil erosion**.
>
> • Some **irrigation techniques** can **erode soil directly**, e.g. surface irrigation, where large amounts of water are added to the soil in a short amount of time, **washing topsoil away**.
>
> • If **too much water** is used to irrigate crops the excess can **sink** into the soil and **raise groundwater levels**. If the aquifer is **saline** this may bring **high concentrations** of **salt** too close to the surface, **increasing** the **salinity** of the **soil** too much for plants to survive.

Aquifers are underground rocks containing water that can be extracted.

5) **Population growth** — **increases pressure** on the **land** as more and more **food** is needed to meet the **growing demand**. This leads to **further overgrazing**, **overcultivation**, **deforestation** and **irrigation**, therefore increasing desertification.

Desertification Impacts on Landscapes, Ecosystems and Populations

Desertification causes change to the **landscape**:

> 1) The ground surface becomes more prone to **erosion**, because:
> - **Vegetation** slows wind speed (see p.27), so reducing vegetation cover **increases wind speed**.
> - **Moisture evaporates** from the soil more **quickly** when it isn't sheltered by plants, so it dries out.
> - **Plants roots** that help to bind the sediment together are **lost**.
>
> 2) Increased erosion can **expose bedrock**.
>
> 3) **Higher** wind speeds and **more mobile** sediment can also cause more sand to be **blown into** an area — **dunes** may encroach, **burying** vegetation and soils.

Increased erosion of soil and encroachment of dunes has major impacts on **ecosystems**:

Loss of vegetation increases erosion, which reduces vegetation cover more — it's a vicious cycle.

> 1) As land becomes less fertile, **less plant life** can grow — this reduces the amount of organic matter that is put into the soil, further reducing vegetation growth. Less vegetation means **less animal life** can be supported, and **biodiversity decreases**.
>
> 2) Desertification is changing the **distributions** of species. Plant and animal populations that were present in regions now transformed by desertification may either **die out** or **migrate** to less degraded areas. Species **adapted** for the **desert** biome can **outcompete** native species in regions that have experienced desertification.
>
> 3) Desertification also **releases carbon** stored in the soil into the **atmosphere** — this contributes to **climate change**, which has widespread impacts on ecosystems.

Brian was hurt by claims that he wasn't adapted to the desert biome.

Changes to landscapes and ecosystems have knock-on effects on **human populations**:

> 1) A reduction in the fertility of land causes a decline in **agricultural productivity** — if it decreases to the point where farmers **can't feed** their **families** or **earn a living** from the land then they have to **migrate** from the area. This **increases pressure** on the **land** in the **areas** that they **migrate to**. Often, people migrate from **rural** to **urban** areas, to seek alternative ways of making a living — this may lead to **overcrowding**.
>
> 2) If people are **unable** to move then desertification can lead to **famine**, as families or whole communities are unable to produce the food they need from the degraded land.
>
> 3) Desertification can also affect human **health** in other ways, e.g. **dust** from soil erosion can cause **respiratory** diseases, and a reduction in **clean water** supplies could increase **water-borne diseases**.

Desertification

It's *Predicted* that *Future Climate Change* will *Increase* Desertification

Future climate change is expected to cause many semi-arid areas to become **hotter** and **drier**:

- Global **temperatures** are expected to **rise** by up to **6 °C** between **2015** and **2100**.
- **Precipitation** is expected to **decrease** in **subtropical** regions, where many semi-arid regions are located.
- **Extreme weather events**, such as heat waves and extreme rainfall, are likely to become more **frequent**.

This is likely to **increase** the **risk** of desertification in many areas by drying out **soil** and **increasing erosion**.

The *Future* of *Local Populations* is *Uncertain*

1) The **future** of people living in areas experiencing desertification depends on the **actions** that are taken to **mitigate** the impacts of desertification and **prevent** more land from being **degraded**.

2) The **uncertainty** surrounding the potential strategies for dealing with desertification mean that there are **alternative possible futures** for local populations:

1 Desertification may continue

- If action isn't taken to reduce desertification, or if strategies aren't **funded** or **managed** properly, then the **rate** of desertification could **increase**, leading to large areas of degraded land.
- The reduction in **agricultural yields** would increase **malnutrition** and **famine**. A lack of **food security** would hinder **development** in affected countries.
- **Overcrowding** of urban areas as people migrate would put extra pressure on **sanitation systems** and **healthcare**, which may increase rates of **disease**.
- There may also be **conflict** within and between countries suffering from desertification, as food and water become more **scarce**.

2 Humans may stop or reverse desertification

- Further desertification could be **prevented** — and some desertified areas could be returned to their previous state — if major action is taken.
- **Locally**, people could **plant** vegetation to **bind** the soil and act as **windbreaks**. Farmers can carry out **crop rotation** to allow the soil to recover, and improve **irrigation** systems.
- **Global** responses to **climate change** could have a major effect. If enough changes are made to **reduce greenhouse gas emissions**, temperature rises and rainfall declines could be slowed. However, this would require major **commitment** and **cooperation** around the globe.

3 Humans may reduce the impacts of desertification

- Local populations may **change** their lifestyles in order to **adapt** to desertification and reduce its impacts.
- For example, local farmers could change their **farming methods** to reduce the impacts of desertification on their livelihoods. This could involve **diversifying** their farms, e.g. keeping small livestock such as goats and chickens, which would be **less affected** by desertification than crops, so would provide **more reliable** produce.
- Improvements in agricultural **technology** could allow farmers to **increase** the amount of food they produce **per hectare**, helping to prevent food supplies from decreasing as more land becomes **unsuitable** for farming.

Practice Questions

Q1 What is desertification?
Q2 How might desertification lead to migration?
Q3 Describe two ways desertification is likely to affect local populations.

Exam Question

Q1 'The impacts of desertification on local populations can only worsen over time.'
To what extent do you agree with this view? [20 marks]

Dessertification — now that sounds like a topic I could get on board with...

If a third of land was at risk of being turned into sticky toffee pudding, the world would be a much better place. Sadly, that's not the case and desertification is causing problems across the globe. The good news is that if you take the time to learn these three pages really well it shouldn't cause you a smidge of a problem in your exam. Every cloud and all that...

Desertification — Case Study

Down to specifics... desertification's causing problems all over the place, including Southern Spain.
The Med may be fantastic for holidays, but all those tourists have an impact...

Desertification is Happening in Southern Spain

1) **Spain** is in **southern Europe**, close to North Africa and the Sahara desert.

2) Roughly **50%** of Spain is classified as **arid**, making it the **driest** country in Europe.

3) In 2008 it was estimated that **37%** of Spain is **at risk** of **desertification** (with **18%** of the land at **high** or **very high** risk).

4) The **most vulnerable areas** of the country are in the **south**, e.g. Andalusia and Murcia.

Desertification is Caused by Climate Change, Agriculture and Development

Climate Change

1) The **average temperature** in Spain has **risen** by **1.5 °C** in the last century, **increasing** the rate of **evapotranspiration**.

2) **Rainfall** has **decreased** throughout Spain, especially in the south.

3) Higher temperatures and lower rainfall have **reduced surface water resources**. Between 1995 and 2015, the volume of fresh water in Spain fell by **20%**. Less water is available to recharge groundwater supplies, leading to **falling groundwater levels**. As there's **less water**, **fewer plants** can grow, meaning there are **fewer roots** to hold the soil together. This leads to **soil erosion** and desertification.

4) As the climate gets hotter and drier there's **increased risk** of **forest fires**, causing **deforestation** and desertification.

Agriculture

1) **Overcultivation** is reducing the **nutrient content** of the soil to the point that it's no longer productive. **80 million tonnes** of topsoil is **lost** each year in **Andalusia** because of intensive cultivation of **olive trees**.

2) **Overgrazing** is **reducing vegetation cover**, causing desertification.

3) Groundwater resources are being pumped to **irrigate crops**. This is **lowering groundwater levels**. Increasingly more water is being used for irrigation because...

- **Agriculture** is carried out in areas that **aren't** really **suitable** for it. E.g. the region of **Almeria** (in Andalusia) is an important agricultural area as produce grown there for export contributes **$1.5 billion** to the economy each year. Almeria is the driest area in Europe though, so this is only possible with **intensive irrigation**.

- **Crops** that need **more water** than the area can **supply** are being grown for **export**. E.g. Spain is Europe's largest producer of **strawberries**, and **95%** of its exports are grown in **Andalusia**. As Andalusia is so arid, **intensive irrigation** is needed to supply the strawberries with the **large amounts** of water they need to grow.

Although there are restrictions in place to protect aquifers, many farmers are using **illegal boreholes** to secure water supplies for their crops.

Development for agriculture and tourism can be done in a more sustainable way — when it's not, it increases desertification.

Development

1) There's been a huge **increase** in **tourism** in southern Spain in the last 50 years. In 2004, an estimated **180 000 holiday homes** were built along the Spanish coast.

2) This is increasing strain on water supplies as there's more and **more demand** for **water** for **swimming pools**, **water parks** and **irrigation** of **golf courses**.

3) Although there are regulations in place to protect water supplies for agriculture, many developments get around them by **reclassifying** grass on golf courses as "**crops**" or holiday villas as "**farms**". This ensures that, like farms, they get **allocated water**. This contributes to desertification by **depleting water levels**. It also **reduces water availability** for **farms**, **reducing** their **productivity**, which leads to desertification spreading.

Desertification — Case Study

Desertification Has Environmental, Social and Economic Impacts

1) The demand for water to fill swimming pools and irrigate crops and golf courses has led to **conflict** over water. A **black market** for water has developed, supplied by water from **illegal boreholes**. An estimated **40%** of land in some parts of the **Segura basin** (Murcia) is illegally irrigated and **10%** of wells in the **Guadalquivir river basin** (Andalusia) are illegal.

2) Exploitation of groundwater has led to **loss of habitats**, such as wetlands, and **reduced biodiversity** in the region. E.g. nearly **150 000 ha** of **marshland** surrounding **Doñana National Park** has been **lost** since 1900 — most of which has been deliberately drained for farming.

3) As groundwater levels lower, the water can become **salinised** (very salty). When this happens the water is no longer suitable for drinking or irrigation and the **resource** is **lost**. Many wells have had to be abandoned.

4) As **aquifers** become **salinised** so do the **soils** around them, which leads to **further desertification**.

5) Desertification leaves soil **unusable for farming** and deprives farmers of their **livelihood**.

There are Various Strategies to Reduce Desertification

People living in southern Spain are **responding** to the changes brought about by desertification in several ways:

- **Resilience** — being **able to cope** with the challenges presented by desertification.
- **Mitigation** — **reducing** the **severity** of desertification or its impacts.
- **Adaptation** — **changing behaviour** to fit with the changes in the environment.

The government's **Programme of National Action Against Desertification** aims to limit desertification and promote **sustainable development** in southern Spain — it involves mitigation, adaptation and increasing resilience:

The **National Hydrological Plan** was adopted in **2001** to ensure that water supply meets demand:

1) The government has proposed various schemes to **transfer water** from areas with a **plentiful supply** to areas with **very little**. However, they are controversial — e.g. in 2002, thousands of people **protested** against plans to transfer water from the **Ebro River** to southeast Spain, claiming that **wetland ecosystems** in the Ebro delta would be destroyed. The plans were **shelved** in 2004, but there are concerns that they may be considered again.

2) **Desalination plants** have been built to produce fresh water from seawater. However, they are very **expensive** to build and run, so customers **can't afford** to buy the water produced. For example, one plant in Torrevieja cost around **€300 million** to build, but is **not running** because of a lack of buyers for the water.

3) Some strategies have been more successful — e.g. investing in drip irrigation has **reduced** the amount of water **wasted** during irrigation, and promoting **efficient use** of **water resources** has helped to limit demand.

1) Areas at **high risk** of **wildfires** have been identified — this helps planners draw up **defence plans** for them so that fires can be dealt with quickly. This helps to **limit** destruction of vegetation and desertification.

2) Some areas are being **reforested** after wildfires or deforestation — this **reduces** soil erosion and helps the soil retain **moisture**. The area of forested land in Spain **increased** from **27.6%** in 1990 to **36.8%** in 2015.

1) An official **water trading scheme** has been set up that allows farmers to buy water. It costs them three times the normal price but is **lower** than the **black market price** and therefore aims to **reduce illegal exploitation** of **aquifers**.

2) However, this will only reduce desertification if water resources are **sustainably managed** instead of **over-exploited**.

Practice Questions

Q1 Which areas of Spain are most vulnerable to desertification?

Q2 Why has the volume of water needed for irrigation increased?

Q3 Describe two impacts of desertification in Spain.

Exam Question

Q1 Assess the extent to which human activities are responsible for desertification. [20 marks]

The rain in Spain stays mainly in the plain — but there's not much nowadays...

You know the drill by now — learn all the specifics, don't skimp on the examples, blah blah blah. The more information you know the more marks you can get. And once you've learnt these pages, you're done with this whole topic. Finally.

The Coastal System

Coastal systems are the areas where the land meets the sea. And they're almost as exciting as they sound...

Coasts are Natural Systems

Coasts are **systems** — they have **inputs**, **outputs**, **flows** and **stores** of **sediment** and **energy** (see p. 2):

Events such as storm surges give high energy inputs — this can increase sediment inputs or outputs.

1) **INPUTS** — e.g. **sediment** can be brought into the system in various ways (see next page). **Energy** inputs come from **wind**, **waves**, **tides** and **currents** (see below).

2) **OUTPUTS** — e.g. sediment can be **washed out to sea**, or deposited **further along** the coast.

3) **FLOWS/TRANSFERS** — e.g. processes such as **erosion**, **weathering**, **transportation** and **deposition** (see pages 40-41) can move sediment **within** the system (e.g. from beach to dune).

4) **STORES/COMPONENTS** — **landforms** such as **beaches**, **dunes** and **spits** (see p. 42-44) are stores of sediment.

Coastal systems are generally in **dynamic equilibrium** — inputs and outputs are **balanced**. A **change** in one input or output often causes **negative feedbacks** that **restore** the balance of the system:

> A **NEGATIVE FEEDBACK** is when a change in the system causes other changes that have the **opposite effect**. For example, as a beach is **eroded**, the cliffs behind it are exposed to **wave attack**. Sediment eroded from the cliffs is **deposited** on the beach, causing it to **grow in size** again.

Coastal systems also experience **positive feedbacks** that change the balance of the system, creating a **new equilibrium**:

> A **POSITIVE FEEDBACK** is when a change in the system causes other changes that have a **similar effect**. For example, as a beach starts to **form** it slows down waves, which can cause more sediment to be **deposited**, increasing the **size** of the beach. The **new** equilibrium is reached when **long-term growth** of the beach **stops**.

There Are Lots of Sources of Energy in Coastal Systems

In the coastal system, energy is **transferred** by **air** (as wind) and by **water** (as waves, tides and currents):

Wind

1) **Winds** are created by air moving from areas of **high** pressure to areas of **low** pressure. During events such as **storms**, the pressure gradient (the difference between high and low pressure) is high and winds can be very **strong**.

2) Strong winds can generate **powerful waves**. In some areas, wind consistently blows from the **same** direction (this is called a **prevailing wind**) — this causes **higher-energy waves** than winds that change direction frequently.

Waves

1) **Waves** are created by the **wind** blowing over the surface of the sea. The **friction** between the wind and the surface of the sea gives the water a **circular motion**.

2) The **effect of a wave** on the **shore** depends on its **height**. Wave height is affected by the **wind speed** and the **fetch** of the wave. The fetch is the **maximum distance of sea** the wind has blown over in creating the waves. A **high wind speed** and a **long fetch** create **higher** and more **powerful** waves.

3) As waves approach the shore they **break**. **Friction** with the sea bed **slows** the bottom of the waves and makes their motion more elliptical (squashed and oval-shaped). The **crest** of the wave rises up and then **collapses**.

4) Water washing **up** the beach is called the **swash**. Water washing **back** towards the sea is called the **backwash**.

5) There are **two types** of wave:

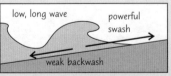

Constructive waves have a **low frequency** (only around **6-8** waves per minute). They're **low** and **long**, which gives them a more **elliptical** cross profile. The powerful swash carries material up the beach and **deposits** it.

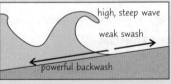

Destructive waves are **high** and **steep**, with a more **circular** cross profile. They have a **higher frequency** (**10-14** waves a minute). The strong backwash **removes** material from the beach.

Wave frequency is how many waves pass a point in a particular time.

6) The waves in an area are usually **mainly constructive** or **mainly destructive**.

The Coastal System

Tides

1) Tides are the periodic **rise** and **fall** of the **ocean surface**, caused by the gravitational pull of the **Moon** and the **Sun**.

2) Tides affect the **position** at which **waves break** on the beach (at high tide they break higher up the shore). The area of land between **maximum high tide** and **minimum low tide** is where most landforms are created and destroyed.

Currents

1) A **current** is the general flow of water in one direction — it can be caused by **wind** or by variations in water **temperature** and **salinity**.

2) Currents move material **along** the coast.

Currants — check. Salinity — check. Karen knew how to make her cake memorable.

Coasts can be **High Energy** or **Low Energy**

1) **High-energy** coasts receive high inputs of energy in the form of **large**, **powerful waves**. These can be caused by **strong winds**, **long fetches** and **steeply shelving** offshore zones. High-energy coastlines tend to have **sandy** coves and **rocky** landforms, e.g. cliffs, caves, stacks and arches (see p. 42). The rate of **erosion** is often **higher** than the rate of **deposition**.

2) **Low-energy** coasts receive low inputs of energy in the form of **small**, **gentle waves**. These can be caused by **gentle winds** (e.g. if the location is **sheltered**), **short fetches** and **gently sloping** offshore zones. Some coastlines are low energy because there is a **reef** or **island** offshore, which protects the coast from the full power of waves. Low-energy coastlines often have **saltmarshes** and **tidal mudflats**. The rate of **deposition** is often **higher** than the rate of **erosion**.

There Are Lots of **Sediment Sources** in Coastal Systems

1) There are lots of **inputs** of sediment into the coastal system:

- **Rivers** carry eroded sediment into the coastal system from **inland**.
- **Sea level rise** can flood river valleys, forming **estuaries**. Sediment in the estuary becomes part of the coastal system.
- Sediment is **eroded** from **cliffs** by waves, weathering and landslides.
- Sediment can be **formed** from the crushed **shells** of marine organisms.
- Waves, tides and currents can transport sediment into the coastal zone from **offshore deposits** (e.g. sandbanks).

2) The **difference** between the amount of sediment that enters the system and the amount that leaves is the **sediment budget**. If **more** sediment **enters** than leaves, it's a **positive sediment budget** and overall the coastline **builds** outwards. If **more** sediment **leaves** than enters, it's a **negative sediment budget** and overall the coastline **retreats**.

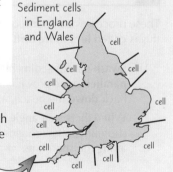

Sediment cells in England and Wales

Sediment Cells

- The coast is divided into **sediment cells** (also called **littoral cells**).
- These are lengths of coastline (often between two headlands) that are pretty much entirely **self-contained** for the movement of sediment (i.e. sediment doesn't move between cells). This means that **processes** going on in **one cell** don't affect the movement of sediment in **another** cell — each cell is a **closed coastal system**.

Practice Questions

Q1 Draw a table to show the main inputs, flows, outputs and stores of a coastal system.

Q2 Describe the differences between high-energy and low-energy coasts.

Exam Questions

Q1 Outline the characteristics of constructive waves. [4 marks]

Q2 Outline the sources of energy in a coastal system. [4 marks]

What did the sea say to the beach — nothing, it just waved...

Lots of technical terms on these pages, but it's worth learning them — they'll really help you understand the rest of this topic. So make sure it's all as familiar as your favourite pair of socks (you know the ones — with the holes and the sausage-dog print).

Coastal Processes

Coasts are affected by two types of processes — marine processes <u>are</u> caused by the sea (erosion, transport and deposition), and sub-aerial processes <u>aren't</u> directly caused by the sea (weathering, runoff and mass movement). Confused? Read on...

There are **Six** Main Ways **Waves Erode** the **Coastline**

Waves don't just erode beaches — they also erode **rocks** and **cliffs**. Here are the six main ways they do it:

1) **Corrasion (abrasion)** — Bits of rock and sediment transported by the waves **smash** and **grind** against rocks and cliffs, **breaking** bits off and **smoothing** surfaces.

2) **Hydraulic action** — **Air** in cracks in cliffs is **compressed** when waves crash in. The pressure exerted by the compressed air breaks off rock pieces.

3) **Cavitation** — As waves **recede**, the compressed air **expands violently**, again exerting **pressure** on the rock and causing pieces to **break off**.

4) **Wave quarrying** — The energy of a wave as it breaks against a cliff is enough to detach bits of rock.

5) **Solution (corrosion)** — **Soluble rocks** (e.g. limestone, chalk) get gradually **dissolved** by the seawater.

6) **Attrition** — Bits of rock in the water smash against **each other** and break into smaller bits.

Transportation is the Process of **Eroded Material** Being Moved

The **energy** provided by waves, tides and currents **transports eroded material**. There are **four** main processes:

Solution — Substances that can **dissolve** are carried along in the water. E.g. **limestone** is dissolved into water that's slightly **acidic**.

Suspension — Very **fine** material, such as **silt** and **clay** particles, is whipped up by **turbulence** (**erratic swirling** of water) and carried along in the water. **Most** eroded material is transported this way.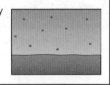

Saltation — **Larger particles**, such as **pebbles** or **gravel**, are **too heavy** to be carried in suspension. Instead, the **force** of the water causes them to **bounce** along the sea bed.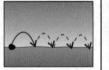

Traction — Very **large** particles, e.g. **boulders**, are **pushed** along the sea bed by the force of the water.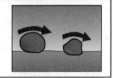

These processes can transport sediment **along** the shore — this is called **longshore drift** (or **littoral drift**):

1) **Swash** carries sediment (e.g. shingle, pebbles) **up** the beach, **parallel** to the prevailing wind. **Backwash** carries sediment back **down** the beach, at **right angles** to the shoreline.

2) When there's an **angle** between the prevailing wind and the shoreline, a few rounds of swash and backwash move the sediment **along** the shoreline.

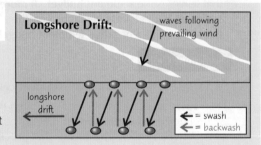

Longshore Drift: waves following prevailing wind

longshore drift

← = swash
← = backwash

Deposition is the Process of **Dropping Eroded Material**

1) Deposition is when **material** being transported is **dropped** on the coast:
   - **Marine deposition** is when sediment carried by **seawater** is deposited.
   - **Aeolian deposition** is when sediment carried by **wind** is deposited.

Deposition forms landforms such as beaches, spits and dunes (see pages 43-44).

2) Both marine and aeolian deposition happen when the **sediment load** exceeds the ability of the water or wind to **carry** it. This can be because sediment load **increases** (e.g. if there is a landslide), or because wind or water **flow slows down** (so it has **less energy**). Wind and water slow down for similar reasons:
   - **Friction increases** — if waves enter **shallow** water or wind reaches **land**, **friction** between the water/wind and ground surface increases, which **slows down** the water or wind.
   - **Flow becomes turbulent** — if water or wind encounters an **obstacle** (e.g. a current moving in the opposite direction, or an area of vegetation), flow becomes **rougher** and overall speed **decreases**.

3) If the wind drops, wave height, speed and energy will decrease as well.

Topic Three — Coastal Systems and Landscapes

Coastal Processes

Sub-aerial Weathering Occurs Along the Coastline

Sub-aerial weathering is the gradual break down of rock by agents such as ice, salt, plant roots and acids. Weathering **weakens cliffs** and makes them **more vulnerable** to erosion. There are several types of weathering that affect coasts:

Salt Weathering
1) **Salt weathering** is caused by **saline** (salty) **water**.
2) This saline water **enters pores** or **cracks** in rocks at high tide.
3) As the tide goes out the rocks dry and the **water evaporates**, forming **salt crystals**. As the salt crystals **form** they **expand**, exerting **pressure** on the rock — this causes **pieces** to **fall off**.

Freeze-thaw Weathering
1) **Freeze-thaw** weathering occurs in areas where **temperatures** fluctuate **above** and **below freezing**.
2) Water enters the **joints** and **crevices** in rocks.
3) If the temperature drops **below 0 °C**, the water in the cracks **freezes** and **expands**.
4) Over time, **repeated** freeze-thaw action **weakens** the rocks and causes pieces to **fall off**.

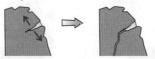
ice expands   rock breaks off

Wetting and Drying
1) Some rocks contain **clay**.
2) When clay gets **wet**, it **expands** and the **pressure** caused by this **breaks fragments off** the rock.

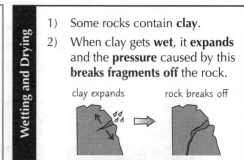
clay expands   rock breaks off

Chemical Weathering
1) **Chemical weathering** is the breakdown of rock by **changing** its **chemical composition**.
2) For example, **carbon dioxide** in the atmosphere dissolves in rainwater, forming a **weak carbonic acid**. This acid **reacts** with rock that contains **calcium carbonate**, e.g. carboniferous limestone, so the rocks are gradually **dissolved**.

Biological weathering — e.g. plant roots growing into cracks in the rock and widening them — can also cause rocks to break down.

Mass Movement is when Material Moves Down a Slope

1) Mass movement is the **shifting** of **material** downhill due to **gravity**. In coastal areas, it is most likely to occur when cliffs are **undercut** by wave action — this causes an unsupported **overhang**, which is likely to collapse.
2) Types of mass movement include **landslides**, **slumping** (a type of landslide), **rockfalls** and **mudflows**. Material can also move gradually downwards by **soil creep**.

Slides — material shifts in a **straight line**

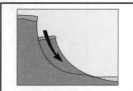
Slumps — material shifts with a **rotation**

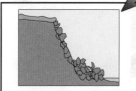
Rockfalls — material **breaks up** and **falls**

Mudflows — material flows downslope

3) **Unconsolidated** rocks (e.g. clay) are prone to collapse as there's **little friction** between particles to hold them together.
4) **Heavy rain** can **saturate** unconsolidated rock, further reducing friction and making it more likely to **collapse**.
5) **Runoff** (the flow of water over the land) can **erode** fine particles (e.g. sand and silt) and **transport** them downslope.

Practice Questions

Q1 Describe two processes of coastal sediment transport.
Q2 Explain why water deposits sediment when it slows down.

Exam Question

Q1 Explain how sub-aerial weathering can cause breakdown of coastal rock.   [4 marks]

Mass movement — what happened when we spotted a spider in the office...

Seriously, it was a bad time — there was running, screaming, one man got trampled... Fortunately, mass movements at the coast aren't normally hazardous (unless you happen to be standing underneath a cliff at the wrong time — do try to avoid that).

Coastal Landforms

Walk this way for some coastal landforms... Geology and the amount of energy in the coastal system affect the type of landforms that occur — areas tend to be dominated by either erosional or depositional landforms, giving distinctive landscapes.

Some **Coastal Landforms** are Caused by **Erosion**

CLIFFS AND WAVE-CUT PLATFORMS

1) **Cliffs** are common coastal landforms — they form as the sea **erodes** the land. Over time, cliffs **retreat** due to the action of **waves** and **weathering**.

2) Weathering and wave erosion cause a **notch** to form at the high water mark. This eventually develops into a **cave**.

3) Rock above the cave becomes **unstable** with nothing to support it, and it **collapses**.

4) **Wave-cut platforms** are **flat surfaces** left behind when a cliff is eroded.

These cliffs and platforms are near Lannacombe Bay in South Devon.

| 1. Notch formed | 2. Cave formed | 3. Collapse and cliff retreats | 4. Repeated retreat leaving a large wave-cut platform |

high tide / low tide (repeated under each diagram)

HEADLANDS AND BAYS

1) **Headlands** and **bays** form where there are **bands** of alternating **hard rock** and **soft rock** at **right angles** to the shoreline.

2) The **soft rock** is **eroded quickly**, forming a **bay**. The **harder rock** is **eroded less** and sticks out as a **headland**.

These headlands and bay are on the Cape of Good Hope, South Africa.

→ = Waves
▢ = Beach
Ⓗ = Headland
Ⓑ = Bay

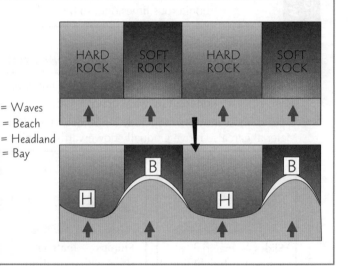

HARD ROCK | SOFT ROCK | HARD ROCK | SOFT ROCK

CAVES, ARCHES AND STACKS

1) Some landforms are found in cliffs — these are called **cliff profile features**.

2) Weak areas in rock (e.g. joints) are **eroded** to form **caves**.

3) Caves on the opposite sides of a narrow headland may eventually join up to form an **arch**.

4) When an **arch** collapses, it forms a **stack**.

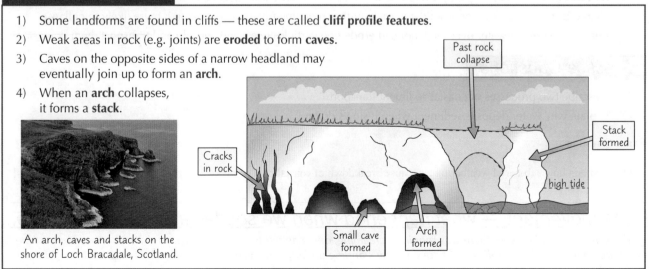

An arch, caves and stacks on the shore of Loch Bracadale, Scotland.

Past rock collapse

Stack formed

Cracks in rock

high tide

Small cave formed

Arch formed

Topic Three — Coastal Systems and Landscapes

Coastal Landforms

Some *Coastal Landforms* are Caused by *Deposition*

BEACHES

1) **Beaches** form when **constructive** waves **deposit sediment** on the shore — they are a **store** in the coastal system.

2) **Shingle** beaches are **steep** and **narrow**. They're made up of **larger** particles, which pile up at steep angles. **Sand** beaches, formed from **smaller** particles, are **wide** and **flat**.

3) Beaches have distinctive features. **Berms** are **ridges** of sand and pebbles (about 1-2 metres high) found at **high tide** marks. **Runnels** are **grooves** in the sand running **parallel** to the shore, formed by **backwash** draining to the sea. **Cusps** are **crescent-shaped indentations** that form on beaches of mixed sand and shingle.

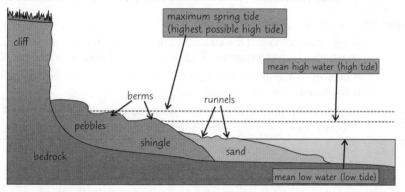

Berms on a beach in
Parque Tayrona, Colombia.

SPITS

Spits tend to form where the coast suddenly **changes direction**, e.g. across river mouths.

1) **Longshore drift** (see p. 40) continues to **deposit** material across the river mouth, leaving a bank of **sand** and **shingle** sticking out into the sea. A **straight** spit that grows out roughly **parallel** to the coast is called a **simple spit**.

2) Occasional **changes** to the dominant wind and wave direction may lead to a spit having a **curved end** (the fancy name for this is a **recurved end**).

3) Over time, several recurved ends may be abandoned as the waves return to their **original direction**. A spit that has **multiple recurved ends** resulting from **several** periods of growth is called a **compound spit**.

4) The area **behind** the spit is **sheltered** from the waves and often develops into **mudflats** and **saltmarshes** (see p. 44).

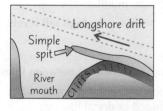
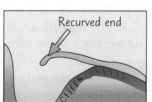

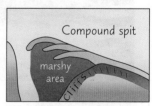

OFFSHORE BARS AND TOMBOLOS

Bars are a type of barrier beach — see next page.

1) Bars are formed when a **spit joins two headlands together**. This can occur across a **bay** or across a **river mouth**.

2) A **lagoon** forms **behind** the bar.

3) Bars can also form off the coast when material moves **towards** the coast (normally as sea level rises). These may remain **partly submerged** by the sea — in this case they're called **offshore bars**.

The Slapton Sands bar at
Torcross, Devon.

Paul and Mary left
the bar to spend some
time enjoying the
lagoon...

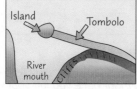

4) A bar that **connects** the shore to an **island** (often a stack) is called a **tombolo**.

5) For example, St Ninian's Isle in the Shetland Islands is joined to a larger island by a tombolo.

Coastal Landforms

BARRIER ISLANDS

1) Barrier islands (also called barrier beaches) are long, narrow islands of sand or gravel that run **parallel** to the shore and are **detached** from it. They tend to form in areas where there's a good supply of **sediment**, a **gentle slope** offshore, fairly **powerful** waves and a **small tidal range**.

> 'Barrier beach' is a general term for any beach that shelters the coast, including barrier islands, spits and bars.

2) It's not clear exactly how barrier islands form, but scientists think that they probably formed after the **last ice age** ended, when ice melt caused rapid **sea level rise**. The rising waters **flooded** the

Ice age — low sea level

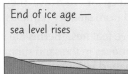

End of ice age — sea level rises

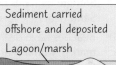

Sediment carried offshore and deposited

Lagoon/marsh

land behind beaches and **transported** sand offshore, where it was **deposited** in shallow water, forming islands.

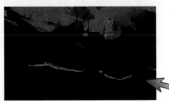

3) Another theory is that the islands were originally **bars**, attached to the coast, which were **eroded** in sections, causing **breaches** in the bar.

4) A **lagoon** or **marsh** often forms behind the barrier island, where the coast is **sheltered** from wave action.

5) Barrier islands are found on many coastlines, including the **east coast** of the **USA**, e.g. Horn Island in Mississippi.

SAND DUNES

1) Sand dunes are formed when **sand deposited** by longshore drift is moved up the beach by the **wind**.

2) Sand trapped by driftwood or berms (see previous page) is colonised by **plants** and **grasses**, e.g. marram grass. The vegetation **stabilises** the sand and encourages **more sand** to accumulate there, forming **embryo dunes**.

3) Over time, the oldest dunes migrate inland as newer embryo dunes are formed. These **mature dunes** can reach heights of up to 10 m.

Sand dunes at Cape Hatteras in North Carolina.

ESTUARINE MUDFLATS AND SALTMARSHES

Saltmarsh, Huntington Beach State Park, South Carolina.

1) Mudflats and saltmarshes form in **sheltered**, **low-energy** environments, e.g. river estuaries or behind spits.

2) As **silt** and **mud** are **deposited** by the river or the tide, **mudflats** develop.

3) The mudflats are colonised by **vegetation** that can survive the **high salt levels** and long periods of **submergence** by the tide.

4) The plants **trap more mud** and **silt**, and gradually they build upwards to create an area of saltmarsh that remains **exposed** for longer and longer **between tides**.

5) **Erosion** by tidal currents or streams forms **channels** in the surface of mudflats and saltmarshes. These may be **permanently flooded** or **dry** at low tide.

Practice Questions

Q1 Name four landforms of coastal erosion and four landforms of coastal deposition.

Q2 Describe where headlands and bays form.

Q3 Briefly describe how stacks are formed.

Q4 Where do saltmarshes form?

Exam Questions

Q1 Explain how a headland and bay coastal landscape is formed. [4 marks]

Q2 Outline how spits form and develop. [4 marks]

Man walks into a bar, gets his feet wet...

The landforms you have to know are pretty much the same ones you have to know for GCSE — you just need to know more detail about how they form. And you thought it was going to be all excitement and glamour once you left your GCSEs behind. Sorry.

Topic Three — Coastal Systems and Landscapes

Sea Level Changes

There's a fair bit to learn on these three pages. Just try and keep your head above the water...

Sea Level Changes are Eustatic or Isostatic

You need to know the difference between **eustatic** and **isostatic** changes in sea level, and the role that **tectonic processes** (processes related to movement of the Earth's **crust**) play in each:

EUSTATIC

Eustatic sea level change is caused by a change in the **volume of water** in the sea, or by a change in the **shape** of the **ocean basins**.

The effects are always **global** and the main **causes** are:

1) **Changes in climate.** Different changes affect sea level in different ways:

- An **increase** in **temperature** causes **melting** of **ice sheets**, which **increases** sea level. It also causes water to **expand**, which **increases** sea level further.

- A **decrease** in **temperature** causes more precipitation to fall as **snow**. This increases the volume of water **stored** in **glaciers** and so reduces the volume of the sea, which **decreases** sea level.

2) **Tectonic movements** of the Earth's crust that alter the shape (and so the volume) of ocean basins. E.g. sea floor spreading **increases** the **volume** of the basin and so **decreases** sea level.

ISOSTATIC

Isostatic sea level change is caused by **vertical movements** of the land **relative** to the sea.

Any **downward** movement of the land causes sea level to **rise** locally, while **uplift of land** causes sea level to **fall**.

The effects are always **local** and the main **causes** are:

1) **Uplift** or **depression** of the Earth's crust due to accumulation or melting of **ice sheets**. Slow uplift of land can continue for thousands of years after the weight of a **retreating glacier** has gone. **Accumulation of sediment**, mostly at the mouths of major rivers, can also cause **depression**.

2) **Subsidence** of land due to shrinkage after **abstraction of groundwater**, e.g. drainage of marshland.

3) **Tectonic** (crustal) processes, e.g. as one plate is forced beneath another at a plate margin (see p. 76).

"There's definitely sea down there somewhere. Nigel, you go first."

Isostatic uplift had caused problems for Chris, Steven and Nigel.

Sea Level Has Risen in the Last 10 000 Years

1) Sea level **varies** on a daily basis with the **tidal cycle**. **Onshore winds** and **low atmospheric pressure systems** also cause the sea surface to rise **temporarily**.

2) On a much **longer time scale**, global sea level has changed by a much **larger** amount:

- During the **last glacial period** (from roughly 110 000 to 12 000 years ago), water was stored in **ice sheets**, so sea level was **lower** than present. At the **last glacial maximum** (around 21 000 years ago) sea level was about **130 m lower** than present.

- As temperatures started to **increase** (about 12 000 years ago), ice sheets **melted** and sea level **rose** rapidly. It reached its present level about **4000 years ago**.

- Over the **last 4000 years**, sea level has **fluctuated** around its present value.

- Since about **1930**, sea level has been **rising** (see next page).

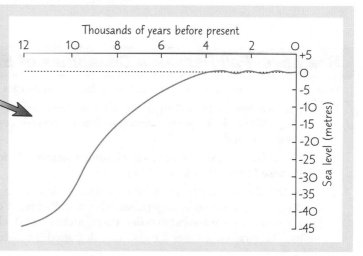

Thousands of years before present

Topic Three — Coastal Systems and Landscapes

Sea Level Changes

Climate Change Causes Changes in Sea Level...

1) Over the **last century**, **global temperature** has **increased rapidly**. This is called **global warming**. There's been a **sharp rise** in average temperature (**1.08 °C** between **1900** and **2016**).

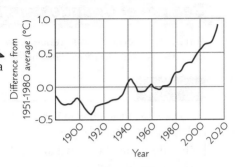

2) The **temperature increase** over the last century has been **very fast**. There is a **consensus** among scientists that the **changes** in **climate** over the last century are a result of **human activities**, such as deforestation and burning fossil fuels.

3) These activities increase the concentration of greenhouse gases in the atmosphere — greenhouse gases absorb **outgoing long-wave radiation**, so less is **lost** to space. As their concentration increases, **more** energy is trapped and the planet **warms up**.

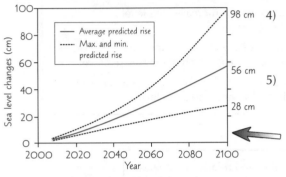

4) Increases in **temperature** are likely to cause increases in **sea level**, through **melting** of ice sheets and **thermal expansion** of water in oceans.

5) Global sea level is currently rising at almost **2 mm** each year. If greenhouse gas emissions remain very **high** during the 21st century, this is predicted to **increase** to **8** to **16 mm** a year by 2100.

The Watson brothers had a plan for dealing with sea level rise.

... and has Impacts on Coastal Areas

1) **Storms** are likely to become more **frequent** and more **intense** due to **changes in ocean circulation** and **wind patterns**. This would cause damage to coastal **ecosystems** and **settlements**.

2) If **sea level rise** continues as predicted, it will have major impacts on coastal areas:

   • **More frequent** and **more severe coastal flooding**. Flooding of low-lying areas has increased with sea level rise and it will increase more with further rises. For example, from 1995 to 2004, **Kings Point** in **New York** state, USA, flooded around **80 times**, but from 2005 to 2014 it flooded nearly **160 times**.

   • **Submergence of low-lying islands**. Lots of low-lying islands are **at risk** of disappearing. For example, if the sea level rises by just **0.5 m** from its current level then most of the **Maldives** will be submerged.

   • **Changes in the coastline**. As sea levels rise the coastline changes — islands are **created** and the **area** of **land** is **decreased**. E.g. if the sea level rises **0.3 m** from its current level, **8000 km²** of land in **Bangladesh** will be lost.

   • **Contamination of water sources and farmland**. Salt water may enter bodies of fresh water (e.g. lakes and rivers) near the coast, damaging **ecosystems** and making the water **unsuitable** for lots of uses. Salt water entering soils may **damage crops** and make land impossible to **farm**.

3) Sea level rise and increased storminess will increase **coastal erosion**, putting **ecosystems**, **homes** and **businesses** at risk.

Sea Level Fall Results in Coastlines of Emergence

When sea level falls relative to the coast, new coastline **emerges** from the sea. This creates different **landforms**:

1) **Raised beaches** are formed when the fall in sea level leaves beaches **above** the high tide mark. Over time, beach sediment becomes **vegetated** and develops into **soil**.

2) Sea level fall also exposes **wave-cut platforms** (**marine platforms**), leaving them **raised** above their former level.

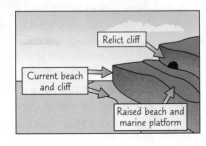

3) The **cliffs** above raised beaches are no longer eroded by the sea, and slowly get covered by **vegetation**. They're called **relict cliffs**. It's not uncommon to see **wave-cut notches**, **caves**, **arches** and **stacks** within relict cliffs. These **raised features** are gradually **degraded** (weathered) over time.

Topic Three — Coastal Systems and Landscapes

Sea Level Changes

Sea Level Rise Results in Coastlines of Submergence

When sea level rises relative to the coast, the sea **submerges** (drowns) the existing coastline. This creates different **landforms**:

RIAS

RIAS are formed where **river valleys** are partially **submerged**, e.g. Milford Haven in South Wales is a ria. Rias have a **gentle** long- and cross-profile. They're **wide** and **deep** at their **mouth**, becoming **narrower** and **shallower** the further **inland** they reach.

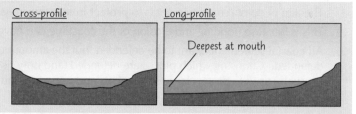

FJORDS

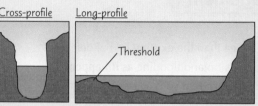

FJORDS are a lot like rias, but they're **drowned glacial valleys** rather than drowned river valleys. They're relatively **straight** and narrow, with very **steep sides**. They have a **shallow mouth** caused by a raised bit of ground (called the **threshold**) formed by deposition of material by the glacier. They're very **deep** further **inland**, e.g. Sognefjorden in Norway is over 1000 m deep in places.

DALMATIAN COASTLINES

In areas where valleys lie **parallel** to the coast, an increase in sea level can form a **DALMATIAN COASTLINE**. Valleys are flooded, leaving **islands** parallel to the coastline. It's named after the Dalmatian coast in Croatia.

 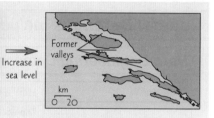

Processes Create and Alter Landforms and Landscapes Over Time

1) Individual **landforms** (e.g. spits, arches) **combine** to form **landscapes** — coastal landscapes can be dominated by processes of **erosion** or **deposition**, but most are formed by **both**.

2) Processes operating in coastal systems can **create new landforms** or **change existing landforms**. This means that coastal landscapes **change** over time. For example:
   - A change in **one factor** can lead to changes in **others**, e.g. a change in **wave direction** might increase **deposition** and eventually change a landscape dominated by **erosive landforms** to one dominated by **depositional landforms**.
   - **Relict** landforms can still experience coastal **processes**, e.g. a relict cliff may be **weathered** by salt and freeze-thaw.

3) Coastal landscapes are therefore often made up of a **mixture** of active and relict landforms that reflect **different periods** of **change**. E.g. a beach that is still being formed may be backed by a relict cliff from an **earlier time** of higher sea level.

4) Changes occur over a **range** of **spatial scales** and **temporal scales**. For example, changes can vary from **short** and **episodic** (e.g. storm waves that last for a few hours) to **long** and **gradual** (e.g. tectonic uplift over thousands of years).

Practice Questions

Q1 State two causes of eustatic sea level change and two causes of isostatic sea level change.

Q2 Give two examples of landforms that show there must have been a drop in sea levels.

Q3 Sketch a diagram showing the cross-profile of a fjord.

Exam Questions

Q1 Outline how coastal submergence can result in a range of landforms. [4 marks]

Q2 Assess the likely impacts of climate change on coastal areas in the future. [20 marks]

I'd start moving up onto high ground now...

You need to know how and why sea levels are rising, and the impacts this might have. Examiners love asking questions about current issues, and rising sea levels are a hot topic in the news at the moment — so make sure you're hot on all the details too.

Topic Three — Coastal Systems and Landscapes

Coastal Management

Coastal management is a complex thing. Fixing up one coastal area can have the unintended effect of messing up another area...

Only **Some Parts** of the **Coast** are **Defended**

1) The aim of coastal management is to **protect homes**, **businesses** and the **environment** from **erosion** and **flooding**.

2) This is because flooding and erosion of the coastline can have severe **social**, **economic** and **environmental impacts**.

3) All coastal settlements want to be defended, but the amount of **money available** is **limited** so not everywhere can be defended. Choosing which places are defended (and how) is based on a **cost-benefit analysis**. The money available is usually used to protect **large settlements** and important **industrial sites**, rather than isolated or small settlements.

There are **Four Options** for **Coastal Management**

1) **Hold the line** — maintain the **existing** coastal defences.

2) **Advance the line** — build **new** coastal defences **further out to sea** than the existing line of defence.

3) **Do nothing** — build **no** coastal defences at all, and deal with erosion and flooding **as it happens**.

4) **Managed realignment** — allow the shoreline to **move**, but **manage retreat** so it causes **least damage** (e.g. flooding farmland rather than towns). See next page.

Coastal Defences Include **Hard Engineering** and **Soft Engineering**

Hard Engineering Defences Involve **Built Structures**

Defence	How it works	Cost	Disadvantage
Sea wall	The wall reflects waves back out to sea, preventing erosion of the coast. It also acts as a barrier to prevent flooding.	Expensive to build and maintain	It creates a strong backwash, which erodes under the wall.
Revetment	Revetments are slanted structures built at the foot of cliffs. They can be made from concrete, wood or rocks. Waves break against the revetments, which absorb the wave energy and so prevent cliff erosion.	Expensive to build, but relatively cheap to maintain	They create a strong backwash, as above.
Gabions	Gabions are rock-filled cages. A wall of gabions is usually built at the foot of cliffs. The gabions absorb wave energy and so reduce erosion.	Cheap	Ugly
Riprap	Boulders piled up along the coast are called riprap. The boulders absorb wave energy and so reduce erosion.	Fairly cheap	Can shift in storms.
Groynes	Groynes are fences built at right angles to the coast. They trap beach material transported by longshore drift. This creates wider beaches, which slow the waves (reducing their energy) and so gives greater protection from flooding and erosion.	Quite cheap	They starve down-drift beaches of sand. Thinner beaches don't protect the coast as well, leading to greater erosion and flooding.
Breakwaters	Breakwaters are usually concrete blocks or boulders deposited off the coast. They force waves to break offshore. The waves' energy and erosive power are reduced before they reach the shore.	Expensive	Can be damaged in storms.
Earth bank	Mounds of earth act as a barrier to prevent flooding.	Quite expensive	Can be eroded.
Tidal barrier	Tidal barriers are built across river estuaries. They contain retractable floodgates that can be raised to prevent flooding from storm surges.	VERY expensive	Really, VERY expensive.
Tidal barrage	Tidal barrages are dams built across river estuaries. Their main purpose is to generate electricity. Water is trapped behind the dam at high tide. Controlled release of water through turbines in the dam at low tide generates electricity. They also prevent flooding from storm surges.	VERY expensive	They disrupt sediment flow, which may cause increased erosion elsewhere in the estuary.

Coastal Management

Soft Engineering *Defences Involve Coaxing* **Natural Processes Along**

1) **Beach nourishment** is where **sand** and **shingle** are added to beaches from elsewhere (e.g. **dredged** from offshore). This creates **wide** beaches, which **reduce erosion** of cliffs more than thin beaches.

2) **Beach stabilisation** can be done by **reducing the slope angle** and planting **vegetation**, or by sticking **stakes** and **old tree trunks** in the beach to stabilise the sand. It also creates **wide** beaches, which **reduce erosion** of cliffs.

3) **Dune regeneration** is where sand dunes are **created** or **restored** by either nourishment or stabilisation of the sand. and dunes provide a **barrier** between land and sea, **absorbing wave energy** and preventing flooding and erosion.

4) **Land use management** is important for dune regeneration. The vegetation needed to stabilise the dune can easily be **trampled** and destroyed, leaving the dune **vulnerable** to **erosion**. Wooden **walkways** across dunes, and **fenced-off areas** that prevent walkers, cyclists or 4×4 drivers from gaining access to the dunes, all **reduce vegetation loss**.

5) **Creating marshland** from mudflats can be encouraged by **planting** appropriate vegetation (e.g. glassworts). The vegetation **stabilises** the sediment, and the stems and leaves help **reduce the speed** of the waves. This **reduces** their **erosive power** and **how far** the waves reach **inland**, leading to **less flooding** of the area around the marsh.

6) **Coastal realignment** (also known as **managed retreat**) involves breaching an existing defence and allowing the sea to flood the land behind. Over time, vegetation will colonise the land and it'll become **marshland**.

Management Strategies *for the Future Must be* **Sustainable**

Some coastal engineering provides habitats for tiny kings and queens.

1) Coastal management has to be **sustainable** — this means that strategies shouldn't cause too much damage to the **environment** or to people's **homes** and **livelihoods**, and shouldn't **cost** too much.

   • Hard engineering is often **expensive**, and it **disrupts natural processes**.

   • Soft engineering schemes tend to be **cheaper** and require **less time** and **money** to **maintain** than hard engineering schemes. Soft engineering is designed to **integrate** with the natural **environment** and it creates areas like **marshland** and **sand dunes**, which are important **habitats**.

   • So soft engineering is a **more sustainable management strategy** than hard engineering because it has a **lower environmental impact** and **economic cost**.

2) There are **two** important ideas involved in deciding how to **manage** coastal areas **sustainably**:

Shoreline Management Plans	1) The coastline is split into stretches by **sediment cells** (see p.39). For each cell, a **plan** is devised for how to manage different areas with the aim of **protecting important sites** without causing **problems elsewhere** in the sediment cell (e.g. starving an adjacent area of sediment could increase erosion).
	2) For each area within a cell, authorities can decide to **hold**, **advance** or **retreat** the line, or to **do nothing**.
	3) The **overall plan** for each sediment cell is called a **Shoreline Management Plan** (SMP). All the **local authorities** in one sediment cell **co-operate** in coming up with an SMP.

Integrated Coastal Zone Management	1) **Integrated Coastal Zone Management** (**ICZM**) considers **all** elements of the coastal system (e.g. land, water, people, the economy) when coming up with a management strategy. It aims to **protect** the coastal zone in a relatively **natural** state, whilst allowing people to **use** it and **develop** it in different ways.
	2) It is **integrated** in various ways:
	• The environment is viewed as a **whole** — the **land** and the **water** are **interdependent**.
	• Different **uses** are considered, e.g. fishing, industry, tourism.
	• **Local**, **regional** and **national** levels of authority all have an **input** into the plan.
	3) It is a **dynamic** strategy — decisions are re-evaluated if the environment or demands on the area **change**.

Practice Questions

Q1 What is the aim of coastal management?

Q2 What are Shoreline Management Plans?

Exam Question

Q1 Distinguish between hard and soft engineering schemes in coastal management. [4 marks]

Do nothing? Retreat? Sounds like a lousy revision strategy to me...

Coastal management sounds like a difficult and unending job. Even after spending millions of pounds on a nice big concrete wall to keep the waves out, it can still go horribly wrong. These days, coastal managers try to use more sustainable methods instead.

Coastal Environment — Case Study

Time to put all the theory into practice — here's a bagful of juicy facts about Holderness in East Yorkshire.

The Holderness Coastline is **Eroding Rapidly**

1) The Holderness coastline is **61 km long** — it stretches from Flamborough Head to Spurn Head.

2) Most of the cliffs are made of **till** (**'boulder clay'**), and the coast is exposed to powerful **destructive waves** from the North Sea during storms.

3) There are a number of **coastal processes** operating in the area:

- **Erosion** — the soft boulder clay is easily **eroded** by wave action. In some places, e.g. **Great Cowden**, the rate of erosion has been over **10 m/year** in recent years.

- **Mass movement** — the boulder clay is also prone to **slumping** when it's wet. Water makes the clay **heavier** and acts as a **lubricant** between particles, which makes it **unstable**.

- **Transportation** — prevailing winds from the northeast transport material **southwards**. These winds also create an **ocean current**, which transports material south by **longshore drift**. Rapid erosion means there is always plenty of sediment to be transported.

- **Deposition** — where the ocean **current** meets the **outflow** of the Humber River, the flow becomes **turbulent** and sediment is deposited.

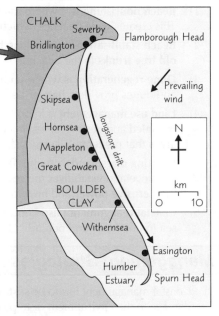

Coastal Processes Have Created **Distinctive Landscapes**

See pages 42-44 for more on coastal landforms.

The coastal **landscapes** around Holderness **vary** — in the north are steep chalk **cliffs**, **wave-cut platforms** and sandy **beaches**. Further south there are less-steep boulder-clay **cliffs**, and around Spurn Head there are **depositional features**.

Headland and wave-cut platforms — to the **north** of the area, the boulder clay overlies **chalk**. The chalk is **harder** and **less easily eroded**, so it has formed a **headland** (**Flamborough Head**) and **wave-cut platforms**, such as those near **Sewerby**. Flamborough Head has features such as **stacks**, **caves** and **arches**.

Slumping cliffs — frequent **slumps** give the boulder clay cliffs a distinctive shape. In some locations several slumps have occurred and not yet been eroded, making the cliff **tiered**. For example, slumps are common around **Atwick Sands**.

Beaches — the area to the **south** of Flamborough Head is **sheltered** from wind and waves, and a **wide sand** and **pebble beach** has formed near **Bridlington**.

Sand dunes — around **Spurn Head**, material transported by the wind is **deposited**, forming **sand dunes**.

Spit — erosion and longshore drift have created a spit with a **recurved end** across the mouth of the Humber Estuary — this is called **Spurn Head**. To the **landward** side of the spit, estuarine **mudflats** and **saltmarshes** have formed.

The Holderness Coastline Needs to be **Managed**

1) The Holderness coastline has retreated by **around 4 km** over the past **2000 years**. Around **30 villages** have been **lost**.

2) Ongoing erosion could cause numerous **social**, **economic** and **environmental** problems, such as:

- **Loss of settlements and livelihoods** — e.g. the village of **Skipsea** is at risk and **80 000 m²** of good quality **farmland** is lost each year on the Holderness coast, which has a huge effect on **farmers' livelihoods**.

- **Loss of infrastructure** — the **gas terminal** at **Easington** is only **25 m** from the cliff edge.

- **Loss of Sites of Special Scientific Interest (SSSIs)** — e.g. **the Lagoons** near **Easington** provide habitats for birds.

Topic Three — Coastal Systems and Landscapes

Coastal Environment — Case Study

Hard Engineering has been Used Along the Holderness Coastline

A total of **11.4 km** of the 61 km coastline is currently protected by **hard** engineering:

- **Bridlington** is protected by a **4.7 km long sea wall** as well as **timber groynes**.
- There's a **concrete sea wall**, **timber groynes** and **riprap** at **Hornsea** that protect the village.
- **Two rock groynes** and a **500 m long revetment** were built at **Mappleton** in **1991**. They cost **£2 million** and were built to **protect the village** and the **B1242 coastal road**.
- A landowner in **Skipsea** has used **gabions** to help protect his caravan park.
- There are **groynes** and a **sea wall** at **Withernsea**. Some **riprap** was also placed in front of the wall after it was damaged in severe storms in 1992.
- **Easington Gas Terminal** is protected by a **revetment**.
- The **eastern** side of **Spurn Head** is protected by **groynes** and **riprap**.

Existing Schemes are Not Sustainable

1) The groynes **trap sediment**, increasing the **width** of the beaches. This **protects the local area** but **increases erosion** of the cliffs **down-drift** (as the material eroded from the beaches there isn't replenished). E.g. the Mappleton scheme has caused **increased erosion** of the cliffs **south** of Mappleton. **Cowden Farm**, just south of Mappleton, is now at risk of falling into the sea.

2) The sediment produced from the erosion of the Holderness coastline is normally washed into the **Humber Estuary** (where it helps to form **tidal mudflats**) and down the **Lincolnshire coast**. Reduction in this sediment **increases** the **risk of flooding** along the Humber Estuary, and **increases erosion** along the Lincolnshire coast.

3) The protection of local areas is leading to the **formation of bays** between those areas. As bays develop the wave pressure on headlands will increase and eventually the **cost** of maintaining the sea defences may become **too high**.

4) All these problems make the existing schemes **unsustainable**.

There are Challenges for All Possible Schemes

1) The **SMP** for Holderness for the next 50 years recommends '**holding the line**' at **some settlements** (e.g. at Bridlington, Withernsea, Hornsea, Mappleton and Easington Gas Terminal) and '**doing nothing**' along **less-populated stretches**. However, this is **unpopular** with owners of land or property along the stretches where nothing is being done.

2) **Managed realignment** has been suggested, e.g. relocating **caravan parks** further inland and allowing the land they are on to erode. This would be a **more sustainable** scheme as it would allow the coast to erode as normal without endangering businesses. However, there are issues surrounding how much **compensation** businesses will get for relocating. Also, relocation isn't always possible, e.g. there may be no land for sale to relocate buildings to.

3) In 1995, Holderness Borough Council decided to **stop** trying to protect Spurn Head from erosion and overwashing — **do nothing** became the new strategy. This **saves money** and allows the spit to function **naturally**, but overwashing may **damage marsh environments** behind the spit. A **coastguard station** on the spit may also be **at risk**.

4) **Easington Gas Terminal** is currently protected by **rock revetments**, and the SMP recommends that these defences are maintained for as long as the gas terminal is operating. However, the defences only span about **1 km** in front of the gas terminal, meaning that the **village of Easington** (with a population of about **700 people**) isn't protected. The defences may also **increase erosion** at legally-protected Sites of Special Scientific Interest (**SSSIs**) to the south.

Practice Questions

Q1 Briefly describe three impacts of coastal erosion in the Holderness area.

Q2 Briefly outline one challenge associated with coastal management along the Holderness coast.

Exam Question

Q1 To what extent do you agree that sustainable management of coastal areas is achievable? [20 marks]

Like easily eroded clay, I'll be gone when the morning comes...

Coastal environments offer loads of opportunities for fieldwork — you could measure beach or cliff profiles, measure sediment size, do vegetation transects, interview residents about their views on management, sun-bathe... OK, maybe not that last one.

Humans at the Coast — Case Study

Oh, I do love a day at the seaside. And I'm not the only one — around half the world's population live near the coast.
Unfortunately, it's not all ice creams and donkey rides — life on the coast can bring some pretty serious risks, too.

The **Sundarbans** Region is in **Bangladesh** and **India**

1) The Sundarbans region is in southwest Bangladesh and east India, on the **delta** of the **Ganges**, **Brahmaputra** and **Meghna** rivers on the Bay of Bengal.

2) Large parts of the region are protected as a National Park or forest reserve. It is part of the largest **mangrove** forest in the world.

> Mangrove is a type of forest found in tropical areas. The trees are adapted to living in salt water and grow on mud flats.

3) The land is very **flat** and **low-lying**. It is intersected by thousands of **channels**, many containing small sandy or silty **islands**.

4) The Sundarbans is home to many **rare species** of plants and animals, including orchids, white-bellied sea eagles, Royal Bengal tigers and Irawadi dolphins.

5) In its natural state, the coastal system is in **dynamic equilibrium**. Material is **deposited** by the rivers, allowing the growth of the mangrove forests. It is also **eroded** by the sea, so the size of the **sediment store** remains roughly the **same**.

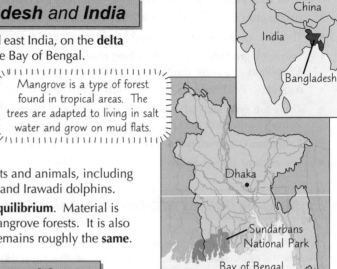

The Sundarbans Region Brings **Opportunities**...

1) The Sundarbans region is home to more than **4 million people**. The area provides a range of **natural products**, which can be used by the people who occupy the area or sold to bring **economic benefits** to the region:

- The flat, fertile land of the river deltas is ideal for growing **crops**, particularly **rice**.
- The rich **ecosystem** of the mangrove forest provides the local population with **fish**, **crabs**, **honey** and **nipa palm leaves** used for roofing and basket-making.
- The mangrove forests provide **timber** for construction, firewood and furniture.

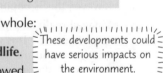

2) The Sundarbans also provides **services** for the people who live there:

- The mangrove forest provides a **natural defence** against **flooding** — it acts as a barrier against **rough seas** and absorbs **excess water** in the rainy (monsoon) season. This makes it easier to **live** and **grow crops**.
- The mangroves also protect the area against **coastal erosion** — their roots bind the soil together.

3) There are also opportunities for **development**, to increase the **wealth** of Bangladesh as a whole:

> These developments could have serious impacts on the environment.

- There are opportunities for **tourism** — visitors are attracted by the mangroves and **wildlife**.
- Since 2011, **cargo ships** transporting goods such as **oil** and food inland have been allowed to use the waterways. Some channels have been **dredged** to make passage easier for the ships.
- A **power plant** has been proposed just north of the national park, providing **energy** for people in the region.

... But Occupation Also Brings **Risks**

The location and nature of the Sundarbans create numerous **risks** for **occupation** and **development**:

1) There is a lack of **fresh water** for drinking and irrigation in much of the area. This is because fresh water is **diverted** from the rivers for irrigation of agricultural land further **upstream**.

2) The **growing population** has led to a need for more **fuel** and more **agricultural land**, so the mangrove forests are being **removed**. This increases the **risk** of flooding (e.g. during tropical cyclones) and coastal erosion.

3) Flooding can lead to **salinisation** (increased saltiness) of soil, making it hard to grow **crops**.

4) The Sundarbans is home to **dangerous animals** that attack humans, including tigers, sharks and crocodiles.

5) There is a lack of **employment** and **income** opportunities.

6) The low-lying land is at risk from **rising sea levels** due to global warming.

7) It is a relatively **poor** region, and only one-fifth of households have access to mains **electricity**. This makes **communication** by e.g. television and radio difficult, meaning that residents often don't receive **flood warnings**.

8) **Access** is difficult — there are **few roads**, and those that exist are of poor quality. This limits opportunities for development, and makes it harder for residents to receive **goods**, **healthcare** and **education**.

Humans at the Coast — Case Study

There are **Attempts** to **Overcome** These Risks

People can respond to risks through **resilience**, **mitigation** and **adaptation**.

Resilience

Resilience means being able to **cope** with the challenges the environment presents. There are attempts to **increase** the population's resilience, for example:

- The Public Health Engineering Department is increasing access to **clean water** and **sanitation**. This will improve **health** and **quality of life**.

- Better **roads** and **bridges** are being built in the region, improving **access** for residents and visitors. However, this can lead to **deforestation** and other environmental damage.

- Mains **electricity** is being extended to more areas, and subsidised **solar panels** are being made available in remote villages to allow them to generate their own power. This will make it easier for **flood warnings** to reach communities, and could create **employment** opportunities.

- There are efforts to **decrease poverty** and **increase food security** in the region, for example by providing **farming subsidies** to increase food production and provide jobs. However, there is a risk that some areas of land may be farmed too **intensively**, causing environmental damage.

- Some NGOs are offering **training** in **sustainable methods** of fishing and farming, to help prevent environmental damage from over-exploitation or poor practices.

> One issue with many of these strategies is that they are expensive. Much of the funding relies on non-governmental organisations (NGOs) such as charities, often based in other countries.

Steve wondered if he'd gone too far with the solar panels.

Mitigation

Mitigation means **reducing** the **severity** of hazards or other problems. For example:

- 3500 km of **embankments** were built to prevent flooding. However, the embankments are gradually being **eroded**, and around 800 km are vulnerable to being **breached** during storms and tsunamis.

- Coastal management projects aim to **protect** existing mangrove forests and **replant** areas that have been removed, to protect against flooding and erosion. However, it is difficult to prevent **illegal forest clearance** throughout the whole region, and it is unclear whether the mangroves will withstand **sea level rise**.

- There are attempts to mitigate the impacts of **extreme events**, e.g. cyclones. For example, the government and NGOs have provided funding for **cyclone shelters** and **early warning systems**, which should help people **shelter** or **evacuate**. However, many people may not have **transport** available to enable them to evacuate quickly.

Adaptation

Adaptation means **adjusting behaviour** to fit the environment. As the environment of the Sundarbans changes (due to e.g. climate change and sea level rise), people will need to adapt to it to **reduce risks** and **increase benefits**. For example:

- In some areas, **salt-resistant** varieties of rice are being grown — this could help residents cope with **flooding** and **sea level rise**. However, relying on a smaller range of crops can **reduce biodiversity** and may increase **vulnerability** to pests and diseases.

- Projects are underway to increase **tourism** to the area, providing **jobs** and **income**. For example, lodges have been built and tour operators run boat trips on the rivers. However, if not properly managed, tourism can cause **environmental damage**.

- People can adapt to sea level rise or flooding, e.g. by building houses on **stilts**. However, infrastructure such as **roads** cannot be protected as easily.

- **Sustainable** adaptations, e.g. using **non-intensive** farming practices and promoting **ecotourism**, will help ensure that the fragile environment remains relatively **undamaged** and **usable** for future generations.

Practice Questions

Q1 Briefly describe the location of the Sundarbans region.

Q2 Outline two ways in which the Sundarbans offer opportunities for human occupation.

Exam Question

Q1 'Human responses will never be sufficient to overcome the challenges posed by living in coastal areas.'
To what extent do you agree with this statement?   [20 marks]

Cup of tea, cake, comfy chair — yep, I'm adapted to my environment...

Resilience, mitigation and adaptation are all interlinked — if you adapt to a threat, you become more resilient and mitigate its impacts. So really this page should just be one big box, called something like 'resilimitigadaptation'. But that would be silly.

Topic Three — Coastal Systems and Landscapes

Cold Environments

You're probably thinking that all cold environments are the same — they're all just, well, cold. Well it turns out that there are different types of cold environment, and it's not quite as simple as chilly, cold and blimmin' freezing.

There are **Four** Main Types of **Cold Environments**

Glacial

1) Glacial environments are areas of land permanently **covered by ice**. Land can be covered by **glaciers** or **ice sheets**:

   - Glaciers are masses of **ice** that flow **downhill**. There are two main types — **valley** glaciers and **corrie** glaciers. Valley glaciers **fill valleys** and can be **several kilometres long** (e.g. the Franz Josef Glacier in New Zealand is 12 kilometres long). Corrie glaciers are **smaller** glaciers that are found in bowl-shaped hollows high up in **mountains** (e.g. the Lower Curtis Glacier in Washington State, USA).

   - Ice sheets are **domes of ice** covering **huge areas** of land, e.g. the Antarctic Ice Sheet.

2) **Climate** — temperatures are cold enough for ice to be present **all year round**, but may be warm enough in summer for **meltwater** to affect glaciers. Most glacial environments have **high snowfall**, but in **extremely cold** areas (e.g. parts of Antarctica), ice sheets and glaciers can persist even when snowfall is very **low**.

3) **Soil** and **vegetation** — glacial environments are **covered by ice permanently**, so there is **no exposed soil**. There are very **few plants**, though **algae** and **moss** may grow on the glacier surface during summer.

Polar

1) Polar areas **surround** the **North** and **South Poles**.

2) Much of the Arctic polar environment is made up of the **northern land areas** of Asia, **North America** and **Europe**. The land-based polar environment can include **glacial** environments, e.g. the Greenland Ice Sheet, and **periglacial** environments, e.g. northern Russia.

3) **Climate** — polar areas are very cold — temperatures are **never** normally above 10 °C. Winters are **normally** below **–40 °C** and can reach **–90 °C**. Precipitation is **low** (no more than **100 mm** a year). There are **clearly defined** seasons — **cold summers** and **even colder winters**.

4) **Soil** — much of the ground is covered by ice. Where soil is exposed, it tends to be **thin** and **nutrient-poor**. There is normally a layer of **permanently frozen ground** called **permafrost** beneath the soil.

5) **Vegetation** — there are **very few** plants in polar areas — some **lichens** and **mosses** are found on rocks, and there are a few **grasses** in warmer areas, e.g. on the **coast** of Antarctica and in some parts of the Arctic.

Periglacial

1) **Periglacial** environments are places where the temperature is frequently or constantly **below freezing**, but which are **not covered by ice**.

2) **Climate** — periglacial areas are **cold** and precipitation is fairly **low** — **380 mm** or less (mainly in the summer). There are **clearly defined** seasons (**brief, mild summers** and **long, cold winters**).

3) **Soil** — soil is **thin, acidic** and **not very fertile**. There is normally a **permafrost layer**, topped with a layer of soil that **melts** in the summer (see p.64).

4) **Vegetation** — plants grow **slowly** and **don't grow very tall** — **grasses** are the most common plants. Some **small, short** trees grow in **warmer, sheltered** areas. Nearer the poles, only **mosses** and **lichens** can survive.

Tribute act Katy Periglacial received a frosty reception.

Alpine

1) Alpine environments are cold areas of land at an altitude **above** the **treeline** (the **limit** of the area where trees can grow — above this it's **too cold**).

2) Alpine environments may include areas of **glacial** conditions (at **higher** altitudes) and **periglacial** conditions (at **lower** altitudes).

3) **Climate** — winters are **cold**, but summers can be **mild**. **Temperature decreases** as altitude increases. **Snowfall** can be **high**.

4) **Soil** — when ice melts in the **summer**, soil is **exposed** in some areas. Higher up, the land is permanently covered by snow and ice, and lower down **periglacial** soils are present.

5) **Vegetation** — seasonally exposed soil means that **plants** can **grow**, e.g. grasses and alpine flowers.

Cold Environments

Different Types of *Cold Environment* are *Found* in *Different Places*

① Polar Environments

1) The Arctic polar environment can be defined either by the **Arctic circle (66° N)** or by the **10 °C July isotherm** (areas north of this line have an average temperature **below** 10 °C in **July**, the **hottest** month).

2) The polar environment around the South Pole is defined by the **10 °C January isotherm** (the hottest month in the southern hemisphere).

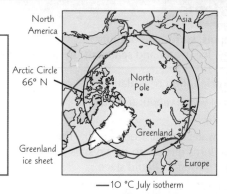

— 10 °C July isotherm   — 10 °C January isotherm

② Periglacial Environments

Periglacial environments are found at:

• **High latitudes**, e.g. the northern parts of Asia, North America and Europe.

• **High altitudes** — periglacial conditions exist **around ice masses** in **mountain ranges**.

③ Alpine Environments

Alpine environments can be found at **high altitudes** at **any latitude**.

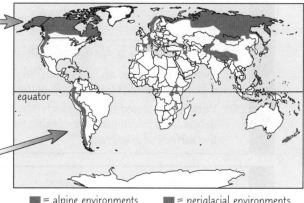

Glacial environments can be found in polar and alpine settings.

■ = alpine environments   ■ = periglacial environments

There Were *Several Periods* of *Glaciation* in the *Pleistocene*

1) The Pleistocene lasted from **2.5 million years** ago to **11 700 years** ago.

2) During this time there were **fluctuations** in global temperatures which led to colder **glacials** (when glaciers advanced and sea levels fell) and warmer **interglacials** (when ice retreated and sea levels rose).

3) The **last glacial maximum** (the point when ice sheets were at their largest size) was about **21 000 years** ago — cold environments extended much further then than they do today, e.g. polar ice sheets covered much of the UK, and most of southern Europe was periglacial.

4) We're currently in an **interglacial** — glaciers are **retreating**.

Global Distribution of Cold Environments, Last Glacial Maximum (~21 000 years ago)

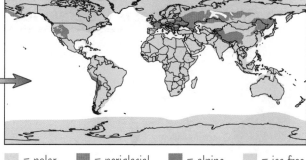

■ = polar   ■ = periglacial   ■ = alpine   ■ = ice-free

Practice Questions

Q1 What is the climate of polar areas like?

Q2 Where are alpine environments found?

Q3 What's the latitude of the Arctic circle?

Exam Question

Q1 Using the maps above, compare the distribution of cold environments today and 21 000 years before present. [6 marks]

So which is better — north or south? Let's take a poll...

It might not seem like it yet, but cold environments are actually pretty interesting. To really get yourself in the mood for these next few pages, try turning the heating off and opening all the windows, and read them with your scarf and gloves on.

Glacial Systems

Since plenty of cold environments contain glaciers, you need to know a fair bit about them. I do like a nice glacier...

Glaciers are Systems

The glacial system has **inputs**, **stores** and **outputs**.
There are **flows** (of **energy**, **ice**, **water** and **sediment**) **between** stores.

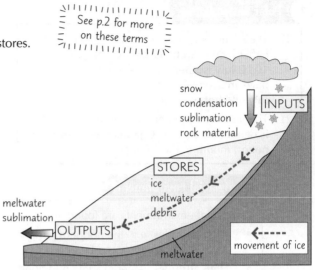

See p.2 for more on these terms

Inputs

1) **Snow** (from **precipitation** or **avalanches**).

2) **Condensation** of water vapour from the air (which then freezes).

3) **Sublimation** of water vapour from the air. This is when vapour turns directly to ice crystals, without passing through a liquid stage.

4) Bits of **rock** collected when the glacier carves away at the landscape, and rocks that have fallen onto the glacier from above.

Stores

1) The **main store** is **ice** in the **glacier** itself.

2) **Meltwater** is stored **on** and **within** the glacier, e.g. in **supraglacial lakes** on top of the glacier.

3) **Rock** is also stored in or on glaciers, e.g. **debris** from freeze-thaw weathering falls onto the **surface** of glaciers.

Flows

1) **Meltwater** flows through glaciers, e.g. from stores in supraglacial lakes to **channel storage** at the base of glaciers.

2) **Debris** flows through glaciers, e.g. from surface storage to **landforms**.

Outputs

1) Ice can **melt** and **flow out** of the glacier as **meltwater**.

2) Surface snow can **melt** and **evaporate**.

3) Ice and snow can **sublimate** to water vapour.

4) Snow can be **blown away** by strong winds.

5) With glaciers that end at the **sea** or a **lake**, blocks of ice fall from the **front** (the snout) of the ice mass into water to create **icebergs**.

A *Glacial Budget* is the *Balance* Between a Glacier's *Inputs* and *Outputs*

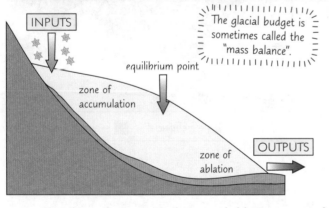

The glacial budget is sometimes called the "mass balance".

1) **Accumulation** is the **input** of snow and ice into the glacial system. Most accumulation is snow.

2) **Ablation** is the **output** of water from a glacier.

3) The **glacial budget** is the balance between accumulation and ablation over a year — it shows whether the mass of ice in the glacial system has **increased** or **decreased**. This determines whether the **front** of the glacier **advances** or **retreats**.

4) You get **more accumulation** than ablation in the **upper** part of a glacier — so it's called the **zone of accumulation**.

5) You get **more ablation** than accumulation in the **lower** part of a glacier — so it's called the **zone of ablation**.

6) The place where accumulation and ablation are **equal** is called the glacier's **equilibrium point**.

7) If there's **more accumulation** than ablation over a year, the glacier has a **positive regime** (or a positive mass balance). The glacier grows and **advances** (moves forward) in response to **high accumulation** in the upper zone.

8) If there's **less accumulation** than ablation over a year, this is a **negative regime** (or a negative mass balance). The glacier shrinks and **retreats** (moves back) in response to **low accumulation** in the upper zone.

9) If there's the **same amount** of accumulation and ablation over a year, the glacier stays the same size and the position of the snout **doesn't change** — the glacier is in **dynamic equilibrium** (see p.2). Dynamic equilibrium is when a system stays the same on **average**, despite **short-term variations** in e.g. inputs and outputs.

Glacial Systems

Feedbacks

When inputs or outputs change, there can be **negative feedbacks**. For example, if the size of the ice input increases, a glacier may speed up so that more water and ice are output and the mass of the glacier **remains constant.**

Glaciers can respond to a change in a way that makes the change **greater** — this is a **positive feedback**. E.g. ice has a high **albedo** (it **reflects** lots of the Sun's **energy**). If glaciers **retreat** there is **less ice** — less of the Sun's energy is reflected and more is **absorbed**, so temperatures **rise** and glaciers **retreat further**.

The Glacial Budget **Changes** Throughout the **Year**...

1) You get **more ablation** during **warmer** times of the year — more ice melts when it's warm.

2) During the **colder** months, there's **more accumulation** than ablation.

3) Over the year, this might **balance out** — the glacier **advances** in winter but **retreats** in summer, so overall the mass in the glacier **stays the same**.

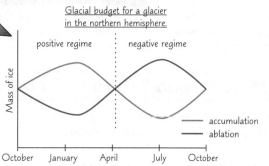

Glacial budget for a glacier in the northern hemisphere.

positive regime | negative regime

Mass of ice

—— accumulation
—— ablation

October   January   April   July   October

Hannah and Betty had a very positive regime.

...Over **Several Years**...

1) There is **variation** in the amount of accumulation and ablation from year to year. Even if the **overall** trend is for retreat, in some years there may be **advances** due to more accumulation or less ablation than usual.

2) For example, the **Kleinelend glacier** in the Austrian Alps **retreated** overall between 2000 and 2011, but recorded **advances** in **2001**, **2004** and **2008**.

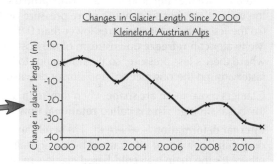

Changes in Glacier Length Since 2000
Kleinelend, Austrian Alps

Change in glacier length (m)

10, 0, -10, -20, -30, -40

2000 2002 2004 2006 2008 2010

...and Over **Hundreds of Years**

Changes in **global temperature** over long periods of time affect the glacial budget. For example:

1) Temperatures in the **Little Ice Age** (a relatively cold period from about 1550 to 1850) were **colder** than the periods before and after it.

2) This meant that many glaciers **advanced** because they had a **positive regime** — the **Mer de Glace** in the French Alps advanced by over **1 km**.

3) Since 1850, global temperatures have **increased** so glaciers have tended to have a negative regime and **retreated** — the Mer de Glace has retreated by **nearly 2.4 km** since 1850.

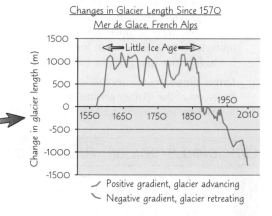

Changes in Glacier Length Since 1570
Mer de Glace, French Alps

Change in glacier length (m)

1500, 1000, 500, 0, -500, -1000, -1500

◄— Little Ice Age —►

1550 1650 1750 1850 2010

1950

╱ Positive gradient, glacier advancing
╲ Negative gradient, glacier retreating

Practice Questions

Q1 What are the main inputs, stores and outputs in a glacial system?

Q2 What are accumulation and ablation?

Q3 How does the glacial budget change throughout the year in the northern hemisphere?

Exam Question

Q1 Explain the concept of a glacial budget.   [4 marks]

Shouldn't have left the cage outside — now I've got a glacial budgie...

No, you're not reading an accountancy revision guide by mistake — glaciers have budgets too. If inputs are bigger than outputs, all is well and the glacier grows. If outputs are bigger than inputs, things aren't so rosy. Much like me with my salary.

Glacial Processes

Glaciers are moving all the time — they don't stop to think about the erosion they might be causing...

Glaciers can be **Cold-Based** or **Warm-Based**

Glaciers can be classified according to the **temperature** of their **base** (the bit where the ice touches the valley floor).

1) **Cold-based glaciers** are found in **very cold** areas, e.g. Antarctica — their bases are usually well **below** the ice's **melting point**, so there's very **little melting**. The ice is frozen to the base of the valley, so there's **very little movement**. There's hardly any melting at the surface either, even in summer. This means that cold-based glaciers **don't** cause very much **erosion** at all.

2) **Warm-based glaciers** occur in **milder** areas — their bases are **warmer** than the melting point of ice because of heat from **friction** caused by the glacier moving, or because of **geothermal heat** from the Earth. The ice at the bottom of the glacier melts, and the **meltwater** acts as a **lubricant**, making it easier for the glacier to move downhill. Ice at the **surface** also melts if the temperature reaches 0 °C, and meltwater moves down through the glacier, lubricating it even more. Lots of movement means **lots of erosion**.

Glaciers Move Downhill *under their Own* **Weight**

1) **Meltwater** underneath a glacier allows the glacier to **slide** over the ground. This is called **basal sliding**, and it's the main way that warm-based glaciers move.

2) There's **more melting** around bits of **rock protruding** from the valley floor, because there's **more pressure** on the ice (so the ice melts at temperatures lower than 0 °C). Meltwater can **refreeze** downstream of the obstruction where there's less pressure, so the flow tends to be faster around the obstruction, and slower downstream.

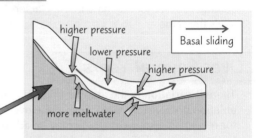

3) Glaciers move in an **arc shape** when they're in a **hollow** (by basal sliding). This is called **rotational flow**.

4) **Internal deformation** is where the ice **bends** and **warps** to flow downhill like a liquid. It's caused by ice crystals shifting past each other. It's the main way **cold-based** glaciers move.

5) At the **head** of a glacier the valley is steep, so there's a strong **gravitational force** pulling the ice downwards. This makes the ice **move quickly**. When ice moves quickly there's more **tension** (pulling apart forces), which causes the ice to **fracture** into thick layers. The **layers** then **slip downwards** — this is called **extensional flow**.

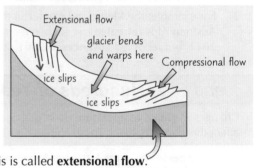

6) **Lower down** the glacier the ice is moving more **slowly** because the valley is less steep. The faster ice from the head of the glacier **pushes down** on the slower ice and **compresses it**. The **high pressure** causes the ice to **fracture** into layers, and the layers **slip forwards** — this is called **compressional flow**.

Glaciated Areas are Affected by **Nivation** and **Frost Action Weathering**

Nivation makes hollows **deeper** by freezing and **thawing**:

1) When snow gets into a **hollow** in the ground, it can **increase** the size of the hollow.

Nivation is especially common in periglacial areas where temperatures often fluctuate around 0 °C.

2) When temperatures **fluctuate** around 0 °C, a lot of **freezing** and **thawing** happens — when the temperature's **above** 0 °C, the snow **melts**, and when it's **below** 0 °C, the water refreezes as **ice**.

3) Every time the ice **freezes**, it **expands**, so **frost shattering** eventually breaks bits off the rock at the base of the hollow. When the snow **melts**, the meltwater carries the broken bits of rock (debris) **away**.

4) Slopes **collapse** because they're **waterlogged** and they've been **eroded** — the material is **washed away** by meltwater.

5) Eventually the hollow becomes **deeper** and **wider**. The processes that cause this are collectively called **nivation**, and the hollows formed by nivation are called **nivation hollows**. Nivation hollows can be the beginning of a **corrie** (see p.60).

Nivation

Glacial Processes

Frost Action

1) **Frost action** (**freeze-thaw** weathering) occurs in areas where there's **moisture** and **temperatures** that fluctuate **above** and **below freezing**.

2) Water from rainfall or melting **enters** the **joints** and **crevices** in rocks and **cliff faces**.

3) When the temperature **drops below 0 °C**, the water in the cracks **freezes** and **expands**.

4) Over time, **repeated** freeze-thaw action **weakens** the rocks and causes pieces to **fall off**.

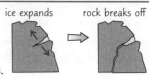
ice expands   rock breaks off

Glaciers *Erode* the *Surrounding Rock*

Glaciers erode the valley floor and sides by **plucking** and **abrasion**:

1) **Plucking** — ice in contact with rock surfaces can thaw slightly then **refreeze around rocks** protruding from the valley sides and floor. When the glacier **moves forward**, it **plucks** the rocks away from the valley sides and floor.

2) **Abrasion** — **debris** carried along by the glacier can **scrape** material off the valley walls and floor.

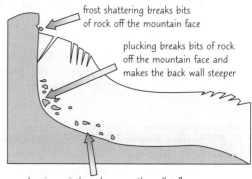
frost shattering breaks bits of rock off the mountain face

plucking breaks bits of rock off the mountain face and makes the back wall steeper

abrasion grinds and gouges the valley floor

The **amount** and **rate** of erosion is increased in areas of **less resistant rock**, and if the glacier is **thick** or if it's **moving quickly**. It's also increased if there's **lots of debris** or if the debris is made of **resistant rock**.

Glaciers *Transport Debris*

1) Glaciers carry large loads of **debris** — this is material that the glacier has gathered by plucking, or bits of rock that have been broken off the back wall or valley sides and fallen onto (or into) the glacier. Debris ranges from **fine sediment** to **huge boulders**.

2) There are **three** main ways debris is transported. **Supraglacial** material is carried **on top** of the glacier's surface. **Englacial** material is carried **within** the body of the glacier. **Subglacial** material is moved along **at the base** of the glacier.

Glaciers *Deposit* their Load as they *Move* and as they *Melt*

1) The **unsorted** mixture of material **deposited** by the glacier is called **till** (it's sometimes called "boulder clay" too). It includes everything from massive boulders down to pebbles and clay. Glaciers drop any size of till anywhere.

2) **Lodgement till** is spread onto the valley floor beneath the ice by **moving** glaciers.

3) **Ablation till** is dropped by a glacier as it **melts**. The till is mainly deposited close to the glacier snout because this is where most ablation happens — the glacier drops debris as the ice around the debris melts.

4) Till **points** in the **direction** that the glacier is flowing.

5) Till is often **deposited** as landforms called **moraines** (see p. 61).

Practice Questions

Q1 What is rotational flow?

Q2 What is nivation?

Q3 What are the main ways that debris is transported by a glacier?

Exam Question

Q1 Outline the impact of basal temperature on glacial processes.   [4 marks]

Glaciers move r e a l l y s l o w l y — bit like me on a Sunday morning...

Alright, I'll admit that these two pages are slightly harder than the last two. It can be tricky at first to get your head around the different ways that glaciers move. Try reading over the first page a couple of times, then at least you'll know that rotational flow isn't a dance move. Don't forget that glaciers erode valleys in two different ways — by plucking and by abrasion.

Topic Four — Glacial Systems and Landscapes

Glacial Landforms

These pages are about the landscapes that glaciers leave behind them. Mountain climbers and geography teachers get very excited about the beauty of glacial landscapes. Whether or not they move you, you still need to learn about them.

Glaciers Create Basins called Corries (also called Cirques or Cwms)

1) Glaciers normally form on one side of a mountain peak — the side that gets **least sun** and the **coldest winds**. That's where there's **most accumulation** and **least ablation**.

2) Snow collects in hollows and turns to **ice**. **Basal sliding** (rotational flow) with **abrasion** and **plucking** deepen the hollow into a **corrie** (a bowl-shaped hollow).

3) When the ice in the hollow is thick enough, it **flows** over the lip and downhill as a glacier. Frost shattering and plucking **steepen** the back wall of the corrie.

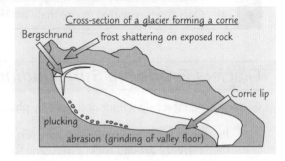

Glacial Erosion Changes the Landscape

Glaciers produce **erosional landforms**, which change the way the landscape **looks** after the ice has **gone**.

1) An **arête** is a steep-sided **ridge** — it's formed when two glaciers flow in parallel valleys. The glaciers erode the sides of the valley, which **sharpens** the mountain ridge **in between** them.

2) A **pyramidal peak** is a pointed mountain peak with at least **three sides**. It forms where **three** or more **corries** form **back to back** (their back walls make the mountain peak).

3) **Glacial troughs** (also called U-shaped valleys) are **steep-sided valleys** with **flat bottoms**. They're formed by the erosion of **V-shaped river valleys** by glaciers. As the glacier erodes through the V-shaped valley it makes it **deeper** and **wider**.

4) **Hanging valleys** are valleys formed by **tributary glaciers** — they erode the valley floor much less **deeply** because they're **smaller** than the main glacier. So, when the glaciers melt, the valleys get left at a **higher level** than the glacial trough formed by the main glacier. You get **waterfalls** from hanging valleys into the main glacial trough.

A tributary glacier is a smaller glacier that flows into the main glacier.

5) **Truncated spurs** are formed when **ridges of land** (spurs) that **stick out** into the main valley are **chopped off** (truncated) as the main valley glacier moves past.

6) **Tarns** are **lakes** that form in **corries** after a glacier has retreated.

7) A **roche moutonnée** is a **resistant** (hard) mass of rock on the valley floor. The **upstream** (stoss) side is **smooth**, because it was smoothed by **abrasion** as the glacier went over it. The **downstream** (lee) side is steep and **rough**, where the glacier **plucked** at it.

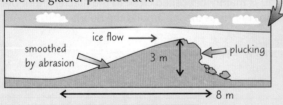

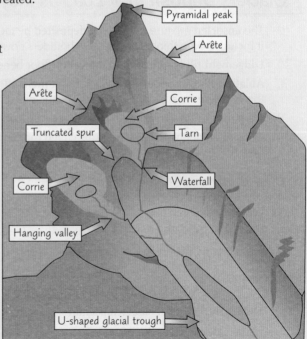

Example: Matterhorn, Swiss/Italian Alps

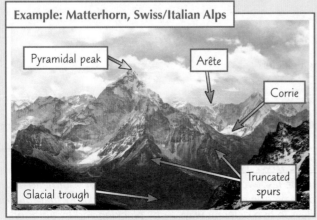

Topic Four — Glacial Systems and Landscapes

Glacial Landforms

Glaciers Form **Moraines** and **Till Plains** by **Depositing Till**

Till is all the stuff that a glacier leaves behind — unsorted boulders, stones and clay (see p. 59). **Moraine** is the name given to particular formations of till:

1) **Lateral moraine** is deposited where the **sides** of the glacier were.

2) **Medial moraine** is deposited in the **centre** of the valley where two glaciers **converge** (the two lateral moraines join together).

3) **Terminal moraine** builds up at the **end** of the glacier, and is deposited as semicircular hillocks of till.

A **till plain** is a **large** expanse of gently rolling hills of till — it forms when an **ice sheet** melts where it is. Northern Ohio, USA is a large till plain.

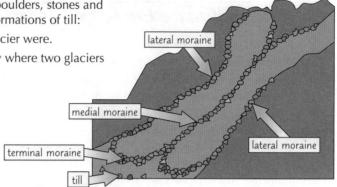

Till can also be Deposited as **Hills** called **Drumlins**

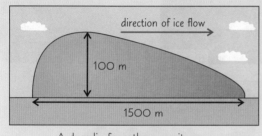

A drumlin faces the opposite way to a roche moutonnée.

1) **Drumlins** are **half-egg shaped hills** of till, up to 1500 m long and 100 m high. The **upstream** (stoss) end is **wide and tall**, and the **downstream** (lee) end is **narrow and low**.

2) Nobody's really sure **how** drumlins formed — it may be that till got stuck around a rock or a little hill sticking out into the glacier. It may be that an original mound of dropped till got streamlined when the ice **readvanced** over it.

3) Drumlins often form in **groups**. There are drumlins in the **Ribble Valley** in Lancashire. There are also a whole bunch of drumlins under the water level in Clew Bay, Ireland.

Erratics are **Boulders** that have been **Carried** a **Long Way** by Glaciers

1) Erratics are rocks that have been **picked up** by a glacier or an ice sheet, **carried along** and **dropped** in an area of **completely different geology**.

2) For example, in the Yorkshire Dales at Norber, loose black **Silurian** rocks sit on top of white **Carboniferous** limestone. They were deposited as ice **retreated** after the last glacial maximum, about 21 000 years go.

Loose, black Silurian rock

Limestone

Practice Questions

Q1 What is the name of the ridge formed by two glaciers in parallel valleys?

Q2 Name three other landforms caused by glacial erosion.

Q3 What is an erratic?

Exam Questions

Q1 Assess the role of glacial processes in the development of the landscape shown in the photograph. [6 marks]

Q2 Outline how moraine is formed. [4 marks]

Corries? I'm more of an Emmerdale fan myself...

There are a fair few features to learn here, but don't let that get you down. You just need to learn the names of the features, what they look like and how they're formed. Even the names of the features are a bit tricky though — cirque, arête, roche moutonnée... anyone would think this was a French exam. At least you don't need to know how to pronounce them.

Fluvioglacial Processes and Landforms

The sad news for all you glacier fans is that glaciers don't always stay around forever. But don't worry, they don't go down without a fight — even when they're melting, they still manage to change the landscape.

Meltwater Streams Erode the Landscape

1) When glacial ice melts, water runs out and forms streams of **meltwater**. **Warm-based** glaciers and **retreating** glaciers produce **lots** of meltwater.

2) **Surface** meltwater **filters** through the glacier (e.g. through crevasses) and flows through **tunnels** underneath the glacier, before running out of the snout of the glacier.

3) Meltwater streams cause **erosion** in the same way as normal rivers (by hydraulic action, abrasion, attrition and solution) — but they cause **more** erosion than rivers of the same size. This is because the pressure of the ice means that meltwater streams flow very **quickly** — so they can carry **lots** of material that **erodes** the landscape.

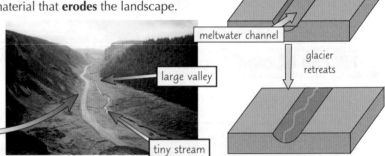

4) Meltwater streams form deep **troughs** in the landscape called **meltwater channels**. Because meltwater streams have a lot of **erosive power**, the meltwater channels they produce are very **wide** and **deep**. After the glacier has **retreated**, the deep meltwater channels are left with very **shallow streams** running through them — e.g. Glen Valtos on the Isle of Lewis in Scotland.

Fluvioglacial Deposits come from Glacial Meltwater

1) Glacial meltwater carries a **large load** of **sediment** of various sizes (from inside, on top of and underneath the glacier).

2) **Traction, saltation, suspension** and **solution** processes transport eroded material in glacial meltwater streams, just like in rivers.

3) Meltwater streams **deposit** their load on the **valley floor** as they flow away from the glacier.

4) Unlike glacial deposition features such as moraine, fluvioglacial deposits are **sorted** — the fine sediment is **separated** from the larger sand, which is separated from the gravel, and so on. This is because **fluvioglacial** deposition features are formed by meltwater **carrying debris** then **depositing** it **away** from the glacier. **Glacial** deposits form by glaciers **dropping material** as they **melt**.

Melting Glaciers leave Outwash Plains

1) An **outwash plain** (also called a sandur) is a layer of gravel, sand and clay that forms in **front** of where the snout of the melting glacier used to be. Meltwater flows out of the glacier, and carries the sediment with it.

2) Sediments on outwash plains are **sorted** into layers. **Gravel** gets dropped **first** because it's **heavier** than sand and clay, so it forms the **bottom layer** of the outwash plain. **Clay** is dropped **last** and gets carried furthest away from the snout because it's the lightest sediment — it forms the **top layer** of the outwash plain.

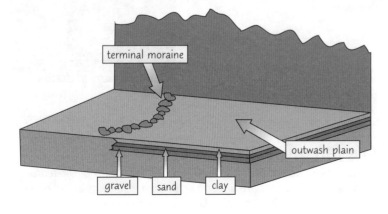

Satellite image of Skeiðarársandur, an outwash plain in southeast Iceland.

Topic Four — Glacial Systems and Landscapes

Fluvioglacial Processes and Landforms

Meltwater Streams Deposit *Kames* and *Eskers*

1) **Eskers** are long, winding **ridges** of sand and gravel that run in the **same direction** as the glacier. They're deposited by meltwater streams flowing in **tunnels** underneath the glacier — when the glacier retreats and the stream dries up, the load remains as an esker. Eskers show you where the glacial tunnel used to be.

2) **Kames** are **mounds** of sand and gravel found on the valley floor. Meltwater streams **on top of** glaciers collect in depressions and **deposit** layers of debris. When the ice **melts** the debris is dumped onto the valley floor.

3) **Kame terraces** are piles of deposits left against the **valley wall** by meltwater streams that run between the glacier and the valley sides. They look like lateral moraine, but they're **sorted** into layers — meltwater streams deposit their **heaviest** loads first, so kame terraces have **gravel** at the **bottom** and **finer sediment** on **top**.

The town of Pispala is built on Pyynikki ridge, an esker that divides two glacial lakes in Tampere, Finland.

4) Eskers, kames and kame terraces look a bit like this.

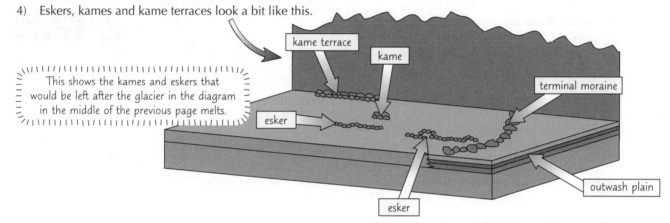

This shows the kames and eskers that would be left after the glacier in the diagram in the middle of the previous page melts.

5) Lakes (called **proglacial lakes**) can form in front of glaciers, e.g. when the flow from meltwater streams gets dammed by the terminal moraine. As meltwater streams flow into a proglacial lake, they **slow down** and **deposit** their sediment on the ice — these deposits are known as **deltas**. When the ice melts, these deltas are dumped on the valley floor, forming **delta kames**.

Practice Questions

Q1 What are meltwater channels?

Q2 What's the main difference between glacial deposits and fluvioglacial deposits?

Q3 What is an outwash plain?

Q4 What are eskers?

Exam Questions

Q1 Outline the role of meltwater in the formation of kames and kame terraces. [4 marks]

Q2 Outline how sediment becomes sorted in glacial outwash plains. [4 marks]

If you're pro-glacial, this section must be a dream come true...

Well, this is just typical of glaciers if you ask me. Not content with ripping bits of rock out of mountains and scattering them all over landscapes, glaciers then have to go and melt, and wash all kinds of bits of rock all over the place. If only they didn't have to be so, well, <u>messy</u> about it — then you wouldn't need to know what a kame or an esker is. Oh well, tough luck, eh.

Periglacial Processes and Landforms

Periglacial areas aren't covered in ice. There's usually ice in the soil though — I knew it'd be there somewhere...

Permafrost is Permanently Frozen Ground

1) **Periglacial** areas contain **permafrost** — **permanently frozen ground** with a top layer that can **melt** in the **summer** (called the **active layer**). **20-25%** of Earth's land surface is **permafrost**. Areas of permafrost can be **continuous** (**all** the ground is frozen), or **discontinuous** (only **patches** of the ground are frozen).

2) For **discontinuous** permafrost to form, the **mean annual temperature** needs to be **below 0 °C** for at least **2 years**. For **continuous** permafrost to form, the mean annual temperature needs to be **below –5 °C**.

3) **Mass movement** can occur in areas of permafrost. It can happen as the ground starts to **thaw**:

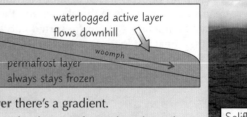

- The layer of permafrost is **impermeable** (water **can't** flow through it). If the temperature gets **above 0 °C** in the summer, the active layer **melts**, but the meltwater can't drain away.
- As a result, the active layer becomes **waterlogged** and **heavy**, and **flows easily**. This flow is called **solifluction** and it can occur **wherever** there's a gradient.
- Solifluction produces **lobe** formations — one section of soil **moves faster** than the soil around it, e.g. if it's on **steeper** ground, so it flows **further** and forms a **tongue** shape.

Solifluction lobes in upland Alaska

4) Mass movement can also occur on slopes due to regular **freezing** and **thawing**:

- Water in soil **expands** when it **freezes**. This expansion causes soil particles to be forced upwards at **right angles** to the slope.
- When the ground **thaws**, the soil particles move **vertically** downwards.
- As a result, they end up **further down** the slope — this is called **frost creep**.

Ice Wedges Develop in Permafrost Soil

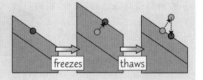
Ice wedges and pingo, northern Canada

1) When temperatures **drop very low** in winter, the ground **contracts** and **cracks** form in the permafrost. This is called **frost contraction**.

2) When temperatures **increase** in spring, the active layer **thaws** and **meltwater seeps** into the **cracks**.

3) The permafrost layer is still frozen, so the water **freezes** in the cracks — the ice-filled cracks formed in this way are called **ice wedges**.

4) Frost contraction in following years can **re-open** cracks in the same place, **splitting** the ice wedge. More water seeps in and freezes, **widening** the ice wedge. The ice wedge gets **bigger** each time this happens.

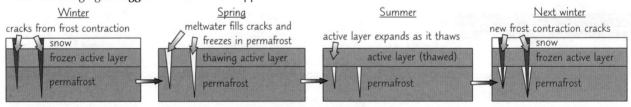

Patterned Ground is Formed by Frost Activity

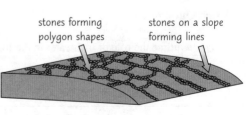

Sometimes **stones** on the surface of the ground are arranged in **circles**, **polygons** or **stripes** — this is called **patterned ground**. Patterned ground can be formed in two ways — by **frost heave** or by **frost contraction**:

1) **Frost heave** happens when water underneath stones freezes and expands, forcing stones upwards. Once they reach the surface, they **roll down** to the **edges** of the **mounds** that have formed, so they form **circles** around them (**polygons** form when the mounds are **close together**). If the mounds are on a **slope**, the stones roll downhill and form **lines**.

2) **Frost contraction** causes the ground to **crack** in **polygon shapes**. The cracks get **filled in** with **stones**, forming polygon patterns on the surface.

Periglacial Processes and Landforms

There are Several Distinctive **Periglacial Landforms**

Pingos

1) A pingo is a **conical hill** with a **core** of **ice**. Pingos can be as large as 80 m high and about 500 m wide.

2) There are **two types** of pingo — **open-system** and **closed-system**.

3) **Open-system pingos** form where there's **discontinuous** permafrost. **Groundwater** is forced **up** through the **gaps between** areas of permafrost (from unfrozen layers lower down). The water **collects** together and **freezes**, forming a **core** of ice that **pushes** the ground above it **upwards**.

4) **Closed-system pingos** form in areas of **continuous** permafrost where there's a **lake** at the surface. The lake **insulates** the ground, so the area beneath it remains **unfrozen**. When the lake **dries up**, the ground is no longer insulated and the permafrost **advances** around the area of unfrozen ground. This causes water to **collect** in the centre of the unfrozen ground. The water eventually **freezes** and creates a **core** of ice that **pushes** the ground above it **upwards**.

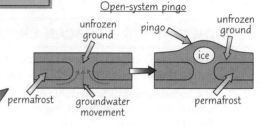

Open-system pingo

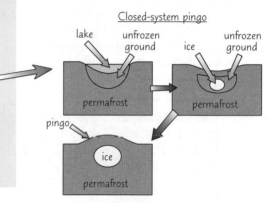

Closed-system pingo

Blockfields

Blockfields are expanses of **loose rocks**. They are formed **in place** by **frost shattering** of the **bedrock** layer due to repeated freezing and thawing.

Blockfield at top of Schiehallion, Scotland

Thermokast

- A thermokarst landscape occurs when ice in the ground (e.g. pingos) **melts**, causing the ground to **collapse** and **holes** to form.

- These holes become **filled** with water, creating an **uneven**, **marshy** landscape.

Terracettes

- Terracettes form when **vegetation** interrupts soil moving down a slope due to **frost creep** or another mass movement process.

- This causes a **flatter** area to build up behind the **obstruction**, which leads to a series of **step-like terraces**.

Terracettes near Pen-y-ghent, North Yorkshire

Satellite image of a thermokarst landscape in the Northern Territories, Canada

Practice Questions

Q1 What is permafrost?

Q2 How does patterned ground develop?

Q3 What's the difference between open-system pingos and closed-system pingos?

Exam Question

Q1 Outline how ice wedges form. [4 marks]

I always thought Pingo was one of the Beatles...

The trouble with this lot is that there are so many different processes going on, and all of them are to do with water freezing and then thawing. But you can sleep soundly now you know that patterned ground is caused by frost activity and not aliens.

Glacial Landscapes — Case Study

Mine's black, about 80 cm tall and has little spiny wheels that get clogged with mud whenever I take a shortcut through a field to the airport... oops, wrong sort of case study. Erm. Pack your bags, we're heading off to Snowdonia...

Snowdonia is a Glacial Landscape in North Wales

1) **Snowdonia** is an area in **north Wales**. It has been repeatedly covered by **ice** during **glacial periods**, including the **last glacial maximum** (see p.55).

2) The **upland areas** of Snowdonia (e.g. the **Glyders** — mountains to the north-east of Snowdon) show many of the **landforms** from pages 60-65. The area is no longer glaciated — since they formed, its landforms have been **modified** by periglacial processes and (more recently) fluvial action, weathering and human processes.

3) Here are some of the **glacial features** that are found on the **Glyders** and the surrounding area:

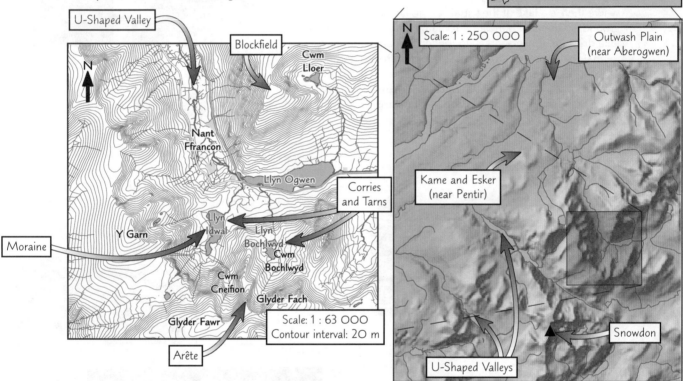

There are Lots of Glacial Landforms in Snowdonia

U-Shaped Valley — Nant Ffrancon

- **Nant Ffrancon** is a glacial trough formed by a glacier that flowed in a north westerly direction towards the coast at Anglesey.
- Today the **River Ogwen** flows in the valley, but it is much **too small** to have created it — it's a **misfit stream**.

Corries and Tarns

- **Llyn Bochlwyd** and **Llyn Idwal** are **tarns**. They sit above the Nant Ffrancon valley in corries (**Cwm Bochlwyd** and **Cwm Idwal**).
- They were formed by **tributary glaciers** that once flowed into the main glacier in Nant Ffrancon.

Glacial Landscapes — Case Study

Truncated Spur — Y Gribin

- Truncated spurs form when **ridges** of land (e.g. **arêtes**) stick out into the **path** of the main glacier and get **cut off** (truncated).
- The **Y Gribin arête** was cut off by the Nant Ffrancon glacier. There may once have been **interlocking spurs** in a **river valley** here, which were **bulldozed** by the glacier.

Arête — Y Gribin

- The **sharp ridge** between Cwm Bochlwyd and Cwm Cneifion, known as **Y Gribin**, is an **arête**.
- Glaciers formed in the corries on **either side** of the ridge and **eroded** the rock in between until it formed the **steep-sided arête**.

Arête   A rat

Moraine

A lot of **moraine** can be found around **Llyn Idwal**, where it was **deposited** by the melting glacier:

- **Terminal** moraine — at the mouth of the tarn.
- **Lateral** moraine — on the west side of the tarn.

These moraine formations have been **eroded** by other processes since being deposited — they are not as **obvious** as in **more recently** glaciated areas.

terminal

lateral

Kame and Esker — Pentir

- There's a **kame** and an **esker** near the village of **Pentir**. The esker is around **400 m long** and up to **10 m high**.
- They were probably formed by **meltwater** from the Nant Ffrancon glacier.
- Both features have been **eroded** by natural and human processes, so they are not easy to see.

Outwash Plain

- The glacier that once flowed in the Nant Ffrancon valley discharged into what is now **Conwy Bay**.
- There is a **flat expanse** of glacial till near **Aberogwen** — this was the outwash plain for the glacier shortly after the last glacial maximum.
- In places where the plain has been eroded to form cliffs, you can see a **clear layer** of glacial deposits.

Blockfields

There are **blockfields** formed by freeze-thaw weathering at the tops of many mountains in Snowdonia, e.g. at the summit of **Glyder Fach**.

Practice Questions

Q1 Give a brief description of the landscape of Snowdonia.

Q2 Give three examples of glacial landforms found in Snowdonia.

Exam Question

Q1 Assess the relative importance of glacial and fluvioglacial processes in forming glacial landscapes. [20 marks]

I just tried to pronounce those place names. Please send wet wipes.

Don't worry, I won't be angry if you've Snow-done a different case study in class — there's no need to rePentir all your hard work. Just be Ffranc with yourself and make sure you've learnt one location well enough to cope if it cwms up in the exam.

Topic Four — Glacial Systems and Landscapes

Human Impacts on Cold Environments

Cold environments might not be great for beach holidays, but they've still got some great resources. There'll always be people who want to exploit those resources, even if it means damaging the environment in the process.

Cold Environments are Fragile

1) Environmental fragility refers to environments that are **easy** to **damage**, and which take a long time to **recover** from **damage**.

2) Cold environments are fragile because of the **harsh climate**:
   - The **short growing season** (when there's enough **light** and **warmth** for plants to grow) means that plants **don't have much time** to **recover** if they're **damaged**.
   - Plants are only able to **grow slowly**, so repairing damage can take a long time.
   - **Plants** and **animals** are **adapted** to the cold conditions, so they find it hard to survive if their **environment changes**.
   - **Decay** is **slow**, so **pollutants** are **broken down** very **slowly** (and so remain in the environment for a long time).

Human Activities have Changed over Time

1) For **centuries**, **indigenous people** like the **Inuit** have lived in cold environments. Their lifestyles are **adapted** to the **landscape** and the **climate**, and populations are **small**. This means their lifestyles are largely **sustainable** and cause minimal environmental damage.

2) More recently, cold environments have been exploited on a **larger scale**. These activities can have **immediate** and **long-term effects** on the **local area** and the surrounding region, and tend to be **more damaging** to the fragile cold environment than small-scale occupation and use. For example:

The O742 to Kettering had also adapted to the cold conditions.

Oil extraction

1) **Oil spills** can occur **during transport** of oil from the area. For example, in **1989** there was a huge **oil spill** off the coast of **Alaska** when the **Exxon Valdez oil tanker** crashed. Over **40 million** litres of oil spilled into the ocean, and over **250 000** birds and fish were killed.

2) **Oil spills** can occur if **pipelines leak**. Between **1977** and **1994** there were, on average, **30 to 40** spills a year from the **Trans-Alaska pipeline**, which runs the length of Alaska. Some of these were caused by **intentional attacks** and **forest fires**.

Fishing

1) Fishing can **disrupt food chains**, e.g. large-scale **krill** fishing in the **Southern Ocean** is depleting food supplies for **whales** and **penguins**.

2) **Overfishing** of a species can severely **deplete** its **population**, sometimes beyond recovery. Overfishing of the **Patagonian Toothfish** in the **Antarctic** is currently a concern.

3) **Bottom trawling** catches fish by dragging nets along the sea-bed. This **disrupts** the **ecosystem** (by **reducing light levels** through increasing turbidity) and **catches other species** as well as the target one. It's carried out in the **Gulf of Alaska**, the **Greenland Sea** and the **Barents Sea**.

Tourism

1) Large **cruise ships** increase **pollution** in the area (from the ships and from tourists).

2) Tourists and tourism developments (e.g. roads, hotels) disrupt **wildlife** and **damage habitats**, leading to **reduced biodiversity**.

Hydroelectric power production

1) **Hydroelectric dams** can **block** the normal **migratory path** of fish. This can prevent them reaching **spawning grounds**, and so cause the fish **population** to **decrease**. Fish can travel **long distances** to spawn, so this can affect fish populations over a **large area**.

2) Hydroelectric dams also **heat up** the water, which can endanger **fish** that are adapted to **colder** temperatures.

Mining

1) Mining can lead to **ground** and **surface water contamination**, either by **chemicals** used **during mining** or by releasing the materials **being mined** into the environment. E.g. a lead-zinc mine in **Maarmorilik** (Greenland) was closed in 1990 but levels of **lead** and **zinc** pollution are **still high** in nearby fjords.

2) Mining produces both **solid waste** and **wastewater** that has to be disposed of. Some mines don't have the facilities required to deal with the quantities of waste produced, so the **waste is released** into the **environment**, polluting the local area.

3) Any development may require **additional infrastructure to** be built, e.g. support **buildings** and **access roads**. These can cause more damage to the environment, and improved access may open the area up to **further development**.

Human Impacts on Cold Environments

Climate Change is Causing Warming in Cold Environments

1) Most climate scientists believe that the climate is **warming**. There are **natural** reasons for this (e.g. changes in the **Earth's orbit**) and human reasons (e.g. increasing concentrations of **greenhouse gases** in the atmosphere).

2) Climate change has **current** and **predicted** impacts on cold environments:

Current Impacts	Predicted Impacts
1) Melting glaciers and ice sheets, particularly those in Greenland and Antarctica, are causing **sea levels** to **rise**. **Globally**, most glaciers are **retreating** due to rising temperatures.	1) **Sea level** will **rise** further as temperatures increase. This could **flood** low-lying coastal cold environments.
2) **Permafrost** is **melting**, e.g. in Alaska. This can cause **buildings** to **collapse** and **ice roads** (essential supply routes to remote settlements) to be usable for **less time** before they begin to thaw each year.	2) **Melting permafrost** could trigger a **positive feedback** as methane (a greenhouse gas) that is trapped in permafrost is **released**. More methane in the atmosphere will cause temperatures to rise, which will cause **further melting** of permafrost and the release of **even more** methane.
3) **Migration patterns** of some species, e.g. caribou, are **changing** due to changes in the seasons.	3) Plants and animals that are **adapted** to cold conditions may find it **harder** to survive. The range of **other** flora and fauna that prefer warmer temperatures may **extend into** cold environments.

Cold Environments are Managed but Under Pressure

1) There are various **management strategies** currently in place to protect cold environments:

- **Protected areas** — some countries have **protected** their cold environments by passing **laws** to prevent activities within them. E.g. some areas of Alaska are **designated wilderness areas**, where development is **forbidden** and access is **limited**.

- **International treaties** — some cold environments are **internationally important**, and there are global management strategies to protect them in the form of **treaties** signed by countries around the world. E.g. the **Antarctic Treaty** was signed by 12 countries in 1959 and now has 53 signatories. It states that Antarctica must only be used for **peaceful purposes**, including **science**.

- **Monitoring and regulation** — exploitation (e.g. number of visitors) can be monitored to assess its **impacts**. Activities can be strictly **managed**, e.g. visitors to Antarctica have to clean and **disinfect footwear** when they land to prevent the introduction of **non-native** species.

- **Fishing quotas** — in some areas, e.g. the Barents Sea, the number of fish that can be caught is **limited**.

2) Cold environments are increasingly under **pressure** — their **natural resources** (e.g. oil, minerals) offer opportunities for exploitation, and demand from **tourists** is increasing. This may influence how they are **managed** in future, for example:

- **Increased protection** — there are growing demands for cold environments to be **protected** from development and human activity. E.g. in 2015, the president of the USA proposed **extending** the wilderness area of Alaska, which would **prevent** oil exploration in that area.

- **Decreased protection** — as global population **increases** and reserves of oil and minerals in other areas are **depleted**, development of cold environments may become more of a **priority** than conservation. Areas that are currently protected (e.g. Antarctica) may be **opened up** for exploitation.

Practice Questions

Q1 What is environmental fragility?
Q2 How have human activities in cold environments changed over time?
Q3 What are the effects of melting permafrost?

Exam Question

Q1 The photograph shows a coal mine in Svalbard. Using the photograph and your own knowledge, assess the potential impact of humans on this environment. [6 marks]

Human impacts on cold environments — a big source of ski holiday injuries...

Ah, those pesky humans are getting in the way of things again. If only they'd manage without things like jobs, energy and houses. If you're itching for more on how humans use cold environments, you're in luck — we're off to Alaska next...

Humans in Glacial Landscapes — Case Study

Alaska is one example of a glaciated environment where the extreme climate creates challenges to development.

There are **Development Opportunities** in **Alaska**...

Alaska is a **glaciated environment** that's part of the **USA**. There are upland areas where **glaciers** still persist, and large areas of **periglacial landforms** in the northernmost parts of the state. The **northern** parts of Alaska are inside the **Arctic circle**.

Opportunities for economic development include:

1) **Oil and gas** — **over half** of Alaska's income comes from the **oil and gas industry**. Most oil fields are in the **tundra** in the north of the country. Oil reserves in **Prudhoe Bay** are currently exploited, but there are more reserves in more remote locations in the north of the state. The **Trans-Alaska oil pipeline** links the oil fields at Prudhoe Bay with **Valdez**, from where the oil can be **shipped** to customers.

2) **Mineral resources** — gold, silver, iron ore, lead, zinc and copper are mined, particularly in the **Tintina gold belt**. Mining in the Tintina belt contributed **$2.2 billion** to Alaska's GDP in 2013.

3) **Fishing** — salmon, crab and pollock are fished. Fishing employs **79 000** people and contributes over **$5bn** to Alaska's economy. The largest fishing ports are in the **Aleutian Islands** and **Kodiak Island**, both to the south-west of the state.

4) **Tourism** — tourists are attracted by Alaska's **wilderness scenery**. Around **2 million tourists** visit Alaska each year, bringing in **money** and creating opportunities for **employment**.

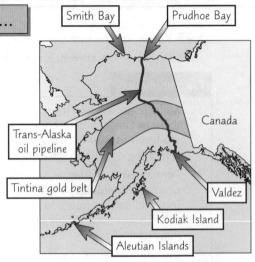

Kodiak Island hadn't been the same since digital cameras came in.

...but there are also **Challenges** to **Development**

1) Alaska's state **population** is one of the **smallest** in the US, despite being the **largest state** by **area**. Most people live in the **south** and **southeast** of the state, near the **coast**, where it is **warmer** and **less remote**.

2) **Development** in Alaska can present **challenges** including getting **access** to resources and finding a **workforce** to exploit them, as well as providing **buildings**, **infrastructure** and protection from the **extreme weather**:

Environmental Conditions

- It's **really cold** — in **Prudhoe Bay** the mean annual temperature is around **–9 °C**. **Snow** and **strong winds** are common. **Exposure** to the extreme cold can cause **injury or death**, and **healthcare** may be a **long distance** away.

- In winter, it is **dark** nearly **all the time** in the north — this makes it hard to live and work there.

Inaccessibility

- Some areas of Alaska are **extremely remote**, and the **mountainous terrain** makes access **difficult** and **expensive**.

- In **winter**, the only way to get to some towns is by **air** or **ice roads**. In summer, the ground is **too soft** so there are **no roads** to some towns.

- Some development opportunities, e.g. oil reserves, are **hundreds** of kilometres from the nearest town — one proposed oil field in Smith Bay is **200 km** from the nearest **existing facilities**. This means it is **very difficult** and **expensive** to transport oil out.

- The population of Alaska is **small** and **scattered** — people in **small towns** may be a long way from **employment opportunities** or **services**.

3) Environmental conditions and inaccessibility create challenges for providing **buildings** and **infrastructure**:

- Most **construction work** can only take place in **summer**, when the days are **longer** and temperatures are **warmer**.

- Development takes a **long time** and is very **expensive**. For example, to exploit oil wells in northern Alaska, building materials have to be **shipped** to the area in **summer**, when seas **aren't frozen**. But prospecting for oil can only occur in **winter**, when the ground is **frozen** and able to support **temporary drilling rigs**.

- Permafrost provides a solid base to build on, but if it **melts** (e.g. due to warmth from buildings or pipelines) the ground becomes **unstable**. This can cause buildings to **collapse** or pipelines to **fracture**.

4) There can also be **conflict** between **development** and **conservation priorities** — the economic benefits of development may come at a high **environmental cost**, and conservation may **hinder** the **local economy**.

Humans in Glacial Landscapes — Case Study

Humans have Responded to the Cold Conditions

There are three main ways that people have responded to the **challenges** that Alaska presents — these responses have allowed them to **occupy** and **develop** the area.

1 Resilience

Resilience means being able to **cope** with the challenges the environment presents.

1) Electricity companies have **emergency generators** that can be started if the **power fails**, and emergency banks of **batteries** that can ensure electricity supplies are not **interrupted** while the generators are starting up. However, remote communities are still **very vulnerable** if there's a fault with their main generator as emergency generators can easily be **overloaded** and may **break down**, leaving the community with **no power at all**.

2) The Alaskan government has **emergency food supplies** to feed **40 000 people** for **seven days** in the event of a natural disaster cutting some people off from regular supplies.

3) When the only road to Prudhoe Bay, the **Dalton Highway**, is **damaged** by the weather, specially designed trucks called **rollagons** with wide, tube-like tyres can cross the tundra to deliver **fuel supplies**. But it's difficult to bring in enough for normal usage this way — this may mean that supplies are **limited** and **prices rise**.

Rollagons crossing snow-covered tundra to deliver fuel after flooding blocked the Dalton Highway in 2015.

2 Mitigation

Mitigation means **reducing** the **severity** of challenges.

1) Utilities such as water and sewage in towns are built in '**utilidors**' — above-ground insulated corridors — to avoid **digging** into permafrost and prevent **melting**. However, they are **expensive** to build and maintain and may still freeze, causing damage and cutting off supplies.

2) Buildings are constructed on **thick** layers of **gravel** or on **stilts** to prevent them from **thawing** the permafrost below. Similarly, some sections of the **Trans-Alaska oil pipeline** are raised on stilts to prevent damage to the permafrost. However, this adds to the **cost** of construction.

3 Adaptation

Adaptation means **adjusting behaviour** to cope with the environment.

1) People **working** in the **cold**, particularly in the oil, gas and mining industries, burn lots of **calories**. Some employers make **food** available **24/7** to ensure employees have enough energy.

2) **Working practices** are **adapted** to the weather — employees may be made to take **warming-up breaks** to prevent **frostbite** and **hypothermia** as often as every **20 minutes** in extreme weather. However, this isn't a very **productive** way of working, so it may not be economically **viable** for some companies.

3) Many vehicles run their engines **continuously** all through winter, otherwise they would struggle to **start** in the cold.

Practice Questions

Q1 Name one important industry in Alaska.

Q2 Give one reason why it is difficult to construct buildings and infrastructure in Alaska.

Q3 Give one example of resilience to cold conditions in Alaska.

Q4 Give one example of a measure taken to mitigate the effects of the cold environment in Alaska.

Exam Questions

Q1 Outline the opportunities for development in a glaciated environment that you have studied. [4 marks]

Q2 "Challenges to development in glaciated environments can and should be overcome."
To what extent do you agree with this view? [20 marks]

Al ask ya again — read this case study until it's drilled deep into your brain...

I mean sure, breaks every 20 minutes and unlimited food sound great, but remember that it's dark all winter long and so absolutely blummin' freezing that even tyres on cars can freeze into shapes that aren't round. You may have studied a different example of human activities in glacial landscapes, which is fine — just make sure you've got one learnt.

Natural Hazards

Time for a bit of mayhem and disaster — it always makes Geography more interesting. Hazards come in all shapes and sizes, and when they happen in populated areas they can be pretty nasty things (as you can probably guess). I'm scared.

There are **Different Types** of Hazard

1) A **hazard** is something that's a **potential threat** to **human life** or **property**.
2) **Natural hazards** are caused by **natural processes**, e.g. a lava flow from a volcanic eruption.
3) Natural hazards can be divided into **three** types:

> **Geophysical hazards** (caused by **land** processes) — these include **earthquakes**, **volcanic eruptions**, **landslides** and **tsunamis**.

> **Atmospheric hazards** (caused by **climatic** processes) — these include **tropical cyclones**, **storms**, **droughts**, **extremes of hot or cold weather** and **wildfires**.

> **Hydrological hazards** (caused by **water** movement) — these include **floods** and **avalanches**.

4) Here are a few more useful terms:
   - **Disaster** — when a hazard actually **seriously affects** humans.
   - **Risk** — the **likelihood** that humans will be seriously affected by a hazard.
   - **Vulnerability** — how **susceptible** a **population** is to the damage caused by a hazard.

   A tropical storm (see p. 86-89) is a hazard, but when it hits land and seriously affects people and property it's a disaster.

5) Hazards can have significant **impacts** while they are **occurring**, and often need an **emergency response** (e.g. evacuating an area). The impacts can also go on for a **long time after** the hazard itself has passed.

People's **Circumstances** Affect Their **Perception** of Hazards

1) People view hazards in **different ways** — for example, some people believe they will **never experience** a particular hazard, others **adapt** their lifestyle to minimise risk, and others **accept** hazards as being beyond their control.
2) People's perception of hazards is affected by their **economic**, **social** and **cultural background**. For example:
   - **Wealth** — e.g. richer people may be able to afford to **move** to areas that are less prone to hazards, or to build their homes to **withstand** hazards, so they may perceive the risk as **smaller**.
   - **Religion** — e.g. some people view hazards as **acts of God**, sent to **punish** people.
   - **Education** — e.g. people with more **education** may have a better **understanding** of the risks of hazards, or they may believe that they are able to **reduce** the risks or **mitigate** the impacts.
   - **Past experience** — e.g. people who live in hazard-prone areas may have experienced hazards **before**, which may affect the perceived risk from **future hazards**.
   - **Personality** — e.g. some people **fear** hazards and others might think of them as **exciting**.

"Hazards? Not a problem. I simply fly away in my platinum rocket."

There are **Many Responses** to Hazards

Individuals and governments might respond to a hazard to try to **reduce** their **vulnerability**, or to **reduce its impacts**:

> 1) People might try to **prevent** a hazard or reduce its **magnitude**. For some hazards (e.g. volcanic eruptions), this isn't possible, but for others (e.g. floods) it may be, e.g. by building flood defences. **Risk sharing** involves sharing the **costs** of reducing a hazard, the **benefits** of preventing it or the **costs** of not preventing it — e.g. people buy **insurance** to help them repair their property after a disaster. Most people **won't** be affected by a particular event, so they won't **claim** on the insurance — this means **lots** of people **contribute**, so the cost is **shared**.
>
> 2) People might try to reduce (**mitigate**) the **impacts** of a hazard. This could be by **prediction** — working out **when** and **where** a hazard is likely to occur, which allows people to respond to it (e.g. by evacuating an area). It could also be by **adaptation** — e.g. adding earthquake-resistant features to buildings.
>
> 3) Governments may **coordinate** responses to a hazard to **manage** it effectively.
>
> 4) Some people believe that hazards **cannot** be avoided, so they must just be **accepted** — this is **fatalism**.

The **success** of attempts to manage hazards depends on **hazard incidence** (how often a hazard occurs), **magnitude** or **intensity** (how **powerful** the hazard is) and **distribution** (the **areal extent** of the hazard). Generally, hazards with **low incidence** and **high magnitude** are most destructive. **Level of development** is also important — less developed countries may lack the **wealth** and **technology** to manage hazards effectively.

Natural Hazards

The **Park Model** Shows How People **Respond** to Hazards

The Park model shows the different phases of **response** to a hazard:

1) **Pre-disaster** — **before** the event, the situation is **normal**.

2) **Disruption** — **during** and **directly after** the hazard event occurs, there is **destruction** of property, loss of life etc. before people begin to respond.

3) **Relief** — in the **aftermath** of the event, rescue efforts focus on **saving** people and **preventing** further damage.

Relief and rehabilitation often involve help from national or international sources, e.g. aid.

4) **Rehabilitation** — once the immediate impacts are under control, people start to **resolve longer-term problems**, e.g. providing **temporary shelter** and **aid** for those affected.

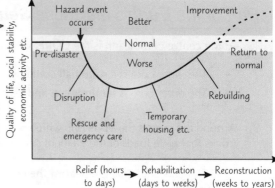

5) **Reconstruction** — this involves **rebuilding** permanent houses, infrastructure etc. This results in one of **two** outcomes:

- If buildings etc. are built to the **same standard** as before, the area returns to **normal**.
- If buildings etc. are built to a **higher standard** than before, the area **improves** (**vulnerability** to hazards **decreases**).

The Park model shows how responses **progress** during a disaster, which may help planners **predict** what resources will be needed at each stage. The model can also help planners to **prepare** for **future** hazard events. For example, the reconstruction phase of the model shows that conditions can be **improved** after a disaster (e.g. by designing hazard-resistant buildings or installing warning systems), which will help to **mitigate** the **impacts** of future hazard events.

There Are **Four Phases** in the **Hazard Management Cycle**

There are **four** stages that authorities go through in **managing** hazards:

1) **Mitigation** — this aims to **minimise** the **impacts** of future disasters. For example, building flood defences or adding fire-resistant roofs to buildings in areas prone to volcanic eruptions. Mitigation can happen **before** a hazard occurs or **afterwards**, when the area is recovering.

2) **Preparedness** — this is about **planning** how to respond to a hazard, e.g. making sure there are warning systems in place or educating people about how to evacuate safely if there is a cyclone.

3) **Response** — this is how people **react** when a disaster **occurs**, e.g. emergency services rescuing people who have been trapped or evacuating people from the danger zone.

4) **Recovery** — this is about getting the affected area back to **normal**, e.g. repairing or rebuilding houses and restoring services such as medical care and electricity.

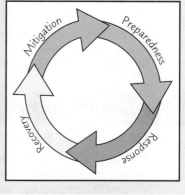

It's a **cycle** because hazard events **keep happening**, so efforts to prepare for them or mitigate their effects are **ongoing**.

Practice Questions

Q1 Name the three types of natural hazards, and give an example of each.

Q2 Explain the 'rehabilitation' stage of the Park model.

Q3 Briefly outline the four stages of the Hazard Management Cycle.

Exam Question

Q1 Assess the extent to which people's perception of hazards is likely to affect their responses to them. [9 marks]

Disruption, relief, rehabilitation — the classic response to exams...

Some of this stuff might seem a bit woolly and theoretical at the moment, but if you can get your head round it it'll help you make sense of the rest of the section. Understanding all the different ways that people respond to hazards, and why, is a really important part of understanding why some disasters have much more severe impacts than others, so learn it well...

Plate Tectonics

The ground beneath your feet is moving all the time — but fear not, it's moving really, really, really slowly (about the same speed as your toenails grow. Yuk, toenails). Plate tectonics theory explains this movement...

Part of the Earth's Mantle is Semi-molten

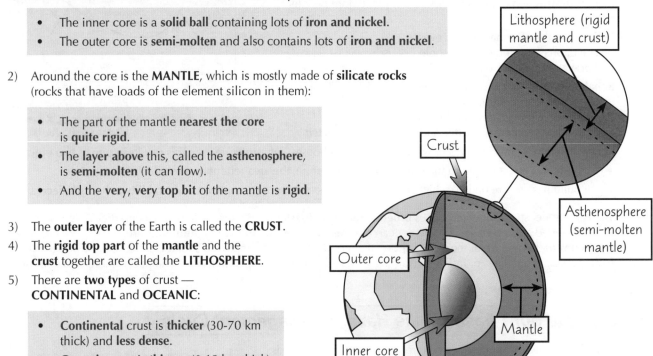

1) At the **centre** of the Earth is the **CORE**, which is split into an **inner** core and an **outer** core:

   - The inner core is a **solid ball** containing lots of **iron and nickel**.
   - The outer core is **semi-molten** and also contains lots of **iron and nickel**.

2) Around the core is the **MANTLE**, which is mostly made of **silicate rocks** (rocks that have loads of the element silicon in them):

   - The part of the mantle **nearest the core** is **quite rigid**.
   - The **layer above** this, called the **asthenosphere**, is **semi-molten** (it can flow).
   - And the **very, very top bit** of the mantle is **rigid**.

3) The **outer layer** of the Earth is called the **CRUST**.

4) The **rigid top part** of the **mantle** and the **crust** together are called the **LITHOSPHERE**.

5) There are **two types** of crust — **CONTINENTAL** and **OCEANIC**:

   - **Continental** crust is **thicker** (30-70 km thick) and **less dense**.
   - **Oceanic** crust is **thinner** (6-10 km thick) and **more dense**.

Lithosphere (rigid mantle and crust)

Crust

Asthenosphere (semi-molten mantle)

Outer core

Mantle

Inner core

6) The core and mantle are **very hot** — the inner core is about **6000 °C** and the mantle is around **1000-3500 °C**. This heat is the Earth's main source of **internal energy**. Some of the heat energy is left over from when the Earth **formed**, and some comes from **radioactive decay** of elements such as uranium.

The Earth's Surface is Separated into Tectonic Plates

1) The lithosphere is **divided** into lots of slabs called **tectonic plates**, which **move** in relation to each other.

2) The places where plates meet are called **plate boundaries** or **plate margins**.

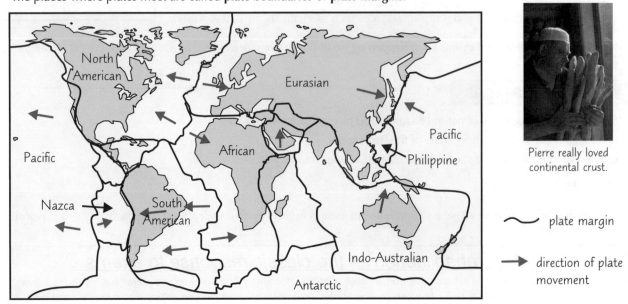

North American

Eurasian

Pacific

Pacific

African

Philippine

Nazca

South American

Indo-Australian

Antarctic

Pierre really loved continental crust.

～ plate margin

→ direction of plate movement

3) The idea that the Earth's lithosphere is made up of plates that move is called the **theory of plate tectonics**.

Plate Tectonics

There Are Several *Theories* About How Tectonic Plates *Move*

Until recently, scientists thought that **convection currents** were the main process causing plate movement. Now, **slab pull** is thought to be the dominant process in most places, with **ridge push** happening in others.

Convection Currents

1) The Earth's mantle is **hottest** close to the **core**, so **lower parts** of the **asthenosphere heat up**, become **less dense** and slowly **rise**.

2) As they move towards the **top** of the asthenosphere they **cool down**, become **more dense** and slowly **sink**.

3) These **circular movements** of semi-molten rock are called **convection currents**.

4) They **create drag** on the **base** of the **tectonic plates**, causing them to **move**.

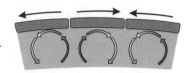

Slab Pull

1) At **destructive plate margins**, denser crust is forced **under** less dense crust (see p.76).

2) The **sinking** of the plate edge **pulls** the rest of the plate towards the boundary.

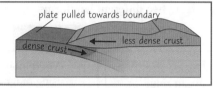
plate pulled towards boundary
less dense crust
dense crust

Ridge Push

1) At **constructive plate margins** (see p.76), magma rises to the surface and forms **new crust**, which is very **hot**. It heats the surrounding rocks, which **expand** and rise above the surface of the surrounding crust, forming a **slope**.

2) The new crust **cools** and becomes **denser**. Gravity causes the denser rock to move **downslope**, away from the plate margin.

3) This puts **pressure** on the tectonic plates, causing them to **move apart**.

4) Ridge push is also known as **gravitational sliding**.

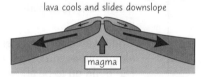
lava cools and slides downslope
magma

Sea-floor Spreading Happens When Plates Move Apart

1) As tectonic plates **diverge** (move apart), **magma rises up** to fill the gap created, then **cools** to form **new crust**.

2) Over time, the **new crust** is **dragged apart** and even **more new crust forms** between it.

3) When this happens at a plate margin under the sea the **sea floor gets wider**.

4) This **process** is called **sea floor spreading**... imaginative name.

5) It creates structures called **mid-ocean ridges** — ridges of higher terrain on either side of the margin.

6) A similar process of spreading occurs at **land margins** where the plates are moving apart.

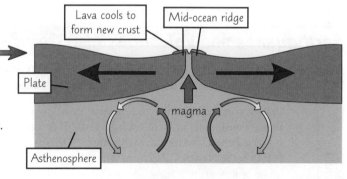
Lava cools to form new crust
Mid-ocean ridge
Plate
magma
Asthenosphere

Practice Questions

Q1 What is the asthenosphere?

Q2 What is the lithosphere?

Q3 Outline the main source of internal energy in the Earth.

Exam Question

Q1 The photograph shows Þingvellir in Iceland, which is situated on the margin between the North American and Eurasian plates. Using the photograph and the map on the previous page, suggest how the landscape is developing tectonically. [6 marks]

Plate tectonics — it's a cracking theory...

What a lovely couple of pages to ease you in to geophysical hazards, but don't think you can get away without knowing this stuff inside out. If you don't get the basics, the rest of this section will be more painful than stubbing your toe on a slab of oceanic crust. A bit of work now will help make the rest of plate tectonics a piece of Victoria sponge. Mmm, cake...

Types of Plate Margin

The next couple of pages build on some of the stuff you should have learnt at GCSE. It's not the most difficult of topics (I'm saving those for later...) but it's vital nonetheless — so put on your favourite revision hat and get ready to take it all in.

Earthquakes and Volcanoes Occur at Constructive Margins

1) A **constructive margin** occurs where two plates are moving **APART** (diverging).

2) The mantle is under **pressure** from the plates above. When they move apart, the pressure is **released** at the **margin**.

3) The release of pressure causes the mantle to **melt**, producing **magma**.

4) The magma is **less dense** than the plate above, so it **rises** and can **erupt** to form a **VOLCANO**.

5) The plates **don't** move apart in a **uniform way** — some parts move faster than others. This causes **pressure to build up**. When the pressure becomes **too much** the plate **cracks**, making a **fault line** and causing an **EARTHQUAKE**. **Further earthquakes** may also occur along the fault line once it's been created.

> *A fault line is where a plate has cracked under pressure.*

6) Constructive margins create **two different landforms**, depending on where they are:

OCEAN RIDGE

1) Where diverging plates are **underwater**, an **ocean ridge** forms (see page 75). For example, the **Mid-Atlantic Ridge** is where the **Eurasian plate** and **North American plate** are moving apart.

2) **Underwater volcanoes** erupt along mid-ocean ridges and they can **build up** to be above sea level. For example, **Iceland** has been formed by the build-up of underwater volcanoes along the Mid-Atlantic Ridge.

RIFT VALLEY

1) Where plates diverge **beneath land**, rising **magma** causes the continental crust to **bulge** and **fracture**, forming **fault lines**.

2) As the plates keep moving apart, the **crust** between parallel faults **drops down** to form a **rift valley**. For example, the **East African Rift System** is a series of rift valleys that stretches from **Mozambique** to the **Red Sea** — about 4000 km. It's formed because the **Nubian** and **Somalian** plates are diverging. Some parts of the system are hundreds of metres deep and thousands of metres wide.

3) **Volcanoes** are found around rift valleys. For example, **Mount Kilimanjaro** and **Mount Kenya** (the two highest mountains in Africa) are volcanoes in the **East African Rift System**.

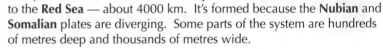

Rift Valley / Faults / Mantle

Earthquakes and Volcanoes Also Occur at Destructive Margins

A **destructive margin** occurs where two plates are moving **TOWARDS EACH OTHER** (converging). What happens at these margins depends on the **types of plates** converging:

Oceanic-Continental

1) Where continental crust and oceanic crust converge, the more dense oceanic crust is forced under the less dense continental crust (it's subducted). This forms a DEEP SEA TRENCH (a very deep trench in the sea — e.g. the Peru-Chile trench in the Pacific Ocean).

2) FOLD MOUNTAINS also form where the plates meet. They're made up of sediments that have accumulated on the continental crust, which are folded upwards along with the edge of the continental crust.

3) The oceanic crust is heated by friction and contact with the upper mantle, which melts it into magma.

4) The magma is less dense than the continental crust above and will rise back to the surface to form VOLCANOES.

5) As one plate moves under the other they can get stuck. This causes pressure to build up. When the pressure becomes too much the plates jerk past each other, causing an EARTHQUAKE.

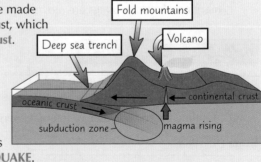

Fold mountains / Volcano / Deep sea trench / oceanic crust / continental crust / subduction zone / magma rising

Oceanic-Oceanic

1) Most of the same processes occur where two plates of oceanic crust are moving towards each other — the denser of the two will be subducted, forming a DEEP SEA TRENCH and triggering EARTHQUAKES and VOLCANIC ERUPTIONS.

2) Volcanic eruptions that take place underwater (e.g. when two plates of oceanic crust converge) create ISLAND ARCS — clusters of islands that sit in a curved line, e.g. the Mariana Islands.

Types of Plate Margin

Continental-Continental

1) Where two plates of **continental crust** move towards each other, **neither** is subducted so there **aren't any volcanoes** — but the pressure that builds up between them can cause **EARTHQUAKES**.

2) **FOLD MOUNTAINS** form when continental crusts converge. E.g. the **Himalayas** were created in this way.

Only Earthquakes Occur at Conservative Plate Margins

1) A **conservative margin** occurs where two plates are moving **PAST EACH OTHER**.

2) The two plates get **locked together** in places and **pressure builds up**. As with destructive margins, this causes the plates to **jerk** past each other (or to **crack**, forming **fault lines**), releasing the **energy** as an **EARTHQUAKE**.

3) For example, the **Pacific plate** is moving past the **North American plate**. Many earthquakes occur along this margin and along its fault lines, e.g. along the **San Andreas fault** in **California**.

AERIAL PHOTOGRAPH OF THE SAN ANDREAS FAULT

This is the fault line

Movement of plates

©PETER MENZEL / SCIENCE PHOTO LIBRARY

Magma Plumes Can Form Volcanoes Away From Plate Margins

Most volcanic activity occurs at **plate margins**, but there are some areas of **intense volcanic activity** that **aren't** near any plate margins. These are caused by **magma plumes**:

1) A **magma plume** is a **vertical column** of **extra-hot magma** that **rises up** from the mantle.

2) **Volcanoes** form above magma plumes.

3) The **magma plume** remains **stationary** over time, but the **crust moves** above it.

4) Volcanic activity in the part of the crust that **was** above the magma plume **decreases** as it moves away.

5) **New volcanoes** form in the part of the crust that is **now above** the magma plume.

6) As the crust continues to move, a **chain of volcanoes** is formed.

7) The chain of islands that makes up **Hawaii** was formed by a magma plume.

The ground above a magma plume is called a hot spot.

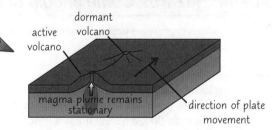

active volcano — plate

magma plume — mantle

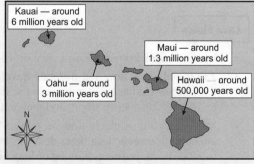

dormant volcano

active volcano

magma plume remains stationary

direction of plate movement

Practice Questions

Q1 Name the two landforms that are created at constructive margins.

Q2 At what type of plate margin do fold mountains form?

Q3 Explain what happens when two continental plates meet.

Q4 Give one example of each type of plate margin.

Exam Questions

Q1 The diagram shows the names and estimated ages of some of the Hawaiian islands. Describe and explain the distribution of the islands in relation to magma plumes. [6 marks]

Kauai — around 6 million years old

Maui — around 1.3 million years old

Oahu — around 3 million years old

Hawaii — around 500,000 years old

N

Tectonic plates are great — but they do have their faults...

Groan... Sorry — I'm running out of tectonics gags. It's not a good sign, since there are still eight pages left on geophysical hazards. I tell you what, you go back and have another read of these pages — make sure you know what happens at each type of plate boundary (and above a magma plume), and I'll see if I can find my sense of humour. See you on the next page...

Volcanic Hazards

Volcanoes — I could talk about them all day. That's probably why I'm such a favourite amongst my friends and relatives.

Volcanic Hazards Usually Occur Near Plate Margins

1) Most volcanic eruptions occur near **constructive** and **destructive** plate margins:

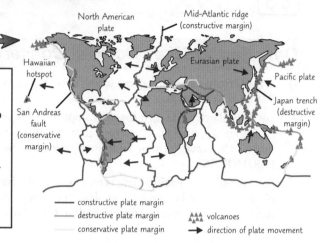

Constructive Margins

- **Basaltic lava** is formed here — it is very **hot** and has a **low viscosity** (it's runny), so it **flows** easily and quickly. Eruptions of basaltic lava are **frequent** and go on for a long time, but they're **not very violent**.
- If the margin is **underwater**, magma rises to fill the space left by plates moving apart, forming **ocean ridges**.
- If the margin is **on land**, as plates pull apart, forming **rift valleys**, they become thinner, and magma is able to break through at the surface.

Destructive Margins

- **Andesitic** and **rhyolitic** lavas are formed here — they are **cooler** and **more viscous** (less runny) than basaltic lava, so they flow **less easily**. Andesitic and rhyolitic lavas usually erupt **intermittently** (every once in a while) and the eruptions are **short-lived**.
- At **subduction zones**, where one plate is pulled beneath another, melting of the plate forms magma, which rises to the surface as volcanoes. Because the lava is viscous, it forms **blockages** in volcanic vents, causing **pressure** to build. The blockage is cleared by a **violent eruption**.

2) A few volcanoes occur **away** from plate margins at **hot spots** above magma plumes (see p.77). Most hot spots have **basaltic lava** that flows quickly, forming volcanoes with **gentle slopes** (shield volcanoes).

Volcanic Hazards Come in Lots of Different Forms

Volcanic eruptions can create **primary hazards** — hazards that come from the eruption itself, e.g.:

Pyroclastic Flows

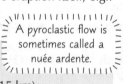
A pyroclastic flow is sometimes called a nuée ardente.

- A **pyroclastic flow** is a mixture of **super-heated gas**, **ash** and **volcanic rock** that **flows** down the sides of a volcano. It travels at **high speed** (often more than 80 km/h) and flows a **long way** (generally around 10-15 km).
- Because they travel **fast** and can happen with relatively **little warning**, pyroclastic flows can cause widespread **death** and **destruction**, through e.g. burning and burial under debris.

Pompeii and Herculaneum were buried by a series of pyroclastic flows from the eruption of Vesuvius in 79 A.D.

Lava Flows

- Lava can **flow** from a volcanic vent down the side of the volcano.
- The **speed** of the flow and **distance travelled** depend on the temperature and viscosity of the lava, as well as the steepness of the slope — **low viscosity** (runny) lava can flow at up to 10 km/h on a steep slope, and may travel tens of kilometres.
- Most flows are relatively **slow**, so people have time to **evacuate** areas that will be affected. However, lava flows **destroy** anything in their path, including buildings and vegetation, by **burning, burying** or **knocking it down**.

Volcanic Gases

- Lava contains **gases** such as **carbon dioxide** and **sulfur dioxide**, which are **released** into the atmosphere when a volcano erupts.
- Some of these gases can be **harmful** to humans and animals if they're breathed in, e.g. sulfur dioxide can cause breathing difficulties.

Topic Five — Hazards

Volcanic Hazards

Pyroclastic and Ash Fallout

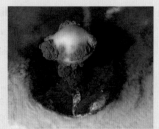

Another name for pyroclastic material is tephra.

- **Pyroclastic fallout** is material that has been ejected from a volcano during an eruption and **falls back** to the ground. When fallout consists mostly of ash, it's called **ash fallout**.

- Fallout consists of material of a **range of sizes** — from large pieces of rock weighing several tonnes to microscopic ash particles. Material can travel **thousands of kilometres** from the volcano. Heavier particles are deposited **earlier** than light ones, so material ends up being **well sorted**, with larger, heavier particles deposited **near** the volcano and smaller, lighter particles (e.g. ash) **further away**.

- Large pieces of falling tephra can **damage buildings** and **kill** or **injure people**. Finer material can form a layer up to several metres in thickness, which can **kill vegetation**, hinder road and rail **transport** and cause buildings to **collapse**. Ash can also be **harmful** to people if it is breathed in.

An ash cloud in Russia.

Eruptions can also create **secondary hazards** — hazards that are **caused by** the primary hazards, e.g.:

Mudflows (Lahars)

- Mudflows occur when volcanic material **mixes** with large amounts of **water** (e.g. from rainfall or from ice melted by the eruption). Flows move very **quickly** (over 80 km/h) and can travel for **tens of kilometres**.

- Mudflows can **bury** or **destroy** natural habitats, settlements and infrastructure (e.g. roads and bridges).

Acid Rain

- Volcanic **gases** can **react** with water vapour in the atmosphere, which then falls as **acid rain** — e.g. sulfur dioxide reacts with water to form weak **sulfuric acid**.

- This can **damage ecosystems**, and can also cause stone and metal to **deteriorate**, damaging buildings, bridges, statues etc.

Eruptions can cause other secondary hazards — e.g. if pyroclastic flows melt ice, it can cause flooding downslope, and if they enter the sea, they may generate a tsunami.

The *Magnitude* and *Frequency* of Volcanic Hazards *Varies*

There are a few more **terms** you need to know to understand volcanic hazards:

- **Magnitude** — volcanic events range from **small**, **slow** lava flows to **huge eruptions** of lava, ash and gas. Magnitude of eruptions can be measured using the **Volcanic Explosivity Index**, which grades volcanoes on a scale from 0 to 8 based on the **amount** of material ejected and **how high** the material is blasted.

- **Frequency** — some active volcanoes erupt only **once every 100 000 years** or so, whereas others erupt **every few months**. Generally, **less frequent** eruptions are **larger in magnitude** and more damaging.

- **Randomness vs. regularity** — some volcanoes erupt at very **regular** intervals, whereas others may be **dormant** for hundreds or thousands of years, then erupt **several times** in quick succession.

- **Predictability** — the regularity with which a volcano erupts can help scientists to **predict when** it might erupt again. They also monitor **tiny earthquakes** and changes in the **shape** of the volcano, which suggest that an eruption is imminent.

Practice Questions

Q1 Briefly summarise where active volcanoes are found

Q2 What is a pyroclastic flow?

Q3 What is meant by the predictability of a volcanic event?

Exam Question

Q1 Analyse the role of plate margin type in influencing the risk posed to people by volcanic hazards. [9 marks]

The Nuée Ardente — sounds like the name of a pretentious synth pop band...

In fact, I might form a band of that name — my first track will be called 'I Will Survive (This Lava Flow by Walking Swiftly in the Opposite Direction)'. Anyway, back to volcanoes — turns out they're not just a great topic for a disaster movie, they're also the basis for some pretty tricksy exam questions. So make sure you know your lahars from your lava flows before you move on.

Volcanic Hazards — Impacts and Responses

So it turns out that volcanic eruptions don't just look scary, they also have some pretty scary impacts.
Nobody panic — there are lots of different ways of managing them, which can make them less damaging.

Volcanic Events Have **Primary** and **Secondary Impacts**

1) **Primary impacts** are a **direct result** of the eruption, e.g. people can be killed by falling tephra.

2) **Secondary impacts** occur as a **result** of the **primary impacts**, e.g. pyroclastic flows can melt glaciers and cause flooding.

3) Volcanic eruptions have **impacts** on people and the environment:

> Have a look at pages 78-79 for the impacts of specific volcanic hazards.

Social
- People are **killed**, and buildings and infrastructure are **destroyed** by pyroclastic flows and fallout.
- Pyroclastic flows and lava flows can **start fires** that damage buildings.
- **Mudflows** and **flooding** from ice melt can cause further **damage** and **deaths**.

Environmental
- Ecosystems can be **damaged** or **destroyed** by flows and fallout of volcanic material.
- **Acid rain** can cause **acidification** of aquatic **ecosystems**, killing some plants and animals. It also damages the leaves of **trees** and **removes nutrients** from the soil, damaging forests.
- Volcanic gases contribute to the **enhanced greenhouse effect** and can add to **global warming**.
- Clouds of ash and volcanic debris can reduce the amount of **sunlight** reaching Earth, **decreasing temperatures** over large areas.

Economic
- Eruptions can **destroy businesses**, and ash clouds can prevent **aircraft** flying and damage **crops**. This damages the **economy** of the region and the country.
- Damage to buildings and infrastructure can be very **expensive** to repair.
- Eruptions and the scenery they form can **attract tourists**, boosting the economy.

Political
- Damage to agricultural land can cause **food shortages**, leading to **conflict** and political **unrest**.
- Governments may have to spend money on **repairing damage** to buildings and roads, rather than e.g. hospitals and schools, so countries may not develop as rapidly.

Volcanic Hazards Need **Short-term** and **Long-term Responses**

1) Hazard **mitigation** is anything that is done to **reduce** the **severity** or **impacts** of a hazard. This can be done through **short-term** or **long-term responses** to the volcanic hazard.

2) **Short-term responses** normally occur **immediately before**, **during** or **immediately after** the hazard begins — they include things like **evacuating** people from areas at risk from an eruption and providing **emergency food** supplies.

3) **Long-term responses** are designed to **reduce** the impacts of future eruptions by managing the **risks**.

4) Long-term responses fall into **three** main categories:

Mark wished the emergency food supplies had included something other than sprouts.

Prevention
- It's **not possible** to prevent a volcanic eruption.
- However, it is sometimes possible to prevent eruptions **posing a risk** to people — e.g. authorities can prevent the **land** around volcanoes from being **developed**.

Preparedness
Preparedness is about what happens **before** an eruption to **minimise risk** or **vulnerability**. For example:
- Authorities can install **monitoring systems** to predict **when** an eruption might occur, and make plans for how they will **evacuate** people if there is an eruption.
- If an eruption is imminent, authorities can **stop people** from **entering** the area around the volcano.
- **Individuals** can make sure they are prepared, e.g. by finding out where their nearest **emergency shelter** is, or making an **emergency kit** containing a torch, medicine, dust masks etc.
- **Communities** can set up **search and rescue** teams or **fire response units** to tackle the impacts of an eruption.

Adaptation
Adaptation is about how people **change** their behaviour or surroundings to **minimise** the **risks** and **maximise** the **benefits** of living near a volcano. For example:
- Buildings can be **strengthened** to reduce the chance of collapse if a layer of ash lands on them.
- People can capitalise on the **opportunities** of living near a volcano, e.g. by **farming** (volcanic ash makes soil very fertile) or by working in the **tourist industry**.

Volcanic Hazards — Impacts and Responses

The **Soufrière Hills** Volcano in **Montserrat** Erupted in **1997**

1) The **Soufrière Hills volcano** is in Montserrat, a small island in the Caribbean Sea. Montserrat is above a **destructive plate margin**, where the **North American plate** is being **forced under** the **Caribbean plate**.

2) Between June and September **1997** there was a series of **large eruptions**. In the largest eruption, about **4-5 million m³** of material was released over a **20 minute period**. **Pyroclastic flows** covered several square kilometres. The eruptions also produced **large ash clouds**.

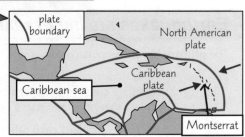

There were **Many Impacts**

ECONOMIC

1) The **total loss in value** of people's homes and investments was estimated to be about **£1 billion**.
2) Over **20 villages** and **two thirds of homes** on the island were **destroyed** by **pyroclastic flows**.
3) **Tourists stayed away** and **businesses** were **destroyed**, disrupting the **economy**. However, **tourism** on the island is now **increasing** as people come to **see the volcano**.
4) **Schools, hospitals**, the **airport** and the **port** were **destroyed**.

SOCIAL

1) **19 people died** and seven were injured.
2) **Hundreds** of people **lost** their **homes**.
3) **Fires destroyed** many buildings, e.g. local **government** offices, the **police headquarters** and **petrol stations**.
4) The **population has declined** — **8000** of the island's 12 000 inhabitants **left** after the eruption, and many still haven't returned.

ENVIRONMENTAL

1) **Large areas** were **covered** with **volcanic material** — the capital city **Plymouth** was buried under **12 m of mud and ash**.
2) **Vegetation** and **farmland** were **destroyed**.
3) **Volcanic ash** from the eruption has **improved soil fertility**.

Responses Included Help from the **Emergency Services** and **Aid**

The responses to the eruption were both short-term and long-term:

1) **People** were **evacuated** from the south to **safe areas** in the north.
2) **Shelters** were **built** to house evacuees.
3) Temporary **infrastructure** was also built, e.g. **roads** and **electricity supplies**.
4) The **UK** provided **£17 million** of **emergency aid** (Montserrat's an overseas territory of the UK).
5) **Local emergency services** provided support units to **search** for and **rescue** survivors.
6) A **risk map** was created and an **exclusion zone** is in place. The south of the island is **off-limits** while the volcano is **still intermittently active**.
7) The **UK** has provided **£41 million** of long-term aid to develop the north of the island — **new docks**, an **airport** and **houses** have been built with this.
8) The **Montserrat Volcano Observatory** has been set up to try and **predict** future eruptions.

Practice Questions

Q1 Describe the difference between short-term and long-term responses to a volcanic hazard.

Q2 Give two economic impacts of the Soufrière Hills eruption.

Exam Question

Q1 'It is possible to manage the impacts of volcanic eruptions, but the impacts cannot be prevented.'
To what extent do you agree with this view?

[20 marks]

Maybe Caribbean islands aren't so idyllic after all...

The scientists at the volcano observatory take thermal images of the dome to see how hot it is, measure earthquakes and monitor how the ground is bulging. If things look like they're hotting up, they issue alerts so everyone knows to hightail it out of there.

Seismic Hazards

Now you're an expert on volcanic hazards, it's time to turn your attention to seismic hazards — that's earthquakes and all the other nasty hazards that they can cause. It's earth-shattering stuff.

Earthquakes are the Primary Hazard Caused by Seismic Activity

The **primary hazard** associated with a seismic event is an **earthquake**:

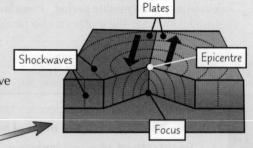

1) Earthquakes are caused by the **tension** that builds up at **all three** types of **plate margin** — see pages 76 and 77.

2) When the plates **jerk past each other** it sends out **shockwaves** (vibrations). These vibrations are the **earthquake**.

3) The shockwaves **spread out** from the **focus**. The focus doesn't have to be a single point — for example, it could be along a **fault line**. Near the focus the waves are **stronger** and cause **more damage**.

4) The **epicentre** is the point **on the Earth's surface** where the earthquake is **felt first**. It's **straight above** the **focus**.

5) Earthquakes cause the ground to **shake**, and sometimes to **rupture** (split apart) along the fault.

Earthquakes can be measured using three different scales:

1) The **Richter scale** measures the magnitude of an earthquake (how powerful the shaking is). It doesn't have an upper limit and it's **logarithmic** — this means that an earthquake with a magnitude of **5** has an amplitude (wave size) **ten times greater** than one with a magnitude of **4**. **Major** earthquakes are **above 7**.

2) The **moment magnitude scale** (MMS) is based on the total amount of **energy released** by an earthquake. Like the Richter scale, it is **logarithmic** and has **no upper limit**. It is **more accurate** than the Richter scale, especially for large earthquakes, so it's more widely used.

3) The **Mercalli scale** measures the **impacts** of an earthquake using **observations** of the event (e.g. reports and photos). The scale is between **1 and 12**, with **1** being an earthquake that's only detected by **instruments**, and **12** being an earthquake that causes **total destruction**.

Earthquakes Can Cause Other Seismic Hazards

Earthquakes cause a range of different **hazards**, including:

> Volcanic eruptions and landslides that slide into the sea can also displace large volumes of water and cause tsunamis.

Tsunamis

1) Tsunamis are **large waves** caused by the **displacement** of large volumes of **water**.

2) They can be triggered by **underwater earthquakes**. The earthquakes cause the seabed to move, which displaces water. Waves **radiate** out from the **epicentre** of the earthquake. The **greater** the **movement** of the sea floor, the greater the volume of water displaced, and the **bigger** the **wave** produced.

3) A tsunami will usually be **more powerful** if it starts **close to the coast**. This is because the waves **lose energy** as they travel towards land. So, the closer to the coast the waves start, the less energy they will lose.

4) The waves travel **very fast** in deep water so they can hit the shore **without much warning**. This means that they can cause a **high death toll**.

Landslides and Avalanches

1) **Shaking** of the ground can **dislodge** rock, soil or snow, causing landslides or avalanches that move **downslope** quickly.

2) Shaking can also loosen ground material, making it easier for **water** to infiltrate. The **weight** of the extra water may trigger a landslide even **after** ground shaking has stopped.

Soil Liquefaction

1) When soil is **saturated** with water, the vibrations of an earthquake can cause it to **act** like a **liquid**.

2) This makes the soil **weaker** and easier to **deform**, so it's more likely to **subside**, especially where it has a heavy **weight** on top of it (e.g. a building).

Seismic Hazards

Seismic Hazards Usually Occur Near Plate Margins

1) Most seismic hazards occur around **destructive** and **conservative** plate margins, but they can also occur around **constructive** margins.

2) The **nature** of an earthquake and its **magnitude** is affected by **three** main factors:

Map labels:
North American plate
Mid-Atlantic ridge (constructive boundary)
Eurasian plate
Pacific plate
Japan trench (destructive boundary)
San Andreas fault (conservative boundary)

constructive plate boundary — earthquakes
destructive plate boundary — direction of plate movement
conservative plate boundary — highest tsunami risk

Margin Type

• The biggest earthquakes occur at **destructive** plate margins, where one plate is forced beneath another at the **subduction zone**. The subduction of a plate causes massive **pressure** to build up, causing a huge earthquake when it is released.

• Earthquakes at **constructive** margins tend to be **lower magnitude** than at destructive or conservative margins.

Rate of Movement

• Tectonic plates move in relation to each other at **different rates**, between about 1 and 15 cm per year.

• There's no clear **relationship** between rate of movement and earthquake **magnitude**.

Depth of Focus

• An earthquake's focus can be **close** to the Earth's **surface** or **deep** below it.

• **Deep** focus earthquakes tend to be **higher** magnitude than **shallow** focus earthquakes. However, deep focus earthquakes generally do **less damage** than shallow focus earthquakes — this is because shock waves generated deeper in the Earth have to **travel further** to reach the surface, which **reduces** their power.

> The severity of the hazard also depends on where the event occurs, e.g. a mid-ocean earthquake may have fewer impacts than one on land.

Low Magnitude Seismic Hazards Occur Frequently

Just a few more bits to get your head round about seismic hazards:

• **Magnitude and frequency** — hundreds of **low magnitude** earthquakes happen around the world **every day**. Fortunately, earthquakes of very **high magnitude** occur much **less often**. The number of earthquakes that occur globally also **varies** from year to year.

• **Randomness vs. regularity** — earthquakes and other seismic hazards don't seem to follow any clear **pattern** or **trend** — their occurrence is largely **random**.

• **Predictability** — scientists can monitor the movement of tectonic plates to predict which **areas** are **at risk** from seismic hazards. However, it's currently impossible to tell **when** an earthquake will strike a particular place, and what **magnitude** it's likely to be.

Nigel's insistence on dressing as a mime was random, yet it happened with more regularity than his friends would ideally have liked.

Practice Questions

Q1 Describe what the focus of an earthquake is.

Q2 Briefly outline the differences between the Richter scale and the Mercalli scale.

Q3 Name two seismic hazards caused by earthquakes.

Exam Question

Q1 Using the map above and your own knowledge, explain the distribution of the areas of highest tsunami risk. [6 marks]

The Beach Boys' earthquake detector — great for picking up good vibrations...

The problem with not being able to predict earthquakes is that nobody knows to get out of the way before one happens. This means that they can have some pretty major impacts, which need to be managed. And that brings us neatly to the next page...

Seismic Hazards — Impacts and Responses

Unless you've been living in a cave, you'll probably be aware that seismic hazards have some pretty serious impacts. My response to this is to live as far away from the hazards as possible — funnily enough, in a cave.

Seismic Events Have **Primary** and **Secondary Impacts**

1) **Primary impacts** are a **direct result** of the hazard, e.g. people can be killed when a tsunami hits a coastal area.
2) **Secondary impacts** occur as a **result** of the **primary impacts**, e.g. earthquakes can break gas pipes, causing fires.
3) Seismic hazards have **impacts** on people and the environment:

Social
- Earthquakes can cause buildings to **collapse, killing** and **injuring** people, and leaving others **homeless**.
- Earthquakes and liquefaction can cause **gas lines** and **power lines** to break, starting **fires** that **kill** more people. Broken water pipes can cause **flooding**, and lack of water can make it hard to put fires out.
- Lack of clean water can cause **disease** to spread.
- Tsunamis can **flood** large areas, **killing** people and causing widespread **damage** to property.

Environmental
- Industrial units, including power plants, can be **damaged** by earthquakes and tsunamis, causing **leaks** of **chemicals** or **radioactive material** that damage the environment.
- **Fires** started by damaged gas and electricity lines can **destroy ecosystems**.
- Tsunamis can **flood** freshwater ecosystems, killing plants and animals and **salinising** water and soil.

Economic
- Earthquakes can **destroy business premises** through ground shaking and liquefaction. This damages the **economy** of the region and the country.
- Damage to **industry** may mean that the country has to rely on **expensive imports** of goods and energy.
- Damage to **buildings** and **infrastructure** can be very **expensive** to repair.

Political
- **Shortages** of food, water and energy can cause **conflict** and political **unrest**.
- Governments may have to **borrow** money to repair damage, putting the country in **debt**. Money that is earmarked for development may have to be spent on **repairing damage** rather than on development.

Seismic Hazards Need **Short-term** and **Long-term Responses**

Helen and Darren's tsunami response was ill-advised.

1) Attempts to mitigate the effects of a seismic hazard can rely on short-term or long-term responses.
2) **Short-term responses** normally occur **immediately before**, **during** or **immediately after** the hazard — they include things like rescuing people from collapsed buildings after an earthquake, and **evacuating** people from areas at risk from a tsunami.
3) **Long-term responses** are designed to **mitigate** the impacts of future hazards by managing the **risks**.
4) Long-term responses fall into **three** main categories:

Prevention
- It's **not possible** to prevent most seismic hazards.
- However, it's sometimes possible to prevent them **posing a risk** to people — e.g. authorities can prevent land that is prone to **liquefaction** from being built on, or build **giant sea walls** to prevent tsunamis hitting land.

Preparedness

Preparedness is about preparing an **area** and the **people** who live there for a future seismic hazard. E.g.:
- Authorities can install **earthquake warning systems** — these detect weaker seismic waves that may be a sign of a more powerful earthquake to come. The systems send out **warnings** by e.g. TV, radio and SMS.
- Individuals and businesses can have **plans** for how people should **respond** during an earthquake, e.g. **staying away** from buildings if possible, finding a strong door frame or desk to **shelter** under if inside.
- Authorities can develop **tsunami warning systems** and make sure **evacuation routes** are well signposted.
- **Communities** can set up **search and rescue** teams or **fire response units** to tackle the impacts of a hazard.

Adaptation

People can adapt their behaviour or surroundings to **minimise** the **risks** of seismic hazards. For example:
- Buildings can be **designed** to **withstand** earthquakes, e.g. by using strong or flexible materials, or by building special foundations that absorb an earthquake's energy.
- Buildings can also be designed to reduce vulnerability to **tsunamis**, e.g. **tall**, **strong** buildings allow people to **escape** the tsunami quickly, and buildings with **raised**, **open** foundations are less likely to be damaged.

Seismic Hazards — Impacts and Responses

The Kashmir Earthquake Happened on 8th October 2005

1) The **Kashmir region** in north **Pakistan** sits on a **destructive plate margin** where the **Indian plate** is being forced under the **Eurasian plate**.

2) An earthquake measuring **7.6** on the Moment Magnitude Scale occurred in the Kashmir region on **8th October 2005**.

3) The earthquake caused **damage** to an area of **30 000 km²**.

4) Over the next few weeks there were nearly 1000 **aftershocks**.

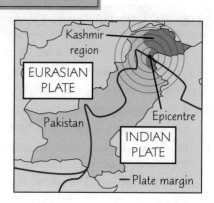

The Earthquake Had a Lot of Impacts

SOCIAL

1) Around **80 000 people died**, and **hundreds of thousands** were **injured**.
2) Around **3 million people** were made **homeless**.
3) **Water pipes** and **electricity lines** were **broken**, cutting off supplies.
4) **Landslides** buried **buildings** and **people**. They also **blocked roads** and destroyed **telephone lines**.
5) **Diarrhoea** and **other diseases** spread due to little **clean water**.

ECONOMIC

1) It's been estimated that the earthquake cost around **US $5 billion** in **total**.
2) **Whole villages** and **thousands of buildings** were **destroyed** or severely damaged. The **total cost of rebuilding** has been estimated to be **US $3.5 billion**.

ENVIRONMENTAL

1) **Landslides** and **rockfalls** occurred throughout the region, affecting habitats.
2) A landslide in Jhelum Valley was over **1 km wide** and over **2 km long**. The debris created a **dam** at the bottom of the valley that **blocked two rivers** where they joined.

People Tried to Respond, But the Response was Delayed

> About US $5.8 billion of foreign aid was provided by the international community in response to the disaster. Some of this was for long-term development.

1) **International aid** and **equipment** such as helicopters and rescue dogs were brought in, as well as **teams** of people from **other countries**.

2) However, the poor roads meant that **help didn't reach** many areas for **days** or **weeks**. People had to be rescued without any equipment or help from emergency services.

3) **Tents**, **blankets** and **medical supplies** were distributed within a **month**, but **not to all areas** affected.

4) The Pakistani government set up the **Earthquake Reconstruction and Rehabilitation Authority** (ERRA) and the **Federal Relief Commission** (FRC) to **coordinate activities** with other international agencies and non-governmental organisations.

5) Around **40 000 people** were **relocated** to a **new town**, from the destroyed town of Balakot.

6) **Government money** was given to people whose homes had been destroyed so they could **rebuild them themselves**.

7) **Training** has been provided to help rebuild more buildings as **earthquake resistant**.

Practice Questions

Q1 Give three possible environmental impacts of seismic hazards.

Q2 Give two possible ways of increasing preparedness for a seismic hazard.

Q3 Describe three social impacts of the Kashmir earthquake.

Exam Question

Q1 Assess whether the secondary impacts caused by seismic hazards are more dangerous than the primary impacts. [9 marks]

Nope, sorry — it's just not very funny...

So, you've reached the end of tectonic hazards. It's been quite a journey — almost to the centre of the Earth. Well, not quite, but 'a journey to a bit below the Earth's surface' sounds far less dramatic. And, let's face it, this section is all about drama.

Storm Hazards

The weather in tropical areas is generally a darn sight better than it is here, but things can get ugly...

Tropical Storms Form Over Warm Water in the Tropics

1) Tropical storms are **huge spinning storms** with **strong winds** and **torrential rain**.

2) They develop over **warm water**. As warm, moist air **rises** and **condenses**, it **releases energy** that increases wind speed.

3) Scientists don't know exactly **how** they're formed but they do know the **conditions needed**. These include:

   • A **disturbance** near the sea-surface that triggers the storm (e.g. an area of low pressure).

   • **Sea water** that's **warm** (above **27°C** to **at least 50 m** below the surface), so lots of water will evaporate.

   • **Convergence of air** in the **lower atmosphere** — either within the ITCZ or along the boundary between warm and cold air masses. This forces warm air to **rise**.

   • A location at least **5° from the Equator**. They **don't form 0-5° either side** of the Equator because the **Coriolis effect** isn't strong enough to make them spin.

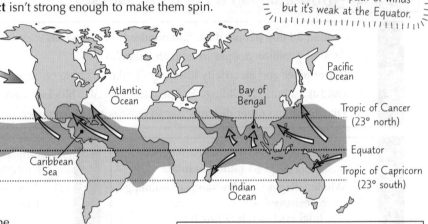

The Coriolis effect is a force caused by the Earth's rotation. It deflects the path of winds but it's weak at the Equator.

4) So tropical storms form in the **tropics** because the water there is **warm enough**.

5) They occur in the **Caribbean Sea** (where they're called **hurricanes**), in the **Bay of Bengal** (where they're called **cyclones**), in the **China Sea** (where they're called **typhoons**) and in **Northern Australia**.

6) Tropical storms **lose strength** when they move **over land** because their supply of warm, moist air is cut off.

7) They initially **move westwards** due to the **easterly winds** in the **tropics**, e.g. trade winds move cyclones west across the Atlantic Ocean.

8) They **move away** from the **Equator** because of the **Coriolis effect**.

path of tropical storm
sea-surface temperature can be above 27 °C

Tropical Storms Are Circular

1) Tropical storms are **circular** in shape, hundreds of kilometres wide and usually last 7-14 days. They spin **anticlockwise** in the northern hemisphere, and **clockwise** in the southern hemisphere.

2) At the **centre** of the storm is an area of very **low pressure** called the **eye**.

3) **Rising air spirals** around the eye in the **eyewall**, causing strong winds.

4) Near the **top** of the storm, there is an **outflow** of moisture-laden air, so cloud cover extends for a long distance either side of the eye.

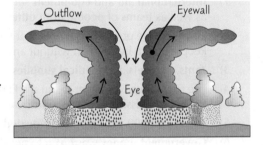

Storm Magnitude is Measured on the Saffir-Simpson Scale

1) Storms are classified using the **Saffir-Simpson Scale**, which is based on wind speed. Category 5 is the **strongest** (with winds over 250 km/h) and 1 is the **weakest** (with winds of 120-150 km/h).

2) The Saffir-Simpson Scale also estimates how much **damage** a storm of a given magnitude will do, from **limited** damage at Category 1 to **catastrophic** damage at Category 5.

3) Tropical storms are quite **frequent** — around one hundred occur each year. Some of these **never reach land**, so they never develop into a major **hazard**. Storms are more frequent in the **northern** hemisphere between June and November, and in the **southern** hemisphere between November and April.

4) There are lots of factors that affect **where** and **when** a tropical storm will form and where it will hit land, so the hazards created by storms are largely **irregular** (they follow no clear **spatial** or **temporal pattern**).

5) Certain cloud formations in tropical areas can be identified from **satellite imagery** and used to tell when a tropical storm is **forming**. The storm can then be **tracked** using satellite imagery and models, helping scientists to work out when and where it is likely to hit land. The path of a tropical storm can therefore be **predicted** fairly accurately.

Storm Hazards

Storms Bring Strong Wind and Heavy Rain

1) Storm hazards can take a number of forms:
   - **High winds** — wind speeds on the ground can reach more than **300 km/h**. Wind can **destroy** buildings, **uproot** trees, and carry debris (e.g. cars and trees) long distances before **smashing** them into other objects.
   - **Storm surges** — a storm surge is a **large rise** in sea level caused by **high winds** pushing water towards the coast, and by the **low pressure** of a storm.
   - **Heavy rain** — as warm, moist air rises it cools and condenses, causing torrential rain. E.g. in 1966, over **1000 mm** of rain fell in 12 hours at La Réunion (an island in the Indian Ocean) during Tropical Storm Denise.
   - **Flooding** — heavy downpours can cause **river discharge** to **increase** suddenly, causing rivers to overtop their banks and flood the surrounding area. Heavy rain and storm surges can also cause flooding in **coastal** areas.
   - **Landslides** — water infiltrates soil and rock, making it **less stable** and increasing the risk of landslides.

2) These hazards can have lots of **impacts**:

Social
- People may **drown**, or be **injured** or **killed** by **debris** that's blown around or carried in flood water.
- Houses are destroyed, so people are left **homeless**.
- Electricity cables are **damaged** and supplies are **cut off**.
- Flooding causes **sewage** overflows, **contaminating water**.
- The **lack** of **clean water** can help **diseases** spread.
- Damage to agricultural land can cause **food shortages**.

Political
- People may blame the **authorities** for **shortages** of food, water and energy, leading to **conflict** and political **unrest**.
- Expensive **repairs** to buildings, infrastructure etc. limit the amount of money that can be spent on **development**.

Economic
- **Buildings** and **infrastructure** cost a huge amount to **rebuild**.
- **Businesses** are **damaged** or **destroyed**, so they **can't trade**.
- **Agricultural land** is **damaged**, affecting **commercial farming**.

Environmental
- **Beaches** are **eroded** and **coastal habitats** (e.g. coral reefs) are **damaged**. Sediment deposited in aquatic ecosystems may damage fish breeding grounds.
- **Environments** are **polluted**, e.g. by salt water, oil and chemicals spilled from damaged factories.
- Landslides can **block watercourses**, so they change course.

Responses Aim to Reduce the Impacts of Storm Hazards

1) **Short-term responses** to a storm hazard normally occur **immediately before**, **during** or **immediately after** the hazard — they include things like **evacuating** people from areas at risk.

2) **Long-term responses** are often designed to **mitigate** the impacts of future storms by managing the **risks**. For example:
   - **Prevention** — storms **cannot** be prevented, but they can be **studied** to help scientists understand which areas are **most likely** to be affected. This means that future developments can be **planned** to **avoid high-risk areas**.
   - **Preparedness** — people and authorities can make sure they are **prepared** for a storm, e.g. **emergency services** can **train** and **prepare** for disasters, governments can plan **evacuation routes** to get people away from storms quickly and **educate people** about how to prepare for a storm (e.g. stockpiling water and food and boarding up windows).
   - **Adaptation** — buildings can be **designed** to **withstand** tropical storms, e.g. by using **reinforced concrete** or by **fixing roofs securely** so they're not blown off. Buildings can also be put on **stilts** so they're safe from floodwater. **Flood defences** can be built **along rivers** (e.g. levees) and **coasts** (e.g. sea walls).

Practice Questions

Q1 Briefly outline the characteristics of a tropical storm.
Q2 Give two social impacts and two environmental impacts of tropical storms.

Exam Question

Q1 Evaluate the role of adaptation in reducing the impacts of storm hazards. [9 marks]

My response to this page is aaaaaaaaaaaaggggggggggghhhhh...
There's a whopping amount to learn on these two pages, so stop eyeing up the TV remote (I saw you) and get learning.

Storm Hazards — Case Studies

And now time for the inevitable case studies — first, a little madam called Katrina, and then a nasty chap called Nargis...

Hurricane Katrina Struck the South East USA on 29th August 2005

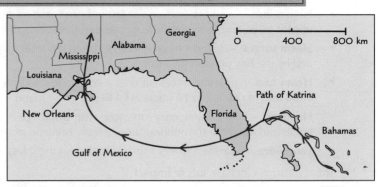

1) A storm hit the south east USA — one of the **wealthiest** countries in the world — in 2005. It **formed** over the **Bahamas** on the **23rd August**.

2) It moved **north west** and **strengthened** as it passed over the warm water of the Gulf of Mexico. By the time it struck Louisiana and Mississippi on the **29th August**, it was a **Category 3** hurricane.

3) It brought winds of around **200 km/h** and **200-250 mm** rainfall to **Louisiana**, and a **storm surge** of up to **8.5 m** in **Mississippi**.

The Hurricane had a Huge Economic Impact

1) The coast of **Louisiana** and **Mississippi** bore the brunt of the hurricane, but south Florida and Cuba were also affected. The storm surge and heavy rainfall **overwhelmed levees** around New Orleans, causing over **80%** of the city to flood.

2) The **high winds**, **storm surge** and **flooding** had the following impacts:

SOCIAL
- **1836** people were **killed**.
- **300 000 houses** were **destroyed**, **hundreds of thousands** of people were made **homeless** and **3 million** people were left **without electricity**.
- One of the main routes out of New Orleans was closed because parts of the **I-10 bridge collapsed**.
- **Water supplies** were **polluted** with sewage and chemicals. **Five people died** from using contaminated water.
- **18 schools** in **New Orleans** were **destroyed** and **74** were badly **damaged**, disrupting **education**.

ECONOMIC
- **230 000 jobs** were **lost** from damaged businesses.
- **Industry** was disrupted — **30 oil platforms** in the Gulf of Mexico were **damaged** or **destroyed**, disrupting the oil industry. **Ports** such as **Gulfport** in Mississippi were **damaged**, affecting the **shipping industry**.
- **5300 km²** of **forest** was destroyed in **Mississippi**, causing around **$5 billion** lost income from logging.
- The total **cost of damage** was around **$300 billion**.

ENVIRONMENTAL
- **Coastal habitats** such as **sea turtle breeding beaches** were **damaged**.
- Some **coastal conservation areas** were **destroyed**, e.g. **Breton National Wildlife Refuge** in **Louisiana**.
- Flooding damaged oil refineries in Louisiana, causing massive **oil spills**.
- Flooding of **salt marshes** led to habitat loss.

Effective Warning Systems Helped the USA Respond Rapidly

1) The USA has a **sophisticated monitoring system** to **predict** if (and where) a hurricane will hit. On **August 26th** the **National Hurricane Center** (**NHC**) in Florida issued a **hurricane warning** for **Louisiana**, **Mississippi** and **Alabama**. It continued to track the hurricane, updating the government on where and when it would hit.

2) This helped the Federal Emergency Management Agency (**FEMA**) and other organisations to start preparing, e.g.:

- The **US Coast Guard** positioned **helicopters** and **boats** around the area likely to be affected.
- **FEMA** organised teams and supplies, e.g. **mortuary teams** with refrigerated trucks to deal with bodies.
- Some areas, including New Orleans, ordered **mandatory (compulsory) evacuation**. It's estimated that around **80%** of New Orleans' residents **were evacuated** before the hurricane reached land.

3) The response continued during the hurricane, and after it had passed. For example:

- **Emergency shelters** were set up for people who hadn't evacuated, e.g. the **Louisiana Superdome** in New Orleans sheltered **26 000 people** during the hurricane.
- The coastguard, police, fire service and army **rescued over 50 000 people** after the hurricane hit.
- Organisations sent **search and rescue** teams, **medical** teams and **supplies** into the area after the hurricane.
- **Charities** collected over **$4 billion** of donations from the public to provide aid (e.g. food) to victims.

Storm Hazards — Case Studies

Cyclone Nargis Struck Myanmar on 2nd May 2008

1) A storm **formed** in the **Bay of Bengal** during the **last week** in **April**.

2) As it approached the **coast of Myanmar** (one of the **least developed** countries in the world, sometimes called **Burma**) it strengthened to a **Category 4** cyclone.

3) On **May 2nd** it **hit** the coast of Myanmar with **wind speeds** of around **215 km/h** and a **storm surge** of **5 m** (storm waves added another 2 m on top of this).

(Map shows India, Myanmar, Bay of Bengal, Irrawaddy Delta, Sri Lanka, and Path of Nargis. Scale: 0 500 1000 km)

The Cyclone had a Huge Social Impact

1) The **Irrawaddy Delta** in Myanmar was the hardest hit area because the cyclone hit it head on. A large proportion of it is only just above sea level and over **14 000 km²** of land was **flooded**.

2) **Sri Lanka** was also affected by heavy rainfall, **flooding** and **landslides**.

3) Across the region, the **high winds**, **storm surge** and **flooding** had the following impacts:

SOCIAL

- More than **140 000** people were **killed**.
- **450 000 houses** were **destroyed** and up to **2.5 million** people were left without **shelter**.
- **4000 schools** and **75%** of **health facilities** were **destroyed** or severely **damaged**.
- **43%** of **freshwater ponds** (valuable sources of fresh water for local people) were **damaged** by salt water. Almost **70%** of people **had no access** to **clean water**.
- A lot of people suffered from **diseases** caused by **poor sanitary conditions** and **contaminated water**, e.g. **dysentery**, **diarrhoea**.

ECONOMIC

- Over **6000 km²** of **agricultural land** was damaged, including rice paddies.
- **Agriculture** was affected — **crops** and **farm animals** were **lost** and over **40%** of **food stores** were **destroyed**.
- **Millions** of people **lost their livelihoods**, e.g. many **fishing boats** were destroyed.
- The **total cost** of damage was around **US $4 billion**.

ENVIRONMENTAL

- **380 km²** of **mangrove forests** were **destroyed**.
- **Flooding** caused **erosion** and **salinisation** (increased salt content) of land.

Mangrove forests protect the coast from flooding. Unfortunately loads had been chopped down to make rice paddies and shrimp farms, reducing the natural protection.

Myanmar Wasn't Prepared for Cyclone Nargis and Responded Slowly

1) Myanmar **doesn't have** a dedicated **hurricane monitoring centre**. **Indian** weather agencies **warned** Myanmar's government that Cyclone Nargis was likely to hit the country **48 hours before** it did, and **Myanmar's weather forecasters issued warnings** the cyclone was coming via **TV** and **radio**. However, it's claimed that they **didn't** say how **severe** it would be or give any advice about **how to prepare** or **evacuate**.

2) There were **no emergency preparation plans**, **no evacuation plans** and the country **didn't** have an **early warning system**.

3) After the cyclone, the **government** initially **refused** to accept any **foreign aid**. On the 9th May they decided to **accept aid donations** of things like food and tents, and organisations such as the **UN refugee agency** (UNHCR) and charities sent shelters, water purification tablets, first aid kits, blankets and food parcels.

4) At the time, Myanmar was ruled by the **military** — they **seized** some **aid**, and some was turned away. Aid workers were not allowed into the country until 19th May — more than two weeks **after** the disaster occurred. The delay in accepting international aid greatly **increased** the **number of deaths**.

Practice Questions

Q1 Give two social impacts, two economic impacts and two environmental impacts of Hurricane Katrina.

Q2 Give two social impacts, two economic impacts and two environmental impacts of Cyclone Nargis.

Exam Question

Q1 'The impacts of tropical storms are always more severe in less developed countries.'
To what extent do you agree with this view? [20 marks]

Make sure you learn two case studies of tropical storms...

If you've studied different tropical storms, that's fine — just make sure you know the impacts and responses inside out.

Wildfires

Fires aren't just for sitting around, telling ghost stories and toasting marshmallows. Nope, when they get out of control they can be pretty devastating. Welcome to the text version of the latest rubbish documentary series... When Fires Go Bad.

Wildfires Normally Occur During **Hot**, **Dry** Periods

1) Wildfires are **uncontrolled fires** that destroy forests, grassland and other areas of vegetation. They usually occur in **rural** areas, but if they reach inhabited areas, they will also destroy **agricultural land** and **settlements**.

2) There are **three types** of wildfire:

- **Ground fire** is where the **ground** itself (e.g. peat and tree roots) burns. It is a **slow**, smouldering fire with **no flame** and **little smoke**.
- **Surface fire** is where **leaf litter** and **low-lying** vegetation burn. Fire can be **low** or **high intensity**.
- **Crown fire** is where fire moves rapidly through the **canopy** (the top layer of vegetation). Fires are likely to be **intense** and **fast-moving**.

All three types of fire can be present at once.

3) There are certain **conditions** that favour **intense** wild fires:

Vegetation Type	• **Thick undergrowth** or **closely spaced trees** allow fire to travel easily. • Some trees, such as eucalyptus and pine, contain a lot of **oil** and so burn very **easily**. • Eucalyptus trees **shed strips** of their bark which helps the fire to **spread** quickly.
Fuel Characteristics	• **Fine**, **dry** material (e.g. long grass, thin twigs) catch fire and burn most **easily**. • **Large amounts** of fuel that form a **continuous cover** will help the fire burn for longer and spread.
Climate and Recent Weather	• Rainfall must be **sufficient** for vegetation to **grow**, so there's plenty of **fuel**. • The area usually has a distinct **dry season** when rainfall is **low** for a **significant time**. **Warm**, **dry weather** causes water in the vegetation to **dry up**, so it's more **flammable**. • **Strong winds** provide more oxygen to help the fire **burn** and **spread** burning embers.
Fire Behaviour	• Fire burns in **different ways** — e.g. a **creeping** fire moves across the ground surface fairly slowly, whereas a **running** fire **spreads** rapidly and is more **intense**. • Fires can throw out **burning debris** (**firebrands**) that help the fire spread and become more intense.

Wildfires Can Have **Natural** or **Human Causes**

Fires need **fuel**, **oxygen** and a **heat source** to ignite the fire. Heat sources can be **natural** or **human**:

1) **Natural causes** — **lightning** is particularly likely to start a fire if it occurs **without much rain**. **Volcanic eruptions** can produce very hot lava, ash or gas, which can start fires.

2) **Human causes** — most fires are started by **people**. This can be **accidental**, e.g. by dropping **cigarettes**, allowing **campfires** and **barbecues** to get out of control, or if **fireworks** or **sparks** from machinery land in vulnerable areas. Fires can also be started **on purpose** (**arson**).

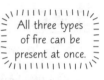

Jed hoped the boys' ability to control their campfire was better than their harmonies.

Wildfires Have a Range of **Impacts**

Wildfires have **primary impacts** — these occur as a **direct result** of the fire, e.g. houses burning down. They also have **secondary impacts** — these occur as a result of the primary impacts, e.g. people have to move. Some impacts are:

Social
- People may be **killed** or **injured** if they don't evacuate in time.
- Homes are **destroyed**, so people may be left **homeless**.
- Wildfire can destroy **power lines** and damage **reservoirs**, leaving people without **electricity** or **clean water**.
- Wildfires can cause **health problems**, e.g. inhaling smoke can cause long-term breathing difficulties.

Political
- Governments can face **criticism** when wildfires have severe impacts.
- Governments may have to **change** their **forest management practices** to reduce the risk of wildfire, e.g. by clearing vegetation to limit fuel.

Economic
- Wildfires destroy **businesses**, leading to loss of **jobs** and **income**.
- **Insurance** premiums increase dramatically after a wildfire.
- The **cost** of fighting wildfires is huge.
- Wildfires may **discourage tourists** from visiting an area, reducing income.

Environmental
- **Habitats** are destroyed. Some species may not return to the area after a fire, changing the **ecosystem**.
- **Soils** are damaged as the fire removes organic matter.
- Smoke causes **air pollution**, and water sources can be **contaminated** with ash.
- Some ecosystems **rely** on wildfires to **clear** dead vegetation, and some plant seeds need fire to **germinate**.

Wildfires

Responses to Wildfires Aim to Reduce Their Impacts

1) **Mitigation strategies** aim to **reduce** the **severity** of the wildfire's impacts. They can be **short-term** or **long-term**.

2) **Short-term responses** to a wildfire normally occur **during** or **immediately after** the hazard. For example:

   - Trying to put the fire out, **diverting** it away from settlements, **evacuating** people from areas at risk and **spraying water** onto the roofs of houses to prevent embers from setting them alight.

3) **Long-term responses** are often designed to **reduce** the impacts of future fires by managing the **risks**. For example:

   - **Prevention** — preventing fires from starting may involve public **education** about the risks of using campfires and barbecues in vulnerable areas. Authorities may also provide **fire beaters** to put small fires out before they spread.

   - **Preparedness** — being prepared for a wildfire may involve households having an **emergency plan** and emergency **supplies** of food, water and medicine, or authorities making **emergency shelters** available.

   - **Adaptation** — individuals and authorities can **change** the way they **live** to help them cope with wildfires, e.g. using **non-flammable building materials** and creating **fire breaks** (gaps in trees) around settlements to stop fire spreading.

Wildfires Hit South-east Australia in February 2009

1) In February 2009, severe wildfires burned for a **month** in the state of Victoria in south-east Australia. The **worst** fires occurred in **forested areas**.

2) **Environmental conditions** added to the intensity of the fires — they followed **ten years** of **drought**, recent temperatures had been **over 40 °C** and there were **strong winds**.

3) **Lack of management** (e.g. controlled burning of forest litter, such as branches and leaves), meant that there was a **large amount** of very dry oil-rich material to **fuel** the fire. Several of the fires were caused by **faulty power lines**.

4) Despite attempts to **manage** the fires, the impacts were **severe**:

Impacts
   - **173** people were killed and around **400** injured. Many more suffered from **stress** and **depression**.
   - **2000 houses** in 78 communities were destroyed.
   - More than **60 businesses** were destroyed, causing loss of jobs and income to the region.
   - The total estimated cost of the fire was more than **AUS $4 billion**.
   - Around **4300 km²** of land was burned, including forest and national parks. Millions of **animals**, **birds** and **reptiles** were killed, including some **rare species** such as the sooty owl and spotted tree frog.

Responses
   - The Australian Bureau of Meteorology **predicted** how the fires would spread and told residents that they could either **evacuate** or **stay** and **defend** their homes. Evacuation **reduced** the number of deaths, but many people were **put at risk** by choosing to stay in their houses.
   - More than **20 000 firefighters** and **volunteers** helped to put out the fires and support victims.
   - More than **AUS $400 million** was donated to help **rebuild** houses and community facilities. However, making new houses more fire-resistant **increased costs**, so not everyone could afford to finish building.
   - Recommendations for **long-term responses** include building **fire shelters** in vulnerable areas, improving **warning systems** and improving the emergency **evacuation** strategy.

Practice Questions

Q1 Briefly describe three conditions that may lead to intense wildfires.

Q2 Give two natural causes of wildfires.

Exam Question

Q1 With reference to a wildfire event, evaluate the impacts of the event and the effectiveness of responses to it.   [9 marks]

Crown fire — the curse of royalty everywhere...

Phew, that's it for wildfires — a pretty hot topic, I think you'll agree. Those of you with sharp eyes may have spotted that similar impacts and responses crop up for a lot of different hazards — that's worth remembering for the exam. Just saying.

Multi-Hazard Environment — Case Study

If you like your surroundings to not try to kill you, the Philippines probably isn't the place for you...

The **Philippines** is a **Multi-Hazard Environment**

The Philippines is a group of islands in **south-east Asia.** The area is vulnerable to a **variety of hazards** with **social, economic** and **environmental impacts**, e.g.:

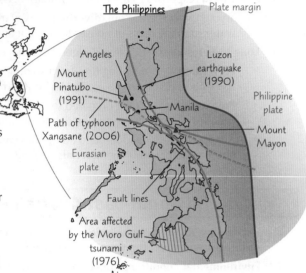

1) **Volcanoes** — the Philippines is near to a **destructive plate boundary**, where the **Philippine plate** is being **subducted** beneath the **Eurasian plate.** E.g. **Mount Pinatubo** erupted in 1991 — more than 700 people **died**, around 200 000 were left **homeless**, buildings **collapsed**, **crops** were **destroyed** and **agricultural land** was **ruined** by falling ash.

2) **Seismic hazards** — earthquakes occur along the plate boundary and at **fault lines** where the plate has **cracked** under pressure. E.g. an earthquake of **magnitude 7.8** occurred on **Luzon island** in 1990, killing over **1500 people**. Earthquakes in the surrounding oceans can cause tsunamis, e.g. in 1976, an earthquake of **magnitude 7.9** caused a tsunami that hit the coastline around the **Moro Gulf. Thousands were killed** and several cities were **devastated**.

3) **Tropical storms** — the Philippines has around **10 tropical storms every year**. They **develop** in the Pacific Ocean and move **westwards** over the islands. E.g. **Typhoon Xangsane** swept across **Manila** and the surrounding **densely populated area** in 2006. High winds and torrential rain **destroyed homes** and caused **flooding, landslides** and the **loss** of power and water. Around 200 people **died**, and the total **cost** of the tropical storm was over US $130 million.

Human Qualities and *Responses* Allow People to *Live* in the Area

1) Despite the risk of disasters, the Philippines is quite **densely populated**, with around 340 people per km².

2) Communities often **understand** the risks of hazards, having experienced them **before**. In many cases, people **prepare** for hazards **themselves**, e.g. by **widening rivers** near settlements to prevent flooding, and by **stockpiling food**. In this way, individuals and communities **increase** their own **resilience**.

3) In the past, funding for dealing with disasters was **only** available **after** the disaster occurred — this meant that the response focused on **reacting** to a disaster that had happened, rather than trying to **prevent** or **prepare** for future disasters.

4) From 2009 onwards, the Philippines' **policy** on disasters has changed — the country is now working to increase large-scale resilience to disasters by **adaptation, mitigation** and **management**. Strategies include:

- Preventing people **building** in areas at high risk of disaster.
- Adapting new and existing **buildings** and other **structures** to cope with earthquakes.
- Building **embankments** to reduce **flood risk** from tsunamis and tropical storms.
- Increasing **public awareness** of hazards and how to respond to them.
- **Monitoring** hazards and developing **early warning systems** so people in at-risk areas have time to prepare.

Practice Questions

Q1 Give one social impact that volcanic eruptions have on the Philippines.

Q2 Give one economic impact that tropical storms have on the Philippines.

Exam Question

Q1 Evaluate human responses to occupying places that experience a range of hazards.   [9 marks]

Just add a swarm of locusts and it starts to look like an apocalypse...

As my geography teacher used to say, case studies 'put the meat on the bones'. However odd that sounds, the point is that it's all very well learning the theory, but it's really important that you know details of real-world examples if you want top marks.

Hazardous Setting — Case Study

Italy — the home of pasta, pizza, Pisa... and a surprising number of earthquakes.

Central Italy has a **High Risk** of **Earthquakes**

1) **Fault lines** run **north-south** close to the **Apennine mountain range** and **east-west** across the centre of Italy. The fault lines are near the **destructive plate margin** between the **Eurasian** and **African plates**.

2) **Earthquakes** are common in the area, for example:

   - Three earthquakes up to magnitude 6.4 hit the area around **Assisi** in **1997**.
   - A 6.3 magnitude earthquake struck **L'Aquila** in April **2009**.
   - A series of earthquakes hit the area around **Amatrice** from August to October **2016**.

3) The **L'Aquila earthquake** was caused by movement along the **north-south fault line**. It **killed** around 300 people, made about 70 000 people **homeless** and **cost** Italy an estimated US $15 billion.

■ North-south fault line

■ East-west fault line

Assisi

Amatrice

L'Aquila

Earthquake Risk Has Affected the **Character** of the Area

1) Before 2009, L'Aquila itself **hadn't** suffered from a **major earthquake** for 300 years. The risks were known, and some steps were taken to mitigate hazards — e.g. there were **strict building regulations** to ensure that **newer buildings** were **designed** and **built** to **withstand earthquakes**. However, much of the city was very old, and some newer buildings didn't comply with regulations, so they were **severely damaged** or **destroyed** by the earthquake.

2) The **character** of L'Aquila reflects the **impacts** of the 2009 earthquake and the **risk** of future earthquakes:

Social

- Many historic buildings in the city centre were **destroyed**, and people were **rehoused** in newly built **earthquake-resistant** homes in suburban areas or in **new towns** outside the city. Many younger people **left** the area to look for jobs elsewhere. All these changes altered the **architectural** and **social** character of the city.
- Attendance at **social** and **religious** activities has **declined** — e.g. around 1000 people attended a Good Friday procession in 2016, compared with around 30 000 before the earthquake. People are **reluctant** to use the shops, bars and restaurants that were rebuilt in the town centre, and many have **closed down**.
- Some residents suffer from **mental health issues** as a result of the earthquake, and **fear** of more earthquakes occurring. However, others have developed **coping strategies** and increased their **resilience** to future hazards.

Economic

- University buildings in L'Aquila were badly damaged, making them **unusable**. The number of students enrolling **decreased**, which caused a major **economic loss** for the city.
- The Italian government plans to **reconstruct** the area to be economically **stronger** than before the disaster, for example by making the city more attractive to students. If successful, this would make L'Aquila a **busier**, more **affluent** place.

Political

- Officials and scientists have been blamed for not giving the public **adequate warning** about the earthquake risk. This has led to **tension** between residents and officials.
- The government has also been blamed for not **rebuilding** L'Aquila quickly enough or **involving residents** in decisions about how it would be rebuilt. This added to residents' feelings of **discontent** and **lack of support**.

3) **Communities** in and around L'Aquila have responded to earthquake **risk** in different ways. Some **accepted** homes in new towns or suburbs, possibly believing that risk would be **lower** there. Others took their own steps to **reduce risk** — e.g. some residents of Pescomaggiore, a village to the east of L'Aquila, worked with professional builders to create new **earthquake-resistant homes** using wood and straw, with **solar panels** to decrease reliance on mains power.

Practice Questions

Q1 Outline why central Italy is prone to earthquakes.

Q2 What magnitude was the 2009 L'Aquila earthquake?

Exam Question

Q1 Assess how the character of a place you have studied has been changed by its hazardous setting. [9 marks]

L'Aquila earthquake? L'Killer more like...

The L'Aquila earthquake killed hundreds of people and had profound physical and psychological effects on thousands more. It's a pretty downbeat end to a fairly depressing topic — unfortunately, we just haven't got that good at coping with hazards yet.

Ecosystems

Don't fret — you haven't picked up your biology book by accident. These three pages cover the basics of ecosystems, so don't skip them unless you want to be exceptionally confused by the end of the topic.

An **Ecosystem** Consists of **Biotic** and **Abiotic** Factors

1) An **ecosystem** is a set of **relationships** between **all** the **organisms** and **non-living factors** in a particular area, e.g. a forest ecosystem includes the **trees**, **animals** and **microorganisms** as well as the **water**, **soil**, **rock** and **air**.

2) The organisms that live there are called **biotic factors** and the non-living things are **abiotic factors**.

3) The **organisms** depend on **physical factors** and **each other** to survive, so **relationships** between them are **important**.

4) Ecosystems **vary in size** — they can be small (e.g. a pond) or large (e.g. a forest, mountainside or ocean).

Energy Flows Between All the Organisms in an Ecosystem

1) **Energy enters** an ecosystem by **photosynthesis** — **producers**, e.g. plants, use **energy** from **sunlight** to grow.

2) **Gross primary production** is the **total** amount of energy that producers get from photosynthesis, but the plant will **use** some of this in the process of **respiration** (converting sugars and oxygen into carbon dioxide and water). What's left over is the **net primary production** (NPP).

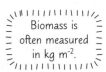
Biomass is often measured in kg m^{-2}.

> net primary production = gross primary production – respiratory loss

3) NPP is the energy available to the plant for growth. It's stored as the plant's **biomass** — the total mass of living matter. It's **transferred** through an ecosystem by **consumers**, which eat other living organisms.

4) When an organism **dies**, it's broken down by **decomposers** (e.g. bacteria) and nutrients are recycled (see next page).

Food Chains and Food Webs Show How Energy Moves Through Ecosystems

1) Each **stage** in a food chain or web is called a **trophic (feeding) level**.

2) **Producers** (**autotrophs**, e.g. plants) occupy the **first trophic level**.

3) **Primary consumers** (**herbivores** or **omnivores**) occupy the next level — they **eat producers**.

4) **Secondary consumers** (**carnivores** and **omnivores**) occupy the next level — they **eat consumers**.

5) **Tertiary consumers** (**top carnivores** and **omnivores**) occupy the next level — they **eat consumers**.

Herbivores eat plants, carnivores eat meat, and omnivores eat plants and meat.

6) **Food chains** tend to over-simplify the relationships — a lot of **consumers** don't just fit in **one trophic level**, e.g. a bird will eat seeds from a plant and also eat the insects that feed on the plant. **Food webs** are more complicated:

Food chains show **one way** the energy from a producer is passed to a consumer:

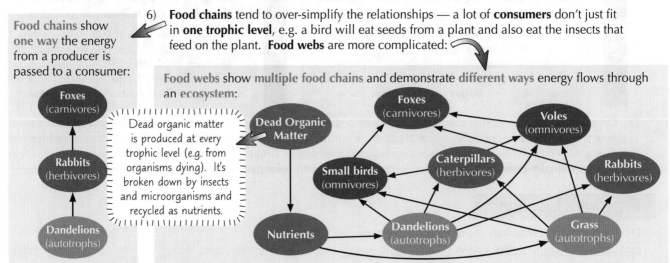

Dead organic matter is produced at every trophic level (e.g. from organisms dying). It's broken down by insects and microorganisms and recycled as nutrients.

Food webs show **multiple food chains** and demonstrate **different ways** energy flows through an ecosystem:

> As you go up the trophic levels in a food chain, the amount of energy and biomass at each level decreases. Around 90% of energy is lost at each trophic level. E.g. a fox doesn't get all the energy in a rabbit, because it doesn't eat the whole rabbit (it leaves the fur and bones), and the rabbit will have lost some energy as droppings, and used some energy for movement and generating body heat.

7) Food webs are more **complicated** in places with a **high NPP** (e.g. rainforests) because there tends to be a **broader range** of species — when there's a bigger range of primary producers, there's a more **varied diet** for the consumers.

Ecosystems

Ecosystems Involve Inputs, Outputs, Stores and Transfers

Ecosystems can be viewed as open systems (see p.2) — energy and matter **enter from** and **exit to** the external environment.

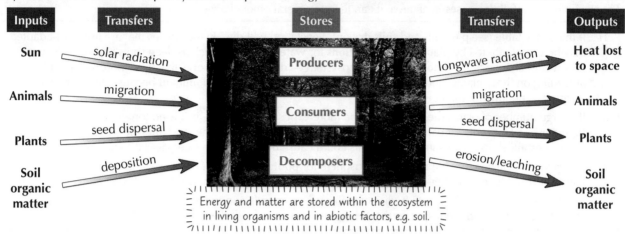

Inputs	Transfers		Stores		Transfers	Outputs

Inputs

Sun

Animals

Plants

Soil organic matter

Transfers

solar radiation

migration

seed dispersal

deposition

Stores

Producers

Consumers

Decomposers

Energy and matter are stored within the ecosystem in living organisms and in abiotic factors, e.g. soil.

Transfers

longwave radiation

migration

seed dispersal

erosion/leaching

Outputs

Heat lost to space

Animals

Plants

Soil organic matter

Mineral Nutrients are Constantly Being Recycled in Ecosystems

Living organisms need large quantities of **carbon**, **hydrogen**, **oxygen**, **nitrogen** and **sulfur**, among other things. These elements are constantly being **recycled** through **ecosystems** — they're recycled between plants, animals, the soil and the atmosphere.

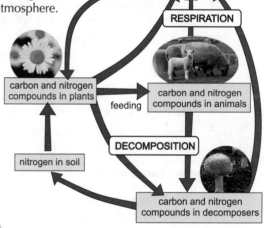

1) Plants take **carbon dioxide** from the **air** and **nutrients** from the **soil**, e.g. **nitrogen**. They use these to create **plant material**.

2) These nutrients get passed along food chains by **feeding**.

3) Dead **animals** and **litter** (dead plant material that's fallen to the ground) are broken down by **decomposers**. This returns **nutrients** to the **soil** to be used again by plants.

4) Plants, animals and decomposers all release **carbon dioxide** back into the air through **respiration**.

Photosynthesis uses carbon dioxide and gives out oxygen. Respiration does the opposite.

Ecosystems Involve Many Inter-Connections

There are many factors that determine the **characteristics** of a **terrestrial** (land-based) ecosystem. For example:

Climate

- **Precipitation** affects **vegetation type** — e.g. whether the ecosystem is forest, grassland or desert. Wetter climates can support more trees.
- **Temperature** determines the type of plant species that grow — e.g. **tropical** or **temperate** forest species.

Soil

- The climate affects the **rate** of **nutrient cycling** and the **availability** of nutrients in the **soil** — warm, wet climates have **high rates** of nutrient cycling, but too much heavy rainfall can **leach** the nutrients down the soil column.
- The **geology** of the area also affects how **nutrient-rich** the soil is, as well as its **depth** and **texture** — this influences the type of vegetation that grows, e.g. in parts of the UK where the **parent rock** is **chalk**, the soil is **alkaline** and **nutrient-poor**, and the main vegetation tends to be **grass**.
- If soil **drainage** is poor, soil becomes **waterlogged** and only plants adapted to wet conditions can grow there — e.g. plants specialised for growing in fens and marshes (see p.119).

Topography

- At high **altitudes** temperatures are lower, which **slows** growth. Plants aren't as tall and there are **fewer species**.
- **Hills** can **shelter** ecosystems from **wind** and **rain** — this is called a **rain shadow**.
- **Steep** slopes are likely to have **thinner soil**, **better drainage** and **lower acidity** than gentle slopes.
- The **direction** a slope faces (the **aspect**) determines how much **light** and **warmth** plants there receive for growth.

Ecosystems

A *Change* in *One* Factor in an Ecosystem *Impacts Others*

Because ecosystems are so **interconnected**, a **change** in any **one** characteristic affects other parts of the ecosystem. For example, if **rainfall decreases** in an area, it can lead to several other changes:

1) If the **water table** (see p.6) **falls** and **soils dry out**, vegetation will **die**. Plant species that are less well-adapted may be **out-competed** by plants with **adaptations** for water shortages, such as deep roots and small leaves. This would change the **composition** of the ecosystem — **different herbivores** might be more **successful** at feeding on these plants, and different **carnivores** might then become **dominant** because they're better **adapted** to hunting for the new herbivores.

2) If a large number of plants die, the soil will be more **exposed to erosion**, as it is no longer **held together** by plant **roots**. It can easily be blown away by **wind**, making the land **infertile** so vegetation can't **re-establish** itself. In some regions, this could cause **desertification** (see pages 33 and 34).

3) Plants take in **carbon dioxide** from the atmosphere for **photosynthesis**. If decreased rainfall kills too many plants, it could lead to further changes in the **climate**, because of the **enhanced greenhouse effect** (see p.233).

4) Rainfall reduction can also cause bodies of water such as **ponds** and **rivers** to **dry up**, so **aquatic** species and other species that **rely** on these for food will **die**.

Climate Change and *Human Exploitation* are *Changing* Ecosystems

1) There are lots of ways that humans have **exploited** the environment and **changed** ecosystems. For example:

- **Urban planning** — e.g. building developments can break up natural ecosystems, which separates populations.
- **Trade** — e.g. trade of animal products such as ivory has resulted in the removal of animals such as elephants and rhinos from their ecosystems.
- **Resource use** — e.g. deforestation for timber destroys habitats that many species rely on for food and shelter.
- **Leisure and recreation** — e.g. diving around coral reef ecosystems can result in accidental damage to the reef.
- **Marine management** — e.g. overfishing removes some species, so there's not enough prey for other species.
- **Flood and erosion management** — e.g. flood walls prevent erosion of river banks, so downstream areas are starved of sediment. This means nutrients aren't added to the soil, which affects the species that grow there.

Any ecosystem change has knock-on impacts. E.g. the loss of one species can reduce the food source for others, so their populations decline.

2) **Climate change** is also causing changes to ecosystems. For example:

- **Temperature increases** will change the **distribution** of some species, if they can only survive within a certain **range** of temperatures. This will change the **composition** of ecosystems.
- Increased **frequency** of **extreme weather events** like **floods** and **droughts** could **kill** species not adapted to withstand extreme conditions.
- **Sea level rise** (from **melting ice** and **thermal expansion** of oceans) will affect **coastal** ecosystems — habitats will be **destroyed** as areas are **flooded**, and **saltwater intrusion** into freshwater ecosystems may **kill** some organisms, or force them to **move** further inland.
- Species may **respond** to climate change and sea level rise in a number of ways — some will **die out**, some will **adapt** to the new conditions, and some will **move** to areas where the conditions are more suitable. **New species** that are **more suited** to the new conditions might **move into** the area.

Practice Questions

Q1 What is an ecosystem?

Q2 What is meant by the term 'trophic level'?

Exam Question

Sparrow ——► Sparrowhawk

Raspberry bush ——► Greenfly ——► Ladybird

Q1 Using the food web on the right, analyse how energy is transferred through the food web, and how it is lost. [6 marks]

Decomposers — bacteria that break down Beethoven's symphonies...

Examiners love food webs and food chains. You might be given one to explain in your exam, so make sure you understand them. Remember the arrows show the transfer of energy up the trophic levels — in other words, who is eaten by who.

Biodiversity

Now you know a bit about what ecosystems are and how they work, it's time to get your head around another key term that'll crop up an awful lot in the rest of this section — biodiversity. It's a pretty hot topic too, so pay close attention.

Biodiversity *is the* Variety of Life *on* Earth *or in a* Particular Place

1) **Biodiversity** means the **variety** of organisms living in a particular area — all the different **species**, **habitats** and **ecosystems**.

2) Globally, biodiversity is **not evenly distributed**. It generally increases from the **poles** towards the **equator** — around **50%** of all the world's **plants and animals** live in tropical rainforests. This is because closer to the equator the climate is **warmer**, more **moist**, and more **stable**. This means **plants grow better** and can support more species higher up the food chain.

3) Biodiversity also varies on a **local** scale — e.g. **farmland** is likely to have **lower** biodiversity than natural habitats.

4) There are different ways of **measuring** biodiversity:

> - **Species richness** is a measure of the total **number** of different species present in an area. However, it doesn't take into account how many individuals of each species there are.
> - The **Living Planet Index (LPI)** is a measure of **global** biodiversity — it brings together **thousands of datasets** on vertebrate populations (mammals, birds, fishes, amphibians, reptiles) that are being monitored around the world, which allows trends to be identified. It's used as an **indicator** of how biodiversity is changing globally.

Biodiversity is Declining *on a* Global Scale

1) In general, biodiversity is currently decreasing **everywhere**. The **LPI** showed a decline of **58%** between 1970 and 2012.

2) The rate of decline varies between regions. In the **tropics**, biodiversity declined by **56%** between 1970 and 2010, whereas in the **temperate** zone it fell by **36%**.

3) Biodiversity has **changed** throughout history. There have been a number of **mass extinctions** in the past, when large numbers of species have **disappeared** within a short space of time. These changes have happened **naturally**, e.g. because of huge volcanic eruptions or meteor impacts.

4) **However**, the **current** rates of biodiversity loss are **much higher** than they would be naturally.

5) This is because **human activities** are reducing biodiversity. For example:

Litter left by humans causes water pollution.

- **Deforestation** (e.g. for farming) results in habitat loss.
- **Draining wetlands** (e.g. for building) results in habitat loss.
- **Pollution** can damage habitats and harm species.
- **Global warming** changes the abundance and distribution of species.
- **Rising sea levels** due to climate change lead to habitat loss.
- **Overexploitation** (e.g. overfishing, overhunting and overharvesting) reduces the population of certain species.

Local *Trends in Biodiversity Vary*

1) Biodiversity is changing at **different rates** on a **local** scale.

2) It's declining **most rapidly** in places where humans are **destroying habitats**, e.g. areas of forest that are cut down for urban development.

3) Other areas are **managed** to **reduce** biodiversity loss. **Conservation areas** such as national parks are **protected** from human activities that might reduce biodiversity, e.g. **agriculture** and **mining**.

4) In some areas, people are making an effort to **increase** biodiversity. For example, urban planners may introduce **green spaces** to town centres, and farmers may plant **hedges** between fields to provide **habitats** for wildlife.

Fashion trends at the local retirement home varied from week to week.

Biodiversity

Maintaining Biodiversity is Important for Humans

Ecosystems provide humans with lots of **goods** and **services**. For example:

1) **Goods** — e.g. food, water, wood, fuels.
2) **Environmental services** — e.g. ecosystems influence the climate and risk of flooding, and help purify water.
3) **Cultural benefits** — e.g. the non-material benefits we get from nature, such as pleasure, spiritual experiences etc.
4) **Ecological services** — e.g. nutrient cycling in ecosystems ensures nutrients are available and helps soil formation.

If biodiversity declines, then these goods and services are **threatened**.

Loss of Biodiversity has Physical and Human Impacts

Physical impacts

- The loss of certain organisms may result in the **extinction** of other species that **depend** on them.
- Fewer plants means that less **carbon dioxide** is taken in from the **atmosphere**, which increases the **greenhouse effect** (see p.233).
- Loss of vegetation affects the **water cycle** (see p.4). In some places, it may lead to **floods** or **droughts**.
- If plants **die** or are **removed**, then the **bare soil** left behind is **vulnerable to erosion**. When this is washed away, the land is left **infertile** — new soil would have to form before plants could be supported again.

Human impacts

- Declining biodiversity may reduce **food supplies**, e.g. through the disappearance of **insects** and **birds** that **pollinate** crops, which could lead to increased **hunger** in many parts of the world.
- Access to **clean air** and **water** may be decreased by loss of biodiversity, which would impact on human **health** — e.g. trees can reduce air pollution in urban areas.
- When species become extinct, humans lose potential sources for new **medicines**.

Humans Need to Develop Ecosystems Sustainably

1) **Sustainability** means meeting the needs of the **present** without preventing **future** generations from meeting their needs.
2) The global **human population** is **growing**, which is putting strain on many ecosystem services. As the population increases, the **products** of ecosystems are getting more difficult to **share** around — trying to provide enough **food**, **water** and **energy** for everyone is a big **challenge**.
3) **Economic development** is **speeding up** the rate of biodiversity loss. As a country becomes more developed, it tends to use more **resources** and **land**, and produce more **pollution**.
4) **Sustainable development** involves **balancing** increases in population size and development with **conservation**.
5) If humans don't **protect** ecosystems, the **goods** and **services** we get from them will be **lost**, which will reduce our **wellbeing**. Pressure on the **remaining** ecosystems may then increase even further.
6) However, if we **protect** ecosystems, we can continue to **benefit** from their goods and services, allowing **sustainable economic development**. This will help to **improve** ecosystem protection further, creating a **positive feedback** loop.

Practice Questions

Q1 What is biodiversity?
Q2 Give three examples of human activities that reduce biodiversity.
Q3 Give two ways that biodiversity decline impacts humans.

Exam Question

Q1 Analyse the potential impacts of declining biodiversity at a global scale. [9 marks]

Biodiversity — it's the spice of life...

Biodiversity supplies us with all sorts of useful things and it's sometimes too easy to take advantage of it. It's already in decline all over the world due to human activities, and if current trends don't change, the wellbeing of future generations is at risk.

Biomes

If you've found this section a bit too biology-heavy so far, don't fear, because on this page we're finally back to dealing with every geographer's favourite image. That's right — our old friend, the map of the world.

Make Sure You Know the **Distribution** of the **Major Terrestrial Biomes**

1) A **biome** is an area with a distinctive **climate** and **vegetation.**
2) Biomes can contain **different ecosystems**, e.g. within a savanna grassland biome there could be areas of open woodland, areas of swamp, lakes and grassland plains.
3) Biomes usually cover a **large area**, often spanning multiple countries.
4) The overall character of a biome is determined by factors such as **climate**, **topography**, **soil**, **plant life** and **animal life** and how these **interact** with each other (see p.95).

Tundra

Found at high latitudes. **Winters are very cold, summers** are **brief** and there is **little rainfall**. There are hardly any **trees** — vegetation includes **mosses, grasses and low shrubs.**

Boreal Forest

Found at relatively **high latitudes**. **Summers** are **short** and **cool** and **winters** are **long** and **cold**. Most of the trees are **coniferous**, and there are also low-growing **mosses** and **lichen.**

Temperate Deciduous Forest

Found mainly in the **mid latitudes** where there are **four distinct seasons**. Summers are **warm**, winters are relatively **mild** and there's **rainfall** all year round. **Deciduous** trees **lose their leaves** in winter to cope with the colder weather.

Savanna Grassland

Found **between** the **tropics**. There are **distinct dry** and **wet** seasons, although **rainfall** is still relatively **low**. Most of the vegetation is **grasses** with a **few scattered trees** (see p.103-105).

Tropical Rainforest

Found around the **equator**, between the tropics, where it's **hot** and **wet all year** round. This is an area of **lush forest**, with **dense canopies** of vegetation forming **distinct layers** (see p.100-102).

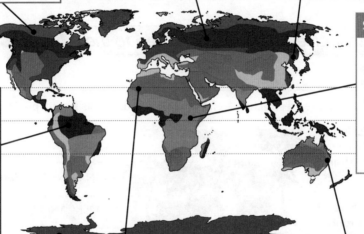

Polar

Found around the **north** and **south poles**. It's very **cold, icy** and **dry**. Not much **grows** at all. It remains **dark** for several months each year so the **growing season** is very **short** — about 2 months.

Desert

Found between 15° and 35° **north** and **south** of the equator where there's **little rainfall**. It's very **hot** during the **day** and very **cold** at **night**. **Shrubs** and **cacti** are **sparsely distributed** in the sandy soil.

Temperate Grassland

Found at **higher latitudes** than savanna grasslands. There is **more variation** in **temperature** and **less rainfall**. There are **no trees** here — just **grasses.**

Practice Questions

Q1 List five factors that affect the overall character of a biome.
Q2 Describe the distribution of deserts.

Exam Question

Q1 Using the map above and your own knowledge, analyse the global distribution of the tropical rainforest biome. [6 marks]

Learn these facts, and you'll get your just deserts...

It might feel like "biome" means the same thing as "ecosystem", but the difference is a biome is on a particular scale, taking up a big area of the world, whereas an ecosystem can be on any scale. Try to learn roughly where each biome's found.

Tropical Rainforests

Rainforests are one of the most important biomes on Earth — they produce oxygen, provide habitats for countless species and they're a great place to make a nature documentary. But human activity is a serious threat in all sorts of ways.

The **Climate** in **Tropical Rainforests** is **Hot** and **Wet** All Year

1) Tropical rainforests are hot. The temperature's generally **20-28 °C** — the sun is overhead all year round.

2) **Rainfall** is **high all year round**, around 2000 mm per year. It rains every day (usually in the afternoon) because the high temperature creates **convectional rainfall**:

   - The sun **warms** the ground, which conducts this heat to the air above and **evaporates** surface water.
   - The **warm air** can hold lots of **water vapour**. This warm, wet air **rises** — and as it rises it **cools**.
   - The cooler air can hold **less water vapour**, so water condenses to form clouds and then **rain**.

3) The **soil moisture budget** (the balance between water inputs and outputs in the soil) is high, because **precipitation** is higher than **potential evaporation**.

4) **Rainforest soils** are known as **latosols**. They are **very nutrient poor** because:

   - Although there is a constant supply of new leaf litter and dead organic matter onto the soil surface, it is broken down very quickly because the warm, wet climate is ideal for micro-organisms.
   - The growing season continues all year, so as soon as dead organic matter is broken down the nutrients are re-absorbed by plants. This means that few nutrients remain in the soil.
   - Nutrients are also leached down the soil column by heavy rainfall.

The **Organisms** that Live There are **Adapted** to the **Abiotic Conditions**

PLANT ADAPTATIONS

1) Tropical rainforests have a **layered structure** — they are **stratified**. Plants are **adapted** to survive in each layer:

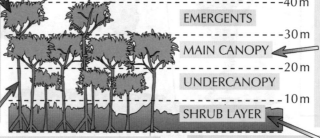

The **emergents** are the **tallest** trees, which poke out of the main canopy layer. They have **straight trunks** and only have **branches** and **leaves** at the **top** where they can get **light**. They also have **big roots** called **buttress roots** to support their trunks.

The main **canopy** is a **continuous** layer of trees. Like emergents, they only have leaves at the **top**. The **dense** layer of leaves **shades** the rest of the forest.

EMERGENTS — 40 m
— 30 m
MAIN CANOPY — 20 m
UNDERCANOPY
— 10 m
SHRUB LAYER

The **undercanopy** is made up of **younger** trees that have yet to reach their **full height**. They can only survive where there are **breaks** in the canopy to let a little bit of **light** through.

The **shrub layer** is **nearest** the ground where it's quite **dark**. Shrubs have **large, broad leaves** to absorb as much **light** as they can.

2) Plants have **thick, waxy leaves** with **pointed tips**. The pointed tips (called **drip-tips**) channel the water to a point so it **runs off** — that way the **weight** of the water doesn't **damage** the plant, and there's no standing water for **fungi** and **bacteria** to grow in. The waxy coating of the leaves also helps **repel** the rain.

3) Plants **drop** their **leaves** gradually throughout the year, meaning they can go on growing **all year round**.

4) **Lianas** root in the soil and **climb** up trees, while **epiphytes** like orchids and bromeliads grow on the trees. These adaptations help plants reach the **light**.

> *When an organism depends on the existence of another to survive it is called a symbiotic relationship.*

ANIMAL ADAPTATIONS

Smoky and Mr Jump had definitely drawn the short straw in their symbiotic relationships.

1) Many animals are adapted to living in the **canopy** because there's plenty of food there. For example, **flying squirrels** have **flaps of skin** for **gliding** between trees.

2) **Jaguars**, **sloths** and **vampire bats** are **nocturnal** — this means they **save energy** by sleeping through the day, and hunting and feeding at night when it's **cooler**.

3) Some animals are adapted to the **low light** conditions underneath the canopy. **Tapirs** and **anteaters** have **excellent senses** of hearing and smell, so they can **detect predators** without **seeing** them.

4) Many **rainforest** animals can **swim**. This allows them to **cross river channels** and cope with **flooding** of the forest floor.

Tropical Rainforests

Deforestation is the Main Threat to Tropical Rainforests

There are lots of reasons why rainforests are chopped down:

Small scale farming — trees are cleared to set up small **subsistence farms**. Often the "slash and burn" technique is used — **vegetation** is **cut down** and left to dry, then **burnt**.

Cattle farming — forest is cleared to make room for **cattle grazing**.

Commercial agriculture — trees are felled for planting **crops** like **palm oil** and **soya**.

Other — for example, land is cleared for **mineral extraction** (e.g. of gold and iron ore) and for **new settlements**. Building **dams** to generate **hydroelectric power** floods large areas of forest.

Commercial logging — wood is used for **timber**, **pulp** and **paper**. Road building for logging also makes new areas of forest accessible for **agriculture**.

Deforestation has Environmental, Social and Economic Impacts

See p.16-17 for human impacts on the Amazon rainforest.

ENVIRONMENTAL

1) **Deforestation** causes **habitat loss**. This **reduces biodiversity** if organisms can't move or adapt.
2) Without a **tree canopy** to **intercept** (catch) rainfall and tree **roots** to absorb it, more water reaches the **soil**. This reduces soil **fertility** as **nutrients** in the soil are **washed away**, out of reach of plants.
3) Reduced interception also increases the risk of **flooding**, because more rainwater reaches the ground at once.
4) The **evapotranspiration rate** is reduced — this means less water vapour reaches the atmosphere, so **less rain** falls.
5) **Deforestation** is a major cause of **global warming**. Trees **remove CO_2** from the atmosphere and store it, so fewer trees means more atmospheric CO_2, which enhances the **greenhouse effect**.

SOCIAL

1) **Quality of life** for some local people improves as there are **more jobs**.
2) The **traditional livelihoods** of some local people are **destroyed** if they lose the **plants** and **animals** that they rely on to make a living.
3) Some **native tribes** are **forced to move** when their land is cleared.
4) Local people are at **risk** because they're not **immune** to **western diseases** introduced by incomers.
5) There can be **conflict** between native people, landowners, mining companies and logging companies over **use of land**.

ECONOMIC

1) Logging, farming and mining **create jobs**.
2) A lot of money is made from selling **timber**, **mining** and commercial **farming**.
3) In the long term, deforestation destroys the **resources** that countries depend on, e.g. timber.

Development Issues are Putting Tropical Rainforests Under More Threat

Changes to **population size**, **economic activity** and **agriculture** are causing further negative impacts on rainforests.

Population change

- Populations in tropical rainforests are **growing**, despite the number of **indigenous** inhabitants decreasing. E.g. the population of **Manaus** in the **Amazon** rainforest grew from about 100 000 in 1950 to **over 2 million** in 2015.
- More people need more **resources** and more **space** for settlements, so more forest has to be cleared.
- There are **many more** small-scale subsistence farmers now, and people who have **no land** or whose land has become **unproductive** are **opening up** more areas of the forest.

Economic development

- The commercial activities that cause deforestation (e.g. **mining, agriculture, forestry**) have brought significant **economic development** to countries with tropical rainforests.
- This has allowed investment in **infrastructure**, e.g. new **roads**, **opening up** previously **inaccessible** areas of forest and leading to more deforestation.
- As countries develop economically, people have more money, so use of **resources** (e.g. food, energy) **increases**. This increases deforestation.

Topic Six — Ecosystems Under Stress

Tropical Rainforests

Agricultural extension and intensification

- There's been a huge **increase** in recent decades in the amount of rainforest **cleared** by corporations to make space for **cash crops** (crops that are grown for their **commercial value**) like **palm oil** and **soya**. These plantations are **monocultures** — only a single crop plant is grown in each area.
- Meat consumption is increasing, so **more room** is needed for **cattle grazing**. 80% of deforested land in Brazil is used for cattle ranching.
- **'Slash and burn'** farming can be carried out **sustainably** if the forest is given enough time to **recover** before being **reused**. However, **deforestation** and **population pressure** has limited the amount of land available to indigenous farmers. This means land is farmed again before the **soil fertility** is restored, so large areas of land become **degraded** and **can't be used** for agriculture any more.

Cattle produce methane, which is a greenhouse gas, so cattle ranching also contributes to climate change.

There are Lots of Implications for Biodiversity and Sustainability

Biodiversity

Tropical rainforests are the biome with the **highest biodiversity**, but humans are causing it to **decline**.

Habitat loss:
- Deforestation directly reduces biodiversity by **destroying habitats**.
- The natural vegetation is replaced with land uses that have much lower biodiversity — e.g. **monoculture** farming means huge areas of land contain only **one** plant species.

Fragmentation:
- With sections of the rainforest being felled and converted to other land uses, the habitat is **split up** into **isolated fragments**.
- Biodiversity is **lower** in the forest fragments than it would be if they were still part of a continuous habitat. This is because populations are **cut off** from each other, so animals and plants can't easily come together to **reproduce**.
- Animals **leaving** their fragment in search of a **mate** or **food** might end up being **killed**, e.g. on the roads that divide up the forest.

Sustainability

1) **Selective logging** and **replanting** make the logging industry more sustainable, and the creation of **national parks** protects rainforest from damage.
2) **Ecotourism** is **nature-based** tourism that **doesn't harm** the environment and benefits **local people**. It is a form of **sustainable development** because:
   - when local people are employed in tourism, they **don't have to log** or **farm** for money.
   - it raises **awareness** of conservation issues.
   - if a country's economy **relies** on ecotourism, there's an **incentive** to put the income it generates into **conserving** the environment, e.g. **25%** of **Costa Rica** is protected from development as a result of ecotourism.
3) Many tropical rainforests are in **less developed countries** that have had to **borrow money** from organisations such as the World Bank. This often leads to **industrial activities** being allowed in the rainforests, to help pay back the debt. However, **debt-for-nature swaps** are an alternative solution — this is when part of a country's debt is paid off by someone else in **exchange** for investment in **conservation**.

There are issues associated with the **governance** of rainforests. Management takes place at a **range of scales** — there are **local** schemes within countries, as well as **international** schemes, e.g. the **Tropical Forest Alliance 2020** is a **global partnership** that aims to reduce deforestation around the world. However, schemes to improve sustainability often have drawbacks, e.g. sustainable forestry generally provides **fewer jobs** for **local people** than conventional forestry.

Practice Questions

Q1 Briefly describe the climate of tropical rainforests.
Q2 Give three causes of deforestation.
Q3 Describe two environmental impacts of deforestation.

Exam Question

Q1 Analyse the ecological response to climate and soil moisture budget in tropical rainforests. [9 marks]

Very few species in the rainforest are adapted to exam conditions...

Wow, we humans really aren't doing the rainforest any favours. This stuff can be pretty disheartening, but you still need to learn it. Make sure you know all about the characteristics of rainforests, and the impacts that humans are having on them.

Savanna Grasslands

Knowing all about one biome just isn't enough, I'm afraid. Now you need to get your head around savanna grasslands too — the environmental conditions, how plants and animals are adapted to them, and how they're being affected by humans.

Savanna Grasslands have a **Wet** and a **Dry Season**

1) **Savanna** grasslands have quite **low rainfall** (800-900 mm per year) and **distinct wet and dry seasons**. Temperatures are **highest** (around 35 °C) just **before** the wet season and **lowest** (about 15 °C) just **after** it.

2) **Grass** is the most **common** type of vegetation — there isn't enough **rain** for a **forest** to grow, but there are a few **scattered trees**.

3) During the dry season, **fires** are common (both **natural** and **man-made**), because the dry plant material **burns** easily.

4) Many species of **large mammals** live in savanna grasslands. Large **herbivores graze** on the **grasses** (e.g. zebras and buffalo) or **browse** on the leaves and fruits of **trees** (e.g. elephants and giraffes). At the top of the food chain are large **predators**, including lions, hyenas and cheetahs.

African elephants feed from the scattered trees.

5) The **soils** of savanna grasslands are usually **acidic** and have only a **thin layer of organic matter** near the surface.

6) The **soil moisture budget** (see p.100) changes through the year. During the **rainy** season, the **porous** soil takes in **a lot** of rainwater — there is a **soil moisture surplus**. During the **dry** season, water is **taken up** by **plants** and lost by **evaporation**, leading to a **soil moisture deficit** (more water is lost than gained) until the rainy season returns.

The **Animals** and **Plants** are **Adapted** to The Environment

PLANT ADAPTATIONS

1) Plants in savannas have to be **adapted** to survive the **long dry season**. Some have long **tap roots**, which allow them to reach water **deep** in the soil when the upper layers of the soil have **dried out**.

2) **Grasses** are able to survive long periods of drought because they can remain **dormant** (they don't grow) for a long time, and then **grow back** quickly when there's enough moisture again.

3) The **leaves** on trees are often **small** and **waxy**. This reduces the amount of water evaporated through the pores on the leaf surface (transpiration). Many trees also **drop** their leaves during the dry season to help them retain water.

4) Grasses tend to **grow** from a point **close to the ground**, instead of from the top. This means that they can **keep growing** despite being **grazed** from above.

5) Many savanna plants are also **fire-resistant**. Some achieve this by **storing water** — e.g. baobab trees have thick trunks with a space below the bark for storing water. Other trees, such as the marula, have thick fire-resistant **bark**.

Baobab trees are adapted to store water in their trunks.

ANIMAL ADAPTATIONS

1) Many birds and mammals **migrate seasonally**, only remaining in the savanna grasslands when there's enough **green vegetation** to feed on.

2) Some **small burrowing animals** remain **dormant** during the dry season when there is a shortage of food. Burrowing also helps them to **avoid predation** and the frequent **fires**.

3) Most **invertebrates** (e.g. insects) in savannas **live** mainly **underground**, where they feed on parts of plants such as roots and tubers. These make up most of a plant's **biomass** and don't die back in the dry season, so there's less **seasonal variation** in food supply.

4) The **wide open spaces** of the savanna make it ideal for predators to hunt in, e.g. large **birds of prey** such as vultures **perch** on the scattered trees to look out for prey.

5) Because savannas are **hot** and provide **little shade**, many mammals, such as **aardvarks** and **leopards**, are **nocturnal** — this means they can **save energy** by hunting and feeding at night when it's **cooler**.

Bruno has tried his best to adapt to his environment since moving to Lapland.

Savanna Grasslands

Humans Have Many Impacts on Savannas

Human activity has been **influencing** the savanna grasslands for **thousands of years**.
Some human activities have helped to **maintain** the grasslands, and some have had **negative** impacts.

Fire

- **Fires** are often started by **humans**, e.g. **farmers** clearing land to make space for new farmland.
- Fire maintains the ecosystem. It burns young trees, which **prevents** woodland from taking over, and removes **dead grass** from the surface. The grass **roots** are left **intact** so grass can grow back when the **rain** starts again.
- Fires also benefit some **animal** species — they kill **insects** and **small animals**, so **birds** have abundant food.
- Human inhabitants of savanna regions have been lighting fires for **thousands of years**, but in some areas changing fire patterns are causing **problems**. E.g. in parts of **northern Australia**, fires have become **more frequent**, which is devastating populations of plants and animals that are not fire-resistant.

Grazing

- Many native people in savannas keep **livestock**, which **graze** on the grassland.
- Like wild herbivores, domestic grazers help to **maintain** the grassland by stopping **woodland** from growing — many young trees are **eaten** before they have a chance to grow.
- Some indigenous people in the savanna biome are **nomadic** — they move from place to place. If livestock are kept in one area, there is a risk of **overgrazing**, which could lead to **soil erosion**. If livestock are **moved around**, the vegetation has a chance to recover.

Many nomadic people keep cattle.

Hunting and poaching

- Hunting on a **small scale** can be sustainable. However, **poaching** (the **illegal** killing of wild animals) is a big problem in the savanna biome.
- The demand for **bushmeat** (the meat of wild animals) is increasing — rather than just hunting for their own food, some people are now **selling** illegal bushmeat.
- Savanna animals are also poached for other products, such as **rhino horn** and **ivory**. Trade of these products is **illegal**, but poaching for them still happens. The population of **elephants** in the African savanna is declining each year.
- Some people travel to the savanna biome for **trophy hunting**, which involves **paying** to **legally** shoot selected animals and keep them as trophies. This can **decrease** populations of at-risk animals. Trophy hunters tend to target **large males**, which can lead to an **imbalance** in the population.

Development is Increasing the Human Impact on Savanna Grasslands

Development issues in savanna grasslands include changes in **population**, **economic activity** and **agriculture**.

Population change

- Savanna grasslands are in **tropical** regions — many are in **developing** countries with expanding human populations. This is increasing **pressure** on the biome.
- There's increasing **conflict** between the animals of the savanna and the people who live there. Sometimes, **crops** are **raided**, and **livestock** or **people** are **killed** by wild animals. This can lead to wild animals being **killed** in retaliation.
- **Nomadic** communities are no longer able to **move** about as much because of their own growing populations, and because of the amount of land now used for **feeding** and **housing** the general population. This has meant livestock are grazed over **smaller** areas, so vegetation doesn't have a chance to **recover**, making **overgrazing** more likely.

Economic development

- As **prosperity** and **development** level increases, demand for **food** also increases. This leads to **agricultural changes** which can damage savanna grasslands (see next page).
- **Tourism**, e.g. safaris and trophy hunting, can **boost** economic development, and some of this income may be used towards **conservation**. However, tourism can also cause **problems**, e.g. **pollution** from vehicles, **habitat loss** from road and building construction, **disturbance** of animals and death of big game from hunting.

Savanna Grasslands

Agricultural extension and intensification

- Savanna grasslands are often thought of as **poorly suited** to **crop** farming, because the soils **dry out** in the dry season, and don't hold many **nutrients**. However, **advances** in agriculture in recent decades have resulted in **commercial farmers** moving into the savanna and planting large areas with **cash crops**, such as corn and wheat. Newly created varieties of **soybeans** are now grown in **Brazil's** savanna, known as the **cerrado**, despite soybeans originally only being suitable for farming in **temperate** climates.

- More land is also being used for **subsistence** crops, to feed the growing local populations in savannas.

- Farmers have tried to increase food production by **reducing** the amount of time that fields are left **fallow** (when no seeds are sown) in **crop rotations**, but this means that soil doesn't have time to **recover** before it's replanted. **'Slash and burn'** farming is used by small-scale farmers, but when this is done too frequently, soil **fertility** decreases. Over time, these practices **decrease yields** — to make up for this, **even more** savanna is converted to farmland.

- Salts in the soil can dissolve in water when land is **irrigated**. As water evaporates, these salts **rise** to the ground surface and form a layer of soil which is **too salty** for many plants. Drawing too much water for irrigation may also **lower** the **water table**, so other plants **can't reach** it.

Human Activity has *Implications* for *Biodiversity* and *Sustainability*

Biodiversity

1) Humans are directly **reducing** biodiversity in savanna grasslands by **destroying habitats** and **killing** wildlife.

2) Changing land use is also causing **fragmentation** (see p.102), which is a problem because grazing animals and predators need **large spaces** to roam.

3) The presence of domestic livestock reduces the amount of vegetation and water available for native **wild herbivores** — domestic species are **replacing** wild species in the ecosystem.

4) Native savanna species are also threatened by invasive species, e.g. **cane toads** were introduced in the **Australian** savanna as a form of crop pest control, but their population rapidly **expanded**, putting native species under **threat** — they eat their food and secrete **poison** when threatened.

Sustainability

1) **Overgrazing** and **intensive agriculture** are unsustainable — they often lead to **soil erosion**, because the soil is no longer held together by plant **roots**. Some areas are experiencing **desertification** because of a lack of proper management of these activities — the poor soil makes it difficult for vegetation to **regrow**, so the area begins to resemble the **desert** biome. This problem is expected to worsen as **climate change** alters **rainfall** patterns.

2) **Controlled fires** are necessary for the sustainable management of savannas. If fires are **prevented** or extinguished too quickly, **organic material** builds up and massive **uncontrolled** fires can occur.

3) **Water** is scarce during the **dry** season, so its usage (for irrigation, domestic use etc.) must be carefully managed.

4) **Game reserves** have been created in many areas — these are areas where **settlements**, **grazing** and **farming** aren't allowed, and **hunting** is strictly controlled. They increase **sustainability** by allowing the ecosystem to operate without too much human interference.

Practice Questions

Q1 How does the soil moisture budget in savanna grasslands change through the year?

Q2 Describe two ways plants in savanna grasslands are adapted to the climate.

Q3 Describe the impact of fire on savanna grasslands.

Q4 How has agriculture in the savanna changed?

Exam Question

Q1 'Population change is the single most important driver of ecological change in savanna grasslands.' To what extent do you agree with this view?   [20 marks]

Why is it hard to play cards in the savanna? There are too many cheetahs...

Savanna grasslands and tropical rainforests are both hot all year long, but the seasonality of the rainfall is the key thing that makes the savanna so different. Make sure you know the main characteristics of savannas, and the human impacts on them.

Ecological Change — Case Study

You're not done with savanna grasslands just yet. You need to be able to write about a specific region that's facing ecological change — so, pack up your binoculars and your safari hat because we're off to the Serengeti...

The **Serengeti** is a **Savanna Grassland** Ecosystem

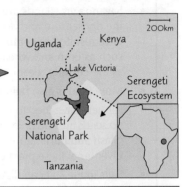

1) The **Serengeti** covers 30 000 km² of Tanzania and south west Kenya. About **15 000 km²** of this is the **Serengeti National Park**, which was established in 1951 to **preserve wildlife** and **reduce environmental damage**.

2) The vegetation is dominated by grasses and shrubs with occasional trees (e.g. acacia). It supports herds of **grazing animals** (wildebeest, zebra, buffalo etc.) and their **predators** (lions, leopards, cheetahs).

3) People aren't allowed to live **inside** the National Park itself, but some communities live elsewhere in the Serengeti ecosystem.

People of the Serengeti

- There are several **indigenous peoples** living in the Serengeti, including the **Maasai**. The **traditional** subsistence Maasai lifestyle works well in the Serengeti ecosystem:

  1) **Social** — the Maasai keep **livestock** (e.g. cattle, sheep and goats), and **subsist** on products from them, such as **meat** and **milk**. They are **nomadic** — this works well in the Serengeti because **moving on** from an area once the herds have grazed there gives the vegetation **time** to **grow back**.

  2) **Political** — the Maasai have **rights** over large areas of land because they have lived there for so long. There are **zones** of land between different groups that both groups can use by **negotiation**.

  3) **Economic** — the Maasai **trade** livestock with **neighbouring** groups for grain, vegetables or other livestock.

- However, the Maasai way of life is under **threat**. Many Maasai groups are being **displaced** by settlers, restricting the areas in which they can roam. Some groups are no longer truly nomadic, and **farm crops** rather than **relying** solely on livestock. Some Maasai have also started trading more **widely** (e.g. in local towns) to earn **money** to pay for their children's education, different types of food etc.

- **New settlements** have also developed in and around the Serengeti, some of which have been illegally built on protected land. Some communities also **hunt** wild animals for their **subsistence**.

The **Serengeti** is Facing **Ecological Change**

This ecosystem faces **ecological change** due to **human pressure** — from **visitors** and from the fast-growing **local population**:

LAND USE

1) Changes to land use include rapidly growing **shanty towns**, **grazing pastures** for increasing numbers of **cows** and **lodges** for the **tourist** industry.

2) Large areas of land are being converted to **wheat fields** — removing the natural vegetation reduces **biodiversity** and can increase **soil erosion**, while **fertilisers pollute** rivers.

3) As areas of the Serengeti are farmed, natural **habitats** are **lost**. The **ranges** of animals are **restricted**, and **migration routes**, e.g. of **wildebeest**, are disrupted by **fences** etc.

POACHING

1) Animals are **killed** by visitors for **sport**, as well as by local people for **food** or for products like **ivory** and **rhino horn** to sell.

2) This has caused serious **declines** in numbers of several species — in the 1980s, the **black rhino** population in the Serengeti fell to just **two animals**.

3) **Legislation** like the **1989 ban** on the **international trade** of ivory has helped to reduce elephant poaching in recent years — elephant numbers have **increased** in the National Park, but the continued **demand** for illegal ivory means poaching is **reducing** elephant populations in the **unprotected** parts of the ecosystem.

4) The **increasing human population** is increasing local demand for **bushmeat**. It's thought that around **100 000 wildebeest** in the Serengeti are killed for bushmeat each year.

INVASIVE SPECIES

1) **Invasive plant species** such as the **Mexican poppy**, which was introduced by accident, can **out-compete native plants** and **crops**, making some areas **unsuitable for farming**.

2) Some **animal species** spread disease, e.g. in 1994 canine distemper virus, spread from **domestic dogs**, killed **a third** of the population of **Serengeti lions**.

CLIMATE CHANGE

1) **Climate change** has **increased temperatures** in the area, and the **dry season** has got **longer**.

2) **Rains** during the wet seasons have become more **intense**, resulting in **soil erosion**.

3) This means that the ecosystem can't produce as much **vegetation**, which reduces its ability to support large herds of **herbivores**.

Ecological Change — Case Study

The **Local Community** is **Responding** to the **Changes**...

The Serengeti National Park is managed by **Tanzania National Parks** (TANAPA) — they aim to balance conservation with the needs of local people. Many schemes **involve local people** in conservation. For example:

Wildlife Management Areas

1) Four **Wildlife Management Areas** (WMAs) have been created, which have a **community-based conservation approach**. For example, the **Ikona Community WMA**, an area of **450 km²**, is managed by communities from five villages. They work together to manage the wildlife, and are allowed to use the resources from the area within **sustainable limits** — either through hunting for their own use, or making money from tourism (e.g. selling local produce or guiding safaris).

2) The WMAs have been **successful** in lots of ways. They provide local people with **food** and **income**, and help to **reduce** illegal **poaching**.

Tourism

1) The Serengeti is a popular destination for **safari** holidays.

2) Money from tourism goes back into the National Park to help pay for conservation projects. It also **boosts the local economy** by creating jobs and a market for local produce.

3) The increased **ranger presence** for tourism has also helped **reduce poaching**.

Conservation education

1) The park supports **conservation clubs** in 74 local primary schools, holds **teacher training workshops** and **informs** local people about work in the park.

2) Involving local people in conservation means they are more likely to **protect the ecosystem** themselves.

Controlled burning

1) TANAPA carries out **prescribed burning** — this means they periodically start carefully **planned**, **controlled** fires.

2) This regularly removes **flammable** materials, e.g. dry grass and twigs, so they can't **feed** any **wildfires** that break out (see p.104).

...but there are still **Threats** to the **Ecosystem**

It's proving difficult to balance **wildlife conservation** with the **needs of local people**:

1) The **human population** around the park is still growing, and more settlements and farms are built near the park each year. There can be **conflicts** between agriculture and conservation, e.g. elephants sometimes raid crops such as sorghum and maize, which can make conservation **unpopular** with local people.

2) Some **local people** are reluctant to become part of a **WMA**, because they have **doubts** about what they'll gain from it. Others have **refused** to stop **farming** or **hunting** within the WMAs, so some areas are still being over-exploited.

3) Outside the WMAs, **poaching** is still a **problem**. Poachers mostly target wildebeest and zebra, but other animals often get caught in poachers' snares or traps. If the human **population** around the park continues to **increase**, it could lead to a **rapid decline** in the **wildebeest population**.

4) **Tourism** can have a number of **negative impacts** (see page 104) — however, a clear **code of conduct** and **limits** to tourism have been set by the National Park to try and reduce these impacts.

Safari vehicles in the Serengeti.

Practice Questions

Q1 How has poaching damaged the Serengeti ecosystem?

Q2 What effect has human population growth had on the Serengeti ecosystem?

Q3 What are Wildlife Management Areas (WMAs)?

Exam Question

Q1 Evaluate community responses to ecological change in a specific region you have studied. [9 marks]

Right, time to get your head down and learn some stuff...

The Serengeti is a great example to pull out in your exam — there's lots to talk about and examiners love answers that are backed up by a truckload of facts. Unfortunately that means there's a lot to remember, so make sure you know it really well.

Coral Reefs

You've looked at some of the major terrestrial biomes, but you'll need to know a bit about marine ecosystems too.
So, it's time to ditch the safari hat and get out your snorkel and diving suit instead, because we're heading underwater...

Coral Reefs Occur in the Tropics and in Cold Water

1) There are two major categories of coral reef:
   - **tropical** coral reefs
   - **deep-sea cold-water** coral reefs

2) **Tropical** coral reefs occur between **30° north and south of the equator**, in waters that stay above **16° C**.

3) These are some of the world's major **tropical** coral reefs:

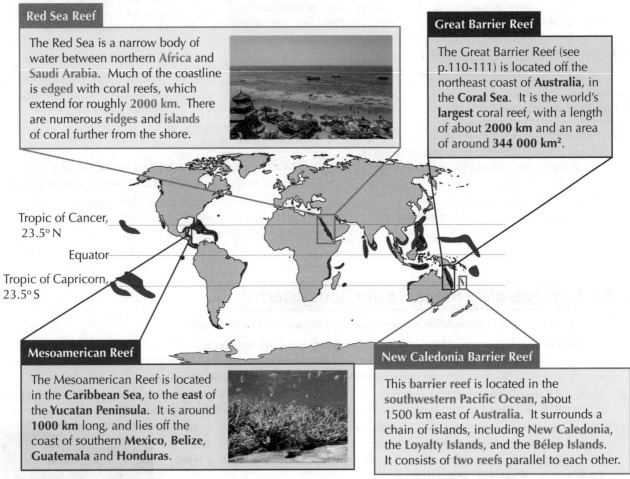

Red Sea Reef

The Red Sea is a narrow body of water between northern **Africa** and **Saudi Arabia**. Much of the coastline is **edged** with coral reefs, which extend for roughly **2000 km**. There are numerous **ridges** and **islands** of coral further from the shore.

Great Barrier Reef

The Great Barrier Reef (see p.110-111) is located off the northeast coast of **Australia**, in the **Coral Sea**. It is the world's **largest** coral reef, with a length of about **2000 km** and an area of around **344 000 km²**.

Tropic of Cancer, 23.5° N

Equator

Tropic of Capricorn, 23.5° S

Mesoamerican Reef

The Mesoamerican Reef is located in the **Caribbean Sea**, to the **east** of the **Yucatan Peninsula**. It is around **1000 km** long, and lies off the coast of southern **Mexico**, **Belize**, **Guatemala** and **Honduras**.

New Caledonia Barrier Reef

This **barrier reef** is located in the **southwestern Pacific Ocean**, about 1500 km east of **Australia**. It surrounds a chain of islands, including **New Caledonia**, the **Loyalty Islands**, and the **Bélep Islands**. It consists of **two reefs** parallel to each other.

4) **Cold-water** reefs can develop in water as cold as **4 °C**, and at depths of **40-2000 m**. So far, most cold-water reefs have been found in the **North Atlantic**, including off the west coasts of **Ireland** and **Scotland**.

5) The largest cold-water reef yet discovered is off the coast of **Norway's Røst Island**. It is **40 km** long and **2-3 km** wide.

Reefs are Made of Coral Polyps

1) Coral reefs are made up of **coral polyps** — small **animals** with tentacles and a **hard outer shell**. A reef can contain **thousands** of polyps.

2) Coral reef formation begins when **free-swimming** coral **larvae** **attach** themselves to any **hard surface** in the water.

3) They then **secrete** a hard skeleton made of **calcium carbonate**. This **protects** the polyps from **predation**.

4) The skeleton provides a **new surface** for polyp **larvae** to **attach** themselves to, so the reef continues to **grow** — reef development is a **self-sustaining** process.

5) The **build-up** of these calcium carbonate skeletons over **hundreds to thousands of years** can form reefs of various shapes and sizes, depending on the coral **species**.

tentacles
mouth
stomach
skeleton

Coral Reefs

Tropical Coral Reefs Need Sunlight to Grow

1) Tropical coral reefs grow at rates of between **0.3** and **10 cm per year**.
2) They need a **hard surface** under the water to begin formation.
3) They can only grow in particular **conditions**:

> *The coral and algae have a symbiotic relationship because they depend on each other for survival.*

- Tropical reefs mainly form in **clear, shallow** (less than about 70 m) waters. This is because their polyps have small **photosynthetic algae** (called **zooxanthellae**) living **symbiotically** inside them — these are what give the reefs their **colour**.
- The zooxanthellae get **nutrients** and **shelter** from the polyp. In return, they provide food for the coral via **photosynthesis**.
- If the reef was **deep** below the water surface, or in **murky** water, not enough **sunlight** would be able to filter through for the algae to **photosynthesise**.
- The polyps can only grow in seawater with moderate levels of **salinity** — between **30 and 40 parts per thousand** — and consistent **warm temperatures**.

There are Three Types of Tropical Coral Reef

1) **Barrier reefs** run **parallel** to a coastline, but are **not attached** to it — they are separated from the shore by a **lagoon**.
2) **Fringing reefs** lie **very close** to the shore, in **shallow** waters — there is no lagoon separating them from the land.
3) **Atolls** are **ring-shaped** coral reefs, **far away** from the shore, that **circle** a lagoon.

Barry O'Reeves always insists on running parallel to the coastline.

Cold-Water Coral Reefs Grow Very Slowly

1) Cold-water coral reefs grow much more slowly than tropical reefs, at rates of about **5-25 mm per year**.
2) There are certain environmental **conditions** they require to develop:

- Cold-water coral reefs form in **deep**, **nutrient-rich** seawater, where the **temperature** and **salinity** levels are more stable than in coastal waters.
- There has to be an initial **hard surface** for the coral larvae to attach themselves to.
- Cold-water coral polyps obtain food by **capturing particles** in the **passing currents** with their **tentacles**, so they grow best in places with **strong ocean currents**.
- Strong currents also carry away excess **sediment** that might otherwise build up on the coral.
- This means they are successful on **slopes** such as **seamounts** (underwater mountains) where there's an **accelerated water flow**.

> *Much less is known about deep-sea coral reefs than tropical reefs, because they're less accessible.*

Practice Questions

Q1 Briefly describe the distribution of tropical coral reefs.
Q2 Name two types of tropical coral reef.
Q2 What conditions do cold-water coral reefs require to develop?

Latitude (°N)	26
Minimum water temperature (°C)	18
Salinity (parts per 1000)	36
Water depth (m)	50
Distance from land (km)	5

Exam Question

Q1 The table gives information about an area of ocean. Using the table and the map on the previous page, assess the likelihood of a coral reef forming in this area.

[6 marks]

Atoll-d you, you might need to reef-er to this page in the exam...

...so stop hiding under your fringe and start learning it. That's right, stretch out those tentacles and try to capture particles of knowledge as they float past your brain. What do you mean, that's not how it works. That's how I've always revised. Hmm.

Great Barrier Reef — Case Study

You look like you could do with another case study. Luckily for you, there's a great one on these two pages. Enjoy.

The **Great Barrier Reef** is Very **Biodiverse**

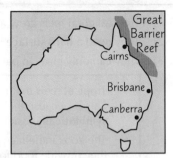

1) The Great Barrier Reef is the **largest coral reef system** in the world. It lies off the **northeast coast** of **Australia**.

2) The reef supports a range of wildlife including many **endangered** species, e.g. green sea turtles. Fish use it for **shelter**, and **feed** on the coral itself as well as on the algae living inside it.

3) The reef **slows down waves** as they approach the shore, which provides a **low-energy environment** where **mangrove forests** and **seagrass meadows** can grow.

4) There are several factors that influence the **health** and **survival** of the Great Barrier Reef:

- Water temperature — if this **rises** above about 29 °C, the coral can become **stressed** and expel the algae that live in it — this is known as 'bleaching'. The coral **needs** these algae to provide oxygen and nutrients — without them it will eventually **die**.

- Salinity — sudden **changes** in salinity, e.g. due to the influx of lots of freshwater after a storm event, can also cause coral bleaching.

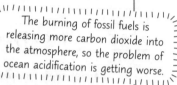

The burning of fossil fuels is releasing more carbon dioxide into the atmosphere, so the problem of ocean acidification is getting worse.

- Acidity — when **carbon dioxide** dissolves in the oceans, it increases their acidity. This makes it harder for corals to produce their calcium carbonate **skeletons**. High levels of acidity can even start to **dissolve** the reef.

- Nutrients — **eutrophication** (when water has an **excessive** amount of nutrients) causes **algae** to grow **too quickly**, forming a thick blanket near the water surface. This is called an **algal bloom**, and it threatens the reef because it reduces the amount of **light** reaching the coral, inhibiting photosynthesis.

Human Activities are **Damaging** the Great Barrier Reef

Human activities **on** or **near** the reef, or in **drainage basins** feeding into it, have **impacts** on the reef system:

(1) Tourism

- Tourism is the **largest commercial activity** around the Great Barrier Reef — over **2 million** people visit each year.

- The tourist industry creates **pollution** in several ways, e.g. through waste disposal, litter and pollution from boats — this affects the coral reefs and the species **dependent** on them.

- Coral can be **damaged** by boat anchors and by poor **diving practices** (e.g. divers stepping on coral or breaking pieces off).

- Coastal developments, e.g. hotels, can damage **coastal ecosystems** such as mangrove forests and estuaries, which are important for **maintaining** the reef (see next page).

Scuba diving and snorkelling are popular on the Great Barrier Reef.

(2) Drainage basin schemes

- There are **35** drainage basins whose rivers drain into the reef system. Changes in these can affect **runoff** into the reef.

- For example, from 2012 to 2014, more than 200 000 hectares of **forest** was **cleared** in Queensland (northeast Australia). Trees intercept rainfall and increase infiltration, so deforestation **increases runoff** and inputs of **pollutants** and **sediment** into the reef.

- Dams, such as the Burdekin Falls Dam in Queensland, which was built to provide water for drinking, industry and irrigation, change the **amount** and **timing** of **freshwater** flows into the reef, which can disrupt the ecosystem.

(3) Fishing

- Fishing can **remove** certain species from the reef, e.g. **predators** such as snapper and coral trout are caught more than prey fish such as damselfish.

- Removing predators means that there are **too many prey fish**, which may lead to **overgrazing** of coral and algae.

- Some fishing methods are **unsustainable** — e.g. **trawling** (dragging a net through water) damages the coral and kills animals other than the fish it's intended to catch. Trawler nets can **drown turtles** — there are now **regulations** in place to protect them, but turtle populations won't **recover** for decades because they breed slowly.

Great Barrier Reef — Case Study

4) Pollution

- **Runoff** from **farmland** in the drainage basins often contains **fertilisers**, which means the water reaching the reef has a high **nutrient** content — this causes **algal blooms**.
- Land-based runoff can also contain other pollutants such as **heavy metals** — these can disrupt **reproduction** or cause **cancer** in marine **animals** living off the reef.
- **Shipping** causes pollution around the reef, e.g. from **waste disposal**, **oil spills** and toxic **paints** used on boat hulls.

If water shortages increase, Australia may become more reliant on **desalination**. Salt from **desalinated water** is often mixed with wastewater and **pumped back into the sea** — if this was done near the Great Barrier Reef, it would change the **water chemistry** and may affect coral growth.

5) Onshore development

- Coastal developments can damage or destroy onshore ecosystems such as **mangrove forests**, which increases the amount of **nutrients** and **sediment** that are added to the reef ecosystem.
- **Too much** sediment prevents **light** from reaching the coral, limiting its **growth**.
- The expansion of **ports** involves **dredging** — this is when the sea floor is dug up so ships can reach the shore. Dredging **destroys** habitats and increases the likelihood of coral **disease**.

The **Future** of the Great Barrier Reef is **Uncertain**

1) Human activities have already caused a lot of **damage** to the Great Barrier Reef and **climate change** is making the problems worse.

2) **Mass coral bleaching** is becoming more **frequent**, which means the ecosystem has less time to **recover** between bleaching events. In **2016**, the reef suffered the **worst** bleaching on record, when **67%** of corals in the northern section **died**.

3) Damage to the Great Barrier Reef puts the **thousands of species** that rely on it at risk.

4) However, if the reef is managed effectively, it may be possible to **minimise** damage. There are many **management strategies** in place to protect the reef:

At least Anita was certain about her bleaching events.

- The **Reef 2050 Plan** is a framework for how the reef should be managed until **2050**. The **government**, **industries**, **environmental groups** and **scientists work together** to improve the reef's **health** while allowing **some development**.
- Much of the reef is managed by the **Great Barrier Reef Marine Park Authority** (GBRMPA) — in 2003, they established a **zoning system** that restricts human activities in vulnerable areas.
- **Fishing** is **strictly regulated** to limit the number of fish that are caught, especially protected species.
- Companies using the reef (e.g. commercial fishing or tourism operations) pay an **Environmental Management Charge** (EMC). This money funds **research**, **education** and **management** of the reef.
- The **tourism** industry can benefit conservation efforts — e.g. tour operators and tourists are **encouraged to help monitor** the reef, e.g. report on the extent of coral bleaching.
- The **Reef Trust** has been set up to improve **water quality** and **habitats** in and around the reef. It has been awarded AU$40 million funding from the **Australian government**, with more money to follow.
- The **Reef Water Quality Protection Plan** was set up in 2003 — it involves the government, farmers and industry working together to **limit pollutants** running off the land into the reef.

5) Protecting the reef from large-scale issues, such as **climate change** and **sea level rise**, is more difficult. These changes are likely to have a significant effect on the future of the Great Barrier Reef.

Practice Questions

Q1 How would a rise in water temperature affect the Great Barrier Reef?

Q2 What causes an algal bloom?

Q3 Describe three ways that tourism can negatively impact the Great Barrier Reef.

Exam Question

Q1 With reference to a named coral reef, assess the impact of human activity on its health. [9 marks]

My urge to go snorkelling is a Great Barrier to my revision...

Another case study, another bunch of ways that humans are killing wildlife. Sorry it's so gloomy. The good news is that there are loads of strategies in place to help protect the Great Barrier Reef, so wipe away those tears and get learning.

Topic Six — Ecosystems Under Stress

Succession

Leave any surface sitting there for long enough and some plant or other will start colonising it. You need to know about two of the ways this can happen: the lithosere and the hydrosere. So, get reading if you want succession success in your exam.

Succession is the Process of Ecosystem Change

1) **Succession** is the process by which an **ecosystem changes** over **time**. The **biotic conditions** (e.g. **plant** and **animal life**) change as the **abiotic conditions** (e.g. **water availability**) change.

2) Succession occurs in **steps** called **seral stages**. There are **two** types of succession:

Primary succession

This happens on land that's been **newly formed** or **exposed**, e.g. where a **volcano** erupts and forms **new rock**.
- The **abiotic conditions** are **harsh**, e.g. there's no soil. **Seeds** and **spores** are blown in by the **wind**.
- The **first species** to colonise the area are **pioneer species** — they're **specialised** to cope with the harsh conditions, e.g. **lichens** can grow on **bare rock** because they don't need soil or much water. This is the **first seral stage**.
- The pioneer species **change** the **abiotic conditions** — they **die** and **decompose**, which forms a **basic soil**.
- This makes conditions **less hostile**, e.g. the basic soil helps **retain water**, which means **new organisms** can grow. These then die and are decomposed, adding **more** organic material and making the soil **deeper** and **richer in minerals**. This means **larger plants** like **shrubs** can start to grow in the deeper soil.

Secondary succession

Secondary succession happens on land that's been **cleared** of all the **plants**, but where the **soil remains**, e.g. after a **fire**. **Secondary succession** happens in the **same way** as primary succession, but because there's already a **soil layer** succession starts at a **later seral stage** — the pioneer species in secondary succession are **larger plants**, e.g. shrubs.

3) At each stage, **different** plants and animals that are **better adapted** for the improved conditions move in, **out-compete** the plants and animals that are already there, and become the **dominant species** in the ecosystem.

4) As succession goes on, the ecosystem becomes **more complex**. New species move in **alongside** existing species, so **species diversity** (the number of **different species** and the **abundance** of each species) tends to **increase**.

5) The **final seral stage** is the **climax community** — the ecosystem supports the **largest** and **most complex** community it can, and the biotic and abiotic factors are **in balance**. This is known as the **climatic climax** and it **won't change** much more — unless the **abiotic conditions change**.

The Abiotic Conditions Control the Type of Community that Develops

Succession can take different routes depending on the **abiotic conditions** at the start of the process. A **lithosere** occurs on exposed rock surfaces and a **hydrosere** occurs on water:

Lithosere example — bare rock to woodland

1) **Pioneer species**, e.g. **lichens**, **colonise** the rocks because they can live with **very little water** and few nutrients. Lichens **break down** rock, which **releases minerals**. As the rock is broken down, its **surface** becomes uneven, which helps to retain **water**.

2) As the rocks get more **damp**, **mosses** begin to grow and **weather** the rock surface. Lichens and mosses **die** and **decompose**, forming a **thin soil**.

3) As the soil **deepens**, **larger plants** that need **more water** move in e.g. **grasses**, **ferns**, **herbs** and **flowering plants**. The soil **gets deeper** as the larger plants die and are decomposed by **bacteria** to form **humus**.

4) **Shrubs**, **ferns** and **small trees** such as **rowan** and **birch** begin to grow. They **out-compete** the smaller plants to become the **dominant** species.

5) Finally, the soil is **deep** and **rich** enough in **nutrients** to support slow-growing **large trees** like **ash** and **oak**. These become the dominant species, and the **climax community** is formed.

6) In the UK, you might find a lithosere in a **quarry**, e.g. Holme Park quarry in Cumbria.

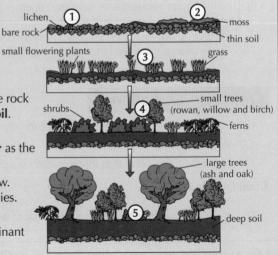

Succession

Hydrosere example — fresh water (e.g. lake) to woodland

1) Pioneer species (e.g. **algae** and floating plants such as **duckweed**) colonise the **water surface**. They die and sink to the bottom, where they accumulate along with other **sediments** (e.g. sediments deposited by rivers).

2) The water gets shallower as sediments and decomposing plant material **accumulate**. Aquatic plants move in, e.g. **elodea** and **starwort**. They are **rooted** in the lake bed and trap and hold **more sediment** on the bottom.

3) The water becomes **very shallow**, and **swamp** and **marsh plants** (e.g. **reeds** and **rushes**) move in. Marsh plants generate lots of leaf litter, which builds up and forms a **wet soil**.

4) Larger plants (e.g. **ferns**) and tree seedlings (e.g. **willow** and **alder**) move in. These plants decrease soil moisture by transpiration, until the soil is no longer water-logged.

5) The **soil deepens** and becomes drier as larger plants die and decompose.

6) This provides suitable conditions for **large climax tree species**, e.g. oak, ash and beech. These are **slow-growing**, but eventually become **dominant**. Herbs, grasses and flowering plants grow on the woodland floor, depending on how much **light** gets through the canopy.

7) In the British Isles, hydroseres have occurred on some **kettle lakes** (shallow lakes formed by retreating glaciers), e.g. **Sweetmere** in Shropshire.

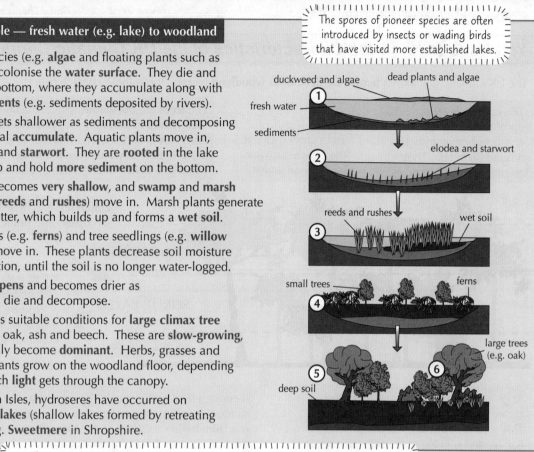

The spores of pioneer species are often introduced by insects or wading birds that have visited more established lakes.

The examples of succession on these pages are for the temperate climate zone, so they can be seen in the UK. Different successions occur in different climate zones.

Sometimes the **Final Seral Stage** is **Different** to the **Climatic Climax**

1) The climatic climax community is only reached if **natural conditions** are **stable** and **uninterrupted**.

2) In many cases, the ecosystem ends up with an **alternative** community:

   - **Sub-climax** — this occurs when succession is **interrupted** by a change in local factors, e.g. fire or the arrival of a new species, so that the vegetation is **prevented** from reaching its climatic climax and is held at an **earlier** stage.

   - **Plagioclimax** — if **human activity** has **permanently influenced** the final community of an ecosystem, it's called the **plagioclimax**. One example in the British Isles is **heather moorland** (see p.115).

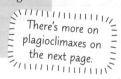

There's more on plagioclimaxes on the next page.

Practice Questions

Q1 What is the difference between primary and secondary succession?

Q2 What is a pioneer species?

Q3 What is meant by the term 'climatic climax'?

Exam Question

Q1 Analyse the role of decomposers in succession.

[9 marks]

A plagioclimax on both your houses...

Both seres follow a similar pattern from bare surface to climatic climax, but it's remembering the details that will get you top marks — you need to talk about specific species and the abiotic changes they cause, and use the scientific terms correctly.

Succession in the British Isles

So after Queen Victoria came King Edward VII, and... oh, hang on — wrong sort of succession. This is about plants and stuff.

You Need to Know the **Characteristics** of the **UK Climatic Climax**

The UK climatic climax is a **temperate deciduous woodland** biome. It has these characteristics:

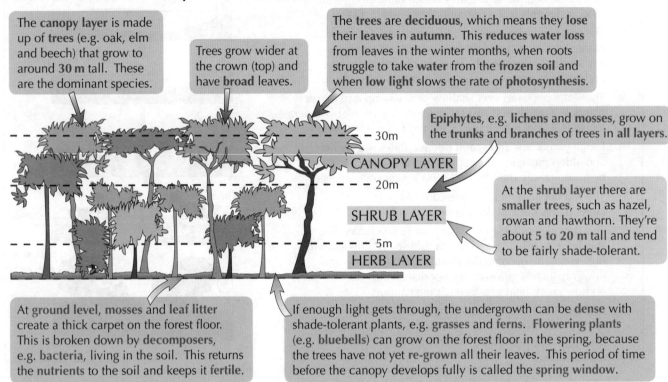

The **canopy layer** is made up of **trees** (e.g. oak, elm and beech) that grow to around **30 m** tall. These are the dominant species.

Trees grow wider at the crown (top) and have **broad** leaves.

The **trees** are **deciduous**, which means they **lose their leaves in autumn**. This **reduces water loss** from leaves in the winter months, when roots struggle to take **water** from the **frozen soil** and when **low light** slows the rate of **photosynthesis**.

Epiphytes, e.g. **lichens and mosses**, grow on the **trunks** and **branches** of trees in **all layers**.

CANOPY LAYER — 30m

— 20m

SHRUB LAYER

— 5m

HERB LAYER

At the **shrub layer** there are **smaller trees**, such as hazel, rowan and hawthorn. They're about **5 to 20 m** tall and tend to be fairly shade-tolerant.

At **ground level**, **mosses** and **leaf litter** create a thick carpet on the forest floor. This is broken down by **decomposers**, e.g. **bacteria**, living in the soil. This returns the **nutrients** to the soil and keeps it **fertile**.

If enough light gets through, the undergrowth can be **dense** with shade-tolerant plants, e.g. **grasses** and **ferns**. **Flowering plants** (e.g. **bluebells**) can grow on the forest floor in the spring, because the trees have not yet **re-grown** all their leaves. This period of time before the canopy develops fully is called the **spring window**.

Although this is the climatic climax, at a **local scale**, **soil**, **drainage** or **relief** can **change** the community that forms.

There are Various **Plagioclimaxes** in **the UK**

Human activities have **stopped succession** in many parts of the British Isles, so that **plagioclimaxes** have formed instead of temperate deciduous woodland. For example:

Human activity	Why it's carried out	Why it prevents the climatic climax being reached	Characteristics of the resulting plagioclimax
Deforestation	To get **wood** for **timber** or **fuel**, or to make **space** for **farming**.	Removing trees **reduces soil quality** because it takes nutrients out of the ecosystem that would otherwise be returned to the soil by **leaf fall** or **tree death**. **Fewer** types of **plants** can **grow** in the poor soil.	**Hardy shrubs**, e.g. heather.
Animal grazing	Domesticated **animals** kept for **meat** (or other **products**) often **graze** for their food.	**Small plants** and saplings are **eaten** or **destroyed** by trampling before they get a chance to grow.	**Fast-growing grasses** and **plants** (e.g. dandelions). Very few trees and shrubs.
Clearance by fire	To **clear** an area for **farming**, to **control** the **plants** growing in an area, or to **improve** the **soil** in an area (ash is a fertiliser).	All the **plants** are **destroyed**, and the **fastest growing** types of plants **re-colonise** the area.	**Fast-growing plants**, whose roots aren't damaged by fire, e.g. heather.
Afforestation (planting trees)	To plant trees for **timber**.	The **trees** in an area may be **cleared** to make way for the **new saplings**. Only **one species** is planted and managed (monoculture), so this species **dominates**.	In **managed areas** like forestry plantations **humans control** the **plagioclimax**.

Topic Six — Ecosystems Under Stress

Succession in the British Isles

Plagioclimax Case Study — North York Moors: **Heather Moorland**

Heather moorland is an area of **open country** mostly covered in **heather**. It's a **plagioclimax** because it's created by human activity. The **North York Moors** are the **largest area** of heather moorland in England, covering **1436 km²** of land.

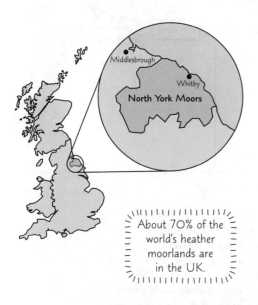

About 70% of the world's heather moorlands are in the UK.

The moors were **created** by human activities:

1) The moors used to be an **oak forest** (a temperate deciduous woodland biome), where only **small amounts** of **heather** grew at ground level.

2) Up to about **5000 years ago** people hunted and gathered in the woodland for food. As the population grew, people began to **clear** the most fertile areas of **woodland** to keep animals and **grow crops**.

3) From around **4000** to **2000 years ago**, the remaining woodland was cleared. Clearing trees **reduced soil quality** — when an area was no longer fertile enough for farming, people moved on.

4) Few types of plants were able to grow in the **poor quality soil**. Heather is a **hardy shrub** — it was able to grow, and it flourished because there was **less competition** from other plants.

5) Around **1000 years ago**, sheep **grazing** became a major form of agriculture in North Yorkshire. This **prevented the re-growth** of other plants (as saplings were eaten or trampled before they got a chance to mature), which **reduced** the level of **competition**. Heather is **fast growing** so it was able to cope with being grazed, and soon it dominated the area.

The moors are also **maintained** by human activities:

1) The **North York Moors** are a **national park** and the moorland is carefully maintained for **environmental** and **economic** reasons. The moors are an **important habitat** for **rare plants**, e.g. sundew and common spotted orchid, and **birds**, e.g. merlin and golden plover. The moors are also used for **sheep grazing** and **grouse shooting**.

2) Without **active management** the heather moorland would eventually return to a **temperate deciduous forest**, and the **moorland plants** and **animals** would **lose their habitat** and **move on** or **die out**.

Heather moorlands in Yorkshire.

3) Although **sheep grazing** helps to maintain the moorland, **controlled burning** is the primary management technique. A few sections are burned each year in an **8-15 year rotation**. If left alone heather becomes **tough** and **woody** and eventually collapses, but burning **encourages** new heather shoots to **grow**, which provides better grazing for sheep and grouse. Burning also **destroys less fire-resistant plants**, which helps to ensure that the heather remains **dominant**.

Practice Questions

Q1 Name the three layers in the temperate deciduous woodland biome.

Q2 Why does deforestation prevent the climatic climax being reached?

Q3 Give two other ways in which human action can prevent a climatic climax being reached.

Exam Question

Q1 With reference to one plagioclimax you have studied, analyse the role of human activity in the development of the ecosystem.

[9 marks]

I don't think I can take much moor of this...

Ecosystems are made of pretty stern stuff — you can burn them down, flood them out or plant trees all over them and they just keep coming back. It's a bit like you and this revision guide really, you just can't keep away (because it's so great, obviously).

Local Ecosystems

You need to know about a local ecosystem — it might be an area of heathland, managed parkland, a pond or a dune system.

A *Sand Dune Ecosystem* is found in *Ainsdale*, Near Southport

1) **Ainsdale Sand Dunes National Nature Reserve** lies between **Liverpool** and **Southport**.

2) It's a **coastal ecosystem** that's part of the **Sefton Coast**, where dunes started to form around **5000 years ago** with **sand blown inland** from the beaches.

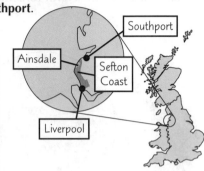

- **Climate** — it's usually fairly **mild** and **wet**. It tends to be **windy** because it's on the coast. Wind **moves** the dunes, and some may be **completely removed** during **stormy** conditions.

- **Soils** — there's **very little** soil in the dunes closest to the sea, so there are **few nutrients** available. Soil depth **increases** with **distance** from the shore, but it is **salty**, **alkaline** and **dry**.

- **Soil moisture budget** — soil moisture budget is negative for most of the year (more water is lost than gained). Sand is **porous**, so water travels through it very quickly. This means the **water table** is **very deep**.

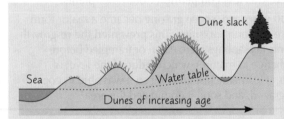

Most of the dune ecosystem is **dry**, but in **dune slacks**, the **water table** is **closer** to the surface, so the sand is **wetter**. The water table **falls** during the **summer**, when **evapotranspiration** is **higher** than **rainfall**, but during the rest of the year, it **rises** — this means the dune slacks usually **flood** during the winter.

Plants are *Adapted* to the Environment...

1) Sand dunes are a very **harsh environment** — plants living in this ecosystem have **adaptations** to cope with the **limited freshwater**, **poor soils**, and the **mobility** of the dunes. For example:

- Many plants, such as **sand couch** and **lyme grass**, can grow rapidly **upwards** to avoid being **buried** by moving sand. These plants grow at the front of a dune system — they trap **wind-blown sand**, forming **embryo dunes**.

- The plants closest to the beach front have a **high salt tolerance** to cope with the spray from the sea. They also have to be able to grow in sediment with **low** organic content.

- Many plants **avoid water loss** by having specially adapted leaves — leaves often have a **small surface area**, **hairs** to trap moisture, and a **thick waxy coating** to prevent water from evaporating.

- Rainwater **drains rapidly** through sand dunes, so many plants have **extensive root systems**, or extremely **long** roots, to **maximise** the amount of water they can take up before it drains away.

- Being on the coast means plants are exposed to the **wind** — many are adapted to this by having **strong stems** that are **flexible** so the wind bends them instead of breaking them.

2) **Marram grass** is important in the formation of sand dunes — it helps to **hold the sand together** so the dunes **stabilise** and **grow**. It's **well-adapted** to the dry, sandy conditions:

Topic Six — Ecosystems Under Stress

Local Ecosystems

... and so are *Animals*

1) Some small **animal** species can be found in the Ainsdale sand dunes, including **rare** species such as **sand lizards**, **great crested newts** and **natterjack toads**. Animals have to be able to cope with the **harsh** conditions of the dunes.

2) For example, **sand lizards** have several adaptations:

- **Freshwater** is difficult to access in a sand dune ecosystem, so much of the **water supply** of sand lizards comes from the **insects** they eat.
- To **retain moisture**, they retreat to **damp** places during the heat of the day, to slow the rate of **evaporation**.
- Sand lizards **hibernate** during the winter when food is scarce.
- **Long toes** help them move **quickly** over bare sand, while their scaly, **streamlined** bodies let them **burrow** into the sandy ground for shelter.
- They also **lay their eggs** in the **loose sand** of the dunes — their egg-laying sites are **exposed** to the **sun** (there are **no large plants** to shade them), so the eggs remain **warm** enough to **develop** and **hatch**.

3) The **natterjack toad** is another **rare** species found in the sand dunes. It is also **adapted** to the conditions:

- Like sand lizards, natterjack toads dig **burrows** in the sandy ground, which they use to avoid **extreme temperatures** — during hot weather, being in a burrow stops them from becoming **dehydrated**. During cold weather, being underground helps them to keep **warm** and **conserve energy**.
- They dig **deeper** burrows to **hibernate** in during the winter when there's little food available.
- Natterjack toads lay their spawn in **shallow pools** of water that form intermittently in dune **slacks**. These pools are usually **warm**, because they are **not shaded** by plants, and the surrounding dunes **shield** them against the wind. **Tadpoles** develop **quickly** in **warm** water — this increases their chance of reaching maturity before the pool **dries up**.
- Natterjack toads **hunt** for **insects** on areas of **bare sand** or **short vegetation**, where they can easily see their prey.

James was keen for little Noah to get the full Natterjack Hibernation Experience.

Pine Tree Plantations Caused *Ecological Change*

1) During the **early 1900s**, large areas of the dunes were planted with **pine trees**.

2) The aim of the plantation was to **stabilise** the dunes and to provide a crop of **wood** and **woodland products**.

3) The plantations have had several **impacts** on the sand dune ecosystem:

- Trees **prevent sunlight** from reaching the ground, so the forest floor does not receive enough light for other plants to **grow**.
- The **needles** dropped by the trees are very **acidic** and change the **chemistry** of the **soil**, which was originally **alkaline**. Pine needles take a **long time** to **break down**, so they build up in a thick **layer** on the surface instead of contributing **organic** material to the **soil**.
- Overall, the pine plantations have caused a major **reduction in biodiversity** in the ecosystem. Specialist dune plant species such as **field gentians**, **yellow bartsia** and **bog pimpernel** could not survive in areas where the dune habitat was **replaced** by the dark, acidic conditions of a pine woodland.

4) The pine plantations had some **positive** impacts too — they were **colonised** by **red squirrels**, a **protected** species.

5) The introduction of pine trees was **planned**, but there have also been **unplanned invasions** of non-native species, e.g. **sea buckthorn**, which spreads quickly, shades out native species, and changes the chemistry of the soil.

Local Ecosystems

Other Human Activities are Also Changing the Ecosystem

Urban change and agriculture have also had impacts on the sand dune ecosystem in the Ainsdale area:

Urban change

- Along the Sefton coast as a whole, around half of all sand dunes have been built on.
- The Ainsdale sand dunes are close to Liverpool and Manchester, and large towns like Southport.
- As urban areas have grown, the number of visitors to the reserve has increased. Visitors drop litter and disturb wildlife, e.g. ground-nesting birds. Trampling erodes dunes.
- New car parks and caravan sites have been built for visitors, which destroy habitats and disrupt the natural ecosystem.
- Increasing demand for water as urban areas grow has lowered the water table, which has affected habitats and increased erosion of dunes.

Agriculture

- During the 17th and 18th centuries, rabbits were bred around Ainsdale for meat and fur. Rabbits grazed on plants and saplings, helping to preserve the dune habitat.
- The sandy soils of the dunes are ideal for growing asparagus. The dunes were levelled to make fields, and some native species were removed. This damaged the ecosystem.

There Have Been Attempts to Manage These Changes

1) The area was established as Ainsdale Sand Dunes National Nature Reserve in 1965 and is now carefully managed.

2) There has been work to restore and maintain the dune ecosystem. For example:

- The pine plantations closest to the sea in the reserve have been removed to recreate the natural dune landscape.

  Some of the woodland has been kept to provide a habitat for red squirrels.

- To preserve the dunes, trees and scrub are cut regularly, invasive species are removed, and marram grass is planted.
- During the winter months, the dunes are also grazed by Herdwick sheep and Shetland cows — they eat any young trees beginning to grow, preventing the woodland from encroaching into the dune ecosystem.
- Asparagus farming is now limited to a small area.
- The nature reserve is open to the public, but access is restricted to footpaths so that visitors don't damage the ecosystem. Campfires and barbecues are prohibited to decrease fire risk. Other potentially damaging activities, such as horse riding, are not allowed, and there are fenced areas of the dunes where dogs cannot go.

3) The North Merseyside Amphibian and Reptile Group aims to conserve amphibians and reptiles in the area:

- They monitor the abundance of local species, especially the rare natterjack toads and sand lizards.
- In the winter, they remove trees and shrubs that would put the habitat of toads and lizards in the shade.
- In the spring, they create bare patches of sand to give a suitable environment for sand lizards to lay their eggs.

Practice Questions

Q1 Describe the location of the Ainsdale sand dunes.

Q2 What are the soil conditions in the Ainsdale dune system like?

Q3 Describe how planting pine trees changed the ecosystem at Ainsdale.

Exam Question

Q1 Evaluate the conservation strategies used in a local ecosystem you have studied. [9 marks]

Dunes may be removed in stormy conditions — just like my uncle's toupee...

You might have studied a different ecosystem in class. Whichever you choose, make sure you know how the plants and animals are adapted to the conditions, how people are changing the ecosystem, and how these changes are managed.

Local Ecosystems — Case Study

You're nearly at the end of the topic — there's just one more case study to navigate your way through...

The **Broads** is the UK's **Largest Wetland** Ecosystem

1) The Broads is a national park made up of a **network of navigable waterways** and **wetlands** in **Norfolk** and **Suffolk** in the east of England.

2) The ecosystem is **man-made**. The natural **climax community** in Norfolk is **woodland**, but most of the trees had been **cut down** by the 12th century. People then started digging **pits** for **extracting peat** (partially decayed organic matter) to use as fuel instead. This was abandoned after about 200 years, and the pits **flooded**, forming **lakes** (known as '**broads**').

3) The Broads has a **temperate** climate, with **seasonal** variations in temperature, like the rest of the UK. However, it gets **less rainfall** and **more sunshine** than the UK average.

4) **Biodiversity** is **high** in the Broads, and there are many **rare species** found in the diverse range of habitats. **Habitats** include:

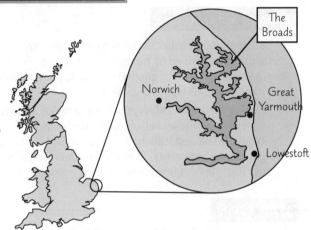

Broads and rivers

- There are **63 broads** of varying sizes, which are connected by seven **rivers**.
- Fish such as **eels**, **pike** and **perch** are found in these waterways, as well as aquatic plants, e.g. **white waterlilies**.
- Many species feed on the fish in these waterways. **Bitterns** are a type of heron that live in the **reed beds** at the water's edge, where they hunt for fish. They're well **adapted** to their habitat — they use reed stems to build a **platform** for **nesting**. If the water level rises, they **add material** to the platform.

Grazing marshes

- **Grazing marshes** are areas of wet **grassland** with **clay** and **silt** soils. **Cattle** are often grazed on these marshes.

- Many **wading bird** species, e.g. **snipe**, breed here, and **migrating** species such as **pink-footed geese** and **whooper swans** use it as their winter habitat.
- These birds are **adapted** to the **marshy** conditions — they have **long legs** so they can wade without getting their feathers wet, and **long toes** to help them keep their **balance**.

Fens

- **Fens** are **boggy** areas dominated by **reeds**, **rushes** and **sedge**, with **water-logged**, **peaty** soil.
- Fens also support a huge variety of other plant species, some of which are **rare**, such as the **fen orchid**.
- The fens of the Broads are now the only place that **swallowtail butterflies** are found, because the larvae feed on **milk parsley**, which rarely grows elsewhere in the UK.

Carr woodland

- **Carr woodland** forms when **fens** are allowed to continue with **succession**.
- It's **damp** and **shady** with **peaty** soils.
- Its main tree species are **willow** and **alder**, and the vegetation also includes **shrubs** such as **guelder rose** and **buckthorn**. Because of the high humidity, many **mosses** and **ferns** also grow.
- Carr woodlands support huge numbers of **insect** species — this attracts a large variety of **birds**, such as **woodpeckers** and **treecreepers**.

Topic Six — Ecosystems Under Stress

Local Ecosystems — Case Study

Humans have Continued to Influence the Ecosystem

Even though peat digging has stopped, humans continue to **influence** the ecosystem. For example:

Drainage and agriculture

1) The **grazing marshes** of the Broads are **estuary** areas that have been artificially **drained** by humans for hundreds of years. This was to make the land suitable for **grazing** livestock, but it also created an important **habitat** for wildlife, especially **wading birds**.

2) During the **20th century**, there were major **improvements** to drainage systems, e.g. the invention of **electric pumps**. This meant that land could be drained sufficiently to allow **arable farming**, which replaced grazing in large areas. This led to a decrease in **biodiversity** — fields of crops support **fewer** species than grazing marshes.

Before electric pumps, the Broads were drained using wind-powered mills.

Water quality

1) The waters of the Broads are **naturally nutrient-rich**, so they are vulnerable to **eutrophication** — this is when there are **too many** nutrients in the water, leading to the growth of a layer of **algae** (an **algal bloom**) on the water surface. Algal blooms prevent aquatic plants from getting enough **light**. The loss of these plants reduces the amount of **food** available for animals living in the water.

2) Around 100 years ago, the waterways in the Broads were **clear** of pollution and eutrophication, but now **58** of the **63** broads suffer from pollution.

3) Humans are contributing to the decline in **water quality** in the Broads:

Eutrophication near Cringleford, Norfolk.

- More nutrients can be added to the water when phosphates and nitrates are washed into the water from **sewage**. The **population** of Norfolk and Suffolk has expanded significantly since the 1950s, which has increased the number of **sewage treatment works** in the area.

- An increase in the amount of land in the drainage basin used for **arable farming** has led to an increase in the amount of **fertiliser** washed into the waterways.

Tourism and recreation

1) The area is a **popular tourist destination** — the national park attracts **over 7 million visitors a year** and tourism contributes **more than £400 million** to the local economy. However, visitors can **damage** ecosystems, e.g. by dropping litter or disturbing wildlife.

2) The Broads is popular for water-based **sports** and **activities**. However, this causes some environmental problems:

- Some **invasive species** have been carried to the Broads on boats, e.g. the non-native '**killer shrimp**', which feeds on the native shrimp.

- **Oil** and **fuel spills**, and **toxic** ingredients in the **paint** used on boat hulls, have **contaminated** the water and threatened **biodiversity**.

- Boat **propellers** and **jet drives** can **churn up** sediment, decreasing water quality. Boat engines can also disturb waterbirds, and the wash from boats can cause **bank erosion**.

Boat mooring area for Hickling Broad.

Climate change and sea level rise

1) The Broads National Park is **low-lying** and situated on the **coast**, which makes it vulnerable to **flooding**. Climate change is expected to increase the **frequency** and **intensity** of floods in the area, because of **rising sea levels** and changing **rainfall** patterns. **Storm surges** cause the intrusion of **saltwater** into freshwater ecosystems in the Broads.

2) If **sea levels** continue to rise, then eventually some parts of the Broads will be **permanently underwater**.

3) Over the next 50 years, the region is expected to experience **hotter, drier summers** and **wetter, warmer winters**. This is likely to affect biodiversity, as some species that are not **adapted** to the new conditions will no longer be able to survive.

Local Ecosystems — Case Study

Sustainable Development can Reduce Damage to the Broads

1) The **Broads Authority** was established in 1989 to manage the Broads.

2) They aim to ensure that the Broads are **managed sustainably** — that is, in a way that considers the **needs** of **local people** and **visitors**, the impact on the **environment** and the **economic costs** and **benefits**.

3) Managing the Broads presents a number of challenges (see previous page), but there are also **opportunities** for sustainable development:

Fen conservation

- **Shrubs** and **trees** that are **encroaching** on the fens are **removed** to protect the diversity of **fen** wildlife.
- This can be done by **mowing**, although **grazing** is often a more efficient method. The Broads Authority keeps 25 **grazing ponies** — they feed mostly on rushes and grass, leaving the more **wildlife-friendly** species to grow. However, the fens tend to be **wet** and **unsheltered**, so the ponies can't be kept at most of the sites over the **winter**.
- In areas where scrub and woodland has **already invaded**, fen can be **restored** by cutting and clearing the large woody plants. However, there are **challenges** to this, e.g. large **machinery** can get **stuck** in the wet ground, damaging the fragile habitat. Some **specialist equipment** that can cope with the conditions has now been developed, but at some sites the **only option** is to get volunteers to cut the scrub **by hand**.

Commercial cutting

- **Reed** and **sedge** are **cut** in the fens to be **sold** to **thatchers**. This **maintains** the fens while providing an **income** for local people, making it a **cost-effective** form of wetland management.
- However, this industry has faced **challenges** — commercial cutting was at risk of **disappearing** in the Broads towards the end of the 20th century. Since 2002, the **Broads Authority** has tried to **reverse** the decline, e.g. by encouraging **young people** to learn the skill, and by offering **incentives** to land managers to cut reed and sedge.
- Commercial cutting is done **sustainably** — often only **small patches** of reed or sedge are cut, and sites are cut in **rotation** and allowed at least two years of **regrowth** before being cut again. This means there is always enough **tall vegetation** to support insects and birds.

Water quality improvement

- Several strategies are used to keep the **water** in the broads and rivers **clean**, so that they continue to support high levels of **biodiversity** and **attract tourists** to the area.
- **Preventing** eutrophication can be difficult, as the **catchment area** of the rivers that flow through the Broads is very large, and land use in any of this can affect **runoff**. However, the **Broadland WaterLIFE Water Sensitive Farming Project 2016-18** is a catchment-wide scheme aimed at reducing agricultural **pollution**, e.g. through a reduction in pesticide usage.
- **Eutrophication** can be reduced by removing **small fish** that **eat water fleas**. Water fleas feed on **algae**, so when extreme algal growth is triggered by an **excess of nutrients**, a large water flea population can help make waters **clearer**.
- There have been efforts to reduce water pollution in other ways, e.g. there's been publicity to encourage **environmentally friendly boating**, and **phosphorus** has been removed from treated **sewage**.

Practice Questions

Q1 How did the wetland ecosystem of the Broads form?

Q2 Give two impacts that humans have had on the Broads.

Q3 Describe one strategy that is used to maintain the fen habitat.

Exam Question

Q1 For a local-scale ecosystem you have studied, assess the challenges and opportunities involved in its sustainable development. [9 marks]

Reed through these pages for a broad understanding...

So there you have it — another jolly little case study to finish off this section. You've made it through an emotional roller coaster of a topic. Now, if you want to sustainably manage your revision, take a well-deserved break before moving on.

Globalisation

In the last few decades it's become a lot easier to communicate with people around the world, and a lot easier to move around. This is causing globalisation, and it affects pretty much everyone. Including you. Yes, you... with the hair...

Globalisation is the Process of Countries Becoming More Connected

1) Globalisation is the process of the world's **economies**, **political systems** and **cultures** becoming more strongly **connected** to each other.

2) If there was **no** globalisation, there wouldn't be any **interaction** between different countries. If there was **complete** globalisation, the whole world would act like **a single community**. The real world is somewhere **in between**, but countries are becoming more and more **closely integrated**.

3) Globalisation is caused by the **movement** of **information**, **capital**, **products**, **services** and **labour** between different countries. People have been **moving between countries** and **international trade** has been going on for ages, but most people think that globalisation as we know it today really started to **accelerate** in the **1980s**.

4) As the world becomes more globalised, countries are becoming more **interdependent** (see p.126) — this has led to global-scale attempts to **manage** a range of international issues (see p.137).

The world's getting smaller and smaller (or else this woman is massive).

There are Five Factors that Promote Globalisation

Flows of Information

1) **Information** (such as financial data or news of current events) can be spread across the world very quickly and easily.

2) The development and rapid spread of **e-mail**, the **internet** and **social media** mean that large amounts of information can be exchanged instantly across the globe. This allows people living in **different countries** to communicate and work together.

3) Increasing **flows of information** are making the world more **interconnected**, e.g. people can learn a lot about different **countries** and **cultures** without leaving their own country.

Flows of Capital

Capital is money that's **invested** — it's spent on something to produce an **income** or **increased profit** from it.

1) Historically, capital was mostly invested **within a country**, e.g. companies would expand by doing things like building new factories or setting up new branches within their country of origin.

2) Over time though, the amount of capital invested in **foreign countries** has increased — this is **foreign direct investment** (FDI). E.g. global FDI increased from about $400 billion in 1996 to nearly $1500 billion in 2016.

3) Improvements in **information and communications technology** (ICT) have encouraged flows of capital round the world — it can **instantly** be moved around the world via the internet.

4) Increasing **flows of capital** are making the world more **interconnected**, e.g. most countries' economies are now **dependent** on flows of investment to and from other countries.

Flows of Products

1) Historically, manufacturing industries were located in **more developed** countries. The products being produced were also **sold** in the country where they were **made**.

2) In recent decades, manufacturing has **decreased** in **more developed countries**, e.g. the number of people employed in manufacturing in the UK fell from more than 5 million in 1985 to around 2.6 million in 2014.

3) Lower labour costs overseas have caused many companies to **relocate** the production **side** of their business **abroad** — they then **import** the products to the countries where they're **sold**. E.g. vacuum manufacturer Dyson moved the production side of its business to Malaysia in 2002, but the vacuums are still sold in the UK.

4) As a result of these changes, **international trade** in manufactured goods is **increasing**, e.g. the UK imported £200 billion of manufactured goods in 1990, and £550 billion in 2008.

5) Changing **flows of products** are making the world more **interconnected**, e.g. many of the manufactured products bought in the UK have been produced in other countries and then imported.

Globalisation

Flows of Services

Services are economic activities that aren't based around producing any material goods, e.g. banking.

1) Improvements in ICT have allowed services to become global industries in recent decades. Things like banking and insurance depend on communication and transfer of information (see previous page). Improvements to ICT mean that services can locate anywhere in the world and still be able to serve the needs of customers anywhere else in the world.

2) During the 1970s and 1980s there was also deregulation (removal of rules to increase competition) and opening up of national financial markets to the rest of the world, e.g. in the USA and UK. This meant that it was made easier for banks and other financial institutions to do business in other countries.

3) Services can be split into low level (e.g. customer service) and high level (e.g. financial services). High-level services tend to be concentrated in cities in more developed countries (e.g. London and New York). Companies are increasingly relocating low-level services to less developed countries where labour is cheaper.

4) Increasing flows of services are making the world more interconnected, e.g. people are connected to other countries just through having a bank account — many banks are huge international organisations.

Flows of Labour

Flows of labour are movements of people who participate in the workforce from one country to another.

1) More people are moving overseas — international migration increased by over 40% between 2000 and 2015. Some people move because they have to (e.g. to escape conflict zones), but many people choose to move for work.

2) Some migrants are highly skilled workers (e.g. ICT and medical workers), moving to more developed countries where wages and working conditions are better. Others are unskilled workers who move to more developed countries to look for work because of unemployment or poor wages in their own countries.

3) Increasing flows of people between different countries are making the world more interconnected, e.g. people bring aspects of their culture with them, and countries are connected because people have family all over the world.

Marketing is Becoming More Global

1) Marketing is the process of promoting and selling products or services.

2) Nowadays, many products and services are sold all over the world, rather than just in the country where they are produced. This means that marketing has had to become global.

3) Global marketing involves treating the world as one single market (a fully globalised world, see previous page) and using one marketing strategy to advertise a product to customers all over the world.

4) Global marketing gives economies of scale — it is cheaper to have one marketing campaign for the whole world, rather than having a different campaign for every country.

5) Global marketing can create a global brand awareness — consumers around the world identify a name or logo with a particular product or service, so they will purchase that product rather than a lesser-known competitor.

6) Marketing needs to be adapted to regional markets though — different populations still have different laws and cultural attitudes, e.g. different countries have different laws and attitudes about consuming alcohol.

Practice Questions

Q1 What is globalisation?
Q2 Name three factors that have driven globalisation since the 1980s.
Q3 What is global marketing?

Exam Question

Q1 Outline how changes in patterns of production have promoted globalisation. [4 marks]

Around the world in (less than) eighty bullet points...

Yep, there's an almost unhealthy amount of jargon on these two pages. Learning it now will give you a boost for the rest of the section though, not to mention for the exam — so better get it memorised before you do anything else.

Factors Affecting Globalisation

What I'm about to say might seem strange to you if you're flying to Barbados or texting your friend in Australia, but believe it or not there was a point in time when globalisation didn't exist. In fact, globalisation has only taken off fairly recently. Here's why...

Globalisation is a Result of *New Systems*, *Technology* and *Relationships*

The **development** of new **systems**, **technology** and **relationships** in a range of sectors including finance, transport and management have been the driving force behind **globalisation**:

- **Systems** include ways of working, procedures and methods of organisation that allow a particular function to be carried out, e.g. the just-in-time manufacturing system is a way of making products in response to the demand for them. Since the 1940s, many **new systems** have been introduced to make it **easier** for flows of information, capital, products, services and labour to **cross national boundaries**.

- The **technology** used for information, communications and transport has advanced rapidly. For example, the Internet allows people from all over the world to **access information**, and aeroplanes allow **people** and **goods** to be **transported** around the world swiftly and efficiently.

- Before the Second World War, most **relationships** between countries involved one country losing and another gaining. Nowadays, relationships are based on **trade** and **common rules** — these allow **everyone** involved to gain.

Financial Systems Promote Globalisation

The **global financial system** governs the **flows of capital** between countries.

1) Financial systems are based on companies called **investment banks**. The main role of investment banks is to help companies raise **capital** by selling **shares** on behalf of those companies. People or groups who buy shares are called **investors**, and they receive a fraction of the **profits** that the company makes.

2) In the 1980s several things happened to make the financial system more **global**:

- **Information technology**, such as the Internet, allowed investors greater access to information. Investors and investment banks could easily find out whether a company was doing well or struggling, and make an informed decision about whether to invest.

- Investment banks created **new financial products** that made foreign investment **less risky**.

- **Governments** around the world undertook a process called **financial deregulation**, where they **relaxed rules** about what banks were allowed to do. Financial deregulation included allowing banks to charge people more for their services, as well as letting banks invest in a greater range of businesses.

- Financial deregulation also involved **removing barriers** to capital coming in and out of a country, making it easier for investment banks to buy and sell shares and other products across the world.

- These changes led to a greater range of companies getting involved in finance — e.g. **commercial banks** also began selling shares. It also enabled investment banks to take on a greater number of services, such as **exchanging currencies** between countries to allow them to trade across national borders.

3) Today, investors, banks and other companies all over the world are part of the **global financial system**. The decisions of banks or investors in one part of the world can affect a company on the other side of the world.

Trade Agreements Remove *Barriers to Trade*

The **global trade system** governs the **flows of products** between countries.

1) Trade is primarily regulated by countries' **governments**, who **control** which products they let into the country and at what price. Controls include **tariffs** (taxes on products coming into the country), **non-tariff barriers** (e.g. rules on the quality of products coming into the country) and the **banning** of certain products (e.g. illegal drugs).

2) Controls make it **more expensive** for companies to sell their products abroad, as well as for **consumers** to buy them.

3) To make it **cheaper**, countries can enter into a **trade agreement**. Trade agreements act like contracts — one country agrees to remove controls in exchange for the other country doing so. This **benefits both** countries' companies and consumers. Trade agreements between two countries are called **bilateral trade agreements**.

4) **Multilateral trade agreements** are trade agreements between several countries — all of the countries involved agree to remove tariffs and other controls. Multilateral and bilateral agreements together make up the global trade system.

5) The global trade system is governed by the World Trade Organisation (WTO, see p.129). Established in 1995, the WTO sets **rules** on how countries can trade with each other, e.g. to stop countries imposing unfair tariffs on each other's companies. It also acts as a **forum** for countries to **negotiate** trade deals with each other and settle **trade disputes**.

Factors Affecting Globalisation

Transport and Communications Systems Have Improved Global Business

1) Improved **transportation** systems (e.g. high-speed rail networks, larger and faster ships and faster planes) have allowed people and products to get to places around the world more easily than ever before.

2) Uniform metal **containers** (known as shipping containers) were introduced in the 1950s — this allowed more goods to be loaded onto ships at once and transferred straight onto other forms of transport, e.g. trains. This has made it easier for goods to be moved **quickly** and **cheaply** around the world.

3) Communications **satellites** were first launched into Earth's orbit in the 1960s. They allow relatively **cheap** wireless communication between two devices, regardless of where they are. This means even people and companies based in **rural** or **remote** areas can access the Internet and communicate with others.

4) **Optic fibre cables** use signals of light to transmit more information than any other cable. They allow **fast** communication between two devices, allowing almost-instant communication between two people or companies.

5) Over the past twenty years there has been a significant growth in **software** that allows **free communication** from anywhere in the world, e.g. email hosts, text messaging services and video messaging services.

Management and Information Systems Have Increased Companies' Efficiency

New ways of working have made companies more **efficient** — they can make the same products more cheaply.

1) Companies' **supply chains** have become **global** — a company's supplier may be in a different country to their factory, which is in a different country to their research and development department (see p.134). This allows companies to **minimise costs**.

2) Large companies can benefit from **economies of scale**. The average cost to a firm of making an item is usually **high** if they don't make very many of them. **Large** companies can **reduce** the average cost of making each item by purchasing **specialised equipment** and **using production lines**. They may also be able to buy raw materials at a **lower price** as they are able to buy in bulk. This gives large companies an **advantage** over smaller companies.

3) **Outsourcing** is when a company pays another company to do work that in the past may have been done in-house, usually to **save costs**. E.g. rather than developing its own call centre, a company might pay another company to take on these services. **Cheap labour** costs mean many companies choose to outsource abroad.

4) Companies' **working practices** have also changed. E.g. **casual** and **temporary** contracts allow companies to take on workers as and when they are required — they don't have to pay them a fixed yearly wage, so they save money.

Countries Work Together to Prevent Security Threats

1) Globalisation creates new trading relationships between countries (see previous page). By forming trade agreements, countries become **interdependent** (see next page) — if two countries need each other to buy and sell their products, it would not be in their interests to be at war with one another. This means **trade** makes **war less likely**.

2) By **working together**, countries are able to improve security. E.g. the North Atlantic Treaty Organisation (NATO) was founded by several countries in 1949, with the aim of providing security during the Cold War — by grouping together, they were able to **deter** common threats.

3) However, globalisation can also make a conflict more likely. E.g. developed countries have **intervened** in conflicts in developing countries to secure **resources** like oil.

Practice Questions

Q1 List three factors that have led to increased financial globalisation.

Q2 Which organisation is responsible for governing the global trade system?

Q3 Give one example of how management systems have changed as a result of globalisation.

Exam Question

Q1 Explain how changes in technology have contributed to globalisation. [4 marks]

I rode my bike into a non-tariff barrier just last week...

Globalisation might crop up in quite a few of the questions in the exam, so make sure you have a good grasp of what causes and contributes to it. If you master it now, the number of marks you'll get could truly be out of this world...

Global Systems

All that movement of people, money, ideas and technology just willy-nilly is bound to have consequences. What are those consequences, you ask? Well, I'm afraid that (inter)depends on the countries involved, so you'll just have to read these pages.

Globalisation Causes Interdependence

1) Globalisation makes countries and people **interdependent** — they **rely on each other**:

- **Economic** — countries rely on each other for **economic growth**. E.g. oil is produced by one group of countries and consumed by another group of countries. Consumers rely on producers to sell them oil, while producers rely on the money the consumers give them when they buy the oil.

- **Political** — countries are dependent on each other to **solve issues** that cannot be addressed by just one country — e.g. in the 2015-16 European migrant crisis, the countries of Europe had to **work together** to support refugees from the conflict in Syria.

Interdependent or not, Carol was still going to sell the other two out at the next available opportunity.

- **Social** — greater connections between people living in different countries creates **social interdependence** between the countries. E.g. in 2015 there were 244 million migrants worldwide — migrants build new relationships and become interdependent with people from other countries.

- **Environmental** — every country in the world is dependent on the rest of the world to look after the **environment**. E.g. in 1986 a reactor at the Chernobyl nuclear plant in Ukraine exploded. Radiation from the explosion led to an increase in some **cancers** and **birth defects** in the Ukraine, Russia and Belarus, and possibly further afield.

2) Interdependence creates **inequality**, both **between countries** and **between people** within the **same country** — it tends to bring more benefits (e.g. increased **wealth** and more **power**) to developed countries rather than less developed countries, and to richer people rather than poorer people. This is because the **flows** of **people**, **money**, **ideas** and **technology** are **unequal**.

Unequal Flows of People Create Benefits and Inequalities

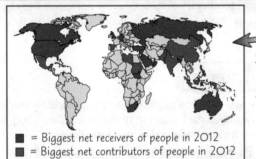

= Biggest net receivers of people in 2012
= Biggest net contributors of people in 2012

1) People tend to move from countries where there are **few jobs** (normally less developed countries) to countries with **plenty** (normally developed countries).

2) People also leave countries to **escape** war, famine or persecution. These **refugees** often try to get to the nearest safe country.

3) The people who move for economic reasons are not usually the poorest in society — money is needed to pay for a **visa**, **transport** and **living expenses** in the destination country. Countries may also only allow people with certain **skills** to enter the country, so migrants are often reasonably **well educated**.

4) It is **easier** for people from developed countries to migrate than people from less developed countries — in 2017, UK citizens could travel to 173 countries without a **visa**, while for citizens of Afghanistan it was only 24.

A visa is an agreement that allows someone to enter and stay in a country.

5) Flows of people bring **benefits** — e.g. immigrants can create **economic growth**, as they do jobs that a country's citizens **can't** do (e.g. skilled jobs like engineering) or **don't want to** do (e.g. dangerous jobs like logging or mining).

6) Many migrants **send money back** to their families or home communities — this is called a **remittance**. Remittance payments can significantly increase the amount of **capital** flowing into **less developed** countries. This can create **economic growth** in the home country because local people can afford to spend more, boosting local industries.

7) However, unequal flows of people can also create **problems**:

- **Inequalities** — Less developed countries suffer from 'brain drain' — skilled people leave and take their knowledge with them. This **reinforces** existing inequalities between countries.

- **Conflict** — Low-skilled migrants are often happier to work for **less money** than low-skilled locals. By employing them, companies may **depress wages** for the local population. This can cause conflict between the local and migrant populations.

- **Injustice** — Migrant workers are sometimes made to work in **dangerous** conditions for **little money**. E.g. in Qatar, several thousand migrants have died building facilities for the 2022 FIFA® World Cup.

Global Systems

Unequal Flows of *Money* Can Cause *Inequalities*

1) Flows of money can include **remittances** (see previous page), **foreign aid** (money given to a less developed country to increase development or help in a crisis), **foreign direct investment** (FDI, see p.129), and income from **trade**.

2) Flows of money are **unequal** — money often flows **from** developed countries **to** less developed countries. E.g. governments and companies from developed countries may **invest** in infrastructure or the extraction of minerals in less developed countries. Less developed countries rarely have the **capital** required to invest in other countries.

3) Flows of money can bring **benefits** to countries — e.g. FDI allows foreign companies and countries to take advantage of cheap **raw materials** and **low labour costs**, while the host country can benefit from foreign **capital** and **expertise**. Foreign aid can be used to improve **living standards** or to rebuild local **infrastructure** after a disaster.

4) However, unequal flows of capital can have **negative impacts**:

- **Inequalities** — Foreign aid can create **dependency**, which gives governments little incentive to improve their own countries. FDI can **force out** local businesses, because foreign companies with superior capital and technology can make products more efficiently.

- **Conflict** — Foreign aid can find its way to **armed groups** and help to fund conflict. FDI can cause conflict between foreign companies and **local people** — e.g. FDI in agriculture can lead to peasant farmers being evicted to create larger plantations.

- **Injustice** — Companies may pressure governments of less developed countries to pass laws that make it **cheaper** to invest there — e.g. by cutting environmental regulation or weakening laws on working conditions.

Ideas About How the World Works are Dominated by *Developed Countries*

1) Before the 1980s, most **national** governments took responsibility for providing **welfare** for their citizens and **controlling imports** through trade barriers (see p.124) to protect their national industries.

2) However, in the 1980s many developed countries began to think that the **economy** would work better **without** state intervention — maximum economic growth would only occur if **barriers** to trade were **removed**, state-owned companies were **privatised** and government spending was **cut**. This is known as **neo-liberalism**.

3) Neo-liberal ideas have increased **free trade**, which has led to **more development** within countries and **less conflict** between some countries. However, other people argue that it has **increased inequalities**, **conflict** and **injustices**:

- **Inequalities** — Neo-liberalism started in **developed countries** and has spread **globally**. It tends to **concentrate wealth** in the hands of a few, e.g. large, wealthy businesses based in developed countries.

- **Conflict** — If private companies and free trade in a less developed country are **threatened** by the decisions of that country's **government**, developed countries may believe that their **intervention** is justified. This could lead to **conflict**.

- **Injustice** — Governments and transnational corporations (TNCs) may argue that free trade and privatisation are the best way to help a country **develop**, and that this **justifies** poor working conditions and environmental degradation in the less developed country.

Most *Technology* is Owned by *Developed Countries*

1) Globalisation has led to unequal flows of **technology** — it mainly flows from developed to less developed countries.

2) Concentration of technology in particular places can lead to rapid **innovation** that can help people all over the world — e.g. technology companies in Silicon Valley, US have developed innovations in communications and healthcare.

3) However, the unequal flows tend to increase **inequalities** and can lead to **conflict** and **injustice**:

- **Inequalities** — Developed countries can **afford** the latest technology, whereas less developed countries can't. Countries that have the latest technology can make products more **cheaply** and have better access to **information** and **services**, due to better **communications** infrastructure — for example, in 2016, 97% of the Netherlands' citizens had access to the Internet, compared to around 20% in Myanmar. This gives developed countries an **advantage** over less developed countries.

- **Conflict and injustice** — **Repressive governments** of less developed countries have used **weapons technology** sold to them by developed countries to stop protests from their own people.

Topic Seven — Global Systems and Global Governance

Global Systems

Globalisation *Makes Some Countries More* **Powerful** *Than Others*

1) The unequal flows of people, money, ideas and technology have created **unequal power relations** between countries, with some countries having much **more power** than others.

2) **Developed** or **emerging** countries with a lot of money and technology are able to drive global systems to their own advantage. These countries have a lot of **control** over the global **economy** and **political events**.

3) Many **less developed** countries lack money and technology. These countries have **limited power** — rather than controlling the global economy and political events, they are only able to **respond** to events.

> ### Example: power relations and climate change
>
> - Many of the **biggest contributors** to climate change are also the **richest countries**. These countries can be **reluctant** to agree to proposals to **limit climate change** as they think they may harm their economy (e.g. through loss of jobs in the fossil fuel industry and higher energy prices).
>
> - In contrast, some of the countries that are **most affected** by climate change are also the **poorest**. For example, countries like Bangladesh and Tuvalu are likely to be impacted by **rising sea levels** but find it **difficult** to influence other countries to reduce greenhouse gas emissions because they lack power.

Global Institutions *Can* **Reinforce** *Unequal Power Relations*

1) The **International Monetary Fund** (IMF) and the **World Bank** govern the **global financial system** (see p.124):

   - The IMF **monitors** the global economy and **advises** governments on how they could improve their economic situation. It also gives **loans** to countries with economic problems.

   - The World Bank provides **loans** to less developed countries to invest in areas like health, education and infrastructure. The money for the loans comes partly from **subscriptions** from its member countries — **all** members pay in, but **only** those who **need** it can take money out. This means funds are redistributed from developed countries to less developed countries. However, less developed countries are expected to **pay back** the loans.

2) Some people think that **global financial institutions**, such as the IMF and the World Bank, are **reinforcing** unequal power relations between different countries:

   - The IMF and the World Bank are both based in the **USA** and are led by the USA and other **developed countries**. Less developed countries (who are most likely to require a loan) therefore have **less influence** over the decisions of the organisations.

   - The IMF and World Bank's loans are **conditional** — the less developed country has to make **changes** (such as **cutting regulation** to make foreign trade and investment easier) in order to receive the loan.

   - The **World Trade Organisation** (WTO, see p.129) generally works to **reduce trade barriers** between countries — however, many developed countries have **kept** trade barriers in place, **reducing imports** from less developed countries. This tends to **boost** the economies of developed countries at the expense of less developed countries.

Developed countries and companies can profit from these conditions, but they can prevent less developed countries from building their own industries.

Elsie was pretty sure the bow did nothing for her unequal power relations.

Practice Questions

Q1 What is interdependence?

Q2 Give two examples of how unequal flows of technology create inequality.

Q3 Briefly describe how one global institution can increase unequal power relations between countries.

Exam Question

Q1 Explain how unequal flows of people can lead to inequalities. [4 marks]

You can't just sit and let the knowledge flow into your brain — get revising...

Make sure you give an example or two in the exam — just saying "technology is bad" ain't gonna cut it, I'm afraid. Also, remember that unequal flows affect countries differently. Now, grab your fishing net and let's find these money flows...

International Trade

Trade is great. I give you an apple, you give me a bag of crisps. We then eat our snack, or trade it with someone else — tasty. What's that? That's not quite how international trade works? Well in that case I'm keeping this apple — you can get your own.

International Trade and Investment have Changed Dramatically

Globalisation affects the **volume** and **pattern** of international **trade** and **investment**:

The global financial crisis in 2008 temporarily reduced the volume of international trade.

Trade

1) International trade is the **import** and **export** of goods and services between countries.

2) The **volume** of global trade has increased dramatically since the 1980s — its value increased by nearly **eight times** between 1980 and 2008.

3) The **pattern** of global trade is also changing. Developed countries remain the biggest global traders, but some **emerging economies** are **catching up** — China is now the **largest exporter** of goods in the world, largely due to the rapid growth of its **manufacturing** sector.

4) **Less developed countries** are also becoming bigger traders, but growth is **slow** — in 1995, African countries accounted for around 2% of world trade, whereas in 2010 they accounted for just over 3%. The poorest 49 countries make up 10% of the world's population, but still only account for 0.4% of world trade.

5) More countries are opening themselves up to international trade by **removing** barriers to trade (see p.124). This is partly due to the formation of **trade blocs** (see next page).

6) There has also been a rise in **fair trade** — this is a way of trading that **supports** people in **less developed countries** who make products that are exported to developed countries. Since the 1970s, nearly a thousand fair trade **producer groups** have been set up in less developed countries. These groups trade with developed countries, who sell their products in shops and supermarkets.

Investment

1) **Foreign direct investment** (FDI) is when a person, company or other group spends money in another country in order to generate a profit, e.g. by opening a new branch of their business or investing in local infrastructure.

2) Foreign investors may be attracted by the **size** of the market (how many people they can sell to), the **stability** of the market (e.g. not in a war zone), the possibility of extracting **resources** for themselves (e.g. from mines in Africa) or the ability to access **financial services**, as in countries like Luxembourg with large banking sectors.

3) The **volume** of FDI has **risen** dramatically from about $400 billion in 1996 to nearly $1500 billion in 2016.

4) The **pattern** of investment has also changed. Until the 1980s, developed countries mainly invested in **other developed countries**. Since the 1980s, developed countries have begun investing more in **emerging economies** and **developing countries**. In the past ten years, China, India, Brazil and Mexico were some of the largest receivers of foreign investment.

5) Another big change has been where the investment has come from. **Emerging economies** now invest heavily in less developed countries, e.g. **China** invests a lot of money in countries in Africa and South America.

6) **Ethical investment** is when a person, company or group only invests in areas that are considered **socially responsible** — e.g. companies that cause **environmental** or **humanitarian** harm are generally avoided by ethical investors. Ethical investment has **grown** since the 1990s — the amount of ethical investment by US companies almost tripled between 2005 and 2016.

Global Trade Rules are Set by the World Trade Organisation

1) Some countries limit trade using **tariffs** and **non-tariff barriers** (see p.124) to shield their industries from foreign competition — this is called **protectionism**. **Free trade** is the policy of removing these barriers.

2) The **World Trade Organisation** (WTO) was set up to increase **trade** and help resolve **trade disputes** between member countries. It sets **rules** about how countries should trade with each other:

- Countries **can't** give another country **special access** to their market without doing the same for every other country in the world. However, there are some **exceptions**, e.g. countries can give special access to members of their trade bloc (see next page).

- Countries should promote **free trade**, e.g. by **removing** as many **barriers to trade** as possible.

- Countries should act **predictably** in their trading, e.g. by not raising tariffs on particular products once a deal has been reached.

- There should be **fair competition** — one company or country shouldn't get an **unfair advantage** over rivals.

International Trade

Trading Blocs are Agreements Between Governments About Trade

1) **Trading blocs** are associations between different governments that promote and manage trade. Trade blocs remove trade barriers between their members, while keeping common barriers to countries who aren't part of the bloc.

2) Many trading blocs are **regional**. They make it easier for countries to trade with their **neighbours**. E.g. in 2016, German exports to other EU countries were €708 billion, compared to €501 billion to countries outside the EU.

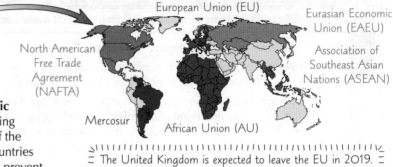

North American Free Trade Agreement (NAFTA)

European Union (EU)

Eurasian Economic Union (EAEU)

Association of Southeast Asian Nations (ASEAN)

3) Other trading blocs are based around **specific industries**. E.g. some of the main oil-exporting countries (e.g. Saudi Arabia) are members of the Organisation of the Petroleum Exporting Countries (OPEC), which aims to **standardise prices** to prevent countries undercutting one another with cheaper prices.

Mercosur

African Union (AU)

The United Kingdom is expected to leave the EU in 2019. Venezuela was suspended from Mercosur in 2016.

4) **Special Economic Zones (SEZs)** increase the volume of trade with emerging economies and less developed countries.

SEZs are areas that have **different** trade and investment rules to the rest of a country, e.g. companies investing there may pay **lower taxes** on land and goods. SEZs **increase** trade while keeping **barriers** in the rest of the country.

Trading Relationships Change Depending on the Countries Involved

Developed countries

Most trade in the world takes place **between developed countries** — in 2013, imports and exports between the United States (US) and European Union (EU) accounted for over 30% of the global products trade. Most of these products, e.g. machinery or chemicals, require a lot of **money** and **expertise** to make.

Less developed countries mostly trade with developed countries — the EU is the largest trading partner of many countries in sub-Saharan Africa.

China has become the EU's second largest trading partner after the US, and the EU imports more goods from China than from anywhere else in the world.

Machinery, medicine

Food, tobacco, crude oil

Machinery, clothes

Cars, chemicals

Examples of the most common imports and exports.

Less developed countries

Most **less developed countries** trade mainly with **emerging economies** and **developed countries**. E.g. Bangladesh mainly exports to the US and EU and imports from China and India, rather than from less developed countries.

Crude oil, minerals

Manufactured goods

Trade between emerging and less developed countries is increasing — China's manufacturing sector relies on lots of energy, so it needs oil, e.g. from Angola.

Emerging economies

Emerging economies like China and India are increasingly important to global trade. China's **manufacturing** sector has grown rapidly, and a highly educated population has grown India's **service** sector.

Developed Countries Have Greater Access to Markets Than Other Countries

1) **Access to markets** is about how easy it is for countries and companies to **trade** with one another. International access to markets is determined by the extent of **export** and **import** barriers between two countries.

2) Access is affected by **wealth**. Developed countries often put **higher tariffs** on goods imported from **less developed** countries — this makes it **harder** for less developed countries to access the market. Developed countries also have more money to **invest**, so they can **avoid high tariffs** imposed by developing countries by opening factories within them. Less developed countries may also rely on **loans** that depend on them **removing trade barriers** and increasing access to their markets.

3) Access is also increased by being a member of a **trading bloc** — member countries have access to the markets of **all** the other **member countries**. Trade blocs of **developed** countries have access to lots of **wealthy buyers**. However, **less developed** countries **outside** the trade bloc may have to pay **high tariffs** to export their goods to those markets. This puts less developed countries at a **disadvantage**.

Topic Seven — Global Systems and Global Governance

International Trade

SDT Agreements Give Less Developed Countries Greater Market Access

1) The WTO forms **special and differential treatment** (**SDT**) agreements — these let the **least developed countries** bypass developed countries' tariffs, which gives them greater **market access**. E.g. the EU's 2001 Everything But Arms (EBA) Agreement allows the least developed countries to export some of their products to the EU without paying tariffs.

2) The profits made from SDT agreements allow less developed countries to **diversify** the range of industries they have, e.g. by introducing manufacturing or tourism sectors.

3) However, some argue that SDT agreements have a **negative impact** on developed countries by allowing **cheap imports** into the country. They suggest that regional **trade blocs** (see previous page), which allow less developed countries to **negotiate** prices **collectively**, are more effective at improving their market access.

Differential Access to Markets has Economic and Social Consequences

Economic Impacts

1) It's **hard** for countries with **poor market access** to establish **new industries** — they face **high tariffs** when they try to sell abroad, making their products **uncompetitive**, and they may be **undercut** in their domestic markets by TNCs producing similar products more **cheaply**.

2) This makes them dependent on selling **low-value primary products** (e.g. agricultural goods) that tend to **fluctuate** in price, so countries with poor market access often have low **Gross National Income** (GNI). This means that they have less money to **invest** in industry, so their economic development is **slow**.

3) Countries with **high** levels of market access tend to see **more economic growth** because they can **trade** more. This means that their citizens are **wealthier**, they can afford to import a range of products and they can develop **high-tech industries** which boost their economy further.

Social Impacts

1) People in countries with **better market access** tend to have higher-paid jobs. This gives them more **disposable income**, which increases their standard of living.

2) Countries with less market access have less money available for **education** and **healthcare** etc., so **quality of life** is generally lower. Better access to **education** in developed countries has created better access to **jobs** for **women** and **ethnic minorities**, giving them more power to shape their own lives and societies.

3) Much dangerous, poorly paid work has **moved** from developed countries to less developed countries. E.g. **sweatshops** are crowded, dangerous factories, whose workers are paid little and work long hours. Some sweatshops employ **children**, which is illegal in developed countries.

Trade and Market Access Affect People's Lives Around the World

You need to think about how **trade** and **market access** affects your life, and the lives of people elsewhere. For example:

- Trade benefits developed countries **more** than developing countries — e.g. many developing countries export mostly **primary** products (e.g. copper ore), which are **processed** in developed countries (e.g. into electronic components) and exported at a **higher price**. The developed country makes more **profit** than the developing country, so **wages** are higher.

- Trade and **high levels** of market access also mean that a **wide range** of goods are available in developed countries. This further increases people's **standard of living**.

- Trade also creates more **interdependence** between countries — if something goes **wrong**, other countries are affected. E.g. the financial crisis in 2008 increased rates of **unemployment** in many countries.

Practice Questions

Q1 Briefly describe how global trade has changed since the 1980s.

Q2 Give two ways that trade blocs affect countries' access to markets.

Q3 Give two economic consequences of differential access to markets.

Exam Question

Q1 The table shows export statistics for a range of countries. To what extent does the data reflect general patterns of international trade? [6 marks]

Country	Main export	Main destination
Afghanistan	Vegetable products	Pakistan
Australia	Mineral products	China
China	Machines	USA
India	Refined petroleum	USA
Germany	Machines	USA
Malawi	Tobacco and foodstuffs	Belgium-Luxembourg
USA	Machines	Canada

FYI, SEZs increase FDI, while SDT is managed by the WTO — OK...

Yep, all those acronyms can be a little confusing. Here's an idea — write down a list of acronyms from this section, close the book and see if you can remember what each of them stands for. You'll get to know your TNCs from your IMFs in no time.

The Global Coffee Trade

A good example of international trade in action is coffee. That's right — the stuff that's getting you through this revision session is also an important global product. It doesn't always give great returns for farmers though, which is where Fairtrade comes in.

Coffee is Grown in Warm Countries Around the Equator

1) Coffee grows in **hot**, **wet** areas close to the **equator**. As a result, coffee production is dominated by countries in South America, the Caribbean, Asia and Africa. The biggest coffee producers are Brazil, Vietnam, Colombia, Indonesia and Ethiopia.

2) There are two main types of **coffee bean** — **arabica** and **robusta**. Arabica is normally **higher quality** but **more expensive** to produce than robusta. Arabica is mainly grown in **South America** and **eastern Africa**, while robusta is mainly grown in **western Africa** and **Asia**, though many countries grow both. Around 70% of world coffee production is arabica.

3) Coffee plants are grown in **nurseries**, and after 6 to 12 months they are moved to **farms** where they produce the **beans** that are used to make coffee. Most coffee is grown on **smallholdings** rather than large plantations.

Issues in coffee production

- Coffee plants can be susceptible to a range of diseases, e.g. bacterial blight and coffee leaf rust, both of which harm the leaves and prevent growth. Coffee Berry Disease causes dark spots to appear on the coffee beans and destroys them within days.

- Coffee farmers also have to look out for insects and other pests. E.g. the Black Twig Borer is an insect native to Asia that tunnels into the branches of coffee plants, destroying the plant.

- Certain weather conditions make outbreaks of disease and pests more likely. Diseases like bacterial blight can be easily spread in very wet weather, while droughts make cicada or other pest infestations more likely.

- Farmers use fertilisers and pesticides, but these are often imported into the country, so can be expensive.

Coffee is Traded Globally

1) Coffee, like many low-value foods and products, is mainly **produced** by **less developed countries** and **consumed** by **developed countries**.

2) **Brazil** is the **largest coffee producer** in the world — in 2015 it exported around **20%** of the world's coffee. It has around 300 000 coffee farms and produces around 2.5 million tonnes per year.

3) The **USA** is the **largest importer** of coffee in the world — in 2015 it imported around **20%** of the world's coffee. **European countries**, **Japan**, **Canada** and **Russia** also import a lot of coffee.

■ = Largest coffee producers
■ = Largest coffee importers

4) The **price** of coffee **fluctuates** depending on the **supply** and the **demand**. Supply is how much coffee is **produced**, while demand is how much coffee consumers want to **buy**:

- If demand for coffee increases and the supply remains the same, then the global coffee price will increase — more people are competing to buy a limited quantity, so they have to pay more for it.
- If supply increases and the demand remains the same, then the global coffee price will decrease — there is more coffee than people need, so people don't need to pay as much for it.
- A low price is good for coffee consumers, while a high price is good for coffee producers.

5) If the **price** is **high**, then people will **produce** more coffee because they are attracted by the idea of making more money — this causes the price to **fall**. If the **price** is **low** then people may **buy more** coffee — this may cause the price to rise.

6) Price **fluctuations** can **affect** coffee farmers. E.g. the amount of coffee exported from Vietnam has increased steadily since 1987. By 1999 Vietnam was exporting over 450 million kg of coffee a year, which caused the price to **fall** dramatically, from $1.19 per kg in January 2000 to $0.68 per kg by March 2001. Many South American coffee growers went **out of business** as they couldn't afford to keep producing it at such a low price.

The Global Coffee Trade

The **Coffee Trade** is Dominated by **TNCs**

1) Only **around 7-10%** of the price of coffee bought in a supermarket goes to coffee farmers, because coffee farmers only sell the unprocessed **bean**, which is of **low value**. **Transnational Corporations** (**TNCs**, see p.134) buy the beans and roast them, increasing their value — they receive the **majority** of the **profits** by selling the processed coffee to consumers.

2) While **coffee farmers** are based in **less developed countries**, the **TNCs** are mainly from **developed countries** — the **profits** go to developed countries rather than being **reinvested** in less developed countries.

Louise's morning coffee only fuelled her obsession for total global domination... of the world's coffee markets.

3) Most coffee producers are **small-scale** farmers with little land who depend on selling coffee, so they have **little power** to dictate prices. In contrast, TNCs have a **lot of control** over the global coffee market — just four companies (ECOM, Louis Dreyfus, Neumann and VOLCAFE) control around **40%** of global coffee exports.

4) TNCs can **pick and choose** where they buy their coffee from, e.g. from the countries or farmers selling their coffee beans at the lowest price. Coffee-producing countries compete with each other to **cut wages**, **labour regulations** and **environmental protection** in order to attract TNCs — this is known as a '**race to the bottom**'. It can cause coffee farmers to go out of business or cause long-term damage to farmland. E.g. much of the coffee in Brazil and Vietnam is farmed intensively as a monoculture (single species), leading to loss of wildlife habitats and biodiversity.

The **Fairtrade Coffee** Campaign **Helps Farmers**

1) In 1992, the **Fairtrade Foundation** was set up to promote brands that support coffee farmers.

> - Fairtrade works with **producer organisations** — groups that are **controlled** by coffee farmers themselves.
> - Fairtrade's aims include setting the **Fairtrade Minimum Price**, which is the minimum price that a coffee buyer has to pay the producer organisation to cover all of the farmer's **costs**. This aims to prevent coffee farmers from going out of business or falling into poverty.
> - Fairtrade works with farmers to maintain **environmental standards** and to **prohibit forced labour** and **child labour**.

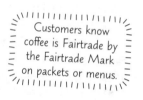

Customers know coffee is Fairtrade by the Fairtrade Mark on packets or menus.

2) The Fairtrade coffee campaign has seen a lot of **growth** since it was founded. The number of Fairtrade producer organisations grew from 175 in 2002 to 329 in 2011. In that time, **global sales** of Fairtrade coffee grew from around 15 000 tonnes to over 80 000 tonnes per year.

3) Fairtrade also pays additional money into a **communal fund** for local communities to help them **develop** — this is called the **Fairtrade Premium**. With this extra money and more economic security, farming communities in less developed countries like Peru have been able to **invest** in computers, farm machinery and schools.

4) The Fairtrade approach is viewed as more **ethical** than traditional trade, particularly in the treatment of coffee producers.

Practice Questions

Q1 Name two of the largest coffee exporting countries.

Q2 What does 'race to the bottom' mean in relation to coffee production?

Q3 Give two ways that the Fairtrade Foundation supports coffee farmers.

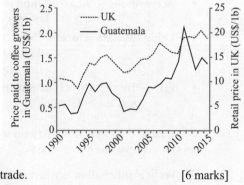

Exam Question

Q1 Using the map on the previous page and the graph on the right, analyse the global coffee trade in relation to the patterns and processes of international trade. [6 marks]

Filter these facts through your brain, and you'll know them in an instant...

Well, there's a case study to raise your mug of arabica to. Coffee's a good example of global trade in action, so remember all the minute details — specific facts and figures show that you know what you're talking about, so be a keen bean and take the time to learn them all. To cappuccino it all off, make sure you know the impact Fairtrade has on the coffee trade.

Transnational Corporations (TNCs)

Oh TNC, oh TNC, you really are enormous! You invest in all the foreign lands. You bring us all our favourite brands.
Oh TNC, oh TNC, you really are enormous! *Cough* don't mind me, just getting in some singing practice...

TNCs are *Companies* that Operate in *Two or More Countries*

1) Transnational Corporations (TNCs) are companies that **produce**, **sell** or are **located** in **two or more** countries, e.g. Sony® manufacture **electronic products** in **China** and **Japan**, and **sell** many of them in **Europe** and the **USA**.

2) They play an **important role** in the **global economy** — in 2013, **80%** of **global trade** was linked to TNCs.

3) TNCs operate in **all types** of industry:

- **Primary industry** (extracting natural resources), e.g. Shell extracts and trades oil and gas.
- **Secondary industry** (making material goods), e.g. Toyota™ manufactures vehicles.
- **Tertiary industry** (providing services), e.g. Aviva™ provides insurance services.

4) TNCs bring lots of **investment** into countries, spread **new technologies** and can promote particular **cultures**, e.g. McDonald's brings Western-style fast food to other countries.

5) **Potential investment**, the **creation of jobs** and provision of **new technology** means TNCs can have **political influence**.

6) They're one of the **main driving forces** behind globalisation because of the economic, political and cultural **interactions** that occur **between** the countries where they operate.

7) TNCs also **connect** countries together because of their **spatial organisation** — they create a **global supply chain** because the different parts of their businesses (from manufacture to retail) are located in different countries:

- TNCs' **headquarters** are usually located in **big cities** in more developed countries (e.g. New York). These cities are well connected in terms of global **transport** and **communications**, and there is a supply of **highly skilled workers**.
- **Research and development** (R&D) facilities tend to be located in cities and towns where there's a supply of **highly educated** people, e.g. scientists and engineers. They are often in the **same country** as the headquarters.
- Some TNCs locate **regional R&D** facilities closer to the markets they are selling to, so they can make products that are specifically **for that market**. E.g. South Korean TNC Samsung has an R&D centre in Warsaw, Poland.
- **Factories** are often located in less developed countries where **production costs** (e.g. labour, materials, land etc.) **are lower**, e.g. Nestlé® have a factory in Bangladesh. Many TNCs also have **factories** in the country where **their market** is, e.g. Nissan™ have a factory in the UK. If a product is made in the country where it is **sold**, the TNC can avoid paying **import** and **export taxes** and can **reduce transport costs** (especially on large items, e.g. cars).

TNCs Form *Linkages* Between *Countries* Through *Investment*

1) TNCs make **links** between countries and companies by expanding their operations:

- Mergers — a merger is when **two companies** (usually of similar size) agree to become **one bigger company**, e.g. the two oil and gas companies BP and Amoco **merged** in 1998. This helps links form between the countries where the two companies operate.
- Acquisitions — an **acquisition** is when one company **buys another** (usually smaller) company, e.g. the US car company Ford bought the Swedish company Volvo Cars in 1999.
- Using subcontractors — TNCs can use **foreign companies** to manufacture products **without** actually **owning** the businesses, e.g. NIKE products aren't always made in factories NIKE own. This links the countries of the TNC and the subcontracted company together.
- FDI — **Foreign Direct Investment** can involve mergers, acquisitions and using subcontractors, e.g. if HSBC acquire a bank in Indonesia, they're investing money there (that's FDI).

See p.129 for more on FDI.

2) TNCs expand their operations to gain more **control** over their **markets**. They can achieve this in two ways:

- **Vertical integration** is when a company **takes over** other parts of its **supply chain**. For example, through mergers, acquisitions and FDI, Shell now owns every part of its supply chain, from extracting and refining oil through to selling it to consumers at petrol stations.
- **Horizontal integration** is when a company **merges with** or **takes over** another company at the same stage of production (e.g. a retail chain might take over another retail chain). For example, in 2006 Disney took over PIXAR Studios — both were film production companies making family-orientated animations.

Transnational Corporations (TNCs)

TNCs *Organise Production* to Take Advantage of a *Global Supply Chain*

1) TNCs create a **global supply chain** (see previous page). This gives them **economies of scale** and means they get the most **value** from the whole of their supply chain (see p.125).

2) TNCs in **primary industry** often invest in countries with **natural resources** that they can extract. E.g. in 2016 Shell acquired fellow oil company BG Group to gain access to oil reserves in Brazil and Australia.

3) TNCs in **secondary industry** often invest in countries with **low labour costs** and **cheap land**, especially where governments encourage investment with **tax breaks**, e.g. Toyota™ invests in Indonesia due to low labour costs and tax breaks on low-emission cars. TNCs also invest where there is a large market for their products, like Nissan™ in the UK.

4) TNCs in **tertiary industry** often invest in countries with a **well-educated population**. E.g. insurance firm Aviva™ has invested in France, Canada and India.

5) TNCs also often invest in countries with **weak labour and environmental regulations**. Weak regulations allow TNCs to **cut costs**, e.g. by making employees work for long hours for low pay, or by disposing of waste cheaply.

TNCs Have a Big Impact on *Global Trade*

1) **Intra-firm trading** is when one division of a TNC trades with another part of the TNC. For example:

   - Technology firm Intel® assembles some of its microchips in **Costa Rica**, but sells them in the **USA**. To get products from Costa Rica to the USA, Intel's Costa Rican subsidiary **'sells'** them to Intel® in the USA.

   - Intra-firm trading is counted in **trade figures** — it is believed to make up between 30% and 50% of international trade. However, intra-firm prices are decided by the **company management** rather than the market, giving TNCs an advantage over smaller businesses, and a **lot of power** over global trade.

2) When a TNC first invests in a new country, it creates a **multiplier effect** — e.g. by opening a new factory, a corporation creates **jobs** for the local area, which means people have more **money** to spend, which helps **local businesses** (who can sell more of their products) and **governments** (who can raise more taxes).

3) TNCs make it **easier** for local companies to trade as part of the **global supply chain** — Taiwanese company Foxconn® is integral to several supply chains as it is the main manufacturer of devices for Apple®, Microsoft® and Amazon®.

TNCs Can Take Advantage of *Global Marketing*

1) TNCs operate in many different countries, so can take advantage of **global marketing** (see p.123). TNCs benefit from having a lot of **money** to spend on **advertising** and large marketing departments.

2) TNCs gain knowledge of **local markets** and adjust their marketing accordingly, even changing their **products** to reflect national **cultures**. E.g. McDonald's sell different products in different countries, such as the McSpicy™ Paneer burger in India and gazpacho soup in Spain.

3) The aim of many TNCs is to create a **brand** that is **recognised globally**, e.g. Coca-Cola®. A recognisable brand means consumers will buy the product without continued marketing.

Wal-Mart® is a *Retail TNC* with *Headquarters* in the *USA*

Wal-Mart is a chain of discount **department stores** (including ASDA in the UK). It's one of the **largest** TNCs in the world and the largest **retail** TNC (many of the top TNCs are **oil companies**).

1) Wal-Mart began in 1962 when **Sam Walton** opened the first store in **Arkansas**, **USA**.

2) More stores opened across Arkansas, then across the USA, and more recently across the globe via the **acquisition** of other retail companies. E.g. **Seiyu** in Japan, **ASDA** in the UK and **Bompreço** in Brazil.

3) Some Wal-Mart stores continue trading under their **own name**, e.g. ASDA, while others are **re-branded** as Wal-Mart.

4) Wal-Mart **divides** its **labour** across different countries. Its headquarters are still in Arkansas, but most manufacturing is carried out where costs are **lower** (cheaper labour and resources), e.g. electronic goods are made in China and clothing is made in India.

■ = Location of Wal-Mart stores in 2017

5) Wal-Mart is starting to **expand** into **emerging economies** like India. For example, Wal-Mart and an **Indian** company called **Bharti Enterprises** are opening new retail outlets **together** in the **style** of Wal-Mart stores.

Topic Seven — Global Systems and Global Governance

Transnational Corporations (TNCs)

Wal-Mart® has *Impacts* in the *USA...*

Economic

- **Employment** — each **new store creates jobs**, e.g. an expanded store in Milpitas (California, USA) opened in 2015, creating 80 new jobs.
- **Low prices** — Wal-Mart is one of the **cheapest supermarkets** in the USA.
- **Decline in manufacturing industry** — Wal-Mart buys a lot of products from suppliers outside the USA, which has caused a loss of manufacturing jobs in the USA.
- **Loss of local businesses** — Wal-Mart stores can cause smaller shops in the area to **shut down** as they can't **match** the low prices. This can cause the loss of **local jobs**.

Social

- Wal-Mart provides consumers with a **wide choice** of goods, e.g. the 'supercenter' stores sell things like garden furniture as well as food and clothing.
- Many Wal-Mart stores are open **24 hours a day**, so consumers are able to shop **when they like**.
- Many jobs at Wal-Mart are **poorly paid** with **few benefits** (e.g. health care), so employees have to rely on **state benefits**.
- Wal-Mart has been accused of having **poor working conditions**. Some employees have to work long and irregular hours.

Environmental

- Wal-Mart produces huge amounts of **polluting gases**, but it has opened '**green stores**' that run on **renewable energy**.
- **Stores** are often **large and out-of-town** — they take up **large areas of land** and **driving** to them **causes pollution**.

...and in its *Host* Countries

Social

- Wal-Mart offers **skilled jobs** in **less developed countries**. E.g. Wal-Mart stores in China are managed by local people.
- In its poorest host countries, working for Wal-Mart can offer a **more reliable** wage than other jobs.
- **Working conditions** may be **poor**, e.g. some Wal-Mart suppliers have **long working hours**.
- Wal-Mart **donates** hundreds of millions of dollars to improve things like **health** and the **environment** in countries where it operates. E.g. in 2015, Wal-Mart **donated over $2 million** to communities in West Africa who were impacted by natural disasters.

Economic

- Wal-Mart creates lots of jobs in **construction**, **manufacturing** and **retail services**.
- **Local companies** and **farmers** supply goods to Wal-Mart. E.g. Wal-Mart works with over 6000 Canadian suppliers.
- **Local suppliers** to Wal-Mart may be able to expand their business by **exporting** their goods to Wal-Mart stores in other countries.
- Wal-Mart has been criticised for forcing its suppliers to accept **low prices** for their products.
- **Local companies suffer** in **competing** with Wal-Mart. **Smaller shops** in the area often have to **shut** — they **can't compete** with the **low prices** and **range of products**.
- **Most** of the **profits** from Wal-Mart stores are sent back to the **USA** rather than put into the host country's economy.

Environmental

- Wal-Mart invests in **environmentally friendly technologies** and **sustainable development**.
- Wal-Mart stores use **large areas of land** for factories and stores.

Greg was disappointed to learn that it wasn't a Wall-Mart that was opening nearby.

Practice Questions

Q1 Outline two factors that influence where TNCs locate their factories.

Q2 What is intra-firm trading?

Q3 Give three economic impacts that Wal-Mart has on its host countries.

Exam Question

Q1 How far do you agree with the following statement? 'Transnational corporations (TNCs) create a lot of opportunities for their home countries, but these benefits are not felt by their host countries.' [20 marks]

And I thought host countries were just for international singing contests...

Wal-Mart is just one of many TNCs, but the impact Wal-Mart has on its home and host countries will be similar for TNCs other than Wal-Mart too. I wonder if Wal-Mart will start paying me if I keep saying Wal-Mart all the time...

Global Governance

Global governance — that's all the rules and organisations aimed at making sure everybody works in a fair way, don'tcha know.

The World is Governed by **Norms**, **Laws** and **Institutions**

1) A lot of the issues the world faces today are **global** and go beyond the scope of national laws, e.g. national governments **can't** tackle climate change alone or coordinate the response to a global disease epidemic.

2) A number of global **norms**, **laws** and **institutions** have been formed to deal with issues like these:

- International **laws** are rules that are established by countries through **international agreements**. They are **legally binding**. International laws cover human rights, labour standards, trade regulations, etc.

- **Norms** are accepted standards of behaviour — there are usually **negative consequences** for countries, companies or individuals who don't follow them. E.g. it is generally believed that people have the right to freedom of speech — countries that restrict this right may face international condemnation.

- **Institutions** are political and legal organisations. They exist to pass and enforce laws, decide whether a law has been broken, or act as a forum for different groups to discuss issues and sort out their differences. At the global scale, they include the United Nations, the World Trade Organisation and the International Criminal Court.

3) Global governance **regulates** global economic and political systems by setting up **rules** countries and companies should follow, **monitoring** whether they follow the rules, and **enforcing** the rules if they aren't followed. Enforcement includes taking a country or company to an international **court**, or imposing **economic sanctions** like withdrawing trade.

4) By setting rules, global governance makes everyone taking part in the global system act in a **certain way**. This ensures that newcomers also act in that way, e.g. in 2011, South Sudan joined the United Nations, agreeing to follow the UN Charter like all other member nations. This means that global systems are **reproduced** and spread.

Global Governance Aims to Promote **Growth** and **Stability**

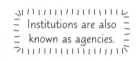
Institutions are also known as agencies.

1) International institutions are designed to provide **growth** (improving the economy or society) and **stability** (making sure there are no sudden changes in the economy or society):

- The **laws** and **norms** that international institutions enforce mean that countries must abide by common rules. This gives **greater stability** because countries know how other countries are likely to react to a situation, making **conflict less likely**. Trade **rules** mean countries cannot take advantage of each other, so all countries can develop.

- The **World Trade Organisation** (**WTO**, see p.129) aims to increase global trade through common rules — more trade leads to **economic growth** and rules make trade more **predictable**, increasing **stability**. The **World Bank** (see p.128) gives development loans to less developed countries to increase their economic growth.

- The **World Health Organisation** (**WHO**) combats epidemics (e.g. the 2014 Ebola outbreak in West Africa), which increases social stability. The **United Nations Educational, Scientific and Cultural Organisation** (**UNESCO**) helps to ensure the benefits of scientific advances are shared amongst all countries.

2) However, there are some **problems** with this system of global governance:

- Countries sign up to international laws and institutions **voluntarily** — if a country doesn't sign or formally approve a particular treaty, then they are **not** bound by the laws that the treaty sets out.

- It can also be **difficult** to make countries and TNCs comply with the rules. E.g. in 2016, China ignored a court ruling that its claims over the South China Sea went **against** international law. Other countries have not brought economic sanctions against China, partly because China is so **important** to the global economy.

- Some people think that global institutions act for **political reasons**, e.g. it is alleged that some countries have used the International Criminal Court to remove people they don't want in power in African nations.

Global Institutions Can Create **Inequalities** and **Injustices**

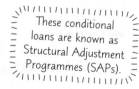
These conditional loans are known as Structural Adjustment Programmes (SAPs).

1) There are **conditions** to receiving a loan from the **IMF** or **World Bank** (see p.128) — e.g. in order to receive the loans, less developed countries have to implement **free trade policies** and cut government spending (often on education and health care). Some people have argued that this has made **poverty** and **inequality** in less developed countries **worse**.

2) Economic groups like the **G7** (a forum for seven of the wealthiest developed countries) **strengthen** the power of **developed countries**, rather than encouraging equality between them and less developed countries.

3) Members of **security** institutions, e.g. the **United Nations Security Council**, can **veto** resolutions — e.g. between 2011 and 2016, Russia and China vetoed several resolutions to intervene in the Syrian Civil War.

Topic Seven — Global Systems and Global Governance

Global Governance

The *United Nations* is a *Global Institution*

1) The **United Nations** (**UN**) was set up in 1945 to establish a **peaceful** and **fair** world.

2) The UN currently has 193 member countries — the UN has a lot of **authority** because practically **every country in the world** is a member.

3) When countries join the UN, they have to sign up to the **United Nations Charter**. This sets out the basic **principles** of global governance and the **functions** of the UN. According the Charter, the UN's **aims** are:

- to maintain **global peace** and **security**.
- to develop **friendly relations** between nations.
- to use **cooperation** to solve international problems.
- to bring countries together to **settle** disputes.

4) The UN is made up of **several organisations**, e.g. the UN Security Council is responsible for maintaining global peace and security and the General Assembly acts as a 'parliament of nations' and makes decisions on a range of issues.

5) The UN works to promote **growth** and **stability**, but some people believe it has made some issues **worse**:

Growth and Stability

- **Growth** — the UN **Millennium Development Goals** have helped reduce the number of people living in **poverty**, increased the number of children in primary **school** and reduced child and maternal **mortality rates**. In 2015, the UN set new targets for 2030 to promote continued **sustainable development**.

- **Stability** — UN **peacekeeping** missions can help to end wars, e.g. peaceful **elections** were held in Côte d'Ivoire in 2015 after years of civil war.

Inequalities and Injustices

- **Inequalities** — **developed** countries hold the **most power** over decisions taken at the UN. Many of the global issues tackled by the UN affect **African** countries the most, e.g. refugee crises, but no African country has a permanent seat at the UN Security Council, which makes the final decision.

- **Injustices** — at times the UN has been **ineffective**. E.g. in 1995, UN peacekeepers failed to protect 8000 people in Srebrenica in south-east Europe when they were massacred by Bosnian Serbs.

Institutions *Work Together* to Make Global Governance a Success

1) Institutions operate at a range of **scales** — they all need to **interact** to ensure that governance is **effective**.

2) Decisions made by **global** institutions **affect** institutions at the **international**, **national**, **regional** and **local** scale. E.g. in 2015, the UN passed the Paris climate change agreement. Institutions from the international level down to the local level had to change their policies to fit with the new agreement.

3) Decisions at the **local** or **regional** level can affect institutions at the **global** level. E.g. in October 2016, a regional government in Wallonia, Belgium temporarily blocked a trade deal between the EU and Canada.

Scale	Examples of institutions
Global	UN
International	European Union (EU)
National	UK Parliament, British government
Regional	Scottish Parliament, Welsh Assembly
Local	Local councils, county courts

4) **Non-governmental organisations** (**NGOs**) also operate on a range of scales to **monitor** and **support** institutions. For example, some NGOs lobby for **national** governments to create **laws**, e.g. Greenpeace campaign for more environmental protection, whilst others act at a **local** scale, e.g. helping communities gain access to safe water.

Practice Questions

Q1 What is the difference between an international norm and an international law?

Q2 State the four main aims of the United Nations.

Exam Question

Q1 Explain how global institutions help to promote growth and stability. [4 marks]

I hope UN-joyed revising global governance...

...what's that? You didn't? Well you've got to learn it anyway, I'm afraid. The UN is one of several global institutions that help govern the global system, but it's the biggest — between all of its agencies, it covers everything from aviation to education.

The Global Commons

Believe it or not, there are some parts of the world that don't belong to anybody. Not you and not me (despite my best efforts). These places are called the global commons, and they're under quite a bit of pressure at the moment.

The **Global Commons** Don't Belong to Any One Country

1) The **global commons** are areas that **aren't owned** by any one country or organisation — they belong to **everybody**, and so should be available for everyone's use and benefit.

2) There are **four** global commons:

> *Some people think that cyberspace is also a global common.*

- **Antarctica** (see p.140-142).
- The **high seas** — areas of the sea that do not belong to any country. Most are more than 200 miles from land.
- Earth's **atmosphere** — the gases that surround the Earth and support life.
- **Outer space** — the moon, the rest of the solar system and beyond.

Having the high seas a little lower might not be a bad thing, mused Colin, as he faced another imminent pounding.

3) The global commons are **governed** by different pieces of **international law**. E.g. the United Nations Convention on the Law of the Sea (UNCLOS) governs the high seas.

4) Environmental **NGOs** (see previous page) want to **protect** the commons from exploitation, as they offer **unique habitats** for wildlife and have a positive impact on **environmental** systems. They are also valuable for **scientific investigation**.

The Global Commons Face Many **Pressures**

1) Countries and organisations may feel they can **exploit** the global commons **without** dealing with the consequences, as the **costs of exploiting** the global commons are **shared by everybody**. This is known as '**the tragedy of the commons**'.

2) **Industrialisation** and **development** are increasing the demand for resources (e.g. food, oil, minerals) — many of these are extracted from the global commons. Industrialisation and development also create **waste** that is pumped into the atmosphere (e.g. carbon dioxide) or into the oceans (chemical waste).

3) New **technology** has made it **easier** to get to areas like the high seas, Antarctica or outer space that were relatively **inaccessible** before — this makes them more **vulnerable** to exploitation.

4) The global commons are under a lot of different **pressures**, which cause problems for the planet as a whole:

- The high seas have been the victim of **overfishing** — taking more fish than is sustainable. This has knock-on effects on other animals in the food chain, and the methods used can damage coral reefs.
- Atmospheric **pollution** is causing **climate change**.
- Increased **carbon dioxide** in the atmosphere also causes **acidification** of the oceans, which affects marine organisms, e.g. it's harder for marine snails to form their shells.

There is a Need to **Protect** the Global Commons

> *Not causing too much environmental damage or using resources faster than they are replaced is necessary for sustainable development.*

1) Institutions around the world have begun to acknowledge that countries' right to **develop** must be balanced by the need to **protect** the global commons.

2) **NGOs** like the World Wide Fund for Nature (WWF®) have called for the global commons to be **protected** by making sure that any development and use of these areas is **sustainable**.

3) Sustainable development of the global commons requires global **cooperation**. E.g. stocks of north-east Arctic cod have increased because of cooperation between Norway and Russia, the two countries which fish for it.

Practice Questions

Q1 Explain what the phrase 'the tragedy of the commons' means.

Q2 Give two ways that development has put pressure on the global commons.

Exam Question

Q1 Explain how globalisation poses a threat to one of the global commons.   [4 marks]

The two of us have a lot in common — the high seas, outer space...

The global commons are a good example of how global governance can face some tricky situations. Learning this page will help you understand the main issues you need to know about — the threats facing Antarctica, which are coming up next...

Global Commons — Antarctica

Antarctica's that lonely, icy continent that sits at the South Pole, surrounded by the Southern Ocean. It's full of penguins and seals and fish and whales. And fishers and whalers and tourists and scientists. Actually, it doesn't sound that lonely after all...

Antarctica Has a Unique **Environment** and **Climate**

1) Antarctica covers an area about **14 million km²**, so it's **larger** than **Europe**. It contains **90%** of all the **ice** on Earth — around **70%** of all the Earth's **fresh water**. The whole of Antarctica, plus the Southern Ocean as far north as the Antarctic Convergence, are considered part of the global commons.

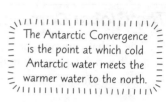
The Antarctic Convergence is the point at which cold Antarctic water meets the warmer water to the north.

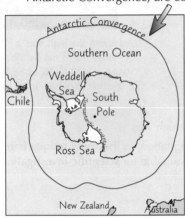

2) There's **very little available water** in Antarctica for plants to grow. Inland areas receive **less than 166 mm** of precipitation per year (which is low enough to classify it as a **desert**) and most precipitation that falls is **frozen**.

3) It's **very cold** — the average temperature is **−49 ˚C**. There's also **very little sunshine** in winter (the sun doesn't rise for several months because of the Earth's tilt).

4) This means that **very few** plants and animals **can survive** there, and the ones that do have to be specially **adapted**. Antarctica's plant life is mainly made up of **mosses** and **lichens**, and only **two** species of **flowering plants** grow.

5) The lack of water, warmth and sunlight in Antarctica means that the terrestrial (land) ecosystem is very **fragile** — it is easily **damaged** and takes a long time to **recover**.

6) At the Antarctic Convergence, there's upwelling of nutrient-rich cold water. Microscopic **phytoplankton** thrive here, which provide plenty of food for **krill** and form the basis of the whole Southern Ocean **food chain**.

7) There's abundant **sea life**, e.g. **fish**, **seals** and **whales**. Birds, like **albatrosses** and **penguins**, survive on the sea life. The marine ecosystem is also **fragile** — if the population of one species **decreases** it affects other species.

There are **Four** Main **Threats** to Antarctica

Climate Change

1) In the past five decades, areas along the **west coast** of Antarctica have warmed by as much as **3 °C** — one of the **fastest temperature rises** on Earth.

2) Warming has caused the **ice shelves** (large sheets of ice) around Antarctica's **Weddell Sea** and **Ross Sea** to melt. As the ice shelves have **retreated**, the Antarctic environment has changed dramatically.

3) Species of **penguin** that are adapted to **sea ice**, like Adélie penguins, have **declined** as the ice has melted. They have been replaced in some areas by chinstrap penguins, which are more **adapted** to open sea conditions.

4) **Antarctic krill** depend on the environment the sea ice provides. The krill population has **declined** by around 80% since the 1970s as the sea ice has melted. Krill are the main food source for penguins, whales and seals, so the decline in the number of krill is leading to declines in the populations of these animals as well.

5) Melting sea ice has an impact on **global sea levels**, which have risen by around 3 mm a year since the 1990s — this could make the edges of the ice shelves unstable, increasing the rate of **melting**.

6) Climate change also causes **ocean acidification** around Antarctica. When carbon dioxide in the air reacts with saltwater it creates carbonic acid, which depletes the amount of calcium carbonate in the water. This can be devastating to Antarctica's plankton, which use calcium carbonate to form their shells.

Fishing and Whaling

1) **Over-fishing** threatens many species, e.g. in Antarctica the **Patagonian toothfish** is being fished unsustainably, making it vulnerable to extinction. **Antarctic krill** are the most fished creature — in 2013 over 200 000 tonnes of krill were fished from the Antarctic. **Reduced fish** and **krill populations** have knock-on effects on other species in the **food chain**, e.g. the larger fish, marine mammals and birds that eat them.

2) There are **legal limits** on how much fish can be caught per year to keep stocks at a **sustainable level**. However, lots of **illegal fishing** takes place, which is difficult to monitor.

3) Other species are also affected by fishing, e.g. **albatrosses** and **petrels** get caught in fishing lines and drown.

4) **Whaling** was common in the mid-20th century, but has declined since 1982 when regulations were brought in to **ban** all commercial whaling (see p.142). Some countries continue to kill whales for 'scientific' purposes.

5) Whaling significantly **decreased** the Antarctic whale population, which is now slowly **recovering**. However, whales are **slow breeders**, so it will take a long time for populations to fully recover.

Global Commons — Antarctica

Search for minerals

1) There are believed to be a lot of **minerals** in Antarctica. E.g. there are large underground deposits of **coal** and **iron ore** in the Transantarctic Mountains.

2) There are also large reserves of **oil** underneath the Southern Ocean.

3) So far there hasn't been any **mining** in Antarctica. It is **currently banned**, but conditions aren't favourable anyway — it is **too far** to transport machinery to Antarctica from any other landmass and the **landscape** and **climate** would make mining difficult and expensive.

4) However, this may **change** in the future due to increasing demand for minerals and oil as supplies are depleted elsewhere. Mining in the Antarctic would **damage** the environment.

Of course Percy didn't agree with the way the humans treated Antarctica, but that wasn't going to stop him posing for photos.

Tourism and Research

1) **Tourism** increases **shipping** and **air travel** to Antarctica, leading to water and air **pollution**. There is also a risk of boats grounding or hitting icebergs, which can cause **fuel spills**.

2) Tourists can **disturb** breeding colonies of birds. **Trampling** damages fragile **vegetation** and **erodes** the landscape. **Litter** and **waste disposal** damages habitats and can harm wildlife, especially because decomposition rates in cold environments are slow.

3) **Non-native species** may be introduced, e.g. on tourists' clothing — these may alter food webs and ecosystems.

4) Antarctica is also important for **scientific** and **environmental research**. This requires lots of **facilities**, including bases for the researchers to live, roads to transport supplies and places to store fuel. Until the 1980s a lot of the **waste** created in these bases was either burned, thrown into the sea or dumped.

International Laws Help to Protect Antarctica

1) The **Antarctic Treaty (1959)** is an agreement about how to sustainably manage Antarctica's ecosystems. It has now been signed by 53 countries. The rules laid out in the treaty include:

- Antarctica should only be used for **peaceful reasons** — no army bases or weapons are allowed on Antarctica.
- Countries should **cooperate** on **scientific research** in Antarctica by sharing plans, researchers and results.
- Antarctica should **remain** in the **global commons** — individual countries cannot make a claim to it.

2) Under the 1959 treaty, all bases and equipment in Antarctica can be **inspected** at any time, with different countries taking responsibility for carrying out inspections. However, inspections **don't** occur very **often**.

3) The **Protocol on Environmental Protection to the Antarctic Treaty** was signed in **1991** and added to the Antarctic Treaty. It focuses on protecting Antarctica's fragile **environment**.

4) The 1991 protocol **banned all mining** in Antarctica. It also set rules to help **protect** Antarctic **plants** and **animals**, **regulate waste disposal** and **prevent pollution**. Under the 1991 protocol, an Environmental Impact Assessment (EIA) is required for any new activities.

5) However, there is **no system** to ensure all countries abide by the rules. If there are **disputes** between countries then they are encouraged to negotiate. Otherwise, disputes can be taken to the **International Court of Justice**.

6) The countries involved must reach a **consensus** over all decisions regarding Antarctica. Tackling problems can therefore be **slow** and **difficult** — e.g. between 2012 and 2016, plans for Antarctic marine reserves repeatedly failed because of opposition from Russia and Ukraine.

Antarctica is Governed by Global Institutions

There are several institutions which help govern Antarctica. These include:

International Whaling Commission (IWC)

- The **IWC** is responsible for regulating whaling (see p.142) and ensuring that the **whale population** is at a **sustainable level**.
- In 1994 the IWC set up a **whale sanctuary** in the Southern Ocean around Antarctica in order to protect whales.
- However, campaigners have **criticised** the IWC for not properly **monitoring** the number of whales in the sanctuary.

United Nations Environment Programme (UNEP)

- **UNEP** is a **UN agency** (see p.138) and is the main institution that governs the world's **environment**. UNEP is responsible for **reporting** activity in Antarctica to the UN.
- The programme in Antarctica is run by the Commission for the Conservation of Antarctic Marine Living Resources (**CCAMLR**), which aims to stop **illegal fishing** and **conserve** the **Antarctic ecosystem**, e.g. by setting up protected areas.
- However, its effectiveness is **limited** by individual countries protecting their **own interests** — it took **5 years** for CCAMLR to negotiate the creation of a **marine protected area** in the Ross Sea, and it hasn't **reduced fishing quotas** in this area.

Global Commons — Antarctica

The **Whaling Moratorium** Banned Commercial Whaling

1) In 1982 the IWC (see previous page) introduced a **Whaling Moratorium** that **banned** all **commercial whaling** around the world, including in Antarctica. It is believed to have helped whale populations in Antarctica to **increase**.

2) The success of the Whaling Moratorium is **monitored** by **estimating** whale populations based on sightings and modelling.

3) Some countries (like the US and Australia) believe there should be a **better** monitoring system, including **registering** all whaling boats with the IWC and placing independent observers on all whaling boats. Other countries (like Japan and Norway) say that the IWC does **not** have the **authority** to do this.

4) **Non-governmental organisations (NGOs)**, including Greenpeace, have said that the Whaling Moratorium is also **poorly enforced**. Countries like Japan have continued to kill large numbers of Antarctic whales for '**scientific research**' despite the ruling.

NGOs Play an Important Part in **Monitoring** and **Enforcing** Rules

1) **NGOs** play an important role in **monitoring** possible threats to Antarctica and **protecting** its environment.

2) As they don't act on behalf of a particular country, NGOs are well positioned to observe whether countries are sticking to the **laws** governing Antarctica and to call **international attention** to those who aren't.

3) One key NGO involved in Antarctica is the **Antarctic and Southern Ocean Coalition (ASOC)**.

- ASOC was formed in 1978 from a group of NGOs who were concerned that some countries were planning to make it legal to search for **oil, gas** and **minerals** in Antarctica. ASOC successfully campaigned to make Antarctic Treaty meetings more transparent, including allowing NGOs to attend.

- As an NGO, ASOC is interested in protecting the environment — it does not have an interest in trying to exploit Antarctica for resources or fishing, and will speak up against exploitation by individual countries.

- Today, ASOC monitors environmental changes in Antarctica and checks whether countries are sticking to the rules — e.g. monitoring whether countries are following the 1991 Environment Protocol (see previous page), protecting the Southern Ocean Whale Sanctuary from attempts to re-establish commercial whaling and ensuring that krill populations are sustainable.

- ASOC also monitors the effects that climate change is having on Antarctica, e.g. by checking melting ice and sea levels around Antarctica. ASOC campaigns with other NGOs to reduce greenhouse gas emissions.

The Way **Antarctica** is **Governed** Affects the Rest of the **World**

Global governance of Antarctica has an impact on people and places in Antarctica and **around the world**. For example:

1) Monitoring of **melting ice** in Antarctica (see p.140) has informed efforts to combat **climate change**. This affects people's daily lives — e.g. using **renewable** energy sources, **conserving** electricity and using cars less.

2) Global governance may **slow down** short-term **economic growth** in some countries, e.g. limits on how many whales and fish can be caught limits the amount that countries can sell. However, it **secures resources** for the future.

3) Global governance allows greater **scientific exploration** of Antarctica. People from **all over the world** can conduct research in Antarctica. Collaboration allows researchers to **pool resources**, e.g. sharing research stations.

4) Global governance allows **tourists** to visit Antarctica safely and securely.

Practice Questions

Q1 State the four main threats to Antarctica.

Q2 Give three rules laid down in the Antarctic Treaty (1959).

Q3 Describe one achievement of the Antarctic and Southern Ocean Coalition (ASOC).

Exam Question

Q1 'The existing governance of Antarctica is sufficient to protect it from the threats to its environment.'
How far do you agree with this statement? [20 marks]

Wailing — one response to what's happening in Antarctica...

It's snow joke — Antarctica's a cool customer, but it's also a key case study for the exam, so make sure you're clued up on the threats to its environment and the rules in place to prevent them. That'll prevent you from slipping up in the exam.

Impacts of Globalisation

Well, that's that then. Globalisation — finished. Fini. Finito. Done and dusted. Wrapped up. Polished off. Flipping Done, Innit (FDI). But wait — there's one more page to go. Wouldn't want to leave globalisation without checking out its costs and benefits...

Globalisation Brings **Benefits**...

Integration — Globalisation allows countries to **pool their resources** to solve **global issues** that are too great for a single country to deal with. Greater integration of information and people creates a better understanding between people of different **backgrounds** and **cultures**.

Development — Foreign **investment** brings **capital** into a country, which can be used to improve **education** and **infrastructure**. This in turn can attract further **trade** and **investment**, which leads to further development. Global institutions like the World Bank (see p.128) can direct **resources** to help countries **develop** further.

Stability — As countries become more **interconnected**, they become more **dependent** on one another. This discourages any actions that would upset global **stability**, because of the **negative** consequences for all countries.

Economic growth — Participation in global trade allows countries to **profit** from their natural resources and specialist industries, generating **wealth**. Countries can also gain **products** and **services** that they would be unable to produce themselves. Greater access to money and products improves people's **standard of living**.

... but it Also has **Costs**

1) **Inequalities** — As companies move low-skilled jobs to less developed countries, low-skilled workers in developed countries find it more difficult to earn money — this creates a **greater divide** between **rich and poor** people within countries. Developed countries have **greater access** to capital and technology, meaning they have an advantage over less developed countries — this increases inequalities between countries.

2) **Conflict** — Developed countries have **intervened** in conflicts in order to secure access to **natural resources** like oil. **Cyber warfare** is a new source of conflict — countries, companies and individuals are now dependent on the Internet, so attacks on their computer systems can have a large impact.

3) **Injustice** — Improved transport and communications systems have made **human trafficking** easier. Many people in less developed countries have to work in **sweatshops** (see p.131) to make products for people in developed countries.

4) Globalisation also has consequences for the **environment**:

   - Global trade increases the amount of **transportation** required, which means more **pollution** and greenhouse gas emissions.
   - Access to resources from around the world causes **deforestation** (e.g. clearing rainforests for oilseed plantations) and **overfishing** (see p.139).
   - Global trade can lead to a **race to the bottom**, in which countries and companies **ignore** environmental impacts in order to produce **cheaper goods** (see p.133).
   - The **abundance** of cheap products around the world means people can afford to be more **wasteful**, creating lots of landfill.

Practice Questions

Q1 Give four benefits of globalisation.

Q2 Give one example of how globalisation causes injustice.

Q3 State four ways that globalisation has a negative impact on the environment.

Exam Question

Q1 'Globalisation has created more costs than benefits.'
To what extent do you agree with this statement? [20 marks]

Globalisation isn't all sunshine and rainbows...

...come to think of it, neither sunshine or rainbows are freely available in the international marketplace. Globalisation isn't all good or all bad — it's a bit of both. It's up to you to assess the consequences and form an opinion about them.

The Concept of Place

Geographers are interested in the location of places, and also all the things that contribute to the characteristics and perceptions (what people think and feel) of those places — this is the study of the concept of 'place'.

Place is More Than Just Location

1) A place can be thought of as a **location** which could be plotted on a **map** or defined by a **grid reference**, e.g. latitude 51.5074°N, longitude 0.1278°W (London).

2) But this doesn't tell us anything **about** that place, i.e. what it's like, who lives there or how it has changed.

3) So to help them study places, many **geographers** use a **broader definition** of the term '**place**'. The idea is that 'place' is made up of **all** the things that **come together** to make a place **what it is**:

> - Its **location**.
> - The **physical characteristics** of the landscape, e.g. the topography or physical features.
> - The **human characteristics** (who lives there and what they're like) plus the human features of the landscape, e.g. the land use or the built environment.
> - All the things that **flow** in and out of that place, e.g. people, money, ideas, resources.
> - The **sense of place**, i.e. the **emotional meanings** the place has, either to individuals or groups of people. For example, an individual may think of a place as 'home', and they may share that sense of place with the other members of their family.

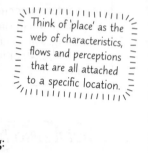

Think of 'place' as the web of characteristics, flows and perceptions that are all attached to a specific location.

4) Apart from location, all aspects of places and the meanings they have are **constantly changing**:

- The **physical characteristics** of a place can change over **long time scales**, e.g. as rivers migrate, or **short time scales**, e.g. when a volcano erupts and alters the landscape.

- The **human characteristics** of a place can change over **whole lifetimes**, e.g. as new people are born in a place and others die, or **shorter time scales**, e.g. as people migrate in and out of a place.

- The **flows** in and out of a place change, e.g. flows of money could change when a multinational corporation (MNC) invests in a new factory or decides to close an existing factory.

- The **sense of place** individuals or groups have may change, e.g. the places a person played in as a child will not have the same meanings to that person when they return there as an adult.

5) Different groups or individuals may also have a **different sense** of the **same place**. For example, one person may think of a city centre as a place of excitement and opportunity, whilst another person may think of it as a place of stress.

Place can Create Insiders and Outsiders

1) The idea of place is important because many people create their **identity** (the sense of who they are) based on the places that they feel **connected** to, e.g. a person may consider coming from Manchester to be a part of who they are.

2) This is because individuals **share characteristics** that they feel bind them together as a group, creating a **shared identity** for all the people from that place. This can be seen at a variety of scales:

- **Local** — e.g. the individuals from a village sharing a positive sense of that village.
- **Regional** — e.g. the individuals from a region sharing an accent.
- **National** — e.g. the individuals of a nation sharing a language, religion or a love for that nation.

3) Relating identity to **particular places** means that people can be perceived as **belonging** to those places or not. This is the idea that people are '**insiders**' or '**outsiders**' in particular places:

> - An **insider** is someone who is **familiar** with a place and who feels **welcome** in that place, i.e. they feel that they **belong** there. E.g. residents of a country, who all share the same cultural values, may feel like insiders in that country.
> - An **outsider** is someone who feels **unwelcome** or **excluded** from a place, i.e. they **don't** feel that they **belong** there. E.g. international immigrants, who don't share the same cultural values as the residents of a country, may feel like outsiders in the country they move to.

4) There are many **factors** that can make a person feel like an insider or an outsider, e.g. **age**, **sexuality** or **gender**. For example, a young person may feel like an outsider in a retirement village, and an elderly person may feel like an outsider in a nightclub.

The Concept of Place

People Can Have a Sense of Place for Experienced or Media Places

People can have a **sense of place** for places they've **been to**, and places they **haven't been to**.

- **Experienced places** are places that people have spent time in. When a person visits or lives in a place their **experiences**, such as the things they see and the people they meet, shape their **sense** of that place.
- **Media places** are places that people have **not been to**, but have created a **sense of place** for through their depiction in **media** (e.g. books, art and films).

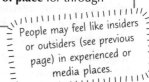
People may feel like insiders or outsiders (see previous page) in experienced or media places.

A person's **sense** of a media place can be very **different** to the **lived experience** of the same place — this is because the media may present a place in a **particular way** and for a **particular purpose**. E.g. tourist websites may present holiday destinations such as the Caribbean as a place of relaxation and opulence, but the reality for people who live there may be that it is a place of poverty and hardship.

Places can be Categorised as Near or Far

1) **Near places** can be thought of as **geographically near** to where a person lives, and **far places** as **distant** from where a person lives.

2) People are more likely to feel like **insiders** (see previous page) in near places, as they are more likely to have **experienced** them and feel **comfortable** in them.

3) Not **all** people will feel like insiders in **all** geographically near places though — people may feel **excluded** from near places for **many reasons**, e.g. their age, gender, sexuality etc.

4) People are more likely to feel like **outsiders** in far places, as they are less likely to have **experienced** them and feel **comfortable** in them.

5) In more recent decades, **globalisation** (the process of the world's economies, political systems and cultures becoming more closely integrated) has affected people's **experience** of geographical distance:

- Improvements in **travel technology** mean that far places are **quicker** to get to, and can therefore be experienced more **easily** and **frequently**.
- Improvements in **ICT** mean that people can be very familiar with **media places** — places they have no lived experience of.
- People can also remain **closely connected** with **people** and **activities** in far places via the **Internet**.

6) So it's **increasingly likely** today that people may feel closely **connected to**, and even like **insiders**, in places that are geographically far away.

7) **Global companies** and **products** also mean that far places can feel **very similar** to near places, e.g. city centres in different parts of the world may have all the same chain stores, selling the same products.

8) Geographers use the term '**placelessness**' to describe how globalisation is making distant places look and feel the **same**.

Practice Questions

Q1 Define the term 'insider'.

Q2 What is a media place?

Q3 Briefly outline the effect of globalisation on people's experience of far places.

Exam Question

Q1 Explain what geographers mean by the concept of 'place'. [4 marks]

This is no plaice for a bad fish joke...

I know there are a lot of definitions on these two pages, and some of them might be a bit tricky, but you will be expected to know all of them for the exam. Examiners are mean like that. So put your reading eyeballs back in and get cracking...

The Character of Places

Here's a bit more about the main factors that give places their character — the physical and human characteristics, plus the flows in and out of them. Take a look back at page 144 to remind yourself of the definition of 'place' if you need to.

Places are **Shaped** by **Endogenous** and **Exogenous Factors**

All places have a unique **character** which is formed by their many different **characteristics**. These factors can be classified as **endogenous** or **exogenous**:

1) **Endogenous** — the **internal** factors which shape a place's character. These could be **physical**, e.g. its location, topography and physical geography, or they could be **human**, e.g. the land use, built environment, infrastructure and demographic and economic characteristics.

2) **Exogenous** — the **external** factors which shape a place's character, including the **relationship** to other places and the **flows** in and out of a place, e.g. the flows of people, resources, money and ideas.

Many **Endogenous Factors Influence** the Character of **Places**

Endogenous factors can include the **physical characteristics** of the landscape. For example:

Location

1) Location refers to **where** a place is, e.g. on the coast or inland, in a rural or urban area, at a bridge point or a confluence of roads.

2) Places can be characterised by the **features** that are present **because** of their location, e.g. a coastal place may be characterised as a port due to its direct proximity to the sea. An inland place may not be a port, but could be a local centre of trade if it was located at a confluence of road routes.

Jack didn't think his character had been influenced by his location at all.

Topography

1) Topography refers to the **shape** of the landscape.

2) Places can be characterised **directly** by their topography, e.g. in a valley, places would be characterised as flat, whereas in a mountainous region, places would be characterised by steep slopes.

3) Topography also affects **other factors** that give places their character. E.g. land use — flat places may be suitable for large-scale arable farming (crops), whilst mountainous regions may be suitable for certain types of pastoral farming (grazing animals).

Physical geography

1) Physical geography refers to the **environmental features** of a place, e.g. altitude, aspect, soil and rock type.

2) Places can be characterised **directly** by their physical geography, e.g. a place could have igneous, sedimentary or metamorphic rocks, which form different landscapes.

3) Physical geography also affects **other factors** that give places their character. E.g. economic characteristics — a place that is rich in natural resources such as iron or coal may be characterised by the industries that can exist there, such as mining or smelting.

Endogenous factors can also include the **human characteristics** of a place and the **activities** that occur there. For example:

Land use

1) Land use refers to the **human activities** that occur on the land, e.g. farming, industry, leisure, residential use etc.

2) Land use is one of the most important human factors in **directly defining** the character of places, e.g. a place could be thought of as rural if the land use is farming, or urban if the land is used for commercial businesses.

3) Land use also affects **other factors** that give places their character. E.g. the built environment — high-rise, high-density buildings are often required for businesses in city centres, whereas residential and leisure land uses often require a lower density built environment.

4) Land use **changes over time**. For example, processes such as deindustrialisation can lead to industrial land use being replaced by other land uses, such as housing or recreation.

Deindustrialisation is the process of manufacturing industries declining in wealthier countries.

The Character of Places

Built environment and infrastructure

1) The built environment refers to aspects of places that are **built by humans**.

2) Infrastructure specifically refers to the **structures** built for **transport**, **communications** and **services**, e.g. roads, phone and broadband networks and sewer systems.

3) Places can be characterised **directly** by their built environment and infrastructure, for example:

   - Town and city centres will have **higher density** buildings, may have **tower blocks** and are likely to have **complex** and **dense** networks of roads and railtracks, as well as **communications** networks and sewers. They may have other built features such as **sports stadia** or **cathedrals**.

   - Villages will have **fewer**, **smaller** buildings at a **lower density** and **less complex** infrastructure networks. They may have built features such as **market squares** or **village halls**.

Demographic and economic characteristics

1) Demographic characteristics are about **who** lives in a place and what they're **like**. Demographic factors include things like age, gender, education level, religion, birth rates, ethnicity and population size.

2) Demographic factors can **directly contribute** to the character of places, e.g. many people retire to seaside locations, which means they can have higher proportions of older people. Seaside places may then be characterised as 'old' places (i.e. places where older people feel like insiders, and younger people feel like outsiders).

3) Economic characteristics are factors to do with **work** and **money**, e.g. income, employment rates and the types of job available.

4) Economic factors can **directly contribute** to the character of places, e.g. places such as Kensington in London have a high proportion of above average earners and low unemployment and as such are characterised as wealthy.

Processes such as gentrification — where wealthy people move into run-down areas and improve the housing — change the built environment, demographics and economics of places over time.

Exogenous Factors are External to Places

Exogenous factors are about how places are **related** to other places, and how these relationships can **affect** their **character**. Places can be **connected** by things like **relative location** and by flows of **people**, **resources**, **money** and **ideas**:

1) The character of places can be **influenced** by their relative location to **other places**. For example, villages and towns outside major cities can be characterised as commuter settlements — people live in the villages for the nice environment, but work in the city where there are greater employment opportunities.

2) Tourism **influences** the **character** of many places. For example, the land use and economic characteristics of Las Vegas are affected by tourism — the casinos and hotels are there for the tourists, and these create employment opportunities for local people.

3) Flows of investment **affect** the **character** of places. For example, Japanese car manufacturer Nissan has a factory in Sunderland. The flow of investment from Japan has influenced some of the characteristics of Sunderland, including the land use around the factory, the built environment of the factory and the type of employment available.

4) Migration can **influence** the **character** of places. For example, parts of the UK have an ethnically diverse population due to migration from other parts of the world. This gives some places their unique demographic characteristics, e.g. 27% of the population of Birmingham are of Asian descent.

Practice Questions

Q1 What are exogenous factors?

Q2 Name three endogenous factors that influence the character of places.

Exam Question

Q1 Outline how physical geography can influence the character of places. [4 marks]

Exogenous Factor — for geographers who dream of making it big one day...

It's a lot to take in, but here's a tip. Think about the place where you live, and what it's like — work out how these endogenous and exogenous factors have contributed to creating that character. You'll be crystal clear on the subject before you know it.

Changing Places — Shifting Flows

As you may have guessed from the topic title, places are always changing. On these pages we'll take a closer look at how flows in and out of places can affect their characteristics, causing the places to change over time.

External Flows cause Places to Change

1) Places are **constantly changing** because all the factors that create their character are constantly changing (see p.144).

2) Historically, the character of a place was heavily affected by the **local** (**endogenous**) factors of that place, e.g. mining towns developed in places with natural resources, or towns were built at naturally defensive points, such as on bends in rivers.

3) The original character of many places has **changed** because of the **external** (**exogenous**) influences that have occurred **over time**, e.g. flows to and from places of things like people, resources, money and ideas.

4) In recent history, flows of **people**, **money**, **resources** and **ideas** between places have **increased** — this is because of improvements to **transport**, which have made it easier for people and goods to be transported, and **communications** (e.g. the Internet), which allow people to communicate with anyone else on the planet **instantly**. These flows have caused more places to become more **strongly connected** to each other, and over increasing distances — this is **globalisation**.

5) You need to focus on how the flows of people, resources, money and ideas have affected **either** the **demographic** and **cultural** characteristics **or** the **economic** and **social** characteristics of places.

Demographic Change is Caused by Shifting Flows

1) Demographic characteristics are to do with **who** lives in a place and what they're **like** — they include factors such as age, gender, education level, religion, birth rates, ethnicity and population size (see p.147).

2) The demographic characteristics of places can **change** due to the effects of **changing external flows**:

> • **Flows of people** can change **any** of the demographic characteristics of a place, e.g. the age or gender balance. For example, on a **local** scale, younger people have been **leaving** the town of Uckfield in East Sussex as they are **unable to afford** to buy a house in the area, leaving an increasingly high proportion of **older** people. On an **international** scale, there are concerns that the **large-scale** migration from North Africa to Europe that started in 2015 altered the **gender balance** of some host towns, as a high proportion of the migrants are **male**.
>
> • **Flows of money and investment**, either by **governments** or **businesses**, can change the demographic characteristics of places. For example, governments can invest money in specific places in order to **attract people** to **live** there. In the UK, the **London Docklands Development Corporation** was a group set up by the government in 1981 to **redevelop** the Docklands area of London. The schemes undertaken by the LDDC improved the **economy** and the **built environment**, which resulted in an **increase** in population in the area — between 1981 and the early 21st century the population more than **doubled**.
>
> • **Flows of ideas and resources** — ideas such as the use of **birth control** can flow to new places and affect their demographic characteristics, e.g. by **reducing** the birth rate and affecting the **population size**. For example, many of the poorest countries in the world have the **lowest** usage of birth control and **rapid population growth**. International organisations such as the UNFPA (United Nations Population Fund) have been set up to spread **knowledge** and **ideas** about birth control, as well as **supplying** resources to aid birth control, such as **condoms**.

These Flows Also Affect the Cultural Characteristics of a Place

1) The cultural characteristics of places are to do with **how** people **live their lives**, e.g. the foods, customs, clothing, traditions, language, art, attitudes, beliefs and values people have.

2) The cultural characteristics of places can **change** due to the effects of **changing external flows**:

The Commonwealth is a group mostly made up of former British Empire territories.

> • **Flows of people** — new people **moving** to a place, or even **visiting** it, bring their **culture** with them, which can **change** the characteristics of the place. E.g. in the 20th century the UK experienced mass international **migrations** from India, Pakistan and other Commonwealth countries. This has created **multi-ethnic** communities in many places, where there is a **greater mix** of languages spoken, religions practised and foods eaten.
>
> • **Flows of money, investment and ideas** — new **cultural ideas** introduced to places can **change** the characteristics of those places, e.g. **fast food** companies from the USA such as KFC®, McDonald's and Pizza Hut® opened restaurants in **China** in the 1980s and 1990s and have **grown rapidly** since. It is thought that **eating habits** have changed in China as a result, with **increasing numbers** of people favouring western-style fast food over traditional Chinese food.

Changing Places — Shifting Flows

Economic Characteristics are Affected by Many Different Flows

1) The economic characteristics of places are to do with **work** and **money**, e.g. income, employment rates and the types of job available (see p.147).

2) The economic characteristics of places can **change** due to the effects of **changing external flows**:

> • **Flows of people** — people visiting places can **change** the economic characteristics of those places, e.g. St Ives in Cornwall used to be a **fishing** settlement, but is now a popular **tourist destination**. The flows of tourism (combined with a decline in the fishing industry) have altered the **types of jobs** available in the area to **service-based** jobs in hospitality, shops and restaurants.
>
> • **Flows of resources** — the outward flow of **local products** or **natural resources** from a place can have a large impact on local economies. Products that may once have been consumed **locally** or **regionally** can now be sold to **global markets**, e.g. the Scottish whisky industry has grown to be one of the **largest industries** in Scotland due to international **exports**. This has brought **employment** and **money** to a wide range of places across Scotland, including **remote** island communities where many distilleries are located.
>
> • **Flows of money and investment** can have **positive** and **negative** impacts on the economic characteristics of places. E.g. **reduced** investment and competition from global markets has led to the **decline** of some primary industries in the UK (**deindustrialisation**), which has **damaged** the economies of many places. For example, thousands of jobs were lost in South Wales when many coal mines were **closed** between the 1950s and 1980s. **Inward** flows of investment can have **positive** effects though, e.g. investment in the **finance** industries in the City of London has created many **high value** service sector jobs and made it a **wealthy** place.

These Flows also Affect Social Inequality

1) The social characteristics of places are to do with what people's **lives** are **like**, e.g. their overall quality of life, their access to adequate food supplies, healthcare, education, sanitation, leisure facilities etc.

2) **Social inequalities** are the **differences** in these factors between different **groups of people**.

3) Social characteristics and inequalities in places can **change** due to the effects of **changing external flows**:

> • **Flows of people** — regional **migration** from **rural** areas to **urban** areas in poorer countries has changed social characteristics and levels of social inequality. E.g. in India, large-scale rural to urban migration has resulted in **slums** (illegal, overcrowded settlements that often lack basic services) developing in cities such as Mumbai. The migrants often have a **very low** quality of life, without access to electricity, sanitation or clean water — this **contrasts** with the **high** quality of life that **wealthier** residents in these cities have, and this gap is **widening**.
>
> • **Flows of resources** — the **outward** flow of **natural resources** from poorer countries can change levels of social inequality. E.g. large amounts of **oil** are extracted around Warri in Nigeria then **exported** round the world, but most of the **wealth** that is generated goes to a **few individuals** who have a **high** quality of life, while **large numbers** of people remain in **poverty** with a **very low** quality of life.
>
> • **Flows of money and investment** — the process of **gentrification** (where wealthier people buy property in run-down areas and improve the housing) has **improved** the social characteristics of some places, but it can also **increase inequality**. E.g. Notting Hill was once one of the **most deprived** areas in London, but now has much **lower** levels of deprivation. As the area has changed though, social inequality between the wealthy newcomers and existing poorer residents has **increased**.

Practice Questions

Q1 Give one example of how shifting flows of ideas have affected the cultural characteristics of a place.

Q2 Give one example of how shifting flows of money have affected the economic characteristics of a place.

Exam Question

Q1 Analyse how shifting flows have affected **EITHER** the demographic and cultural characteristics **OR** the economic characteristics and social inequality of a place you have studied. [20 marks]

External flows — nothing to do with going to the loo...

The trouble with this lot is that there's so much of it. Flows of this and that affect these characteristics... and maybe these too... and don't forget about these. Nothing for it but to get your brain box in gear and set a course for Revisetown, USA.

Changing Places

Use the external force... this page is about the external forces that cause change and affect the character of places. The next page is about how places have been shaped by their connections to other places and the way they developed in the past.

External Forces are Driving Changes in Many Places

You need to know about **at least one** of the **external forces** below, and how they can affect the **demographic**, **cultural**, **economic** and **social** characteristics of places.

Government policies

- Governments can directly affect the **demographic** characteristics of places, e.g. by introducing policies to **control population**. In China, the **one-child policy** was introduced as a method of **reducing** rapid population growth, but in France the government introduced policies (such as lower taxes and better maternity leave conditions) to **increase** the birth rate. Both were **successful** at altering the demographic characteristics of their countries.

- Other government policies can affect the **cultural** characteristics of places, e.g. by **controlling immigration**. For example, in the 1960s the German government **invited** Turkish people to **live** and **work** in Germany — many people migrated and stayed **long term**. As a result, aspects of Turkish culture have become a **part** of German culture, e.g. Turkish fast food outlets are common across Germany, Turkish is the second most widely spoken language and Islam is widely practised.

- Some government policies can affect the **demographic**, **economic** and **social** characteristics of places. For example, governments can fund schemes aimed at **regenerating** run-down urban areas. In 1992 in Manchester, the **Hulme City Challenge Partnership** rebuilt houses, created a new park, refurbished shopping areas, built an arts venue and a business park. This scheme led to an **increase** in the population in the area, created jobs, reduced unemployment and increased quality of life for some residents.

Decisions of multinational corporations

- The decisions of MNCs can have **major impacts** on the demographic, social and economic characteristics of places. For example, **Detroit** in the USA was a major global centre of **car manufacturing** in the early and mid 20th century, with MNCs such as Ford, General Motors and Chrysler all located there.

- The investment from the MNCs gave the city a **massive economic boost** — large numbers of **jobs** were created, many of which offered comparatively **high wages**.

- This altered the **demographic** characteristics of the city by attracting large numbers of **migrants**, both from the USA and other parts of the world — the population **grew** to a peak of around **1.8 million** in the 1950s.

- After the 1950s, many of the manufacturing MNCs **closed** or **relocated factories** to places with **cheaper labour**, such as Mexico. These decisions had a number of effects:

  - Massive **population decline** — the population of Detroit at the 2010 census had reduced to around 700 000.

  - Huge **reductions** in **employment** — at the 2010 census, 24.8% of the workforce in Detroit was unemployed.

  - **Social deprivation** — Detroit has some of the highest crime rates in the USA.

D. Trout, at your service — car manufacturer extraordinaire.

Impacts of international or global institutions

- The **World Food Programme** (WFP) is an international organisation that provides **food assistance**, often as emergency **aid**, wherever it is needed. The WFP affects the social and demographic characteristics of places by ensuring that people have **enough food**, and preventing **deaths** from famine and starvation. For example, there has been intense conflict in **Yemen** since 2015, which has meant that millions of people don't have **regular access** to food. The WFP has distributed **food aid** to millions of malnourished people.

- The **World Bank** is an international organisation that **invests in**, and helps to **set up**, thousands of **projects** round the world that are aimed at **reducing poverty**. Many of these projects affect the demographic, cultural, economic and social characteristics of the places where they are set up. For example, between 2010 and 2016 the World Bank provided funding for the **Ningbo New Countryside Development Project** in Ningbo, China. This project improved the **social conditions** in the area by providing wastewater disposal services to 144 rural villages that previously had no wastewater collection or treatment services.

Changing Places

Past and Present Connections and Developments Shape Places

1) **Connections** between places in the **past** shape their **character** in the **present**, e.g. for centuries London and New York have been connected to each other and other major cities by **sea trade routes**. These connections helped them to become more **wealthy**, attract more people, and be more **closely linked** to other cultures. They gradually became **world cities** — global centres of trade, politics, finance and culture often with huge, diverse populations.

2) **New connections** are made between places in the present which can affect their character. E.g. London and New York have made new connections which **strengthen** their character as world cities — they are now more closely connected through industries such as **finance** and **banking** because of the **internet** and **faster air travel**.

Take a look at pages 158-160 for more about urbanisation and urban change.

3) The way in which places **developed** in the **past** also strongly affects their **character** in the **present**. For example, the past development of cities shows how their present-day character was created:

- Many settlements in the UK **initially developed** because of factors to do with their **location** (endogenous factors, see page 146). E.g. Sheffield originally located at the confluence of two rivers, near to coal and iron ore reserves — these would have been important factors for the early development of industry.

- During the **Industrial Revolution**, large industrial cities developed that were **globally connected** through the trade of the goods produced. This resulted in large-scale rural to urban **migration** as people moved to the cities in search of work in the factories. Today, these old industrial centres **remain** as large cities, e.g. Sheffield became a major centre of the steel industry, trading items such as cutlery all round the globe. The work available in the steel industry attracted workers and made Sheffield a major population centre.

- In the later part of the 20th century, many UK cities were heavily affected by **deindustrialisation** — the closure of factories due to increased automation, competition from abroad and the removal of manufacturing to developing countries where labour is cheaper. These cities **remained** as large population centres, but were **less well connected** globally due to the loss of trade, and suffered **economic** and **social decline**. E.g. the steel and mining industries collapsed in Sheffield in the 1970s and 1980s, which resulted in factories being abandoned, mass unemployment and a reduction in population.

4) The **character** of places is shaped by a **mix** of all the **connections** and **developments** they have undergone throughout their **history**, and the **present-day** connections and developments that are occurring. For example, the character of Sheffield is now a mixture of its **industrial past** and the **redevelopment** work that is being done today:

- Sheffield is still characterised as an **industrial city** — steel works such as Sheffield Forgemasters still supply steel to **international markets**, and the heritage of the city has been retained by creating a **conservation area** (the Cultural Industries Quarter) to preserve historically significant roads and buildings. New **art installations** around the city, such as the Cutting Edge sculpture, also reflect the industrial character of the city.

- **New connections** have been made that add to the character of Sheffield — today it is also characterised as a **student city**, with over 50 000 students in two universities, and a place of **academic** and **research excellence** (both universities have strong international academic reputations).

- The city has developed and made new connections in **high-tech industries**, e.g. the Advanced Manufacturing Research Centre (AMRC) carries out research into cutting-edge manufacturing techniques. In 2017, the car maker McLaren Automotive announced that it will build a plant near to the AMRC to build carbon fibre chassis for its new vehicles.

- Sheffield City Council has been **re-branding** the city as 'The Outdoor City'. The aim is to encourage **tourism** and **boost events** surrounding activities such as running, cycling, climbing and walking.

Practice Questions

Q1 Give one example where the decision of an MNC has affected the character of a place.

Q2 Briefly outline how the past development of a place can influence its character.

Exam Question

Q1 'The decisions of governments, MNCs and global institutions are the most important control on the characteristics of places.' With reference to **one or more** places you have studied, how far do you agree with this statement? [20 marks]

Changing places — when the seating plan just isn't right...

The story of Sheffield above is a great example of how you could approach your own place studies — look back through the history of your places to understand all the things that have made them what they are today, and how they've changed.

Meanings and Representations of Place

Yep, it's more detail about sense of place right here. Take a look back at page 144 if you're already feeling confused...

People Perceive and Present Places Differently

1) Places have **meaning** to the people that **know** them — this is their **sense** of those places, i.e. how they **feel** about them.

2) Different people, or groups of people, can attach **different meanings** to the **same places**, e.g. different people may think of the same place as beautiful or unattractive, exciting or boring, stressful or peaceful.

3) How people **feel** about a place is often dependent on their **experience** of that place, e.g. people may feel like **insiders** or **outsiders** (see p.144) in a place depending on whether their experience of that place has been **positive** or **negative**.

4) How people feel about places can also be affected by how places have been **represented** to them.

> The **representation of place** is how individuals, or organisations such as businesses or councils, **portray** places they **know about** to others.

See below and the next page for more about how places are represented.

5) People or organisations can represent places in **different ways** depending on what their **perspective** is. For example:

- Individuals who are **proud** to come from a place may present it to others in a **positive** way, whilst individuals who have had a **bad experience** of a place may present it **negatively** to others.

- Organisations, such as **tourism companies** or **local councils**, may present places **positively** as they stand to **gain** from how the places are perceived. **Newspapers** may choose to focus on the **negative** aspects of a place in circumstances where it may help them to **sell more copies**.

6) Meanings and representations of places are important as they can change how people **behave** towards those places, e.g. **positive** feelings about a place may make a person decide to go on **holiday** or **invest** in a business there, whilst **negative** feelings may make them **avoid** that place.

7) Meanings and representations of places are also important as many people generate their **identity** (their sense of who they are) based on the places they feel **connected to**.

Come to Porkpiesville — the perfect place for your family holiday.

Many Groups Influence Our Perceptions of Place

1) Some groups try to **influence** people's sense of place, or even create **new meanings** for particular places, so that they can **change** people's **behaviour** towards those places:

- **Governments**, both nationally and locally, might do this to **attract people** or **investment** to particular places.

- **Corporate bodies** (e.g. businesses, government-funded agencies) might do this to **generate profit**, or because they have been set up for a **specific purpose**, e.g. VisitBritain is an agency set up to **promote tourism** to the UK.

- **Community** or **local groups** might try to change the **perception** of their place to improve the **local economy** or the lives of **local people**, e.g. local people and business owners in Ludlow promote the town through organising a **food festival** every year — this associates Ludlow with **good food** and **attracts visitors** to the area.

2) Here are three of the main **strategies** used to alter perceptions of place:

- **Place marketing** is how places are 'sold' like products to consumers — the people who will potentially **visit**, **move** to the area or **invest money** there. **Marketing companies** may be employed to produce websites, design logos, run advertising campaigns and social media pages — all of which are designed to **promote** a particular place. E.g. the Lake District is being promoted as the 'Adventure Capital' of the UK through a website and related social media pages which have details of all the available activities in the area.

- **Reimaging** is about **changing** existing **negative perceptions** of places. E.g. in the 1980s and 1990s some people's image of Birmingham was that it was a place of high unemployment, abandoned factories and poor architecture. Many places in Birmingham have been reimaged by turning old industrial areas into new developments, e.g. Brindleyplace is a former industrial site that has been repurposed into a town centre mixed development that include shops, offices, residential areas, restaurants, bars, a gallery and a theatre.

- **Rebranding** is about giving a place a **new identity** that is **appealing** to people and investors. It is achieved through reimaging, place marketing and regeneration schemes. As part of rebranding, many places create **logos** and **slogans** that are designed to be **instantly recognisable** and create **positive associations** with the place they're representing. For example, Glasgow's rebranding included the slogan 'People Make Glasgow' to highlight what makes Glasgow a great place — the people that live and work there.

Meanings and Representations of Place

Places Can be Represented Using a Variety of Different Forms

1) Some forms of representing places are **quantitative** — they can be quantified **numerically** and **statistical analyses** can be performed on them. E.g. representations based on data, such as tables of statistics, graphs and charts are quantitative.

2) Other forms are **qualitative** — they can't be quantified numerically and may be more **descriptive** or **creative**. E.g. representations such as art, poetry and photography.

3) Different forms can create **contrasting** representations of places. When investigating places, it's important to look at a **variety** of different sources to build up a **complete picture** of what a place is like.

> *Objective means based on facts, subjective means based on feelings or opinions.*

Statistics

- Statistics, such as **census data**, can give you lots of **quantitative information** about what places are **like**, e.g. population, population structure, average income, crime figures etc. They can be in the form of raw data, or visually represented through things like charts or graphs.

- Statistics themselves are **objective**, but they can be used **subjectively**, e.g. people can **select** which data they use to show what they want to show. Statistics also don't usually tell you anything about **sense of place**.

Maps

- Maps can be used to show any sort of **data** that has a **location**, e.g. they can show where physical features are. They can also show **quantitative** demographic and economic data, e.g. different levels of income by location.

- Some maps can also show **qualitative** information, such as maps of indexes that show levels of **happiness** — these may be more helpful than quantitative maps for information about **sense of place**.

- Maps can show you **reliable** data, but they can also be **misleading**, e.g. historical maps may be inaccurate.

Films, photography and art

- Visual representations show what places **look like**, and can give some sense of the **character** of places. However, they only represent what the artist **wants** to show you, and can therefore be **misleading**.

- Photographs only show what a place looks like in a **given moment** — photographs taken at different times of day can make a place **look** and **feel different**. Photographs can also be **altered** so places look different to the reality.

- Films and television evoke a **sense of place** that is dependent on the **nature** of the story being told, e.g. a crime drama set in a city might give a different sense of place to a romantic drama set in the same city.

- Paintings or sculptures can be **less reliable** than films and photography at showing what a place **looks like** as they are the artist's **interpretation**. They can be more effective at conveying **sense of place** and character though.

Stories, articles, music and poetry

- Written representations can be used to **describe** places, and can also evoke a sense of how it **feels** to be in that place. They usually only offer the perspective of the **author** though, so they don't show a **complete picture**.

- Newspaper articles can give lots of **detail** about places but they may be **biased**, e.g. newspapers may focus on the topics and ideas that are likely to sell more copies, rather than give a balanced perspective on a place.

- Stories, music and poetry can give an **emotional impression** of places, but only from the **writer's perspective**.

Practice Questions

Q1 What is the meant by the term 'representation of place'?

Q2 Give three strategies that could be used to alter people's perception of place.

Exam Question

Q1 The painting shows Venice, Italy. Assess how useful qualitative representations of place, such as this painting, are in helping you to understand the character of a place.

[6 marks]

Exam halls — places of stress or places of relaxation...

Once you start looking for it, you'll see place marketing everywhere — logos, slogans, events, festivals. All these things and more are done to create positive meanings for places. In fact, I think I feel a song about my home town coming on...

Place Studies

And so we come to it at last... the place studies. You need to bring together everything you've learnt about this topic to do the place studies properly — so these pages may well be the most important in the section so far... gulp.

You need to do Studies of Two Places

1) One of your place studies needs to be about a place that is **local** to you, i.e. where you **live** or where your **school** is. The other needs to be about a place that **contrasts** with your local place, and is likely to be **distant** from it.

2) Your distant place should contrast with your local place in terms of its **economy**, **demographics**, **social inequality** or **cultural characteristics** — ideally a **combination** of these factors so there are lots of ways to **compare** them.

3) The distant place could be in the **UK** or **abroad**, but think carefully about how easy it will be to **find information** about the place. Sources on UK places may be easier to find and more **comparable** to the sources on your local place.

4) Your places shouldn't be **too big** — think about places that are the size of a **village**, **small town** or **part** of a larger city.

5) Your research should focus on the **material** that's been covered throughout **this topic**, i.e. the characteristics of the places and how they've changed, the external forces that have caused change, past and present connections and developments, the meanings of those places to different people and how the places have been represented.

6) You also need to make sure that you've got a **mix** of **quantitative** and **qualitative** sources from both the **past** and the **present**.

7) Over the next four pages, we'll go over some **tips** for putting together your place studies, and give examples using two places we've chosen — central **Liverpool** and **Lerwick** on the Shetland Islands.

Take a look back at pages 146-147 for more about the character of places.

Research the Characteristics and History of Your Places

1) **Maps** are a good source for the **basic characteristics** of places — they can show you the **physical characteristics**, e.g. the location and topography, and some **human characteristics**, e.g. the built environment and infrastructure.

2) The **Ordnance Survey®** is the UK's mapping agency, providing a variety of types of map. OS® maps are available to view **online** or as paper maps that can be found in **libraries**.

3) **Google Maps™** can be viewed **online** and can provide both **maps** and **satellite images**. **Google Street View™** gives images at street level of many places round the world (this could be particularly helpful for your distant place).

4) **Historic maps** are also available, which can be **compared** to modern maps to show **change over time**. You could find these via **Internet searches** for organisations such as **local history societies**.

5) You should research the **history** of your places too — to see how they've **changed over time** and the **forces** that have affected their **development**. Your school or local library will have books, such as atlases and encyclopedias, that may provide more information on the history of your places.

6) Internet searches will allow you to find a **wide variety** of other sources about your places. For example, **local tourism websites** and **local government websites** may provide a lot of local information, and **news articles** can give you detailed information about **past** and **present** issues affecting your places.

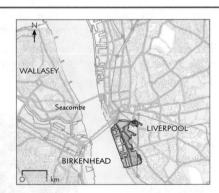

Central Liverpool, located on the River Mersey estuary, is the centre of one of the UK's largest cities. Liverpool was a major port for global trade and a centre of manufacturing between the 18th and mid-20th centuries, during which time the city grew and attracted immigrants from around the world. The docks and factories declined in the 1960s, leading to large scale deprivation. Recently though, Liverpool has attracted a lot of investment for regeneration and was chosen as the European Capital of Culture in 2008.

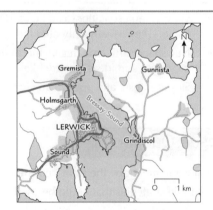

Lerwick, the capital of the Shetland Islands, is a small town and port located on the east of the main island. In its earlier history, the island was populated by Vikings but has been part of Scotland since the 15th century. Its major industry has traditionally been fishing, but North Sea oil was discovered in the 1970s which, along with increases in tourism, has led to improvements in the economy.

Place Studies

Demographic Characteristics are About People

1) The demographic characteristics of your places are about **who** the people are and what they're **like**. E.g. you might research the population size, density and structure (e.g. age and gender), birth rate or ethnicity of your places.

2) You need to look at how demographic characteristics have **changed over time**, and the **reasons why** they've changed — think about the external **flows** and **forces** and the changes they've caused (see pages 148-151).

3) A great source of demographic data is the **census** — the survey of the UK population conducted every ten years. This data, along with other statistics, can be accessed through the website of the **Office for National Statistics** (ONS).

4) It's possible to generate statistics and summaries about **specific places** through the ONS website ('neighbourhood' statistics).

5) The website **DataShine.org.uk** and the **Consumer Data Research Centre** also show demographic data, using interactive tools for displaying the data on maps.

Take a look back at page 148 for more about changing demographic and cultural characteristics.

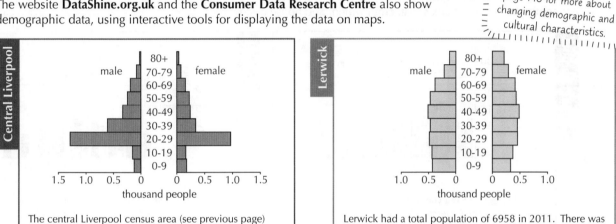

The central Liverpool census area (see previous page) had a population of 5436 in 2011. A large proportion of the population were young and working age (20-39) due to the high availability of work in the area (see p.156), and there was a high proportion of males.

Lerwick had a total population of 6958 in 2011. There was a lower proportion of people of working age, and a higher proportion of older people compared to central Liverpool. As a result of the population structure, there are concerns that the Shetlands have an increasingly ageing population.

Cultural Characteristics Could be Shown Using Qualitative Sources

1) The cultural characteristics of your places are about **how** people live their lives. E.g. you might research the languages spoken, foods eaten, clothes worn, literature read, music listened to or the attitudes and beliefs people have.

2) Think about how these have **changed over time** and what **caused** those changes.

3) Sources for cultural characteristics may be **quantitative**, e.g. census data may be available on the religions practised or languages spoken in your places.

4) They could also be qualitative, e.g. **literature** or **music**. There may be **travel writing** or **biographies** of people who have experienced the **culture** of your places, and local people may also have written **poems** or songs that reflect their culture.

Central Liverpool

Many people consider poetry and music to be a key part of Liverpool's culture, and there are famous musicians and poets that are closely associated with Liverpool. For example, The Beatles were one of the most successful bands of all time. They wrote songs about places in Liverpool and gave the city global connections — with fans when they were playing in the 1960s, and by continuing to attract tourists from around the world.

Famous poets, such as Roger McGough, are also closely associated with Liverpool. In 2007, Roger McGough was involved in a project to celebrate the 800th birthday of the city. He wrote the opening and closing lines of an 800-line poem (The Liverpool Saga), with all the other lines written by the people of Liverpool — the idea was that the poem would reflect the varied history, people and culture of Liverpool. Lines such as, "Eight hundred different cultures, eight hundred different tongues" give an insight into the mixed cultures found in the city, which are the result of immigration throughout Liverpool's history.

Lerwick

Shetland has a distinct dialect (variety of a language) that is still in use today. The dialect is similar to other Scottish dialects but contains many features, words and sounds from an old form of Norwegian. This reflects the cultural history of the island, which has been populated by a mix of Vikings and Scottish people. Many of the place names on the islands reflect this, e.g. Lerwick is a similar name to Leirvik, a place in Norway, which means 'bay of clay'.

The dialect has been represented through poetry, and some poets are particularly associated with the Shetland Islands. For example, T.A. Robertson was a poet who wrote in Shetland dialect, and about Shetland, in the mid 20th century. The poem 'Kwarna Farna?' is about depopulation on the islands and contains lines such as, "Bit noo da laand is bare", to evoke the sense of emptiness on the island caused by emigration.

Place Studies

Yet more place study stuff on here. Well, we wouldn't forget the economic and social characteristics now, would we...

Economic Characteristics are About **Work** and **Money**

1) The economic characteristics of your places are to do with **work** and **money**. E.g. you might research employment and unemployment statistics, income, the types of job available or house prices for your places.

2) You need to look at how they've **changed over** time, and the reasons **why** they've changed — think about the external **flows** and **forces** and the changes they've caused (see pages 148-151).

3) You'll find data on economic characteristics in a lot of the **same places** as for demographic characteristics — data from the **census** and **Office for National Statistics** covers things like **employment** and **income**.

4) Other websites, such as **CheckMyStreet.co.uk** and **uklocalarea.com**, give reports of **economic** data for local areas, e.g. employment and house prices.

These websites also have data on social characteristics, e.g. crime and education.

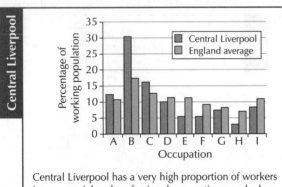

Central Liverpool

Central Liverpool has a very high proportion of workers in managerial and professional occupations, and a low proportion of the workforce in skilled trades and elementary occupations. This reflects the decline of the docks and manufacturing employment, and the rise of employment in the service sector — much redevelopment work on the city centre has focused on the creation of office space.

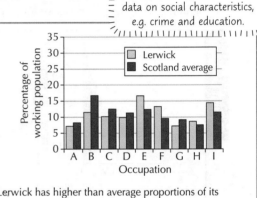

Lerwick

Lerwick has higher than average proportions of its workforce in skilled trades and elementary occupations, and lower than average proportions of its workforce in managerial and professional occupations. This reflects the continued importance of the seafood industry to Lerwick — the catching, processing and sale of fish around the harbour employs many people.

Key

A Managers, Directors and Senior Officials
B Professional Occupations
C Associate Professional and Technical
D Administrative and Secretarial
E Skilled Trades
F Caring, Leisure and Other Services
G Sales and Customer Service
H Process, Plant and Machine Operatives
I Elementary Occupations (e.g. labourers)

Social Characteristics can **Highlight Social Inequality**

1) The social characteristics of your places are to do with what people's **lives** are **like**. E.g. you might research things like quality of life, level of deprivation, crime, access to healthcare, education and leisure facilities for your places.

2) Think about how these have **changed over time** and what **caused** those changes.

3) **Compound indicators** of social and economic characteristics are a good overall indicator — these are indexes that take into account lots of different social and economic factors, e.g. the **Index of Multiple Deprivation** (IMD).

4) Data on **health** can be found at the website for the **Public Health Outcomes Framework**, and mapped **crime data** for local areas can be sourced at **police.uk**.

5) Social characteristics may be represented through **qualitative** sources as well, e.g. television programmes or films may highlight social issues in your places.

Take a look back at page 149 for more about changing economic and social characteristics.

Central Liverpool

Central Liverpool has a high crime rate. In January 2017 alone, there were 2076 crimes reported, including 362 violent and sexual offences.

Gang crime has historically been a problem across Liverpool, and media reports in the early part of 2017 have continued to highlight this, particularly in relation to gun crime. E.g. between April 2016 and February 2017 there were 79 shootings across the city, including 4 fatalities.

Central Liverpool continues to be associated with historic incidents of civil unrest, e.g. the Toxteth riots in 1981. Social and economic problems in the area led to a period of 9 days of rioting, in which many people were injured and 70 buildings were destroyed.

Lerwick

The Shetland Islands have a very low crime rate — in the year 2012-2013, a total of 1057 crimes were reported for the whole of the Shetland Islands.

Some media reports highlight this, e.g. the Shetland News reported in 2014 that "one of the safest communities in Scotland is becoming safer still". Other media reports highlight the rise of particular crimes. For example, in 2008 The Guardian highlighted a rise in drug crime on the islands.

Crime on Shetland has also been presented through a BBC crime drama, 'Shetland', which started in 2013. Fictional TV shows such as this may affect people's perception of the types of crime that occur in Shetland.

Place Studies

Meaning and Representation of Place are Important too

1) You need to cover the **lived experience** of people in your places, both in the **past** and in the **present**.

2) To do this you'll need sources that tell you, or show you, how people **feel** about the places you're studying (their sense of place).

Have a look at pages 152-153 for more about meaning and representation of place.

3) You also need to look at sources that show how your place has been **represented** — this can affect and create people's **perceptions** and therefore their **sense** of those places.

4) Sources that reflect the meaning and representation of places are likely to be **qualitative**, e.g. works of art, photographs, news articles, interviews with local people, stories or poems.

5) Art and photographs could be sourced from **image searches** on the **Internet**, or **image bank websites**. Older photographs may be available through **local history societies**.

6) News articles are available **online** via newspaper or news outlet websites. You should also consider **local newspapers** — they may offer **different perspectives** to national newspapers.

7) For your local place, you could conduct **interviews** or **surveys** of people's sense of place through **fieldwork**.

8) Stories and poems can be sourced through **libraries**, and many older poems are freely available online. Many authors and poets are **strongly associated** with particular places, and may have written a lot about the place and the **issues** that have affected it over time.

Central Liverpool

Stanley Dock tobacco warehouse

Some major buildings in central Liverpool, such as the Stanley Dock tobacco warehouse, have been disused following the industrial decline of the mid to late 20th century (though there are current plans to redevelop them). Albert Dock was also abandoned but has been redeveloped as a multi-use attraction, including a major art gallery (Tate Liverpool).

Photographs such as these represent central Liverpool differently — the disused warehouse image shows decline and abandonment, whilst Albert Dock is presented as modern, exciting and attractive.

Albert Dock

Lerwick

Burning longship at Up Helly Aa

The Viking heritage of the Shetlands is represented by an annual festival held in Lerwick. During Up Helly Aa (which means 'the end of the holiday') local people dress as Vikings and have a torchlit procession, which culminates in the burning of a Viking longship. Though the festival celebrates the Viking heritage of the Shetlands, its origin is relatively recent — it has been going in its present form since the late 19th Century. Local people are involved in the preparations throughout the year, including creating the costumes and building the longship.

Images such as this convey a sense of drama around the festival, which helps to communicate the lived experience of the people and create a sense of the place.

The festival also connects Lerwick to the world through tourists who come to experience it.

Whatever sources you find (quantitative or qualitative), it's important to be **critical** about them — for each source think about what its **strengths** and **weaknesses** are. It might be that some sources are **biased**, or it might be that some are **inaccurate**. Other sources may be more **reliable**, but only offer the viewpoint of **one particular individual**.

Practice Questions

Q1 Briefly describe Lerwick's population structure.

Q2 Briefly describe the cultural characteristics of Liverpool.

Q1 Assess the extent to which the experiences of people living in a place that you have studied have been affected by the past development of that place. [20 marks]

Liverpool and Lerwick — like peas in a pod...

Having a good mix of qualitative and quantitative sources for your places studies, to show what they were like in the past and what they're like today, is vital. So take the time to do the research properly and it'll pay off big time come exam day.

Urbanisation

Ahh cities, at last. This is a section you'll know a little bit about already. You might live in a city, or maybe you've visited a few on holiday. These first couple of pages will help you get to grips with the basics of urban areas...

The **Population** of **Urban Areas** is **Increasing**

1) Globally, the **number** and **proportion** of people living in **urban** areas has **increased** dramatically since 1945. In **1950**, **30%** of people **lived** in **urban areas**. In **2014**, just over **50%** lived in **towns** or **cities**.

2) In the developed world, the **majority** of people **live in cities**, but the **urban population** has only **increased slightly** since 1945. This is because urbanisation **began** much **earlier** in the **developed world** than in the **developing world** — during the **Industrial Revolution**, many people **moved** to cities in search of **work** in **mills** and **factories**. Although people are still **moving** to **cities** such as **London** and **New York**, **similar** numbers of people are leaving these cities.

3) In the developing world, **most people** currently live in **rural areas** — but this is **changing** fast. In many developing countries and emerging economies (countries with a rapidly growing economy), **old cities** are **growing** in size and **new cities** are **forming**. For example, in **Beijing, China**, the **urban population** increased from **4.4 million** in **1970** to **20.4 million** in **2015**.

With her cool new look and sassy attitude, Sam knew she'd fit in just fine in the city.

Four **Processes** Affect the **Populations** of **Cities**

There are **four processes** that involve the **movement of people** into and out of urban areas:

People move because of push factors (things that make them <u>leave</u> an area) and pull factors (things that attract them <u>to</u> an area).

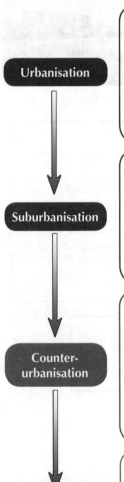

Urbanisation

- This is the **growth** in the **proportion** of people living in **urban areas**.
- It usually occurs because of **migration** (especially **rural-urban migration**) and **natural increase** (when birth rate is higher than death rate). People often migrate to cities for easier access to **schools** and **healthcare**, and because there are **more jobs** available.
- Many migrants are **young adults** — if they have **children**, the population increases further.
- In **developing countries**, urbanisation can result in **shanty towns** — **unplanned** and often **illegal** settlements made out of any material available.

Suburbanisation

- This is the migration of people from **city centres** to the **outskirts** of cities.
- As **urbanisation increases**, city centres become **overcrowded** and people desire **more space**. Improvements to **transport links** mean people can **live further away** and **commute** to work. Many people choose to move to the suburbs when they have **children** or **retire**.
- A **complex pattern** of **wealthy** and **poorer** areas develops. **Wealthier middle-class people** may move to the **suburbs** where there is a **better quality of life**. Those left behind are **poorer** and may include **foreign immigrants**. This can lead to economic and ethnic **segregation**.

Counter-urbanisation

- This is the movement of people **out of the city** into surrounding **villages** and **rural areas**.
- Improvements in **transport** mean people can **commute** to work and better **communications** (e.g. internet access) allow people to **work from home**.
- People leave cities because of **high property prices** and **overcrowding**. Some people may just **prefer quieter rural areas**.
- Counter-urbanisation can lead to new **housing estates** being built in rural areas. House prices may **increase**, meaning that some local people (e.g. young people) **can't afford** to live there. It can change the **age structure** of the area, e.g. average age may increase.

Urban Resurgence

- This is the **movement** of people **back** to the **city centre**.
- People may move back to city centres because of a **lack of jobs** in rural or suburban areas. People are also attracted by new developments (e.g. high quality housing).
- Urban resurgence is **common** in many **post-industrial countries**, like the UK and USA.
- New **shops** and **services** may open in the city as people move back, boosting the local **economy** and creating **jobs**. However, original residents may not be able to **afford** to live in the area any more, and may be forced to **move** to cheaper locations.

Urbanisation

Urbanisation has led to the Emergence of Megacities

Population growth in urban areas has **increased** the number of **big cities** in the world:

1) A **megacity** is an urban area with **over 10 million people** living there, e.g. Istanbul, Turkey.

2) In 1950 there were only **two** megacities — Tokyo and New York. By 2014 there were **28**, and this is predicted to rise to **41** by **2030**. More than **two-thirds** of megacities are in **developing nations**, e.g. Lagos, Nigeria.

3) Megacities develop because of **rural-urban migration** and **natural increase**. Migrants tend to move to **large** cities, and to cities that are experiencing **rapid economic growth**, so their population increases rapidly.

4) Megacities **dominate** the national and regional **economies** of countries. This is because companies choose to build their **headquarters** in cities with a **high number** of **skilled workers** and good **transport links**, e.g. international airports.

5) Megacities often have people living at **opposite extremes** — some are **really rich**, while others live in **extreme poverty**.

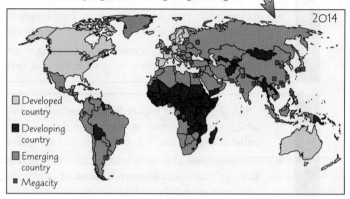

World Cities are Global Centres for Finance, Business and Culture

1) A **world city** is a city that has political and financial **influence** over the **whole world,** e.g. London and Sydney. Most are in the **developed world** but **some**, e.g. Dubai and Rio de Janeiro, are in **emerging economies**.

2) The **number** of world cities is **increasing**. In **1950**, the only world cities were London, Paris, Tokyo and New York. More recently, **economic growth** in **oil-rich countries** such as Nigeria has allowed cities such as **Lagos** to become **contenders** for **world city status**. These cities are **increasingly important** in **global economics** and **business**.

3) Since 1945, **world cities** such as London and New York have **emerged** as the **leaders** of **banking** and **finance**. Many **banking companies**, such as HSBC, Lloyds and RBS, have **headquarters** in these cities.

4) **World cities** usually **dominate** international **trade** and **regional economies** in their area. For example, **Tokyo** is extremely **influential** in international **trade** between the **East Asian nations**. World cities have good international **transport links**, which allow them to trade with the rest of the world.

5) World cities are generally home to world-renowned **universities**. They also tend to be centres for **science** and **innovation**, with high-quality **research and development** facilities.

6) They are also centres for **culture** — they are often home to large, globally influential **media** and **communications** corporations, as well as a range of theatres, museums and other cultural attractions.

7) They tend to attract high numbers of **people** from other countries, including **migrants**, **business visitors**, **students** and **tourists**.

The City of London is the main business and financial centre of London.

Practice Questions

Q1 What is counter-urbanisation?

Q2 What is a megacity?

Q3 Give two characteristics of world cities.

Exam Question

Q1 Assess the possible reasons for the global distribution of megacities shown in the map above. [9 marks]

Megacity — not quite an awesomecity, but better than a coolcity...

It all seems very confusing. First people move to the city for jobs, then into the suburbs for space, then back to the city once they realise that they're missing all the amenities of the city. I'm surprised they don't get dizzy and fall over more.

Urban Change

In the developed world in particular, cities have gone through rapid change since the 1970s.

There are **Many Processes** Associated with **Urbanisation**

Cities **develop** in lots of different ways as they **urbanise**:

Economic
- Cities attract people from **rural areas** because they offer more **job opportunities**, and jobs are often **better paid**.
- As the urban population increases, **businesses** such as factories and shops **grow** in size and become **more profitable**. This leads to more **jobs** and **wage rises**.
- As countries develop, **commercial farming** overtakes subsistence farming as the **primary method** of **food production**. The **decline** in agricultural jobs **drives** even more **people** into **towns** and **cities**.

Social
- Cities tend to have **higher living standards** than rural areas, e.g. better access to healthcare and education, which attracts people. As more people move to a city and the economy grows, it can become a **centre** for **cultural expression**, e.g. **museums** and **art galleries** open.
- The **migration** of people into urban areas **increases** the **mix of people** from different social backgrounds. This can make people **more tolerant** of others, creating a **welcoming environment** that attracts more migrants. However, **segregation** of people from different social backgrounds is also common (see pages 164-165).

Technological
- With the emergence of **factories** in cities, **urban areas** become **hotspots** for **technological advancement**. For example, in the 19th century, **Manchester** became the **first industrialised city** in the world and was branded '**Cottonopolis**' because of its **cotton-processing factories**.
- More recently, areas with a large number of **high-tech industries** have emerged, e.g. **Silicon Valley** in California. These areas attract people because they offer **specialised** and **highly paid jobs**.

Political
- Urban growth may lead to increased **inequalities** between rich and poor people. A new '**working class**' emerges, often made up of people who work in **manufacturing industries**.
- New **political movements** emerge to represent the '**working class**' population. **Political reform** focuses on **issues** that **affect urban life**, e.g. poor sanitation, quality of housing, working conditions in factories.

Demographic
- As **cities** become **larger** and **wealthier**, they **attract migrants** from all over the world. Urban areas become more **culturally** and **ethnically diverse** and **new areas** emerge, e.g. Chinatown in New York City.
- Many **young people** are **attracted** by **jobs** and **entertainment** (e.g. bars and clubs). They often choose to stay and **raise families** in the city, so cities tend to have a **younger population** than rural areas.

Developed Countries Have Experienced Deindustrialisation Since the 1970s

Cities in developed countries have undergone several **processes of change** in the last **fifty years**:

1) **DEINDUSTRIALISATION** — in the **1960s**, some **developing nations**, such as Singapore and Taiwan, became **industrialised**. These countries were able to **produce goods** at a **cheaper price** than Europe or North America, mainly due to **lower labour costs**. By the 1970s, the **developed world** was **struggling to compete** with the products being manufactured in the developing world. Entire **industries collapsed**, e.g. steel in Sheffield, which led to mass **unemployment** and **poverty**. In the UK, **deindustrialisation** caused **unemployment** to rise above **3 million** in 1983. This was the **highest rate** of unemployment since the **Second World War**.

2) **RISE OF THE SERVICE ECONOMY** — during the 1980s, many **service industries** (e.g. retail and banking) began to expand and **dominate western economies**. These industries have been **responsible** for the majority of **economic growth** in developed countries since deindustrialisation.

3) **DECENTRALISATION** — as **land prices** in city centres increase, businesses such as shops and offices may **relocate** to suburbs. This has led to the rise of out-of-town **retail parks**, e.g. Meadowhall near Sheffield. Decentralisation has caused city centre shops and offices to **close** — this has led to buildings being **abandoned**, **job losses** and urban **poverty**.

Topic Nine — Contemporary Urban Environments

Urban Change

Since 1979 British Governments Have Tried to Regenerate Cities

There have been **lots of schemes** to improve cities in the UK since 1979:

Urban Development Corporations — 1979-1990s

- By 1979, many UK city centres were in **catastrophic decline**. The government created agencies called **Urban Development Corporations** (UDCs), which used private sector funding to restore derelict areas.
- The first UDCs were established in 1981 in the **London Docklands** and Liverpool. The main aims of the London Docklands UDC were to attract **new businesses**, improve the local **environment**, create **jobs** and build **new houses** for professionals. Between 1981 and 1998, the Corporation built **24 000** new homes and created **85 000** jobs. In addition, the Corporation built **new schools**, **parks** and **community facilities**, including a sailing and watersports centre and Surrey Quays shopping centre.
- By 1993, **twelve UDCs** had been established, helping to redevelop some of the most rundown areas of the country. However, the UDCs were criticised for **ignoring** the needs of **local residents**, e.g affordable homes and suitable jobs.

Enterprise Zones — 1981-Present

- In 1981, **Enterprise Zones** (EZs) were **established** in areas with **high unemployment**. Their aim was to attract **start-up companies** to the area to **create jobs** — they did this by **reducing tax**, e.g. on corporations and land.
- By 1990, the EZs housed over **5000 companies**, employing more than **125 000 people**. However, tax reductions encouraged many **existing companies** to **move** their premises and staff to the EZs, which **limited** the number of **new jobs** that were created.

City Challenge — 1991-1997

- In the **City Challenge** programme, local authorities **competed** for government funding to regenerate deprived urban areas. They worked with the local community and private companies to improve the **physical**, **economic** and **social environment** of the area.
- Funding was allocated to projects that **benefited** the **local community**, e.g. improving housing, providing vocational training and creating jobs for local people. By 1997, over **50 000 jobs** had been created and **40 000 houses** improved. However, many deprived areas didn't receive any **funding**.

Partnership Schemes — 2010-Present

- Since 2010, the government has worked with private companies to provide **financial support** and **expertise** for urban regeneration — these are called **partnership schemes**.
- These schemes are designed to improve **physical**, **economic** and **social** conditions in deprived areas, e.g. by building new **homes**, providing **parks** and **sports centres**, and **reducing unemployment**.
- For example, the **Liverpool City Region Local Enterprise Partnership** was established in 2012 — it aims to increase **business activity** in Liverpool and create new **jobs**.

Peter and Lara's partnership scheme was heading straight for divorce.

Practice Questions

Q1 Give one economic reason why people might move from the country to the city.

Q2 What is deindustrialisation?

Q3 Name three regeneration schemes used by the UK government since 1979.

Exam Question

Q1 Assess the extent to which urbanisation affects the character of cities. [9 marks]

Wonder if I can get funding to redevelop my local area...

Ideally, I'd like to improve my environmental conditions (by replacing the floors of my house with trampolines) and my social conditions (by making life an endless party). You grab the party hats, and I'll start putting together a bid for funding...

Urban Forms

From the smallest city in the world (Vatican City, in case you're wondering) to megacities and world cities (see p.159), every city has its own unique form. Here's a reminder of exactly what that means — try not to get too excited.

Urban Form is Affected by Physical and Human Factors

1) Urban form is the **physical characteristics** that make up a city, including its **size** and **shape**, **population density** and how the city is **arranged** (e.g. **land-use patterns** in different areas).

2) Many cities were initially established in areas with good **water supplies**, **fertile soil** for growing food, plentiful natural **resources** (e.g. woodland for fuel) and good **defensive** positions (e.g. on top of a hill).

3) Over time, the urban form of cities **changes**. These changes are influenced by a number of factors, including:

Physical Factors

- **Topography** — **physical features** often influence the growth of cities. E.g. **steep slopes** are harder to build on and **less accessible**, so poorer housing (e.g. slums) may be built on them. Large **flat** areas encourage **low density** developments because there's lots of space to build.

- **Water** — the presence of **lakes** and seas **limits** urban growth in those areas, while cities may grow **along** the course of a **river**. City centre shops and businesses are usually located close to the **waterfront**, rather than at geographical centre of the city.

- **Natural resources** — rich resources (e.g. coal, metal) **encourage growth** in size and population of cities.

- **Land type** — some ground surfaces are more difficult or expensive to build on than others, e.g. **swamps** and **wetlands** can **limit** urban growth.

Human Factors

- **Planning** — urban expansion can be **planned** or **unplanned**. For example, a lot of urban growth in **developing countries** is caused by the unplanned expansion of **slums**. In contrast, **planned** developments often include open space, leisure facilities etc.

- **Infrastructure** — new developments are often built along **transport links** (e.g. motorways), leading to **linear growth**.

- **Land value** — the **highest** value land is often found in the **city centre**, so **profitable** businesses (e.g. chain stores) normally locate there, while **less profitable** businesses (e.g. independent shops) may be found **further** from the centre.

Cities in the Developed World Have Different Land-Use Patterns...

1) Cities in **developed** countries tend to have a **Central Business District** (CBD) — a central zone of shops and businesses.

2) The CBD is **surrounded by housing**. Although **land value** tends to be **highest** in the city centre, **houses** generally increase in value with distance **away** from the centre:

- **Inner city areas** have **high** land value, so housing is typically **high density**, e.g. **skyscrapers**. Wages are often low, and many residents live in relative **poverty**. The proportion of people from **ethnic minorities** tends to be high.

- Land value is **lower** in rural and semi-rural areas, so residential areas are **less dense** and have more **open space**. Houses are usually **larger** and **newer** than those in inner city areas. Residents are generally quite **wealthy** and earn relatively high wages. The proportion of people from **ethnic minorities** tends to be low.

3) Because of the availability of **cheap land** in **semi-rural areas** close to urban centres, many **science parks** and large **shopping centres** are constructed there, e.g. Bristol and Bath Science Park, the Trafford Centre in Manchester.

...To Those in the Developing World

1) Cities in the developing world also have **CBDs** — these zones contain shops, offices and entertainment services.

2) The CBD is surrounded by housing, which **decreases** in **value** with distance away from the centre:

- Land value is **highest** around the city centre, so **high-cost housing** (e.g. luxury apartments) is built there. Wages are generally **high**, and residents are **wealthy**. These areas are often home to **wealthy immigrants** from developed countries and emerging economies.

- Surrounding the high-cost housing there is often a zone of **medium-cost** housing. It may have started as an **informal settlement**, but gradually the housing has been **improved** and some **services** have been provided.

- Land value is very **low** on the **outskirts** of cities, so **low-cost** and **informal** housing is built there, often with **limited access** to services such as clean water and electricity. Most residents have **poorly paid** jobs and **poverty** levels are high. Immigrants from **elsewhere** in the country and from **other** developing countries may settle there.

3) **Industrial areas** are often located along **transport links**, e.g. major roads.

Urban Forms

Cities in Developed Countries Have Seen Recent Changes

Modern urban areas have a **range** of **recent features**:

Town Centre Mixed Developments
- These are areas where **land use** is **mixed** — luxury flats, offices, shops and entertainment facilities (e.g. bars, cinemas, gyms) are all located there, so **residential**, **commercial** and **leisure** uses are combined.
- Developments are **planned** by local councils, often with **private investment**. The aim is to **attract people** back to city centres by giving them opportunities to live, work and relax there.

Cultural and Heritage Quarters
- These areas focus on the **history** or **character** of a city, e.g. Southampton's Cultural Quarter includes SeaCity Museum, which has exhibits about the city's maritime history.
- Such areas are often home to **theatres**, **art galleries** and **historical buildings**.
- They are often developed by **local councils** to **regenerate former industrial areas**. They attract **visitors**, encouraging **economic development** and creating jobs.

Fortress Developments
- These are developments (e.g. for residential or retail use) with lots of **security**, such as CCTV, guards and high walls. They are often located in **suburban** areas of large cities, and only those with permission can enter them.
- They are designed to give a **safe environment** for families, but they are very **divisive** — only rich people can afford to live in or use them.

Gentrified Areas
- Gentrification is when **wealthier people** move into **rundown inner city areas** and regenerate them by improving **housing**.
- Gentrified areas often have a large range of **services**, e.g. shops and restaurants, and contain **high-quality housing**. However, **poorer residents** may be **displaced** as the cost of living increases, leading to social and ethnic segregation.

Edge Cities
- Edge cities are new areas of **offices**, **shops** and **leisure facilities** that develop close to major **transport links**, e.g. motorway intersections outside city centres, where land is **cheaper**. They often contain some housing, but most people **travel to them** for work or to use the services available.
- The majority of edge cities have developed since the **1950s** and **1960s** as **car ownership** has **increased**. They are most common in the USA, e.g. Las Colinas near Dallas, Texas.

Many Cities Are Evolving to Become Post-modern

Many cities, especially in developed countries, are gradually moving **away** from **uniformity** in **architecture** and from clear-cut patterns of **land use** — these are known as **post-modern western cities**. They have a number of characteristics:

1) **Multiple centres** with different purposes (e.g. high-tech industry, retail, heritage) rather than a single centre.
2) A focus on **tertiary** and **quaternary industry** (e.g. IT, media) instead of secondary industry.
3) Less uniform architecture — buildings have a wide range of styles.
4) Planning **prioritises** the **aesthetics** of the city (how it looks) over practical use.
5) Higher **social** and **economic inequality**.

Many cities have **elements** of post-modernism — e.g. in London, buildings such as the **Gherkin** and **Cheesegrater** are examples of **post-modern architecture**, and social and economic **inequalities** are **growing**.

Practice Questions

Q1 What is meant by the term 'urban form'?
Q2 Give two characteristics of post-modern western cities.

Exam Question

Q1 Assess how far traditional urban forms are being challenged by new urban forms in the developed world. [9 marks]

Move to Las Colinas — live life on the edge...

If you're stuck for something to do tonight, and there's nowt on telly, have a think about a town near you and all the things that give it a unique urban form. Or just watch some footage of cats falling off fences on the internet. Your call.

Urban Issues

With all those people crammed together, it's no wonder cities face social and economic problems...

All **Cities** Face **Economic Inequality**

"Looks, charm, dress sense... it's not just money that's unevenly distributed," brooded Hugo.

1) **Economic inequality** is the **unequal distribution** of **money** amongst a **population**.

2) Economic **inequalities** are **higher** in the **developing world** than in developed countries. This is because many developing countries **lack the resources** to **support** their **poorest citizens**, whereas most developed nations have **welfare states** which **provide basic services** and **income** for people who are struggling financially.

3) Economic inequality can cause lots of **issues** in cities, for example:
   - **Political** and **social unrest**, e.g. rioting.
   - A **rise** in **crime**, **drug use** and **violence**.
   - **Health** problems, e.g. cities with **higher levels** of **income inequality** have more **malnourished children**.

Cities Are *Culturally Diverse* but Often Experience *Social Segregation*

1) Cities tend to be **culturally diverse** — they have a wide mix of people from different **ethnic** and **cultural** backgrounds.

2) This can have lots of **benefits** — ethnic diversity can **enrich** a city's **character** and increase **tolerance**, while cultural events and ethnic quarters within a city can attract **tourists**, boosting the city's **economy**.

3) However, cultural diversity can also cause **problems** in cities, for example:

   - **Tensions** between different groups, sometimes leading to **violence**.
   - Increased pressure on **services**, e.g. schools may need extra staff for pupils who can't speak the native language.
   - Minority communities can feel **isolated** and **under-represented politically**.

4) Cities with high diversity, including people from different **ethnic**, **social** or **cultural backgrounds**, may also experience **social segregation**. This is when different groups are **separated** from each other, e.g. poorer people or people from a particular ethnic background are **concentrated** in a specific area of a city.

5) This can be **voluntary**, e.g. followers of a particular **religion** may choose to **settle** close to their **place of worship**. It can also be **forced**, e.g. many Roma people in Italy can't access social housing, so they end up in **camps** on city outskirts.

6) Social segregation can cause **issues** in urban areas, for example:

   - Lack of integration between different groups can cause **prejudice** and **discrimination**.
   - People in some areas may have less access to **education** and **jobs**, widening **inequalities**.
   - Segregation can lead to **anxiety** and have negative impacts on **health** and **life expectancy**.
   - In developing countries, poorer areas may lack access to **facilities**, e.g. electricity, clean water, public transport. They are also more likely to be close to industry and rubbish dumps, affecting **health** and **wellbeing**.

There Are **Strategies** *to* **Manage** *Urban* **Issues**

There are lots of strategies to **reduce poverty** and **economic inequalities** in urban areas:

   - Improving transport systems can make it easier for the urban poor to access jobs.
   - Subsidising the construction of affordable housing can help less wealthy people to buy property.
   - Introducing minimum wages can help to stabilise wage inequalities between the poor and rich.
   - Governments can offer subsidies for new companies, increasing local employment opportunities.
   - In developing countries, many cities have introduced upgrading programmes for slum settlements. Investments in road-building, sanitation, drainage and water supply increase the quality of informal housing.

There are also strategies to encourage **social and cultural integration**:

   - Governments can encourage political participation of minority groups, e.g. by sending postcards and text messages encouraging them to vote. This ensures minority groups have opportunities to influence decision-making.
   - Governments can pass laws, e.g. to prevent companies discriminating against employees on the basis of race.
   - New developments can include luxury homes and lower-cost housing, reducing divisions between rich and poor.
   - Communities can help ease racial tensions, e.g. by involving different groups in projects to clean off racist graffiti.

Urban Issues

London has Tried to Manage its Social and Economic Issues

London, a city in the **developed** world, has issues associated with **economic inequality**, **cultural diversity** and **social segregation**:

1) London is home to some of the **richest** and **poorest** people in the UK — this gap has **widened** since the 1980s.

2) The average annual **income** in Kensington and Chelsea is more than **£130 000**, but in Newham it's less than **£35 000**. Low wages and few job opportunities in some areas mean that more than **25%** of people in London live in **poverty**.

3) Many **inner city** areas, e.g. Notting Hill, have been **gentrified** — this has **forced poorer residents** out of the area.

4) London is culturally diverse — more than 50% of the population is **not white British**. Proportions of ethnic minorities **differ widely** between boroughs — e.g. in **Brent** over **60%** of people are not white British, whereas in **Havering** the proportion is only around **16%**, suggesting that ethnic segregation is an issue.

5) **Hate crime** based on race and religion is a problem in London, e.g. in the twelve months before July 2015, there were over 800 **anti-Muslim** incidents (including verbal abuse and violence) in the city.

6) Social segregation based on **age** and **class** is also an issue — London residents have less interaction with people of different age groups and classes than people elsewhere in the UK. This could lead some residents to feel **isolated**.

There are **strategies** in place to tackle these issues, e.g.:

1) From 2016, the **London Living Wage** increased to **£9.75** per hour (compared to £8.45 in the rest of the country). This should **increase income** and **social mobility** in deprived areas.

2) London mayor, Sadiq Khan, plans to build more **affordable homes** in London — this could allow less affluent people to remain in more expensive areas, **reducing** social segregation.

3) The police are working to tackle **hate crime**, e.g. by encouraging people to **report** it and offering **support** to victims.

4) Some charities are calling for better access to English **language classes** for immigrants, and **mentoring** schemes to help recent immigrants adjust to life in the UK, with the aim of **increasing integration** between groups.

São Paulo is Struggling to Tackle its Issues

São Paulo in Brazil, an **emerging** economy, also has issues of **economic inequality** and **social segregation**:

1) Economic inequality is **high** — the richest 10% of households earn nearly **forty times** more than the poorest 10%.

2) There is clear **segregation** between the richest and the poorest residents:

- The city's poorest residents live in slums (favelas), e.g. 80 000 people live in **Paraisópolis**, São Paulo's largest favela. It has **high crime** rates, **poor sanitation** and high incidence of illnesses such as **cholera**. The favelas **lack educational facilities** — this limits job options and social mobility.

- The wealthiest residents live in the **southwest** of São Paulo, in areas such as **Vila Nova Conceição**. These areas have more **green space**, better **healthcare** and access to amenities such as luxury **shops** and **restaurants**. These areas have large numbers of **white immigrants**, but the **lowest** proportion of **black people** in the city.

There are **strategies** in place to tackle these issues, e.g.:

1) In 2016, the **minimum wage** was raised by nearly **12%**, to increase **income** for the poorest workers.

2) In 2001, the government passed a law that allowed favelas to be recognised as **legitimate** residential areas. This led to investment in **sanitation**, **road building** and **housing improvement** in favelas, e.g. **10 000** new homes are currently being built to **replace** slum housing or housing in high-risk areas.

Practice Questions

Q1 Give two possible consequences of economic inequalities.

Q2 What is meant by 'social segregation'?

Exam Question

Q1 Analyse how social and economic issues can affect the character of cities. [9 marks]

Brown leather, small heel, slightly muddy — these are my urban-ish shoes...

Don't talk to me about managing social issues — I'm just try to arrange a nice birthday dinner, but Helen's fallen out with Raj, and Tom won't speak to Laura after she laughed at his hair. So yeah, I totally get the difficult issues that cities are facing.

Urban Climate

Urban climate characteristics — or 'what the weather's like in cities' to you and me. Geographers and their fancy names...

Urban Areas are Warmer than the Surrounding Rural Areas

1) The phenomenon of urban areas being warmer than rural areas is called the **urban heat island effect**.

2) Urban areas with higher air temperatures than the surrounding rural areas are called **urban heat islands** (UHIs). For example, **London** has a clearly defined UHI.

3) The **highest temperatures** are found in **industrial areas** and in the most **densely built up** areas, e.g. the **CBD** (Central Business District).

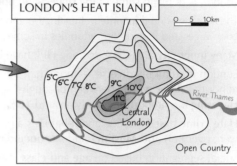

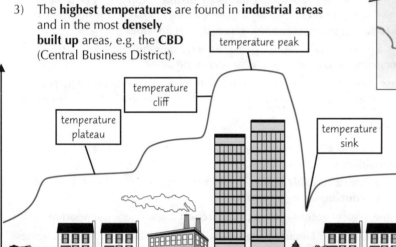

4) There are **pockets** of **cool air** above **parks** and **bodies of water** (e.g. rivers or ponds). These are called temperature '**sinks**'.

5) Areas within the city with the **same land use** (e.g. industry) generally have the **same temperature**. These are called temperature '**plateaus**'.

6) Temperature can **change rapidly** when **land use changes** (e.g. from inner city housing to CBD high rise buildings). Rapid changes are referred to as temperature '**cliffs**'.

There are Four Main Causes of the UHI Effect

Urban surfaces have a low albedo — they absorb lots of energy instead of reflecting it.

1) **ABSORPTION OF HEAT BY URBAN SURFACES:**
Concrete, brick and tarmac surfaces **absorb** and **store heat from the sun** during the **day**.
They slowly **release** the heat as **long wave radiation** — this is most noticeable at **night**, when it warms the air.

2) **AIR POLLUTION:**
Air pollution from cars and factories **increases cloud cover** over the city. It also creates a '**pollution dome**' — a layer of pollution over the city. Both these things **trap outgoing heat radiation** and **reflect it back** to the surface.

3) **HEAT FROM HUMAN ACTIVITY:**
Cars, factories, offices, central heating, air conditioning units and people themselves all release heat.

4) **LESS EVAPOTRANSPIRATION:**
When it rains the water's quickly removed by **drainage systems**, so there's **little surface water** to evaporate. Also, there isn't much **vegetation**, so there's **little transpiration**. **Evapotranspiration** uses heat energy, so less evapotranspiration means higher temperatures.

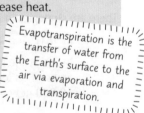

Evapotranspiration is the transfer of water from the Earth's surface to the air via evaporation and transpiration.

The Effect Varies Seasonally and Diurnally (Between Day and Night)

1) The UHI effect is stronger at **NIGHT**. Urban **daytime** temperatures are on average **0.6 °C warmer** than surrounding rural areas, but **night time** temperatures can be **3-4 °C warmer**. This is because rural areas cool down at night, but **urban areas don't cool as much** because **urban surfaces continue to release heat** that they've absorbed during the day.

2) It's stronger in **SUMMER** (in mid-latitude cities like London). Average **winter** temperatures can be **2 °C warmer**, but average summer temperatures can be up to **5 °C warmer**. This is because there's **more solar radiation in summer**, so urban areas absorb more heat.

3) It's stronger when there's an **ANTICYCLONE**. Anticyclones cause **clear skies** and **low winds**. If there are no clouds, **more solar radiation** reaches and heats the ground. **Low winds** mean **warm air isn't blown away**.

Urban Climate

Winds are Affected by Buildings in Urban Areas

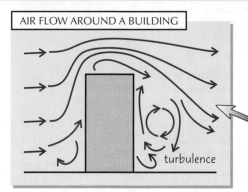

AIR FLOW AROUND A BUILDING

turbulence

1) **Average wind speed** is usually **lower** in cities than in rural areas. This is because **tall buildings create friction** that slows down the moving air.

2) There are areas where **wind speed** is **zero**, because some areas are **totally sheltered** from wind by **buildings**.

3) You get **turbulence around buildings**. This happens when **wind hits** the **face** of a **building** — some of it's **deflected down**, some **around the sides** and some **over the top**. When these winds hit other buildings or the ground they causes **vortices** (bodies of swirling air).

4) You get **powerful gusts** of wind when wind is **channelled down streets** — this is known as the **canyon effect**.

The canyon effect has implications for building design and town planning, e.g. positioning of buildings, and the location of doorways on larger buildings.

There's More Rain, Fog and Thunderstorms...

1) It **rains more often** in urban areas than in the surrounding countryside.

2) The rain is also **more intense** and there are **more thunderstorms**.

3) There are **two** main reasons for these things:

- The **UHI effect** means the air in urban areas is warm, and warm air can hold more water. The **warm, moist air rises** — this is called **convectional uplift**. As it rises it **cools**, the **water vapour condenses** and it **rains**. This type of rain is called **convectional rainfall**.

- Urban areas generate huge amounts of **dust** and **pollution**. Particles of dust and pollution floating about in the air act as **condensation nuclei** (they trigger water to condense around them). This **encourages clouds** to form, rather than allowing the warm, moist air to disperse.

4) The higher concentration of **condensation nuclei** in urban areas also **increases** the frequency of **fog**.

...but Less Snow and Frost

1) It **doesn't snow as often** in urban areas, and when it does, the **snow melts faster**. This is because it's **warmer** due to the **UHI effect**.

2) Urban areas have **fewer days of frost** for the same reason.

Darn that UHI effect — now I've gone and got my sleigh stuck.

Practice Questions

Q1 What is the urban heat island effect?

Q2 Give the four main causes of the urban heat island effect.

Q3 Explain why the urban heat island effect is stronger at night than during the day.

Q4 What effect do urban structures have on average wind speed?

Q5 Why is fog more frequent in urban areas than in rural areas?

	City A	City B
Annual average rainfall (mm)	1200	1300
Average July temperature (°C)	21	23
Average number of thunderstorms per year	18	25
Average number of days with fog	17	23
Average number of days without cloud cover	180	120

Exam Question

Q1 The table on the right shows climate data for two cities.
Analyse the possible reasons for the differences between the two urban climates. [6 marks]

UHI — I'm sure you can buy cream for that...

If you know what causes the UHI effect, you should be able to use your common sense to answer any exam question on it, e.g. if you're asked why parks are cooler than built up areas, talk about the fact that they have more vegetation and less tarmac. If you're asked why one city has a stronger UHI than another think about whether it might be more polluted, or more built up.

Urban Air Quality

Urban air pollution causes a range of pretty horrible health problems. Today, *cough* — sorry. Today, most pollution comes from road traffic. Cities all over the world have tried to solve the pollution problem simply by reducing traffic.

There's a lot of **Particulate Pollution** in Urban Areas

1) **Particulates** are **tiny pieces** of **solids** and **tiny droplets** of **liquids** floating in the air.

2) **More** particulates are found in **urban areas** than in rural areas. The concentration of particulates in urban areas is around 10-40 $\mu g/m^3$, compared to less than 10 $\mu g/m^3$ in rural areas.

3) **Sources** of particulates include:

> - **Vehicle exhausts** — they produce very **fine particulates** (0.01 µm-1.0 µm). About **80%** of fine particulates in urban areas are from vehicle exhausts.
> - **Burning** of refuse, cigarettes and fuel, e.g. coal — this produces both **fine** and **coarse particulates**, e.g. sulfates, nitrates, soot and ash.
> - **Construction**, **mining** and **quarrying** — these activities produce **coarse particulates** (10 µm-100 µm), e.g. tiny fragments of rock, brick and cement dust.
> - **Plants and moulds** — also generate **coarse particulates**, e.g. pollen and mould spores.

A microgram (µg) is one millionth of a gram and a micrometre (µm) is one thousandth of a millimetre.

4) Particulates can cause **health problems**. **Coarser particulates** are usually **filtered out** by the nose and throat, but **finer particulates less than 10 µm** in diameter (often called PM10) can enter the **lungs**. PM10 could **cause** or **make worse** problems like asthma, bronchitis, lung cancer and heart disease.

Other Types of Pollution Lead to **Photochemical Smog**

Smog over Mexico City.

1) Pollutants such as **nitrogen oxides**, **sulfur oxides** and **hydrocarbons** come from **burning fossil fuels** (e.g. in vehicles and factories).

2) When these **pollutants** come into contact with **sunlight**, the **UV light** causes them to **break down** into **harmful chemicals** (e.g. ozone) which form **photochemical smog**.

3) Photochemical smog is a **problem** in **many cities**, e.g. Los Angeles (USA), Beijing (China), Mexico City (Mexico) and Barcelona (Spain). It's more common in places with **hot** and **sunny climates** because there's **more sunlight**.

4) These locations often have a **temperature inversion** (a layer of warm air trapped below denser cooler air), which keeps the pollutants at **ground level**.

5) Photochemical smog is linked to **health problems** such as **breathing difficulties** (coughing, shortness of breath), **respiratory disorders** (e.g. asthma) and **headaches**.

Ozone is useful in the upper atmosphere (protecting us from UV radiation), but when it's in the lower atmosphere it causes health problems.

There are Lots of Different Ways to **Reduce Air Pollution**

Lots of cities have tried to **reduce pollution** by **reducing traffic**. There are various ways that this can be done:

CONGESTION CHARGING

- **People** are charged if they **use their vehicles** in **certain places** at **certain times**.
- This reduces pollution by **reducing road traffic**. In **Central London** congestion charging reduced traffic and emissions in the congestion zone by around 15% in its first year of operation.
- However, some people **travel around** the edge of **zones** to avoid being charged, increasing traffic in these areas.
- It's hard to enforce the charge because the **volume of traffic** is so large that it's hard to process all the fines correctly.

PEDESTRIANISATION

- **Vehicles are restricted** from **entering certain places** at **certain times**. It reduces pollution by **reducing road traffic**.
- Many cities have pedestrianised zones — including London, Cardiff, Manchester and Liverpool.
- Pedestrianisation can lead to shops receiving **fewer customers** because people can only get to them on foot.

Urban Air Quality

PUBLIC TRANSPORT IMPROVEMENTS

- Encouraging people to **use public transport** instead of their cars reduces pollution. For example, many cities have:

  - **Improved bus services** to make bus journeys cheaper, faster and more efficient. E.g. many cities have introduced bus lanes so buses don't get caught in slow-moving traffic.
  - **Park and ride schemes** (car parks on public transport routes) to make it easier to **access public transport**.
  - **Trams** and **light railway services** which run on lines, so they don't get caught in **road congestion**. They also **pollute less** than **buses**. E.g. The Metrolink in Manchester opened in 1992. It links the city centre to the suburbs and has been very successful — the line to Bury and Altrincham has taken about **2.6 million** cars off the roads.

- Public transport improvements are often **expensive** — e.g. construction of the Metrolink cost over £1 billion.
- New developments can also cause problems — e.g. **park and ride schemes** can shift traffic problems to rural areas.

OTHER SCHEMES FOR REDUCING TRAFFIC

- In **Mexico City** drivers are **banned** from using their cars **one weekday** per week, based on the last digit of their number plate, e.g. number plates ending in 5 or 6 can't be used on Mondays. However, some richer households get around the system by **buying two cars**.
- **Birmingham**, **Bristol** and **London** have council-run **car sharing** schemes to encourage people making the same journey to share a car. However, some people find car sharing inconvenient, or worry about sharing a car with a stranger.

There are **larger scale** ways of tackling urban air pollution too. For example:

LEGISLATION (LAWS)

Laws aim to **reduce pollution** by **limiting emissions** and setting **air quality standards**. For example:
- The **UK Clean Air Acts** of 1956 and 1968 reduced domestic pollution by introducing **smoke control areas** where only smokeless fuels could be burned, and **reduced industrial pollution** by introducing the use of **tall chimneys** (which mean that pollutants are dispersed higher in the atmosphere, so they're less harmful to people in the city).
- The **Road Vehicles Regulations** reduce exhaust emissions by ensuring cars pass an **emissions test** in their MOT.
- In Scotland, legislation allows local authorities to do **roadside emission tests**, where they can **issue fines** if the vehicle fails. Throughout the UK, local authorities can issue fines to people who leave their engines running unnecessarily.

ALTERNATIVE FUELS

Petrol and diesel are replaced with **cleaner fuels** that **pollute less**. For example:
- **Biofuels** (e.g. **bioethanol** and **biodiesel**) are produced from **plants**. They can **directly replace** petrol and diesel, and have **lower particulate emissions**. However, growing the crops needed to make biofuels can **reduce biodiversity**, e.g. biofuels like corn-based ethanol need a lot of land to grow, which means clearing other vegetation.
- **Liquefied petroleum gas** (**LPG**) is a **gas** produced from **fossil fuels** that has **lower emissions** than petrol or diesel. However, cars have to be **converted** to use LPG, and **service stations** have to be **adapted** to distribute it.
- **Electric vehicles** have **lower emissions** because they run off **batteries**, rather than **conventional fuel**. Electric vehicles need **recharge points**, and **producing** and **disposing** of the **batteries** can cause environmental problems.

Practice Questions

Q1 What are particulates?
Q2 How is photochemical pollution produced?
Q3 Why is photochemical pollution more common in hot climates?

Exam Question

Q1 Assess the extent to which air pollution in urban areas can be managed. [9 marks]

Country Mouse came to visit Town Mouse... and died due to poor air quality

Ah, the lesser known version of the classic tale. The health and environmental problems caused by urban air pollution really are serious — make sure you learn about the potential solutions and their drawbacks. If only we could all live in the country...

Urban Drainage

Attention all human geographers — these pages may look a bit too much like physical geography.
But don't worry, there's still plenty of human geography to get your teeth into.

Infiltration is Low and Surface Runoff is High in Urban Areas

1) Urban areas are covered in **impermeable materials**, e.g. concrete and tarmac. Many urban structures are designed to **shed water quickly**, e.g. camber on roads funnels water to drains.

2) This means that **infiltration** is **low** in urban areas, so replenishment of groundwater stores is slow. Groundwater feeds rivers, so during **drier periods**, river **discharge** in urban areas is **low**.

3) **Precipitation** is higher in urban areas than in rural areas, and storms are more intense (see p.167) — this increases surface runoff.

4) **Runoff** is channelled through man-made pipes, which transport water to rivers and streams.

5) **Low infiltration rates**, **high surface runoff** and channelling of water means that water enters rivers quickly. This gives a **short lag time** and **high peak discharge** (see page 8), with a **fast** return to **base flow**.

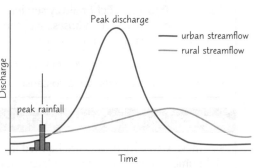

Catchment Management Aims to Reduce Urban Drainage Issues

1) **Catchment management** is a way of managing rivers and improving drainage systems by looking at the **whole** river catchment, and the **interactions** between water and land.

2) It aims to minimise issues such as **flooding**, **drought**, **water pollution** and **erosion** in sensitive areas, and to improve **river ecosystems**.

3) There are two main methods that can be used to **manage river catchments**:

Catch men? Man-agement? James didn't like the sound of this.

- **Hard engineering** — this involves man-made structures such as **dams**, **floodwalls** and **reservoirs**, which are often used to prevent **flooding** and ensure a constant **water supply**. However, hard engineering schemes are often **expensive** and can **disrupt natural systems**, e.g. silt can be trapped behind dams, starving downstream areas of sediment and increasing erosion. They can also alter wildlife **habitats**, e.g. dams can prevent salmon migrating upstream to breed.

- **Soft engineering** — this uses knowledge of the river basin and its **processes** to try to **work with nature**. It involves **land use management**, e.g. planting trees to decrease flood risk and water pollution, and preventing building on the flood plain. It can also involve **river restoration and conservation** (see next page). It is generally **cheaper** than hard engineering, and it can **improve** the local environment. However, **planning restrictions** can limit the construction of new homes and businesses, and land use management is hard in areas that are already urbanised.

4) Decisions about what methods to use are made by **experts** in water management rather than **residents** — what is best for the catchment as a whole may not be best for all individuals, so some residents and communities may feel **ignored**.

5) Catchment management schemes can also be **disruptive** — e.g. construction of the **Three Gorges Dam** in China flooded 13 cities and 140 towns, forcing over **1.2 million** people to move.

SUDS can Make Urban Drainage More Sustainable

1) **Sustainable Urban Drainage Systems** (SUDS) aim to imitate **natural** drainage systems, rather than channelling water through pipes and drains. They use several methods to decrease **flooding**, **water pollution** and **drought** in urban areas:

- **Vegetated trenches** increase interception of rainfall, and **retention basins** store water. They help to increase infiltration and water storage — this **decreases runoff** and **channel flow**, which lowers **flood risk**. Increased infiltration also decreases the amount of **pollutants** entering watercourses.

- **Vegetated roofs** intercept rainfall and increase **evapotranspiration**, which reduces **flood risk**.

- **Containers** on the roofs of buildings catch and **store rainwater** for reuse. This helps to reduce **drought risk**.

2) SUDS are **more sustainable** than traditional urban drainage methods because they **work with** the **natural environment** to improve drainage and water quality. Vegetated trenches and roofs also provide new **habitats** and increase **biodiversity**.

Topic Nine — Contemporary Urban Environments

Urban Drainage

Enfield is Restoring its Water Systems

1) River **restoration** and **conservation** aims to restore river systems to a more **natural** state. It can help to reduce **flood risk**, decrease **water pollution**, create new **habitats** and increase **biodiversity**.

2) One area that is restoring its rivers is **Enfield**, north London. Enfield has had **regular floods**, e.g. in 2006, 2007 and 2008.

3) The area is heavily **urbanised** — this has caused **problems** for drainage and water quality, including:

- The spread of urban structures has **increased surface runoff** and channel flow, e.g. in the River Lea. This has increased the frequency and intensity of **floods** — over **9000** homes in Enfield are at risk of flooding.
- Surface runoff from roads has increased levels of **pollutants** such as oil and heavy metals in watercourses.
- Water pollution also comes from **domestic sources** — up to **10%** of houses in Enfield have wastewater pipes (from e.g. toilets, showers and dishwashers) that feed **directly** into rivers.

4) In 2012, a project began to **restore** rivers in the area, with the following **aims**:

- **Reduce flood risk** and limit the **impacts** of flooding on habitats and residential areas.
- **Reduce surface runoff** from roads and pollutants entering rivers in order to improve **water quality**.
- Provide more **habitats** for wildlife and new **recreational areas** for residents.

5) The project has used **SUDS** to help restore river systems and meet these aims, for example:

- **Vegetated trenches** have been created around roads to **absorb runoff** and decrease **flood risk**.
- **Rain planters** have been installed in schools — these collect rainwater and **manage** the **flow of water** into drains, lowering flood risk. This also provided opportunities to **educate** children about water management.
- **Wetlands** have been constructed to improve **water quality**. E.g. reed beds were created around Salmons Brook to decrease surface runoff from roads and **filter** water before it enters the river.

6) Lots of **groups** have been **involved** in the project, for example:

- **Defra** and **Thames Water** are providing **funding**. In 2012, Defra granted **£340 000** to the project to construct more SUDS.

  Defra is the Department for Environment, Food and Rural Affairs.

- **Local residents** — reactions from the community have been **very positive**. Volunteers have been involved in **water quality monitoring** and **litter pickups**.
- **Local schools** — Thames21 offers education sessions for local schools to **increase engagement**. In 2015, **1000 students** were involved in litter picking and wildlife monitoring.

7) The project is ongoing, but it's had some **successes** already:

- **Flood risk** seems to be **reduced** — e.g. high rainfall in December 2013 and January 2014 did not cause significant flooding in Enfield.
- SUDS have reduced **ammonia** levels in Salmons Brook by 67% and **nitrogen** levels by 43%.
- Populations of **eels** and some species of **insects**, e.g. dragonflies, have increased.

8) However, **pollution** and **litter** are still an issue in many rivers.

Practice Questions

Q1 Give two reasons why surface runoff is higher in cities than in rural areas.

Q2 Give one issue that catchment management can cause in urban areas.

Exam Question

Q1 Assess the extent to which river restoration and conservation can reduce urban drainage issues. [9 marks]

When I hear the word 'revision', I always runoff...

So that's that — your one-shop, whistle-stop, tip-top guide to urban drainage. Read back over these pages until they're as familiar as your favourite pair of socks. It's more likely you'll get a question on this stuff than on your favourite socks, too.

Topic Nine — Contemporary Urban Environments

Urban Waste

Urban waste may sound like a load of rubbish. But there's a lot of important stuff on this page, so keep focused...

There Are Three Primary Sources of Waste in Urban Areas

CGP Moral Guidance Tip #31 — your younger brother doesn't count as personal waste.

1) **Industrial waste** — any waste that has been produced in the **manufacturing** process or from **industrial** activity, e.g. in power plants or building sites. Industrial waste can include scrap metal, solvents and chemicals, which can be **toxic** or **corrosive**.

2) **Commercial waste** — any waste that is produced by **businesses**, e.g. shops, restaurants, offices. Commercial waste often includes food, paper, cardboard and plastics.

3) **Personal waste** — any waste produced by **private homes**. This can include plastic bottles, food packaging, newspapers, food waste, etc.

Types of Waste and Methods of Disposal Vary Between Countries

1) Globally, the largest components of waste are **organic material** (46%), **paper** (17%), **plastic** (10%) and **glass** (5%). The majority of waste is easy to manage, but some material is **hazardous**, e.g. medical waste.

2) A **waste stream** is the **flow** of waste from its **origin** through to its eventual **disposal**:
   - Some products (e.g. paper, glass) can be **recycled**.
   - Others need to be **broken down** into their component parts and each part disposed of **separately** (e.g. by recycling, sending to landfill, processing to extract useful chemicals or metals, or treating to reduce risk).

3) Waste streams and components of waste vary depending on **many factors**, including:

1 Economic Characteristics

   - As people get **richer**, they tend to consume more goods. This means that **developed** countries produce **more waste** (**2.1 kg** per person per day) than **developing** countries (**0.6 kg** per person per day).
   - The **components** of waste also vary depending on the development level of the country. In developed countries, the main components are **paper** (31%), **organic material** (28%) and **plastic** (11%). In developing countries, the largest components are **organic material** (64%), **plastic** (8%) and **paper** (5%).
   - **Waste streams** vary between countries, but there is **no clear-cut link** to wealth. For example, Austria recycles 63% of all waste, whereas Japan only recycles 21%. Most developing countries do not have **formal** recycling systems, but many people collect recyclable goods from landfill and sell them to **make a living**.

2 Lifestyles

   - **Amount** and **type** of waste produced varies depending on whether people live in the city or the country — **urban** dwellers produce **more waste** than **rural** residents. People in rural areas produce **more organic** waste (e.g. food), and people in cities produce more **manufactured waste** (e.g. plastic, glass).
   - The **facilities** available to people affect the **waste streams** they use — for example, people are more likely to **recycle** waste if recycling facilities are easily **accessible**, and if authorities **encourage** them to.
   - **Diet** is likely to affect waste **components** and **streams** — e.g. producing **processed food** creates waste, and finished products tend to come in a lot of **packaging**. In contrast, fruit and vegetables tend to produce more **compostable waste** (e.g. vegetable peelings) and **less packaging**.

3 Attitudes

   - Many developed countries have a **throw-away culture** — e.g. electronics are replaced regularly, and clothing may be bought, worn a few times then thrown away. This results in high levels of waste, much of which cannot be **recycled** or has a long and **complex waste stream**.
   - Increasing concerns about **health** may cause people to throw away food that is near or just past its **sell-by date**, resulting in high levels of **food waste**.
   - People have different attitudes towards the **environment** — people who are concerned about the environmental **impacts** of excess waste are more likely to **reuse** or **recycle** waste.
   - In some groups, there has been a recent move towards a decrease in **consumption** and **waste**. For example, many **freegans** forage for food, including **salvaging** it from supermarket bins, **repair** broken goods and **give away** things they don't need, instead of throwing them away.

Urban Waste

There Are **Many Ways** to **Manage Urban Waste**

There are **lots** of **methods** of **waste disposal**, all of which have environmental impacts:

1) **UNREGULATED** — waste is **dumped** in places that aren't official disposal sites — e.g. solid waste is left on the street, or untreated liquid waste enters water courses. Waste that isn't properly disposed of can **damage ecosystems**, e.g. if chemicals from it enter the environment. **Animals** and **birds** can be harmed if they swallow or get tangled in plastic waste.

2) **RECYCLING** — waste is **reprocessed** into **new** products, e.g. plastic bottles can be turned into fleece jumpers. Recycling **reduces demand** for **raw materials**, which decreases the environmental impacts of resource extraction, e.g. deforestation. Producing recycled products generally uses **less energy** than making them from scratch, so less **greenhouse gases**, such as CO_2, are emitted. However, recycling requires **separate collections** and the construction of **new facilities** to process waste — these contribute to **greenhouse gas emissions** and **air pollution**.

3) **INCINERATION** — this is when waste is **burnt**. It **reduces** the amount of waste going to landfill, but it emits **greenhouse gases** and causes **air pollution**. Waste that is burnt can be used to generate **electricity** — this is called **energy recovery**. This reduces use of **fossil fuels**, but burning some waste can release **toxic chemicals** into the air or water.

4) **RECOVERY** — this involves using **waste** instead of **new products**, e.g. waste concrete can be crushed and used as a base for new roads and buildings. This **reduces** the amount of waste being sent to landfill and means that fewer **natural resources** are exploited because goods are reused.

5) **BURIAL (LANDFILL)** — waste is placed in disused **mines**, quarries or **landfill sites**. Many sites are **lined** with e.g. clay or plastic to prevent leaching of chemicals into the environment, but if sites are not properly regulated, hazardous chemicals can contaminate **groundwater**, while gases such as methane from decomposing waste cause air **pollution**. Some countries collect gases for **energy production**, reducing air pollution and fossil fuel use.

6) **SUBMERGENCE** — disposing of waste by dumping it in **oceans** is illegal, but it is still common in some areas, e.g. off the coast of Somalia. Submerged waste can release **toxic** or **radioactive** substances, damaging ocean **ecosystems**.

7) **TRADE** — waste can be **bought** and **sold** by countries. For example, developed countries may pay developing countries to take their **hazardous waste**. However, developing countries may not dispose of hazardous waste safely, meaning that it can **damage** local environments, e.g. heavy metals can **pollute groundwater** and local watercourses.

Singapore Has Moved From **Landfill** to **Incineration**

1) Singapore is an **island** off Malaysia. It is almost entirely **urban**. The amount of **waste** produced in Singapore increased from **1260 tonnes per day** in 1970 to **8400 tonnes** in 2015. **Land** is **scarce**, so waste management is important.

2) In the 1960s and 1970s, most waste was sent to **landfill sites** around the city. However, in the late 1970s the government changed their main waste disposal method to **incineration** with **energy recovery**.

3) The first incineration plant was constructed in **1979**. Today, there are four plants across the city, which provide about **3%** of Singapore's **energy needs**. Each incinerator is fitted with **pollution control systems** to limit greenhouse gas emissions.

4) Singapore now has only one landfill site, Semakau, which was built on reclaimed land between two small islands. It is lined with an **impermeable membrane** and a layer of **clay** to prevent leaching of chemicals. Once each area of the site is full, it is covered with topsoil to support vegetation. The landfill is now home to rare species, e.g. Malaysian plovers.

5) Singapore's waste disposal systems are effective. In 2015, only **2% of waste** was sent to **landfill** — **38%** was **incinerated** and **60%** was **recycled** (recycling facilities were built in 2001). Only waste that **can't** be recycled or burnt goes to landfill.

6) However, pollution control systems cannot remove **all** harmful emissions from **incinerators**, and incinerators only last around **ten years** before they need to be replaced. The current landfill site is expected to be **filled** by around **2040**.

Practice Questions

Q1 What are the three main sources of waste in urban areas?

Q2 Briefly describe how economic development affects urban waste.

Exam Question

Q1 Evaluate the environmental impacts of different approaches to urban waste disposal. [9 marks]

Waist recovery — that's what the post-Christmas diet is for...

We can all do our bit towards environmentally friendly waste disposal — for example, you could write your revision notes on scrap paper and then recycle them once you've passed your exam. Just make sure you read them carefully in the meantime...

Urban Environmental Issues

As if problems with climate, drainage and waste aren't enough, cities also have issues with air pollution, water pollution and dereliction. But there's no need to panic just yet — there are loads of ways to fix these problems...

Urban Atmospheres Are Being Polluted by Human Activities...

1) Atmospheric pollution is often a **problem** in **urban areas** (see pages 168-169).

2) In many **developed** countries, reliance on **fossils fuels** is **decreasing**, and use of less-polluting energy sources (e.g. natural gas) is increasing. As a result, **air quality** in many cities has **improved since 1950**. However, **car ownership** is **increasing**, and congestion can cause significant atmospheric pollution.

3) Many **developing** countries and **emerging** economies still rely heavily on **fossil fuels** to meet their energy needs. **Increases** in **industrial activity** and **car ownership**, combined with a **lack of regulation** of emissions, mean that atmospheric pollution is often severe.

4) In many developed countries, there are **strategies** to **limit air pollution**, such as promoting 'green' modes of transport, e.g. cycling, and expanding **green spaces** (e.g. parks) in urban centres. Other strategies are outlined on pages 168-169.

5) In the developing world, there has been **some progress** towards reducing urban air pollution. For example, most countries have phased out the use of **leaded petrol**. However, **progress** is **slow**.

Yep, I've got this green transport thing licked.

...and so are Urban Rivers and Streams

1) Water pollution is also common in cities (see pages 170-171). There are several reasons for this:

   - Cities have a **high population density**, so they produce a lot of waste. This includes **wastewater** and **sewage**, as well as **oil** and **metals** on road surfaces from cars. These pollutants can enter **watercourses**, e.g. if sewers are inadequate, or in runoff when it rains.
   - Many cities have a high concentration of **factories**, which may **discharge** industrial waste into watercourses.

2) Water pollution can cause **damage** to **ecosystems**, and **contaminated drinking water** can cause **health problems**, e.g. dysentery and cholera.

3) Water pollution can be managed through **laws** to stop discharge of untreated waste from industries and provision of plants to treat wastewater. Strategies such as **catchment management** and **SUDS** can also help (see page 170).

4) In **developed** countries, there are strict **regulations** about discharge of untreated water, and water quality is **monitored**. However, **litter** dropped in or around water and pollutants in **surface runoff** still cause pollution.

5) In many **developing** countries and **emerging** economies, there are **few regulations** and inadequate provision of **treatment facilities**. This means that untreated industrial waste and sewage often enter watercourses and water pollution is **common**.

Litter in the River Tees in Stockton.

Urban Dereliction can Impact on Local Environments

1) **Urban dereliction** happens when **economic activity** in urban areas **declines** and buildings become run down. It often follows a pattern:

   - The **movement** of **manufacturing overseas** and the **decentralisation** of industry leads to industrial decline. Many unemployed people **leave** urban areas in **search of work**.
   - If lots of people leave the area, shops may be forced to close and services go into decline. As industry, people and services move out, they leave **empty buildings** — e.g. factories, homes and shops.
   - Empty buildings and derelict areas often have problems with **vandalism**, **graffiti** and **crime**.

2) Urban dereliction is more **common** in **developed** countries where widespread deindustrialisation has occurred.

3) Strategies to manage urban dereliction include the **redevelopment** of former factories into **commercial** and **residential properties**, the construction of **new housing** in derelict areas and the creation of **green spaces**, e.g. parks.

4) However, some cities **lack investment** and large areas remain derelict, e.g. Detroit.

Urban Environmental Issues

Bangkok Has Lots of Environmental Issues

Bangkok is in Thailand, an **emerging** economy. Lack of regulation and poor planning has led to **environmental problems**:

Air Pollution
- A rapid rise in **car ownership**, coupled with poor vehicle maintenance, is causing high levels of air pollution. In 2011, some pollutants, e.g. benzene, were more than **three times** acceptable levels in some areas.
- In the early 21st century, air pollution caused around **5000 premature deaths** per year in Bangkok.
- The government has taken steps to reduce air pollution, including improvements to **public transport**, such as bus lanes and a new subway. Drivers can be **fined** if their cars are found to emit high levels of exhaust fumes.

Water Pollution
- Poor **sewage systems** and ineffective **waste management** mean that water pollution is severe. River water contains **unsafe** levels of ammonia and coliform bacteria, which come mostly from **human waste**.
- Since the 1960s, there have been various plans for **improving** sewage systems in the city in order to reduce pollution levels in the rivers. However, these plans have been too **expensive** to implement.

Dereliction
- A lot of buildings in Bangkok were left **half-finished** when Asia experienced a **financial crisis** in 1997. Some have since fallen into disrepair, and suffered from **vandalism** and **graffiti**.
- However, **economic growth** since 2010 has led to the **completion** of many unfinished buildings. The government offers incentives for **foreign investment** — this may help to decrease the number of empty buildings.

Manchester has Overcome Many Environmental Issues

1) Manchester is in the UK, a developed country. During the **19th** and **early 20th centuries**, Manchester was **very polluted**. Factories and mills produced huge amounts of greenhouse gases and industrial waste, which polluted **air** and **water**.

2) **Deindustrialisation** and **strategies** to improve the urban environment have had a big impact on the city:

Air Pollution
- **Closure** of factories and better **management** of air quality has **reduced** air pollution. This has reduced the frequency of **illnesses** associated with poor air quality, e.g. bronchitis.
- **Cars** are the largest contributor to air pollution in Manchester today. To reduce car use, the local government is improving **bus services**, constructing **cycle paths** and expanding **pedestrian walkways** across the city.

Water Pollution
- Until the late 20th century, the River Irwell and Manchester Ship Canal were badly polluted by **industry** and **sewage**. Since 1987, extensive work has been done to clean up these waterways, e.g. by increasing the **oxygen** content of the water, encouraging **aquatic plant growth** and collecting **litter**.
- To reduce water pollution caused by **surface runoff** from roads, the local government is installing **SUDS** (see p. 170), e.g. green areas and porous pavements have been installed in Salford Quays.

Dereliction
- In the late 1980s and early 1990s, **deindustrialisaton** and **job losses** had caused many people to leave the city. The city centre was **underpopulated** and many shops and residential areas were **abandoned**.
- Large-scale **redevelopment** of the city began in **1996**. Former mills and factories were **converted** to luxury flats, **open spaces** were improved and funding was provided for **new businesses**, such as the Lowry Gallery in Salford Quays. From 2001 to 2011, the population of the city centre nearly **tripled** to around **18 000**.

Practice Questions

Q1 Give one cause of urban air pollution.
Q2 Briefly describe one strategy to manage water pollution.

Exam Question

Q1 With reference to contrasting urban areas, evaluate strategies to manage environmental issues. [9 marks]

Noise pollution from snoring — a major environmental issue in exam halls...

It may seem like there's a lot to take in on these pages, but it's worth learning — Geography examiners love it when you can relate theoretical issues to the real world using facts and figures. Almost as much as they love tweed jackets with elbow patches.

Sustainable Urban Development

I know it seems like cities have a million and one problems. But there's still hope — with a bit of effort, cities can become clean, green, energy-efficient models of sustainability. Well, maybe...

Urban Areas Have **Environmental Impacts**

1) Cities **impact** on the **environment** at a **local scale**, for example by increasing **air pollution** (see pages 168-169), **water pollution** (see page 170), **flood risk** (see page 170) and by generating large amounts of **waste** (see page 172).

2) Urbanisation also causes **loss** of **open space** in and around cities, resulting in loss of habitats and biodiversity.

3) At a global scale, cities increase **demand** for **resources** such as **food**, **water** and **energy**. Cities are home to around half the world's population, but account for about **three-quarters** of **resource use**. This is putting **pressure** on **finite resources**, leading to food, water and energy insecurity.

4) Cities are also responsible for about **60%** of **greenhouse gas emissions**, which contribute to climate change.

Many Factors Influence a **City's Ecological Footprint**

1) An individual's **ecological footprint** is the amount of land that is needed to produce **everything** they consume, e.g. food, water and fuel, and to absorb their **waste**. The ecological footprint of an **area combines** the footprints of its **residents**.

2) The ecological footprint of a **city** depends on a range of factors, including:

- **Wealth** — e.g. **consumption** and **waste production** is **higher** in cities in richer countries.
- **Size of city** — e.g. **compact** cities are easier to travel around on foot or by bike, so they produce **less pollution**.
- **Quality of public transport** — **efficient** public transport systems decrease car use, and therefore reduce **pollution**.

There Are **Many Ways** Urban Areas Can be **Sustainable**

Clive hoped his tightrope would prove physically sustainable.

1) To be sustainable, a city must meet the **needs** of people **today** without preventing **future generations** from meeting their **needs**.

2) There are different **dimensions** to sustainability — how sustainable a city is depends on its **natural**, **physical**, **social** and **economic** characteristics. Sustainable cities have a range of **features**:

(1) Natural

- Natural sustainability is about how the **environment**, **resources** and **waste** are managed.
- Cities with a high level of natural sustainability rely on **renewable energy** sources (e.g. wind). They produce relatively little **waste**, and **reuse** or **recycle** the waste they produce.
- Cities where people **walk**, **cycle** and use **public transport** a lot produce **less pollution**, so they are more sustainable.

(2) Physical

- Physical sustainability is about **how well** a city is able to **support** the people living there.
- To be sustainable, a city must provide enough **resources** to **support** the population and let them be **productive**, e.g. have jobs.
- Features of physically sustainable cities include plentiful **high quality housing** and **secure supplies** of nutritious **food**, safe **water** and **energy** for all residents.

(3) Social

- Social sustainability is about how people **live together**, their **quality of life**, and the availability of basic **services**, e.g. healthcare.
- Cities offer good living conditions for all residents, with **access** to basic **services**, e.g. hospitals, schools etc. are within easy reach.
- Socially sustainable cities are **peaceful**, **tolerant**, **respect human rights** and are politically stable.

(4) Economic

- Economic sustainability is about maintaining **economic growth** without causing long-term **negative effects**, e.g. environmental damage, social inequality.
- Cities with high levels of economic sustainability are **wealthy**, have low levels of **inequality** and **little debt**. They are home to **profitable**, **ethical** businesses that offer plenty of **well-paid jobs**.

3) Sustainability can affect the **liveability** of a city — this is a measure of how good **living conditions** in an area are.

4) Liveability depends on many factors, including **job opportunities**, **crime rates**, **open space** and access to **education**. Different factors matter more to **different people**, so everyone's **view** of what makes a city liveable will be different.

Topic Nine — Contemporary Urban Environments

Sustainable Urban Development

There are **Opportunities** to **Make Cities** More **Sustainable**...

There are several **factors** that make **sustainable development** of urban areas easier than rural areas, including:

1) People are more **densely concentrated** in cities than in rural areas, so the **provision** of services such as clean water and public transport is **easier** and **cheaper**.

2) Understanding of the **importance** of **urban sustainability** has increased — this has encouraged **more research** and **investment** into how urban areas can be made more sustainable.

3) Governments may **invest** more in **urban** sustainability initiatives than **rural** ones, because they benefit **more people**.

... But There Are Also **Challenges**

Increasing urban sustainability can be **difficult** — there are many reasons for this, such as:

1) It requires significant **investment**, which many cities **cannot afford**.

2) Many cities are **growing**, so public services need to expand rapidly to meet the needs of a larger population.

3) Some people are **unwilling** to **change** their **habits**, e.g. driving less or using less water.

4) Some cities don't have appropriate **infrastructure**, e.g. roads may be **too narrow** to build **cycle lanes**.

In the **developing world**, **urbanisation** is **happening** at a **faster rate** than in the developed world, and growth is often **unplanned** — this makes it **harder** to **increase** urban **sustainability**.

There Are Lots of **Strategies** for **Increasing Urban Sustainability**

Different **strategies** for increasing sustainability are used in different cities:

1) **Reducing the number of cars on the road** — strategies can include constructing new **cycle lanes**, introducing **park and ride schemes** and improving **public transport provision** (see pages 168-169 for more strategies). E.g. in Freiburg, Germany, cycling routes, pedestrian-only zones and a light rail system have reduced car use.

2) **Increasing the amount of green space** — green spaces, e.g. parks, can reduce **pollution** and increase **biodiversity**. Programmes such as **river clean-ups**, **wetland restoration** and **tree planting** can provide **habitats** for wildlife.

3) **Improving urban waste disposal** — many cities have introduced measures to **reduce** the amount of **waste** being **sent to landfill**. These include expanding **recycling facilities**, converting to **incineration with energy recovery** (see p. 173) and encouraging people to **compost** green waste.

4) **Increasing renewable energy use** — using **renewable energy sources**, such as wind and solar power, **decreases** fossil fuel use and carbon emissions. For example, UK and Welsh governments are currently considering building a **tidal lagoon** in Swansea Bay to supply renewable energy to the UK.

5) **Reducing water use** — authorities can insist that new buildings are fitted with **water meters** and **water-efficient fittings**, and ensure that people use less water. E.g. in Cape Town, South Africa, water pressure was **reduced** so that showers, hosepipes etc. would use less water.

6) **Making buildings more energy efficient** — governments can offer **incentives** to encourage homeowners and businesses to improve the **insulation** in buildings, install **solar panels** and use **energy-efficient** light bulbs.

I'm a big fan of renewable energy.

Practice Questions

Q1 Give one way that cities impact on the environment on a global scale.

Q2 What is a person's ecological footprint?

Q3 Briefly describe two challenges to urban sustainability.

Exam Question

Q1 Assess the extent to which cities can be made sustainable. [9 marks]

Reusing toilet paper — when sustainability goes too far...

Sustainable living does seem like a chore — we'd have to change our lifestyles quite dramatically in order to be entirely sustainable. But even doing a little bit, e.g. recycling paper or using less electricity, can make a massive difference.

Mumbai — Case Study

Cities in the developing world are growing faster than in the developed world. This means that some — like Mumbai — have grown very rapidly and are facing significant social, economic and environmental issues.

Mumbai Has Many **Social** and **Economic Inequalities**

1) **Mumbai** (formerly Bombay) is a **megacity** (see p. 159) on the west coast of **India**.

2) Mumbai is **globally important** — it is a major **port** on the Indian Ocean, India's **financial centre** and a hub of **industry** and **services**. The city is also a **cultural centre** — it's home to the **Bollywood** movie industry.

3) Migrants from **rural** areas of India have moved to Mumbai in search of jobs. The population of Mumbai **increased** from **5.9 million** in 1971 to **20.7 million** in 2016.

4) This rapid urbanisation has created a number of social and economic **issues**:

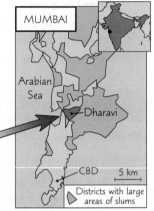

Dharavi is one of the largest slums in Mumbai and is home to more than 1 million people.

- **More than half** of the population live in **poverty** in slums — these cover large areas of the city. **Living conditions** in the slums are poor — homes are **cramped** and **poorly built**, often without water supply or sanitation. The **lack of toilet and sewage** facilities is a risk to **health** (e.g. raw sewage spreads disease).

- In contrast, over a **quarter** of all India's **millionaires live in Mumbai**. The urban rich **live close** to Mumbai's **CBD**, usually in **high-rise apartments**. Some of the richest districts of Mumbai include **Bandra** and **Andheri**, both of which offer **amenities** such as shopping centres, restaurants and private hospitals.

- There are also **inequalities** in **education** — literacy rate is around **60%** in the slums, compared to about **90%** in the city as a whole. Literacy rates are **lower** for **women** than for men.

- There are **few opportunities** for **women** in **slum areas**. With **no qualifications**, some women resort to **prostitution** to earn a living. This leads to **higher rates** of **HIV** and other **STIs** among **poorer communities** than in wealthy areas.

- Only around **30%** of slum residents have access to **public healthcare**. Outbreaks of **disease** (e.g. malaria and dengue fever) are common, and the **infant mortality rate** is relatively high (26 deaths per 1000).

- Psychological problems such as **depression** are more common in **slum areas** than in richer districts.

- As Mumbai has developed economically, there has been an influx of **African migrants**. Many have experienced **racial discrimination** — e.g. they struggle to find formal jobs or rent apartments, and are forced to live in **slums**. They also face **racial prejudice**, including **verbal abuse** and greater risk of **arrest** by police.

> Despite these inequalities, 42% of Mumbai's residents class themselves as very happy with life.

Mumbai is **Vulnerable** to **Natural Disasters**

1) Mumbai is at risk of **flooding**. There are several reasons for this:

- India has a monsoon climate — a long dry season is followed by a period of intense rainfall. Mumbai has one of the highest amounts of annual precipitation in India — average precipitation in July (monsoon season) is 960 mm.

- Five rivers flow through Mumbai, including the Dahisar and Mithi. Mumbai has limited room to expand, so many new developments have been built on floodplains.

- Mumbai experiences tropical storms, which bring heavy rain and may cause storm surges.

> In **July 2005**, monsoon rains caused the **Mithi River** to burst its banks — the flooding killed about **400** people and left thousands homeless. Flooding of drainage systems caused water contamination and an increase in **waterborne diseases**, e.g. cholera and leptospirosis, which killed more people.

2) Mumbai is also vulnerable to **tectonic hazards**:

- It is located in a seismically active area, so it is at risk from earthquakes (although they are quite rare).

- Earthquakes can cause tsunamis (see p.82) — Mumbai is low-lying, so a tsunami could cause extensive damage.

3) **Slum areas** are more **vulnerable** to natural disasters than richer areas. Slums have **poorly constructed houses** and are often built on **floodplains** — e.g. 70% of the Mithi River's embankments are occupied by informal settlements.

Mumbai — Case Study

Current Conditions in Mumbai are **Unsustainable**

1) Most slum areas in Mumbai **lack adequate sanitation** — this is causing **water pollution**. Contaminated water is contributing to the spread of **illnesses** such as hepatitis, and reducing local fish populations.

2) Mumbai's water supply is dependent on the **monsoon rains**, and in dry years water has to be strictly **rationed**. As population increases, **demand** for water grows — this is unsustainable in the long term.

3) The **road network** in Mumbai carries millions of cars each day. There are problems with **long journey times**, **congestion** and **air pollution**.

4) **Economic growth** is leading to the construction of factories and increased car ownership — there are around 450 more vehicles on Mumbai's roads **every day**. This is adding to air pollution, and Mumbai regularly suffers from **acid rain**.

5) The increasing population produces **more waste**. This can cause problems, e.g. in the neighbourhood of Chembur, waste on open rubbish dumps is burnt, adding to **air pollution**. This has **health impacts** on local residents, e.g. **25%** of deaths in Chembur between 2008 and 2010 were caused by **respiratory problems**.

6) **HIV** and **AIDS** rates are **increasing** in Mumbai, putting extra pressure on **healthcare** services. HIV/AIDS-positive people regularly face **discrimination** — e.g. some have been **refused treatment** in hospitals, **sacked** from their jobs or **prevented** from entering communal areas.

There are Efforts to Make Mumbai **More Sustainable**

The Indian government, local authorities and non-governmental organisations are working on **strategies** to make Mumbai a **cleaner**, **safer** and more **pleasant** place for residents. For example:

1) In 2004, the government first announced a **redevelopment project** to clear the Dharavi slum and create a new independent township. Plans include building new **apartments**, a **water** and **sewage** system, **hospitals** and **schools**. Some residents of Dharavi **object** to the redevelopment — it's an established community with successful industries, e.g. **recycling** rubbish from all over the city, and residents are worried that the redevelopment will destroy their **livelihoods** and the **community spirit** of the area.

2) To increase water security, the local authority has made **rainwater harvesting** systems (collecting rainwater from rooftops) compulsory on all **new residential buildings** in Mumbai on plots larger than 300 m². However, since 2007 only **half** of the eligible buildings have actually installed rainwater harvesting systems.

3) Mumbai's **public transport** system is being upgraded, with the aim of improving air quality. In 2011, the World Bank provided **$1 billion** of funding to **upgrade roads**, **rebuild** train tracks and purchase more **fuel-efficient buses**. However, many families have had to be **relocated** to make space for upgraded roads.

4) The **Clean-Up Mumbai Campaign** is cleaning up the streets by clearing litter and **educating** local residents and shopkeepers about **how to recycle** and **dispose of waste** to limit environmental damage.

5) The National AIDS Control Organisation runs **condom promotion campaigns** in Mumbai to reduce HIV rates. New government legislation plans to make it **illegal** to discriminate against HIV/AIDS-positive people.

Practice Questions

Q1 Give one reason why Mumbai is at risk of flooding.

Q2 Briefly describe one way that conditions in Mumbai are environmentally unsustainable.

Exam Question

Q1 "For every problem caused by urbanisation there is an effective solution."
To what extent do you agree with this view?

[20 marks]

Poverty management strategy #12 — win the lottery...

Phew — the first case study of the section and it's a bit of a whopper. Mumbai is a big city with some big problems — make sure you learn the issues with urbanisation and sustainability thoroughly. Oh, and everything else on these pages as well...

Birmingham — Case Study

From the sun-drenched, monsoon-battered slums of Mumbai to the... well, slightly less exotic Birmingham.
On the plus side, there's a lower risk of contracting cholera if you end up doing fieldwork there.

Birmingham *is a* Post-Industrial City *in the* UK

1) **Birmingham** is a city in central England. It is a political, social and economic **hub**. In the 19th century, the growth of metalworking and heavy industry caused a **boom** in **population** and **economic growth**.

2) During the 1970s and 1980s, Birmingham suffered from **deindustrialisation**. The **decline** of the metalworking industries led to widespread **unemployment**, **poverty** and **dereliction**.

3) **Urban regeneration** programmes have helped to **redevelop** Birmingham's city centre (see next page). However, the city still suffers from **social** and **economic issues**:

- Birmingham is **divided** into **rich** and **poor** areas. The poorest areas tend to be close to the city centre, e.g. Sparkbrook and Aston, whereas richer areas tend to be further from the centre in more **rural areas**, e.g. Sutton Coldfield.

- The average **income** in Handsworth, the poorest area of Birmingham, is **£19 000** per year, compared to **£37 000** in Edgbaston, the richest area.

- More than **100 000 children** in Birmingham live in **poverty**, and many families rely on **food banks**.

- Average **life expectancy** is **8 years lower** for **men** and **6 years lower** for **women** in the **most deprived areas** of Birmingham than in the least deprived.

- Around **6%** of people in Birmingham are **unemployed** — unemployment is higher in **poorer areas** such as Hodge Hill (10.7%) than in richer areas, e.g. Sutton Coldfield (1.6%).

- **Crime rates** in Birmingham city centre are high. In 2016, an average of around **1100 crimes** were reported **every month** — the most common crimes were **anti-social behaviour** and **shoplifting**. In comparison, only about 270 crimes a month were reported on average in Edgbaston.

- Birmingham's **population** is **ethnically diverse** — in 2011, around 40% of the population were **non-white**. The **largest** minority **groups** were **Pakistanis** (13%), followed by **Black or Black British** (9%). There are **social** and **economic inequalities** between ethnic communities. For example:

  - **Life expectancy** is **higher** in **areas** with a majority white population than in minority communities.
  - **White families** are **more likely** than minority groups to **be homeowners** — 64% of white people own their home, compared to 48% of Bangladeshis and 29% of Black Africans.
  - Many ethnic minorities face **prejudice** and **discrimination**, e.g. verbal abuse and difficulty finding a job.

Birmingham's *Physical Environment* Affects *Environmental Sustainability*...

Birmingham's **environment** has **improved** since the industrial decline of the 1970s and 1980s, but there are still **issues**:

1) **Air pollution** — some areas of central Birmingham have very **poor** air quality, e.g. high levels of **nitrogen dioxide**, which is produced by burning fossil fuels (e.g. in **cars** and **factories**). Air pollution can cause acid rain — this may contribute to **acidification** of rivers and canals, which can **harm aquatic life**.

2) **Water pollution** — many rivers and streams in Birmingham are very polluted. Pollution comes from surface **runoff** from roads, wrongly connected **drains** and incorrect disposal of waste such as **engine oil**. High levels of pollution have reduced populations of some species of **insects**, with **knock-on effects** on other wildlife.

3) **Lack of green space** — central Birmingham has relatively little **green space**. This reduces the city's ability to absorb greenhouse gases and other pollutants, and to moderate its climate (see p.166).

4) **Flooding** — lack of green space also contributes to high **surface runoff** and **flash flooding**. Flooding can increase erosion and deposition of sediment, which can damage **ecosystems**, e.g. by silting of fish breeding habitats.

5) **Urban waste** — Birmingham produces **3.2 million tonnes** of **waste per year**. The majority of waste is sent to **landfill** or incinerated — only around **25%** is **reused** or **recycled**. This is adding to air and water **pollution** in the city (see p.174).

6) **Extreme weather events** — Birmingham has a **temperate** climate with relatively little extreme weather. However, extreme events seem to be increasing in **frequency** — recent events including storms, drought and tornadoes.

Birmingham — Case Study

... And Has Impacts on **Residents**

Birmingham's physical environmental conditions affect the **social sustainability** of the city and people's **experiences** of living there:

1) High levels of **air pollution** can cause **respiratory** problems, e.g. bronchitis, and worsen conditions such as asthma. Air pollution is linked to over **500 deaths** in Birmingham each year.

2) Lack of **green space** impacts on the **health** and **well-being** of residents — levels of **obesity** in Birmingham are high, and around **40%** of adults who don't do enough exercise claimed they would exercise **more** if they had better access to attractive open spaces.

3) **Flooding** causes **damage** to **properties** and businesses. For example, heavy rainfall in June 2016 flooded hundreds of **houses**, disrupted **train services** and forced several **schools** to close temporarily.

4) Extreme **weather events** can also cause damage to property, e.g. in 2005 a **tornado** damaged hundreds of houses — over 100 families were **evacuated** and there was about **£50 million** of damage. Heatwaves and icy conditions also cause **health problems**.

5) Some parts of Birmingham, e.g. Aston, have large numbers of **derelict buildings**. These can be targets for **vandalism**, and some residents feel **unsafe** in abandoned areas.

There Are Attempts to **Increase Sustainability**

Birmingham City Council is **redeveloping** the city to increase its sustainability. They have **four key objectives**:

1) **Improve transport links** — the council is expanding New Street **train station** and constructing **cycle lanes**. This will help to **limit** the number of **cars** in the city centre, reducing **air pollution**.

2) **Redevelop derelict areas** — there are ongoing projects to **regenerate** derelict areas, e.g. by demolishing abandoned buildings and building new ones. For example, the council is undertaking extensive **redevelopment projects** in Eastside, including **restoring** canal-side properties for residential use and creating new **museums** and **art galleries**.

3) **Increase green spaces** — the council is creating new **parks** and green areas to improve the local **environment**, limit **air pollution**, reduce the **risk of flooding** and provide habitats for **wildlife**.

4) **Improve waste management** — there are plans to decrease the amount of waste going to **landfill**, e.g. by encouraging **composting** and expanding facilities for **recycling** and **energy recovery**.

The redevelopment of Birmingham's city centre has changed its **character** and people's **perceptions**:

1) **Regeneration** of derelict areas and creating a more **pleasant** urban environment is attracting people back to the city. Since 2004, the city's population has **increased** by about **10%**.

2) **Redevelopment** of city centre shopping areas, e.g. the Bullring, has increased the number of people **visiting** — Birmingham is now the second most popular **shopping** destination in the UK, after London.

3) Birmingham has become a major **tourist destination** — about **37 million people** visited the city in 2014. Visitors are drawn to the city by its **industrial heritage**, e.g. canals and historic buildings. Campaigns by **Visit Birmingham** have also raised national and international **awareness** of the city, e.g. by marketing the city's German Christmas markets.

Practice Questions

Q1 Briefly describe some of the social and economic issues in Birmingham.

Q2 Give three ways in which environmental sustainability in Birmingham is being improved.

Exam Question

Q1 To what extent do you agree with the view that urban issues affect poorer communities more than richer ones? [20 marks]

Get the defibrillator — we need to revive the city centre...

If you've studied different cities and want to use them in the exam instead, that's fine. I mean, just because I've gone to all this effort tracking down everything you need to know and putting it in pretty boxes, don't feel you need to use it. No, no, it's fine.

People and the Environment

Populations are dynamic — they're always changing. This topic is all about how and why.

People are **Spread Unevenly** Around the World

1) The **size** of the **population** in an area is influenced by how many people the **environment** of that area can **support**.

2) **Environmental conditions** (e.g. climate, soils and resources) differ around the world — this means that populations are **not evenly spread out**, but are **concentrated** in certain places. There are two terms you need to know:

Distribution

- **Population distribution** is the **pattern** of where people live.

- People live in **some** areas (those with favourable conditions, e.g. coastal plains) but not in **others** (those with unfavourable conditions, e.g. on glaciers).

- For example, the population of **China** is very **unevenly** distributed — over 90% of the population live in the **eastern** part of the country. Much of the western part is covered by mountains and desert, so large areas are **uninhabited**.

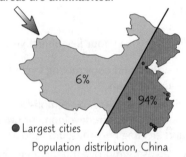

6%

94%

● Largest cities

Population distribution, China

Density

- **Population density** is the **population** of an area **divided** by the size of that **area** (e.g. number of people per square kilometre).

- Population density is **high** in some countries and **low** in others, e.g. Bangladesh has about **1200** people per km², whereas Libya has about **4** people per km². Areas of **high population density** tend to be found **between 20°N** and **60°N**. The areas of **highest** population density are located in **South** and **East Asia**.

- Population density can vary **within** a country — some areas are more densely populated than others.

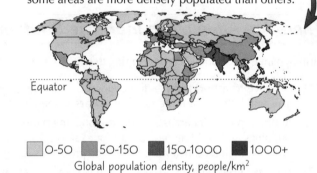

Equator

☐ 0-50 ☐ 50-150 ☐ 150-1000 ☐ 1000+

Global population density, people/km²

The **Global Population** has **Risen Rapidly** since **1800**

1) It took until **1804** for the world's population to reach **1 billion**. Before this, **famine**, **disease** and **war** prevented the population from growing rapidly.

2) Until **1950**, most population growth was limited to **developed** countries:

There's more about the reasons for population change on pages 200-201.

> 1) During the 19th century, the **populations** of North America and many countries in western Europe **grew rapidly**. Improvements in **medicine** and **food production** increased **life expectancy** and reduced **infant mortality rates**. For example, the population of **England** and **Wales** increased from approximately **9.4 million** in **1801** to **32.5 million** in **1901**.
>
> 2) During the same period, the populations of **developing countries** remained **stable** — **infant** and **maternal mortality rates** were **high**, and **famine** was **common**.

3) Since 1950, global population has **increased rapidly** — from around **2.5 billion** in 1950 to **7.5 billion** in 2017. Population is predicted to reach **9 billion** by 2050.

4) Most of the growth since 1950 has been driven by **developing countries**, where **life expectancy** has increased and **death rates** have decreased significantly.

5) Some countries are now experiencing **population decline**, e.g. Ukraine's death rate is higher than its birth rate, but globally population is still **increasing**.

6) The distribution of populations has **changed** — globally, **urban** populations are increasing **faster** than rural ones, so populations are becoming **less evenly distributed**, with higher **densities** in **cities**.

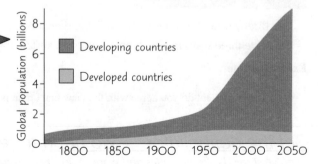

Developing countries

Developed countries

People and the Environment

Population is Affected by the Physical Environment

See pages 186-190 for more on the interactions between people, climate and soils.

There are **three** main aspects of the **physical environment** that affect populations:

Climate

- **Climate type** affects the **global distribution** of population. **Few people** live in **arid** (dry) areas, e.g. the Sahara Desert, but **many** live in **temperate** (moderate) areas, e.g. the UK. **Tropical** (hot and wet) and **temperate climates** usually have the **largest populations** and **highest population densities**, because it's easier to produce food.
- **Climate change** is affecting **population distribution**. For example, in **coastal areas** where **sea levels** are **rising**, people are moving **inland**, and some people living on **small islands** are having to abandon their islands. Climate change is causing **levels of nutrition** to fall in some developing countries.

Soils

- **Soil fertility** determines the **amount** and **type** of food that can be produced in a region.
- It has played a role in determining **where** human settlements have developed, and the **size** of populations. For example, many **cities** (e.g. Naples) are built near **volcanoes** where soil fertility is **high**.
- Some countries, such as Bangladesh, have large **floodplains**, which are very **fertile**. This supports **large-scale agriculture**, which **feeds** the **large population**.
- **Soil erosion** can cause people to **migrate** to other places as agriculture becomes more **difficult** (see p.189).

Resource distribution

- **Population growth** and **distribution** are linked to the **availability** of **fresh water** and other **natural resources**, e.g. most **deserts** have **small populations** because of the **lack of water**.
- Lack of **safe water** can lead to **food insecurity**, **health problems** and, in extreme cases, **death**. This can cause populations in these areas to **decrease**.
- Places with lots of naturally occurring **food** and **fuel** (e.g. tropical rainforests) are able to support fairly large populations.
- **Energy** and **mineral** resources (e.g. oil, coal, gold) can cause local **concentrations** of people.

"Resource distribution? I don't think so — the bananas are all mine."

Development Processes Also Affect Population Change

1) In the past, major **advances in development** have affected **population size** and **distribution**. For example:

- **Neolithic Revolution** — around **12 000 years ago**, people in some areas (e.g. western Asia and eastern China) developed **agriculture**. Their lifestyles changed from **hunting** and **gathering** food to **farming** in permanent **settlements**. Population in these areas **increased** as **food supply** became more **reliable**.
- **Industrial Revolution** — from approximately 1760 to 1850, there was a rapid rise in the use of **machinery**, **factories** etc. in developed countries. It coincided with major **population growth**, e.g. Britain's population **more than doubled** between 1750 and 1850. This was for many reasons, e.g. **death rates fell** because of increased **food production** and more **money** meant people had better **diets**. As farming became less **labour intensive**, people moved to **cities** for work, leading to more **concentrated** populations.

2) Development still influences population change. As countries develop, the rate of **population growth** tends to first **increase** and then **decrease** (see p.200-201), and populations generally become more **concentrated** in urban areas.

Practice Questions

Q1 Define population density.

Q2 Briefly explain how soil can affect population size.

Exam Question

Q1 Assess the extent to which population size, density and distribution are affected by the physical environment. [9 marks]

Evenly distributed revision will prevent you from feeling dense in the exam...

Phew... you've dipped your toe into a big complicated subject here — try not to turn and run if it feels a bit intense. Lots of these ideas are covered in more detail later in the topic, so these pages will get you nice and prepared for what lies ahead.

Food Production and Consumption

These pages are all about one of my favourite topics of conversation — grub. So tuck in.

Global Food Production is Unevenly Distributed

1) Food production has **increased** globally over the last 50 years — the **area** of land used for producing food has **increased** since 1965, and **technological advances** (e.g. rotary combines, pesticides and modern irrigation techniques) have made it possible to produce **more food** from **less land**.

2) Some countries produce **large amounts** of food and some produce **very little**. The map below shows the production of cereals by country from 2012 to 2014. The production of a lot other food follows a similar pattern.

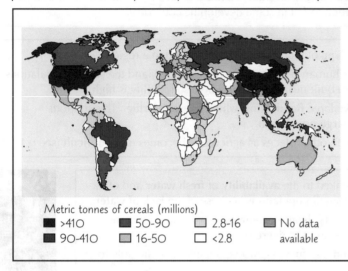

Metric tonnes of cereals (millions)
- ■ >410
- ■ 90-410
- ■ 50-90
- ■ 16-50
- □ 2.8-16
- □ <2.8
- ■ No data available

East Asia and **North America** produce a lot of food due to:
- **Climates** that are **good** for farming.
- Lots of **investment** in farming.

Central America and **Africa** produce relatively small amounts of food due to:
- A **lack of resources** and **funding** for farming equipment.
- Large areas of **land** that are **unsuitable** for farming as they are either **mountainous**, or have **poor quality** or **little soil**, e.g. the Sahara desert.
- **Unsuitable climates** — some areas don't get enough **rainfall** or are **too hot**.

Global Food Consumption is Also Unevenly Distributed

1) The global **population** is increasing — more people means **more food** is being consumed.

2) Food consumption **per person** is also increasing globally — as the world becomes more economically developed, people are **eating more**.

3) However, food consumption, like production, **varies** between countries. The map below shows the **daily per capita calorie intake** of people in different countries from 2011 to 2013.

- **More developed** areas, like **North America** and **Europe**, **consume a lot**. They can afford to import a large variety of foods, have a **culture** of **consumerism**, and many people have **high disposable incomes** so can afford **more food**.
- **Less developed** areas, like **Africa** and parts of **South America** and **Asia**, **consume less food** per person as they **can't afford** as much.
- **China** and other **emerging economies** are **consuming more** as their **wealth increases**.
- However, the map doesn't show **variations** within countries — even in a country with a **high calorie intake**, **some** people may have **limited access** to food.

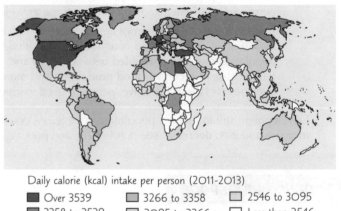

Daily calorie (kcal) intake per person (2011-2013)
- ■ Over 3539
- ■ 3358 to 3539
- ■ 3266 to 3358
- □ 3095 to 3266
- □ 2546 to 3095
- □ Less than 2546
- ■ No data available

4) The **types** of food consumed vary between countries at different levels of **development**. E.g. **meat** costs more to produce than plant-based food, so it makes up a **bigger** proportion of the diet in more **developed** countries — the average amount of meat consumed per person per year in developed countries from 2013-2015 was **65.7 kg**, whereas in **developing** countries it was **26.6 kg**.

Hugh tried to make out he was loaded, but his dinner was a dead giveaway.

Topic Ten — Population and the Environment

Food Production and Consumption

Farms are **Open Systems**

1) In an **open system**, **energy** and **matter** can be lost or gained from the **environment**.
2) Some of the **inputs** to farmland are **natural**, e.g. **solar energy** and **rainwater**, and some are introduced to the system by **humans**, e.g. **seeds** and **fertilisers**.
3) Energy and matter are **transferred** to and **stored** in the **soil**, **crops** and/or **animals** on the farm.
4) The main **output** is the **food** produced, although there are also other outputs, such as **runoff**.

See p.2-3 for how natural systems work.

Agricultural Productivity Measures **Agricultural Output**

1) **Agricultural productivity** is a measure of the **amount of food** that is **produced** in an area — it's the ratio of agricultural **output** (i.e. amount of food produced) to **inputs** (e.g. human labour, capital).
2) Agricultural productivity is affected by the type of **agricultural system**:

Farms can grow plants (arable farming), raise animals (livestock farming) or both (mixed farming).

1) **Commercial** farming — the production of crops or livestock to make a **profit**. It has **high agricultural productivity** and is more common in developed countries than developing countries.
2) **Subsistence** farming — when just enough food is grown to **feed the family**. It's common in Africa and Asia, and has **lower** agricultural productivity.
3) **Intensive** farming — **as much as possible** is produced from the land. There are two types of intensive farming:

   - **Capital-intensive** farming has a high input of capital (money), and a low input of labour for the area of land. It often involves using fertilisers, pesticides and labour-saving machinery.
   - **Labour-intensive** farming doesn't involve much capital but uses a lot of labour.

4) **Extensive** farming — the **opposite** to intensive farming. It has **low capital** and **labour input** for the area of land so produces **less food** than intensive farming. Small numbers of livestock grazing large areas of land is an example, e.g. livestock farms on the grasslands of North America. Extensive farming tends to have **less impact on the environment**, and provides **better animal welfare** than intensive farming.
5) **Nomadic** farming — farmers **move** from place to place to grow crops or graze animals on different land, e.g. many livestock farmers in sub-Saharan African countries roam over large areas to let their animals graze.

3) Agricultural productivity is affected by the **physical environment**:

Climate
- The climate affects how **successfully** plants can **grow** in an area and the **animals** that can survive there.
- Some crops are **adapted** to particular climatic conditions, e.g. pineapples suit tropical climates.
- Some climates make farming more **difficult** — e.g. if the ground is frequently **frozen**.

See p.186-190 for more on the effects of climate and soil on agriculture.

Soil
- Some areas are unsuitable for farming because there is **not enough** soil, or the soil is of **poor quality** — this is often the case in **deserts**.
- Different **soils** are suited to different **types of farming**, e.g. some soils are too shallow or not fertile enough to grow **crops** so are used for **grazing**.

Practice Questions

Q1 Give two reasons why global food production has increased over the last 50 years.
Q2 Define the term 'agricultural productivity'.
Q3 Describe two agricultural systems.

Exam Question

Q1 Using the maps on the previous page, analyse global patterns of food consumption and production. [6 marks]

Food fights — a serious threat to the even distribution of food...

OK, I'm fully aware that your main interest in food is probably the part where you shovel it into your mouth — but you need to know a bit about where and how it's produced, how much is eaten in different parts of the world, and the factors that can affect productivity. So, fetch a snack if it's making you peckish, but make sure you take the time to learn these pages properly.

People and Climate

The climate affects human life, and I don't just mean our wardrobe choices and our topics of small talk at the bus stop...

Human Activities and Numbers are Influenced by the Climate

1) The world can be broadly classified into five **climatic zones** — arid, continental, polar, temperate and tropical.

2) **Climate** affects things like **agricultural productivity** and **water availability** — this means that **population sizes** and **lifestyles** in different climatic zones are often **different**.

3) You need to know the **characteristics** and **distributions** of **two** climate types and how their characteristics **affect people**. These pages cover **polar** and **arid** climates, but you might have studied different examples.

Polar Climates are Cold and Dry

There's more on the distribution and characteristics of polar environments on p.54-55.

1) Polar climates are mainly found **above 66° latitude** in the northern and southern hemispheres, and experience the **coldest temperatures** on the planet.

2) Polar regions are cold and have **little precipitation**. The precipitation that does occur falls mainly as **snow**.

3) There are two polar regions — the **Arctic** is at the **north** of the globe:

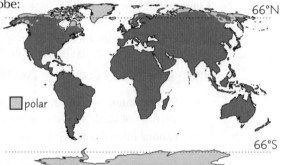

66°N

- It covers the **Arctic Ocean**, much of which has a surface layer of **ice**.
- Areas around the Arctic Ocean, such as **northern Canada**, **Greenland** and **northern Russia**, have a polar climate.
- In winter, temperatures are often **below -40 °C**. In summer they range from about **-10 °C** to **+10 °C**.
- Precipitation is generally less than 100 mm per year.

□ polar

66°S

4) Antarctica is an **ice-covered** continent at the **south** of the Earth:

- Antarctica is **colder** than the Arctic — temperatures in the winter can fall **below -80 °C**.
- The **interior** of Antarctica is very dry — it gets **less than 50 mm** of precipitation each year. Precipitation is higher in **coastal** areas, especially in the **west**.

5) Polar climates produce **two** main types of environment — **ice caps**, which are layers of ice **permanently covering** an area, and **tundra**, which has permanently frozen ground called **permafrost**.

The Polar Climate Makes Human Occupation Difficult

A small number of scientists stay in Antarctic research bases temporarily, mostly in the summer.

1) **Populations** are **low** in the polar climatic zone — the population of the Arctic is around **4 million**, and nobody lives permanently in **Antarctica**.

2) The low temperatures and low precipitation affect **traditional lifestyles** in the **Arctic**:

- Agricultural productivity is **low**, so traditional lifestyles are based on **subsistence** (people produce enough for themselves without any extra for trade).
- **Arable farming** generally **isn't possible** because few plants can **survive** such **cold** temperatures, and the ground is often **frozen** solid. Therefore, Arctic diets are usually **meat-based** — much of this meat comes from **hunting**, **trapping** and **fishing**, but many Arctic people also raise **reindeer** for meat and milk.
- Many of the species that Arctic people eat **leave** the **most extreme** environments in **winter** — this causes some native peoples to **migrate seasonally**, so they're closer to a food source all year round.
- People have **adapted** to the **cold temperatures** with **clothing** and **building** methods that provide **insulation**, e.g. **Inuit people** build **stone** houses into **hillsides**, which are **insulated** by coverings of **turf** and **snow**.

3) The climate also affects **development** in polar regions:

- The low temperatures and frozen ground make it hard for people to **work** in polar environments or **construct** buildings there — this means that development is **difficult**. Buildings and roads have to be designed so they don't **melt** the permafrost, e.g. by building on thick **concrete slabs**.
- There are several types of **seasonal work**. **Tourism** is popular during the summer months, especially on **cruise ships**. **Oil** and **gas** reserves are more accessible in the summer, which also creates jobs.
- The **melting** of **Arctic sea ice** during the summer opens up **shipping routes** that make **trade** between northern countries easier. **Commercial fishing** can also take place when there is less sea ice.

People and Climate

Arid Climates are Very Dry

1) Arid areas usually get less than 250 mm of rainfall per year — places in this zone are classed as **deserts**, which can be **hot** or **temperate**:

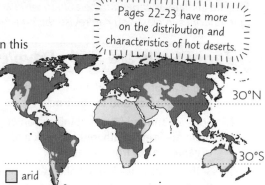

Pages 22-23 have more on the distribution and characteristics of hot deserts.

- **Hot deserts** occur around **30°** north and south of the equator, e.g. the Sahara in northern Africa and the Namib in southern Africa. Maximum air temperatures are **above 40 °C**.
- **Temperate** deserts occur at **higher latitudes**, e.g. central Asia. They are **cooler** than hot deserts, but still as **arid**.

2) Rain is **rare** and **unreliable** — it falls in infrequent **heavy storms**.

3) **Temperature ranges** can be **huge** — nights are usually much colder than days.

People Living in Arid Regions are Affected by the Climate

1) **Population** in arid areas is **low**, e.g. the **Sahara Desert** has around **2.5 million** inhabitants (**about 0.4 people per km²**). **Distribution** is **uneven** — there are **clusters** of settlement around **water sources**, and other areas are **uninhabited**.

2) The dry climate is a **challenge** for human occupation of arid regions, and affects **traditional lifestyles**:

- **Agriculture** is **impossible** in most areas because **rain** only falls very **infrequently**, usually in the form of **heavy convectional rainstorms**. Rainstorms can cause **flash flooding** and **soil erosion**.
- Water can be drawn from **oases** to **irrigate** crops nearby. Crops such as **cereals** can be grown in the **shade** of taller food plants, e.g. **date palms**. These methods have allowed some people to **settle** around oases.
- Other native people are **nomadic** — they move from place to place. This allows people to keep **grazing** livestock despite the **sparse vegetation** — animals eat the plants in one place, then **move on**.

3) There are also more **modern** solutions to the challenges of arid climates.

- **Groundwater** for irrigation can be more easily accessed with **motorised pumps**. Modern **irrigation** techniques include **drip irrigation**, where water slowly drips onto crops, minimising **evaporation**.
- **Economic development** is often **hindered** by the climate, but major **cities** can develop if there is enough **money** to invest in obtaining water. For example, **Las Vegas** in the **Mojave Desert relies** on water from Lake Mead, a **reservoir** created by a huge **dam** on the Colorado River, for 90% of its water supply.

Climate Change has Impacts on Agriculture

See p.13 for more on the causes of climate change, and p.15 for its impacts.

1) Climate change is **decreasing agricultural productivity** (p.185) in some areas. E.g. **reduced rainfall** in Africa and Australia may damage harvests and limit the food available for grazing livestock.

2) **Agricultural productivity** may **increase in other areas**. E.g. **increased temperature** and **rainfall** may increase productivity in North America and Europe by encouraging crop growth.

3) There may be **changes** in the **types of crops** grown. Crops that **prefer warmer conditions** (e.g. melons) could be grown further **north**. Crops that **prefer cooler conditions** (e.g. potatoes) could produce **lower yields** in their current locations.

4) **Agricultural pests** and **diseases** may **increase** in some areas. E.g. the range of the European Corn Borer (a pest of maize) is shifting northwards due to increased temperatures.

Practice Questions

Q1 Describe the characteristics of the polar climate zone.

Q2 Briefly describe two ways that climate change is affecting agriculture.

Exam Question

Q1 Analyse the relationships between climate and human numbers and activities in one major climatic type. [9 marks]

The Arctic also has the world's largest population of toy-making elves...

If you've studied different examples in class, just make sure you know what the climate is like and how it affects human numbers and activities in both. And don't forget that you also need to know how agriculture is being affected by climate change.

People and Soils

Just like climate, you need to be able to write about two soil types and how they affect humans — if you've learnt about different ones in class you can revise them instead, but make sure you also know about soil problems and their management.

Zonal Soils are Fully Developed Soils

1) Soil is all of the material between the ground **surface** and the **bedrock**.

2) Soils are formed from a combination of **minerals** from **weathered bedrock** and **organic matter** from **vegetation**.

3) Soil formation is closely linked with the **climate** of the area. Climate determines the **rate of weathering** of the bedrock, the **type of vegetation** that grows there, and how **quickly** this vegetation **decomposes**.

4) **Zonal soils** are **mature** soils that have developed from the **interaction** between climate, vegetation and parent rock across a **significant period of time**.

5) Different parts of the world have different dominant zonal soil types, e.g. **podzols** and **latosols**.

6) Soil types can be **identified** by looking at the **distinct layers** in the **soil profile**, which are known as **soil horizons**. There are **five** main horizons (although not all soils have all five).

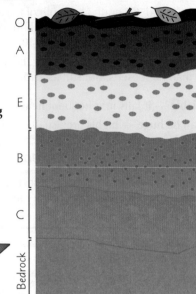

Loose, partially decayed organic matter.

Topsoil with high humus (organic matter) content.

Pale layer of silt and sand, from which clay, iron and other minerals have been leached.

Zone in which minerals leached from above accumulate.

Mainly broken bedrock

Leaching is when water moves minerals and nutrients down through the soil profile.

Podzols are Acidic and have Distinct Horizons

1) Podzols occur in **cool temperate climates** in the **northern hemisphere**, where there is more **precipitation** than **evapotranspiration**.

2) They're usually found under **coniferous woodland** or **heather moorland**.

3) The **O horizon** is a layer of **needles** from the coniferous trees or heather **leaf litter**, and below this is a **narrow, acidic A horizon**. **Nutrients** are **leached** from the A horizon by water.

4) Because of the acidity, **water** travelling through the soil is more able to **dissolve** certain minerals such as **iron** and **aluminium compounds**. **Leaching** of these minerals creates a pale **E horizon** formed mainly of **quartz** sand and silt.

5) Minerals **accumulate** in the **B horizon**, forming a **reddish-brown** layer. In very **well-developed** podzols, a 'hard pan' or 'iron pan' forms in the B horizon — this is a hard, continuous layer of deposited **iron**.

23.5°N
Equator
23.5°S
podzols

Podzols are acidic because the leaf litter from coniferous trees and heather is acidic, and they often form on acidic sandstones or clays.

Podzols are Not Good for Agriculture

1) Some **livestock** can be **grazed** in areas with podzols. However, **arable** farming is difficult:

- The **acidity** and **lack of nutrients** means that few crops are able to grow.
- Formation of a **hard pan** can prevent water draining away, making the soil vulnerable to **waterlogging**, damaging crops (see p.190). Waterlogging also makes **ploughing** difficult because machinery sinks into the ground.
- **Some** arable farming does take place on podzols, but this requires treatment with lime to **reduce acidity**, and extensive artificial **fertilisation**.

2) Because **coniferous trees** grow successfully in podzols, **forestry** is a common **human activity** in this soil type. **Low soil temperatures** mean that it can take up to 100 years for a tree to reach **maturity** and be ready to **harvest**.

Carl insisted that his farm didn't have a problem with waterlogging.

People and Soils

Latosols are Deep and Red

1) Latosols are found under **tropical rainforests**.

2) The **high temperature** and **humidity** in the tropics encourage **fast chemical weathering** of the bedrock, forming soils up to **30-40 m deep**.

23.5°N

Equator

23.5°S

■ latosols

3) Year-round plant growth means the **O horizon** is quite **thick**. However, as soon as **leaf litter** decomposes to **humus**, its nutrients are **absorbed** by vegetation rather than staying in the soil — this means that the **fertile A horizon** is very **thin**.

4) **Rainfall** is **higher** than **evapotranspiration** in rainforests, causing a **soil moisture surplus**. This means there is a lot of **leaching** — silicate minerals are leached from the **B horizon**, but **less soluble** iron and aluminium compounds are **left behind**. The **iron compounds** give the B horizon a **red** colour.

5) The **build-up** of minerals in the soil can form a **laterite horizon**, which acts like **clay**.

Latosols Influence Human Activities

1) Latosols are **poor for agriculture** due to their low nutrient content. Once the rainforest trees are **removed**, the soil has **no protection** from the **heavy rainfall** — **leaching** increases and the latosol becomes even more **nutrient poor**.

2) **Humans** living in the rainforest have **adapted** to this soil type:

- Traditional agriculture using 'slash and burn' clears one small area for growing crops at a time.
- **Burning** vegetation to clear the plot **adds nutrients** to the soil. After **one** growing season, a **new** plot is cleared, and the first is left to **recover** fully.

3) However, farming has **expanded** in areas with latosols. Large areas of land are cleared for **agriculture**, and soil isn't given a chance to **recover** — this has led to **permanent** soil **degradation**.

4) The laterite horizon is **soft** when it is **moist**, but **hard** when it **dries out** — this makes it useful for **building**.

Soil Erosion Has Impacts on Agriculture

Soil erosion can lead to desertification — see p.33-34.

1) Soil erosion is the **wearing away** of soil by **wind** or **water**. There are several factors that can make soil more **vulnerable** to erosion, for example:

- **Clearing vegetation** — rain falls directly onto the soil instead of being **intercepted** by plants, and the **roots** that were **binding** the soil together are removed. Vegetation also **slows down** the **wind**, so removing it exposes the ground surface to **stronger winds**.
- **Topography** — e.g. soil is more likely to be **washed down a steep slope**.
- **Climate** — e.g. **high rainfall** increases **water erosion**. **Low rainfall** and high temperatures mean soil is **dry**, which makes it more vulnerable to **wind erosion**.
- **Land use** — e.g. **ploughing loosens** soil and **exposes** it to wind and rain, making it more **vulnerable** to erosion.

2) Soil erosion is a major **threat** to **agriculture** because it **removes nutrients** and reduces the soil's **ability to hold water**. In the last 40 years, **almost a third** of the world's arable land has become **unproductive** because of soil erosion.

3) There are several management strategies to **reduce** soil erosion on farmland, such as:

- **Crop rotation** — instead of leaving fields **bare** after the **main crop** is harvested, farmers can plant **cover crops**, which help to maintain the soil until a main crop is sown again.
- **Windbreaks** — **hedges** or **trees** can be planted around fields as barriers against **wind erosion**.
- **Terracing** — **steps** can be **cut** into a steep **hillside** to **slow down** the movement of water down the slope.
- **Contour ploughing**, i.e. ploughing **across the slope** instead of downslope — this stops rainwater from **flowing** downhill as quickly.
- **Mulching** — covering the soil with a **layer of plant material** protects the soil from wind and rain, and **slows down runoff**.

A row of poplars acting as a windbreak around a barley field.

People and Soils

There are Other Soil Issues Related to Agriculture

1) **Waterlogging** is when the spaces between soil particles fill with **water**:

Causes	Problems for agriculture	Management strategies
• Soils with **few airspaces**, e.g. clay, fill up with water quickly. • **'Hard pans'** or **laterites** (see p.188-189) hinder **drainage**, which can cause waterlogging of the soil above. • **Precipitation** is **higher** than **evapotranspiration**. • Too much **irrigation**.	• Plant **roots** are surrounded by water, which limits their **growth** and can **rot** them. • Water decreases **soil temperature**, which can reduce crop growth. • Crops may be out-competed by **weeds** that can cope better with the wet conditions. • Land is hard to **plough**.	• Avoid **over-watering** crops. • **Drain** the soil using underground **pipes** or **ditches** around the fields. • Change the **composition** of the soil, e.g. add **sand** to **clay** soil.

2) **Salinisation** is the build-up of **salts** in the soil:

Causes	Problems for agriculture	Management strategies
• **High temperatures** draw water to the surface, where it evaporates, leaving behind salts. • In **dry** climates, there isn't enough rainfall to leach salts away. • **Irrigation water** contains salts — when the water is absorbed by plants or evaporated, the salts are left behind. • Some **fertilisers** contain salts — applying **too much** means that some salts are left in the soil.	• Salt can stop crops from **absorbing** the **water** they need from the soil. • Some salts are **toxic** to plants, so they may reduce the yield or kill the crop. • Water flows **from** areas of low salinity **to** areas of high salinity. High soil salinity means water may flow from **plant roots** to the **soil**, **dehydrating** plants.	• Avoid **waterlogging** (see strategies above). • Only use as much water for irrigation as is needed (e.g. using drip irrigation). • Add the appropriate **amount** and **type** of **fertiliser**.

3) **Structural deterioration** is when the **pore spaces** in the soil are lost:

Causes	Problems for agriculture	Management strategies
• Use of heavy machinery, or **trampling** by livestock or people, can compact soil. • Removal of **vegetation**, as plant **roots** help to maintain soil structure. • **Salinisation** in clay soils, as salt causes clay particles to **clump** together.	• If the soil is too compacted, it's difficult for plant **roots** to grow. • A **loss of pore spaces** in the soil means that there is a reduced capacity for **water**, so plants can dry out. • Land is hard to **plough**.	• Avoid compaction by **moving livestock** regularly. • Maintain **vegetation cover**. • Change the structure of soil by **adding sand** to clay soils. • Avoid **salinisation** (see strategies above).

Practice Questions

Q1 Briefly describe the characteristics of podzols.

Q2 Briefly explain why latosols aren't good for agriculture.

Q3 Give two ways in which soil waterlogging can be managed.

Exam Question

Q1 'As more land is converted to agricultural use, the worsening of soil problems is inevitable.'
To what extent do you agree with this view? [20 marks]

Chuck some soil in the air — now it's an aerosol...

Well. It turns out soil is a lot more complicated than it looks. There are a few new words on these pages, but don't let them put you off. Just take it a little bit at a time — you need to know about two zonal soil types, and the four main soil problems.

Increasing Food Security

There's more to meeting the food needs of the population than just producing enough grub...

Food Security Means Having Reliable Access to Affordable Food

People have **food security** when they have **enough nutritious food**. This depends on:

1) **Food availability** — a country must **produce** and/or **import** a **sufficient** amount of food.
2) **Food access** — people must be able to **regularly** obtain food, e.g. by **buying** it or **producing** it themselves.
3) **Food quality and use** — the food that people consume must be **nutritious** enough for them to maintain a healthy life. It must be stored and prepared in a way that is **safe** and **hygienic**.

There are Different Strategies to Improve Food Security

Food security can be increased by **producing more** food, **sharing** it out more evenly, and reducing the amount **wasted**:

1 Increasing food production

- **Agricultural expansion** — more land can be **converted** to agricultural use. However, this **destroys** ecosystems.
- **Intensive farming** — this means producing as much food as possible from the land available. This reduces the need for **clearing** natural land, but it may result in **artificial chemicals** (e.g. pesticides and fertilisers) damaging the natural environment.
- **Changing the types of food produced** — e.g. producing **plants** needs less land and water than producing **meat** and **dairy**, so converting to arable farming (where possible) means **more food** can be produced. However, as countries become more **developed**, people tend to eat more meat, so demand is **increasing**.
- **Technology** — e.g. crops can be **genetically modified** to produce higher yields or to resist pests and diseases. This limits the need for artificial pesticides, but it reduces biodiversity. **Hydroponics** (growing plants in a **nutrient solution** rather than soil) means crops can be grown in places where there's a lack of **fertile soil**. However, it's very expensive, so it may not increase food production in poorer countries.

2 Increasing food access

- **Trade** — food can be **imported** to countries that don't have enough. However, **prices** have to be **low** enough for countries to be able to **afford** sufficient food. Cheap imports may **undercut** local farmers, making it hard for them to earn a living.
- **Improving access to markets** — e.g. improving transport links makes it easier for farmers to sell their produce. However, some countries can't afford to invest in the **infrastructure** needed.
- **Aid** — e.g. food is **donated** during a famine. This may not be **sustainable** in the long term.

To ensure **long-term** food security, strategies must be **sustainable** — e.g. they shouldn't use too many **resources** or cause too much **environmental damage**.

3 Reducing waste

Waste can be reduced at all stages of the process:

- **Production** — e.g. crop loss due to pests and disease can be decreased by **educating** farmers on **prevention** and providing them with better **resources** (e.g. equipment, pesticides).
- **Distribution** — many shops **discard** food that they don't sell. Improving **storage** and **packaging**, and **speeding up** the time it takes for food to reach consumers, increases **shelf life**. Some supermarkets donate surplus food to **food banks**.
- **Consumption** — campaigns like '**Think.Eat.Save**' encourage consumers to be less wasteful, e.g. by sharing recipes to use up leftovers. However, it can take a **long time** for populations to **change their behaviour** on a large scale.

Practice Questions

Q1 What is food security?

Q2 Describe one way that food production could be increased.

Exam Question

Q1 Analyse the likely impacts of climate change on attempts to increase food security. [9 marks]

Ensure your food's secure — install a burger alarm...

Just a single page to learn here, but it's important stuff — as the global population grows, food security gets harder to achieve.

Global Patterns of Health, Disease and Death

This section's all about global health issues. Where you live in the world affects your health in many different ways.

Health is Better in More Developed Countries

1) **Health** is defined as your **physical**, **mental** and **social well-being**, and the **absence of disease**.

2) Health **varies** between different parts of the world. It's measured using **health indicators**, such as **healthy life expectancy (HALE)** — this is the **number** of **years** a newborn child can **expect** to **live** in **full health** without major disease. The **global pattern** of HALE is shown on the map below:

Global pattern of healthy life expectancy (2015)

Units = years

No data
40.0 to 46.9
47.0 to 53.9
54.0 to 60.9
61.0 to 67.9
68.0 to 74.9

• The map shows HALE is **highest** in **more developed countries** such as the **UK, USA** and **Australia**.

• HALE is lowest in **less developed countries** such as those in **sub-Saharan Africa**.

Sub-Saharan Africa includes all the countries south of the Sahara Desert.

3) How **healthy** a country is **depends** on how much **disease** there is in the country, and what **types** of **diseases** there are.

Global Morbidity Patterns are Different Depending on the Type of Disease

1) **Morbidity** means the **rate of disease in a population**. Morbidity **indicators** include:
   • **prevalence** — the **total** number of **cases** in a **population** at a **particular time**.
   • **incidence** — the number of **new cases** in a **population** during a **particular time period**.

2) **Global patterns** of morbidity **differ** depending on the **type** of **disease** you're looking at:

(1) Morbidity pattern of infectious diseases

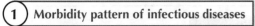

Global morbidity pattern of tuberculosis (TB) (2015)

• **Infectious** diseases can be passed between people, e.g. malaria, HIV/AIDS.

• The map shows the **global morbidity pattern** of the **infectious** disease tuberculosis (TB).

• There's **high TB morbidity** in **less developed** countries, e.g. countries in **sub-Saharan Africa**.

• There's **low TB morbidity** in **more developed** countries, e.g. the **UK, USA** and **Australia**.

Units = new cases per 100 000 of the population

No data
0 – 24.9
25 – 99
100 – 199
200 – 299
> 300

Reasons for the **high morbidity** of **infectious disease** in **less developed** countries include lack of **clean water**, **sanitation** and **health care**, limited **health education** and **overcrowded** conditions in urban areas.

(2) Morbidity pattern of non-communicable diseases

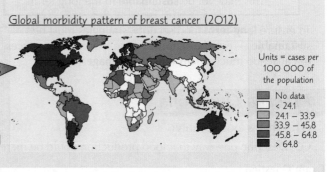

Global morbidity pattern of breast cancer (2012)

• **Non-communicable** diseases can't be caught from someone else, e.g. cancer, heart disease.

• The map shows the **global morbidity pattern** of the **non-communicable** disease breast cancer.

• There's **high breast cancer morbidity** in **more developed** countries, e.g. the **UK, USA** and **Australia**.

• There's **low breast cancer morbidity** in **less developed** countries, e.g. countries in **Africa** and **Asia**.

Units = cases per 100 000 of the population

No data
< 24.1
24.1 – 33.9
33.9 – 45.8
45.8 – 64.8
> 64.8

Reasons for the **high morbidity** of **non-communicable disease** in **more developed** countries include:
• **Higher proportion** of **older people** (due to higher life expectancy) — if there are more old people **more** people are **likely** to suffer from **diseases** associated with **old age**, e.g. **cancer** and **heart disease**.

• **Unhealthy lifestyle** — the **risk** of **some diseases** (e.g. cancer, heart disease) **increases** if you're **overweight**, eat **unhealthy food** and don't do enough **exercise**. These **factors** are **more common** in **developed** countries.

Global Patterns of Health, Disease and Death

Mortality Patterns Depend on Morbidity and the Ability to Treat Morbidity

1) **Mortality** means **death**. In general, **high morbidity** is associated with **high mortality**.

2) The **mortality rate** is how many people **die** in a **population** over a **period of time**. You use mortality rates to **compare global patterns of death**.

   Global incidence and mortality rates from all forms of cancer* (2012)

   - The table shows that **more developed** areas, such as **Australia** and **North America**, have a **higher incidence rate** of cancer than **less developed** areas, such as **Africa** and **Asia**. The **mortality rate** is also **higher** in more developed areas.

   - However, the **percentage** of cases resulting in **death** is much **lower** in **more developed** areas than in less developed areas.

Area of the world	Incidence rate (cases per 100 000)	Mortality rate (deaths per 100 000)	% of cases resulting in death
Africa	79	55	70
Asia	159	106	67
South America	202	110	54
Europe	461	237	51
North America	510	197	39
Australia/ New Zealand	506	191	38

*excluding non-melanoma skin cancer

3) The **risk** of **dying** from a disease is **much higher** in **less developed countries** due to:

   - **Malnutrition** — **reduces** the body's **ability** to **fight** disease.

   - **Poor access** to **health care** — people **can't access** the drugs or other treatments (e.g. surgery) they need to **treat** the disease.

The Epidemiological Transition Refers to Changing Mortality Patterns

1) The **epidemiological transition model** states that the main cause of **mortality** changes from **infectious** diseases to **non-communicable** diseases over time. The original model had **three stages**, but further stages have been suggested:

Stage 1	Stage 2	Stage 3	Stage 4?
Age of pestilence and famine	Age of receding pandemics	Age of degenerative and man-made diseases	Delay of degenerative diseases?
High number of deaths from infectious diseases.	Number of deaths from infectious diseases falls due to better living conditions and health care.	Non-communicable diseases replace infectious diseases as the main cause of death.	Non-communicable diseases may be prevented or their onset delayed, and death rate reduced by better treatment.
Average life expectancy is low (~50 yrs).	Average life expectancy starts to increase (~60 yrs).	Average life expectancy continues to increase (~70 yrs).	Average life expectancy is high (~80 yrs).
E.g. Angola	E.g. Haiti	E.g. Russia	E.g. UK

2) The model suggests that countries move through the stages as they become more **economically** and **socially developed**. This is because as they develop:

   - **malnutrition** decreases because food availability increases — this **increases** the body's **ability** to **fight** disease.

   - **clean water** becomes more widely available and **sanitation** improves, **decreasing** the **spread** of diseases.

   - there is **better access** to **health care** — people can access drugs etc. to **prevent** and **treat** diseases.

   - there is **better health education** — people are **better informed** about how they can **avoid** diseases.

3) Some people think that there is also a **Stage 5**. This is the **re-emergence** of **infectious** diseases due to the evolution of **antibiotic-resistant** bacteria, along with increasing **travel** and **trade** allowing diseases to spread more easily.

4) The stages in this model can be linked to those of the **demographic transition model** (DTM, see p.200-201).

Practice Questions

Q1 Describe the global pattern of life expectancy.

Q2 What is morbidity?

Q3 Briefly outline the epidemiological transition model.

% of obese males
- No data
- <10
- 10 - <20
- 20 - <30
- >30

Exam Question

Q1 The map shows the global distribution of obesity in males. Using the map, assess the extent to which global patterns of obesity are similar to global patterns of non-communicable disease morbidity. [6 marks]

Disease — it's morbid stuff...

This isn't the cheeriest of sections, I know, but that doesn't mean you can get away with not learning it. Just remember morbidity means illness and mortality means death and you'll be at least part way there. Chin up, brave face, then onwards...

The Geography of Disease

Illness is affected by a whole host of factors, both physical and human. Take exams for instance — I mean, I feel sick just thinking about them. Anyhow, it's time to take a look at these factors, and at what's being done to fight disease.

The **Incidence** of **Disease** is Affected by **Environmental Variables**

Some **environmental** factors can **increase** the risk of disease:

Disease vectors (or transmission vectors) are living organisms that can pass diseases between people.

Climate

1) **Precipitation** — many disease vectors need **water** to survive, so there are more infectious diseases in **wetter** climates. **Higher** than average rainfall can also cause **growth** in the populations of disease vectors, e.g. ticks that carry Lyme disease.

2) **Temperature** — many disease vectors can only survive **above** a certain **temperature threshold**, e.g. mosquitoes carrying dengue fever are only found where winter temperatures are above 10 °C. This means that many infectious diseases occur only in **tropical climates**. High temperatures can also **increase** the **likelihood** of disease from **food-borne vectors** if food isn't stored properly (e.g. salmonella). Higher temperatures also increase the abundance of **pollen**, which can lead to allergies, e.g. hayfever.

3) **Extreme events** — heavy rainfall can lead to **flooding**, causing **sewage** systems to **overflow**. This **contaminates** water supplies, making **water-borne diseases** such as cholera more likely (see below). Very low rainfall can lead to water-borne disease vectors becoming **concentrated** in water sources, making it more likely that people will become **ill** if they use the water.

4) **Seasonality** — **Arctic areas** experience very **little daylight** during the winter. This can affect **mental health**, e.g. Arctic countries tend to have a higher rate of **seasonal affective disorder** (SAD) than other countries.

5) **Sunlight** — **lack** of sunlight can result in **vitamin D deficiency**, which can lead to bone loss, kidney disease and intestinal problems. **Overexposure** to sunlight increases the risk of diseases such as **skin cancer**.

Topography

1) **Drainage** — the **flood plains** of rivers tend to have high population densities. When they flood, drinking water can be **contaminated**, leading to the spread of **water-borne** diseases such as cholera and typhoid. Floods can also force people to **move**, increasing pressure on **resources** (e.g. water, health care) in the areas they move to.

2) **Relief** — **standing water** collects at low points in the landscape, which provides an ideal breeding ground for mosquitoes carrying diseases such as yellow fever. **Urine** from infected animals can also become **concentrated** in areas that don't drain well, leading to diseases such as leptospirosis.

3) **Altitude** — high altitudes can increase the risk of **skin cancer** because of increased exposure to ultraviolet rays.

Poor Air Quality Can Cause **Health Problems**

1) **Burning fossil fuels**, e.g. in factories and vehicles, produces **poisonous gases** (e.g. sulfur dioxide and nitrogen oxides) and tiny particles of **soot**. Long-term exposure to these can cause **respiratory problems** such as asthma and bronchitis, as well as various **cardiovascular (heart) diseases** and types of **cancer**.

2) **Urban areas** are most likely to be affected by **poor air quality** — **urban air pollution** is estimated to cause around **1.2 million deaths** every year.

3) **Indoor** air quality can also be poor if buildings aren't properly **ventilated** — the air can be polluted by **tobacco smoke**, **mould** and **pollen spores**, or polluting **appliances**, e.g. wood- or kerosene-burning stoves. These can also lead to respiratory diseases, cardiovascular diseases and cancers.

Poor Water Quality Can **Spread Diseases** and Lead to **Poor Health**

Water quality can be affected by both **disease-causing organisms** and **chemical toxins**:

1) Many disease-causing microorganisms (pathogens) live in water that has been **contaminated** with **faeces**. Diseases are spread either by **drinking** the contaminated water or by **bathing** in it — pathogens can enter the body through cuts or through the eyes and nose. Around **3.4 million people die** from **water-borne diseases** every year.

2) Examples of water-borne diseases include:

   - **Hepatitis A** — a liver disease which leads to fever and nausea.
   - **Cholera** — a **bacterial** infection that causes diarrhoea and dehydration.

3) **Chemical toxins** include heavy metals released into the water by industries, and pesticides from agricultural runoff — these can cause some **cancers**, as well as damage to the **nervous system**.

Boris knew that good water quality was something to shout about.

The Geography of Disease

International Organisations are Important in the Fight Against Disease

1) **International organisations** such as the United Nations (UN) aim to **prevent infectious** diseases spreading within and between countries, and to **coordinate research** and **best practice** in limiting the rise of **non-communicable** diseases.

2) The UN acts through agencies such as the **World Health Organisation (WHO)**, the **World Bank** and **UNICEF**. For example, the **World Bank** provides **loans** to less developed countries for **health programmes** and **UNICEF** helps **mothers** and **children** access **food**, **clean water** and **vaccinations**.

3) The **WHO** has the broad aim of improving health on a **global** scale:

> **World Health Organisation**
>
> 1) The WHO works alongside governments and other agencies to **promote health** around the world by:
>   - **advising national governments** about health issues.
>   - working with other international bodies and NGOs (see below) to **limit outbreaks** of **infectious** diseases.
>   - promoting **research** into health issues and providing **training** for health professionals.
>   - **monitoring deaths** and **diseases** to identify global patterns and send resources where they are needed.
>
> 2) One example of a successful WHO project was a **global immunisation campaign** against **smallpox** between 1966 and 1980, which led to the disease being **eradicated**.
>
> 3) More recently, the WHO has helped to **coordinate** the **response** to the outbreak of **Ebola** in west Africa — their actions included increasing the number of **treatment centres** in the region, helping to find a **vaccine** and implementing measures to **prevent transmission** of the disease to other countries (e.g. by advising countries on controls at airports for people travelling from at-risk areas).

NGOs Also Provide Essential Health Care

1) Non-Governmental Organisations (NGOs) are **not-for-profit groups** which are **independent** from governments. They're often **charities**, e.g. the Red Cross, Oxfam.

2) NGOs **promote global health research** and **provide** a significant proportion of the **health care** available in **less developed countries**. They provide health care for **poor** and **remote communities** with little **infrastructure** and **minimal resources**, often working alongside local people to gain **understanding** of their needs.

3) However, the impact of NGOs can be **small-scale** (they often don't have the resources of international organisations) and they rely on **continued donations** and **aid** from people in more developed countries.

4) Some examples of NGOs that work to **improve health** are:

- **Médecins Sans Frontières** Doctors Without Borders) provide **emergency medical assistance**, such as **vaccinations** and **surgery**, wherever it is most needed, e.g. in war-torn areas. They work with **local health care professionals**, providing them with **extra training** and **equipment** so that they can help their communities.

- **Cancer Research** fund **research** into the causes of cancer and treatments for it, provide **support** to sufferers and supply **resources** to healthcare professionals (e.g. information on new treatments). Their work helps to **inform government policies** on issues such as the prevention and diagnosis of cancer and access to treatment. E.g. the Test Cancer Sooner campaign in 2015 meant that the UK government committed **more funding** to the NHS to ensure cancer patients are **diagnosed** as **early** as possible, giving them a better chance of recovery.

Practice Questions

Q1 Give one way that climate affects disease.

Q2 Name one disease caused by poor water quality.

Q3 Outline one way that an international agency acts to promote global health.

Exam Question

Q1 Assess the extent to which the incidence of infectious disease is affected by environmental variables. [9 marks]

Environmental variables also affect the rate of knowledge transmission...

For example, the presence of your geography notes under your pillow... will do nothing at all for how much you remember in the exam. So get your head down and learn these pages until you've got health and disease facts coming out of your ears.

The Geography of Disease

Time to brush up on your knowledge of a couple of specific diseases — and they're a proper pair of nasties...

Malaria is Common in the Developing World

1) Malaria is an **infectious disease** caused by **parasites**, which are transmitted by **mosquitoes**.

2) Most **cases** of **malaria** occur in **tropical** areas, e.g. **sub-Saharan Africa**. In **2015** there were more than **200 million cases** of malaria worldwide — around **90%** occurred in **Africa**.

3) Cases of malaria show **seasonal variation** in **some** regions — most cases occur at the **peak of** or **just after the rainy season**. However, in tropical regions with little seasonal variation in climate, there is a risk of malaria **all year round**.

4) The incidence of malaria is affected by both **physical** and **socio-economic** factors:

Physical	Socio-economic
• **Mosquitoes** that carry **malaria** can only **survive** in **warm countries**, e.g. in Africa. • **Higher temperatures** decrease the time taken for the parasite to develop inside the mosquito, so **increase** the likelihood of **infection**. Mosquitoes also **breed** and **feed** more often when it's warmer, so it's more likely that people will be infected. • Mosquitoes like to **breed** in **still** bodies of **fresh water**, e.g. swamps or pools. The rainy season creates lots of **small puddles** and turns low-lying areas into **wetlands**, providing an ideal habitat for breeding.	• Limited health education — people **aren't informed** about how to **avoid malaria** (e.g. by using **bed nets**). • **Low incomes** may mean people cannot **afford treatment** or means of **prevention**. • In areas where **health care** is limited, there are **more infected people** and **more sources** of the **parasite** for mosquitoes to pick up and transmit. • **Poor health reduces** the body's **ability to fight infection**. • **Poor quality housing**, e.g. windows and doors that don't fit well, puts people at **risk**. • **Human activities**, e.g. digging irrigation ditches or canals, can **increase** the number of breeding sites.

Malaria Affects People's Health and Well-Being

1) Malarial symptoms include **fever**, **chills**, **nausea** and **headaches**. **Organ failure**, **respiratory** problems, **coma** and **death** can follow in **severe** cases of the disease or if it's left **untreated**.

2) Apart from physical symptoms, malaria has a range of impacts on the **well-being** of individuals:

- There may be **lost income** from inability to work, as well as the financial **cost** of **treatment** and **hospital visits**.
- Children may have **extended absences** from school — this affects their education and future job prospects.
- Repeated bouts can affect **children's development**.
- Malaria may hinder a **country's development** — the government has to spend money **treating** the disease, and **productivity falls** when workers are ill. This means that there's less to spend on **improving living standards**.

There are Many Strategies to Manage Malaria

1) In 2015, the WHO set three **goals** for 2030 — **reduce** global malaria **incidence** and **mortality** rates by at least **90%**, **eliminate** malaria in at least **35 countries** and **prevent** malaria **returning** in countries that are currently malaria-free.

2) The **most effective** strategy in reducing malaria incidence is to **get rid of** the **mosquitoes** that carry it, for example:

- by **spraying** the **inside walls** of buildings with insecticide (Indoor Residual Spraying, IRS).
- by **spraying mosquito nets** with insecticide. Providing bed nets also prevents people from being **bitten** (malarial mosquitoes are mainly active from **dusk** to **dawn**).

3) However, IRS can be very **expensive** and may have to be **repeated** several times a year. The chemicals used can have **ecological impacts** and effects on **people's health**, e.g. DDT kills aquatic insects and fish, and can lead to cancers and miscarriages in humans. **Mosquitoes** can evolve **resistance** to insecticides, so **new** insecticides need to be developed.

4) Other strategies include:

- giving **anti-malarial drugs** or **vaccines** to vulnerable people, e.g. pregnant women and young children.
- **monitoring** the breeding of mosquitoes, e.g. so that insecticides can be used where they are needed most.
- **improving diagnosis** (making accurate tests more widely available) so that people are given **prompt treatment**.

5) These strategies can also be very **effective**. However, many people affected live in **remote** rural areas with **limited access** to health care. In practice, a **combination** of strategies is needed.

The Geography of Disease

Coronary Heart Disease is Linked to Unhealthy Lifestyles

1) **Coronary heart disease** (**CHD**) is a disease where a build-up of fatty substances in the arteries means the heart doesn't get enough blood. It is one of the **world's biggest killers** — it caused **15.5%** of **deaths** worldwide in **2015**.

2) CHD is a **non-communicable disease** that is mainly caused by **socio-economic** factors, for example your **risk** of developing CHD **increases** as you get **older**. The **biggest** risk factors are from **lifestyle** — risk is higher for people who are **overweight**, don't **exercise**, consume too much **alcohol**, have a diet high in **unsaturated fat** or **salt**, and **smoke**.

3) The risk of developing CHD is also increased by **physical** factors, e.g. long-term exposure to high levels of **air pollution**.

4) CHD is **more common** in **wealthier** countries, e.g. the **UK** and **USA**. However, **death rates** in these countries are **falling** because of **improvements** in **diagnosing** people **at risk** of CHD, **effective treatments**, and **awareness campaigns**.

5) **Cases** of CHD are **increasing** in **developing countries** and **emerging economies** (e.g. **sub-Saharan Africa** and **India**), as their **wealth increases**. **Death rates** are still **high** in many less developed countries because of **poor health care** (e.g. treatments aren't available) and **limited health education** (e.g. people **aren't aware** of the **effects** of **lifestyle**).

CHD has an Impact on Health and Well-Being

1) Symptoms of CHD include **chest pain**, **shortness** of **breath** and **sweating**. It can lead to a **heart attack**, which can **permanently damage** the heart — this may leave people feeling **fatigued** and unable to perform **physical activities**.

2) Coronary heart disease can affect people's **well-being**. For example:
   - It can make people **anxious** or **depressed** and put a **strain** on **relationships**.
   - People may have to take **medication** for the rest of their lives or visit the **doctor frequently** for check-ups.
   - People may have to **take time off work** or reduce their hours — this has a financial cost that can put **stress** on families.
   - Treatment costs put a large **economic burden** on the country as a whole — this may mean there's less money available for **other** things that may **improve** people's **well-being**, e.g. education, provision of open spaces.

There are Many Strategies to Manage CHD

1) There are different ways of helping individuals with CHD to **manage** their condition:

   - **Lifestyle changes** — people are encouraged to eat a **healthy diet** that is low in saturated fat, **exercise regularly** and **stop smoking**. This reduces the **risk** of further CHD and makes other forms of treatment more **effective**.
   - **Drugs or surgery** — people can take drugs to reduce **cholesterol** or **blood pressure**, or have an **operation** such as a heart bypass or replacement. However, drugs can have **serious side effects**, e.g. kidney failure and liver damage, and heart surgery is a major procedure with a risk of **blood clots** and **infection**.

2) There are also **national strategies** to mitigate the effects of CHD. These include:

   - Help to **quit smoking**, e.g. the NHS Stop Smoking service. Having help makes people more likely to give up **successfully**, but only a **small percentage** of people decide to stop smoking due to campaigns like this.
   - **Taxing foods** that are high in fat, sugar and salt to **discourage** people from buying them and **promote** healthier diets, e.g. there is a tax on soft drinks in France. However, people quickly **get used** to paying higher prices.
   - Providing **healthy school meals** for children, e.g. there is a UK scheme to provide free **fruit** to primary school children. This improves children's diets in the **short term**, but many children go back to their **usual diet** once they are no longer eligible for the scheme.

Practice Questions

Q1 Give three effects of malaria on people's health and well-being.

Q2 Describe one national strategy used to manage coronary heart disease (CHD).

Exam Question

Q1 Assess how far non-communicable disease morbidity is due to socio-economic factors. [9 marks]

Knock, knock — Who's there? — Amos — Amos who?*...

You don't have to study these examples, but you do need to know about both an infectious and a non-communicable disease.

* A mos-quito just bit me.

Health in Knowsley — Case Study

Time for the obligatory case study. We're off to north-west England, but feel free to revise a different case study if you wish.

Knowsley *is a Borough of* Merseyside

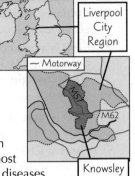

1) Knowsley forms part of the **Liverpool** city region in the north-west of England. It is a mix of large **industrial** estates, **housing** estates and **farmland**.

2) In 2015, Knowsley had a population of around **147 000**, with a slightly higher proportion of people **under 14** than the rest of UK and an **increasing** number of people **over 65**.

3) **Health** in Knowsley is generally **worse** than the UK average — e.g. it is one of the worst areas in England for **premature deaths**, ranking 145 out of 150 areas.

4) **Life expectancy** in Knowsley is **lower** than average — in 2011-2013, it was **76.7** years for men and **80.8** years for women, compared with 79.4 and 83.1 years in England as a whole. The most common causes of death are **cancer** (especially lung cancer), and **circulatory** and **respiratory** diseases.

5) However, life expectancy **varies** across Knowsley — it is significantly **higher** in **less deprived** areas.

Health is Related to the *Physical* and *Built* Environment

Open Space

1) Knowsley has lots of open space — over **60%** of the area is designated as **green space**. **Open spaces** are important for **recreation** and **physical activity** and are also places where people can **meet** and **interact**. This can have a positive effect on **health**, **social cohesion** and **mental well-being**.

2) However, only **10%** of Knowsley's residents use outdoor space for **exercise** or **health reasons**, compared to 17.1% of people in England as a whole. Lack of exercise can lead to excess weight — **69%** of Knowsley residents are classed as **overweight** or **obese**, compared to an average of **65%** in England. Excess weight can contribute to health issues such as **heart disease** and **diabetes**.

3) In 2013, the Knowsley Health and Wellbeing Board came up with a strategy to **improve health**, partly by encouraging **healthier lifestyles**, such as regular **exercise** and healthy **diets**.

Housing

1) In 2011, over **27%** of private homes in Knowsley failed to meet the Decent Homes Standard — this means that they have issues such as **leaking roofs**, **inadequate heating** or **insufficient insulation**.

2) These issues can make houses **cold** and **damp** , which increases residents' risk of **respiratory diseases**, such as bronchitis, asthma and pneumonia. In 2011 to 2013, the rate of **premature deaths** from respiratory diseases in Knowsley was **58.3** per 100 000 of the population compared to **33.2** in England as a whole.

3) Knowsley Council has introduced schemes to improve **housing**, e.g. **Healthy Homes Assistance** provides **grants** to help people improve their homes — this should help to reduce housing-related health issues.

Air Quality

1) Air quality in urban areas is generally worse than in rural areas — in Knowsley, air quality is affected by **traffic** and **industry**, e.g. two motorways run through the area, and there is a coal-fired power station nearby.

2) **Air pollution** is associated with a number of health conditions, such as **respiratory** problems, **cardiovascular** disease and **lung cancer** (see p.194), as well as **premature births** and **low birth weight**.

3) Steps have been taken to **reduce air pollution** in Knowsley over the last few years, e.g. by improving roads to reduce traffic congestion. This is likely to have a **positive impact** on health.

Socio-Economic *Conditions also Influence* Health

Unemployment can also contribute to mental health issues, such as depression.

Employment

1) Knowsley has **high unemployment rates** — in 2015, **7.7%** of working-age people were out of work, compared to a national average of around **5.3%**.

2) Unemployment is linked to **unhealthy lifestyles**. For example, unemployed people are twice as likely to **smoke** as those who are employed. Approximately **30%** of adults in Knowsley **smoke** (compared to 20% nationally) and 24% of deaths for people aged over 35 in Knowsley are due to **smoking-related illnesses** (compared to 18% nationally). Knowsley Council runs **free services** to help people stop smoking.

3) Knowsley Council is also working to **increase** the number of jobs available in the area, e.g. by encouraging businesses to locate in the **Knowsley Industrial Park**. It also aims to improve **public transport** to make jobs more **accessible**. Unemployment rates in Knowsley have **decreased** since 2011.

Health in Knowsley — Case Study

Income

1) Income in Knowsley is lower than the UK average — in 2016, the gross weekly median **earnings** for a Knowsley resident working full time were **£475 per week**, compared to the national average of £539.

2) People living in **poorer** areas tend to have **lower life expectancies** than those in **wealthier** areas and are more likely to suffer from **ill health** at an earlier point in their lives. **Healthy life expectancy** (the number of years a person is expected to live in good health for) is significantly **lower** in Knowsley than in England as a whole.

3) Low incomes can contribute to mental health issues such as **stress and depression**. **8.7%** of people in Knowsley suffer from depression, compared to a UK average of **6.5%**.

4) People with **higher incomes** are able to access a greater range of goods and services, such as **leisure facilities**. In contrast, people on low incomes often **don't** have access to these things, which may affect their health. For example, **children** in low-income households are more likely to suffer from **asthma**, **obesity** and **mental health** issues. When children from poorer families reach adulthood, they have a **higher risk** of dying from diseases such as **lung cancer**, **coronary heart disease** and **respiratory illness** than people from wealthier families.

Education

1) **25%** of people aged 16-64 in Knowsley don't have **any qualifications**, compared to 15% across England and Wales, and on average students achieve **lower grades** in their GCSEs.

2) Education is linked to **income** (see above), and it also has an impact on **lifestyle** — on average, people with more education are less likely to **smoke** or be **overweight**. Generally, people with **lower levels** of **education** have a **lower life expectancy** and **higher morbidity** rates for many common diseases, e.g. heart disease, diabetes and asthma.

3) In 2016, the Knowsley Education Commission was launched to **improve** education in the area, e.g. by attracting outstanding **teachers** and improving school **facilities**. If it succeeds, this is likely to have a **positive** effect on health.

I can't think of a joke, so here's a picture of some tiny horses.

Health is also Affected by People's Attitudes and Experiences

1) People's **attitudes** towards their **health** and **lifestyle** can affect their well-being:
   - **More than half** of the residents of Knowsley think it is too hard to achieve a **healthy lifestyle** — people with this attitude may be less **motivated** to improve their health, e.g. by eating healthily or giving up smoking.
   - However, around a **quarter** of people in Knowsley believe that achieving a healthy lifestyle can be **enjoyable**. Average consumption of **fruit** and **vegetables** is higher in Knowsley (**3.9** portions a day) than in England (**3.6** portions a day), suggesting a positive attitude towards **diet**.

2) The **experiences** that people have can also impact on their health. For example:
   - Living in a **lively**, **safe place** with a strong sense of **community** is more likely to make people feel **happy**. This increases **well-being** and encourages **healthier lifestyles**. However, living in a place with **few facilities** and **little** sense of community, or where people feel at **risk**, can have a **negative** effect on health.
   - Knowsley's **crime rate** is **higher** than the average for England, and **fear** of crime has a negative effect on people's quality of life — e.g. it can cause **stress** and prevent people from using **public spaces**. However, crime rates in the area are **decreasing**, and instances of **violent crime** are **lower** in Knowsley than in England as a whole.
   - Knowsley has a number of **community centres** and **leisure centres**, as well as two **art galleries** — these help to build a sense of community. The council organises **heritage walks** to encourage people to engage with their local area and to promote **physical activity**, and has set up **Healthy Knowsley**, a service that aims to help people develop **healthier lifestyles**, e.g. by offering cookery courses and advice on giving up smoking.

Practice Questions

Q1 Describe the socio-economic character of a place you have studied.

Q2 Give an example of how the physical environment affects health in a place you have studied.

Q3 Briefly explain the impact of income on health in a place you have studied.

Exam Question

Q1 Assess the extent to which socio-economic factors influence health in a place you have studied. [9 marks]

It's my nose-ly neighbours that affect my health...

Who'd have thought that where you live could have such a big impact on your health. Don't let it get you down though — maintaining a positive attitude throughout your revision could have a bigger effect on your life than you thought...

Natural Population Change

Natural population change is all to do with birth and death rates. And don't forget the famous DTM.

There are **Loads** of **Terms** and **Definitions** to Learn

Reproductive age is often considered to be between the ages of 15 and 44.

1) **Birth rate** — the **number** of live **births** per 1000 people, per year.

2) **Death rate** — the **number** of **deaths** per 1000 people, per year.

3) **Total fertility rate** — the **average number** of **children** a woman will have when she is of **reproductive age**.

4) **Infant mortality rate** — the **number** of **children** (out of every 1000 born **alive**) who **die before their first birthday**.

5) **Dependency ratio** — the **proportion** of the population that has to be **supported** by the **working population** (aged **15-64**). **Young people** (aged **0-14**) and **older people** (**over 65**) are generally **dependent** on the working population — they need to be **looked after** or **supported financially**.

The **Demographic Transition Model (DTM)** Shows **Population Change**

The **demographic transition model** (**DTM**) shows how the **population** of a country **changes** over time through **five stages**. The model shows changes in **birth rate**, **death rate** and **total population**.

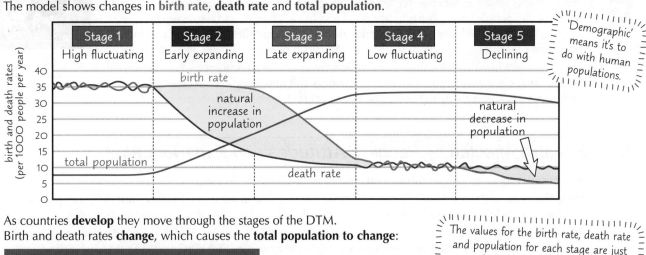

'Demographic' means it's to do with human populations.

As countries **develop** they move through the stages of the DTM. Birth and death rates **change**, which causes the **total population to change**:

The values for the birth rate, death rate and population for each stage are just rough estimates, not exact figures.

Stage 1 — high birth rate and high death rate

Birth rate and death rate **fluctuate** at a **high level** (both are around **35/1000**) — the population remains **stable but low**. There **aren't any countries** in **Stage 1**, but some **tribes** in the rainforests of **Brazil** are in this stage.

1) **Birth rate** is high because there's **no birth control** or **family planning**, and **education is poor**.

2) It's also high because there's **high infant mortality**, so people have **more children** to replace those who've **died**.

3) **Death rate** is high and life expectancy is low because there's **poor health care, sanitation and diet** — leading to **disease and starvation**.

Stage 2 — high birth rate, death rate falls

Death rate **falls** to around **15/1000**, but birth rate remains **high** (about **35/1000**) — the population **increases rapidly**.

1) **Birth rate** is still **high** as there's still **little birth control** or **family planning** and **education is poor**.

2) Birth rate also stays **high** for **labour reasons** — family members (including **children**) **all** have to **work**, e.g. on **farms**. A **larger** family can tend to a **larger** farm, helping to bring in **more food** and **money**.

3) **Death rate** falls and **life expectancy increases** due to improved **health care, sanitation and diet**.

Chad and Afghanistan are in Stage 2.

Stage 3 — birth rate falls a lot and death rate falls slightly

Birth rate **declines rapidly** to around **13/1000**, while death rate **falls slowly** to around **10/1000** — the population **increases at a slower rate**.

1) **Birth rate decreases** due to the **increased** use of **birth control** and **family planning**, and **improvements** in **education**.

2) The **birth rate** also **drops** as the **economy** moves towards **manufacturing** — **fewer children** are needed to **work** on farms, so having a **larger family** isn't as **advantageous** as it once was.

3) **Birth rate falls** further still as **more women work** rather than stay at home to have children.

Morocco is in Stage 3.

Natural Population Change

Stage 4 — low birth rate and low death rate

Birth rate and death rate **fluctuate** at a **low level** — both are around **10/1000**. The population remains **stable** but **high**. **Birth rate stays low** because **increased access** to and **demand** for **luxuries** like **holidays** and **material possessions** means there's **less** money available for having children (they're **expensive** to raise). Also, there are **fewer** **advantages** to having children, e.g. they're **not needed** to work for the family.

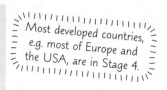 Most developed countries, e.g. most of Europe and the USA, are in Stage 4.

Stage 5 — birth rate drops below death rate

Birth rate begins to **decline** further (**below 10/1000**), while death rate remains **stable** (about **10/1000**) — the population begins to **decrease**.

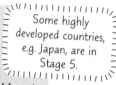 Some highly developed countries, e.g. Japan, are in Stage 5.

1) The **birth rate decreases** because children are **expensive** to raise and many people have **dependent** elderly relatives, so lots of people choose **not** to have children.

2) **Death rate** remains **steady** as there are **more elderly people** so more people die (of **old age**).

It's easy to **compare countries** using the DTM — if you know a bit about how the **population** and **birth** and **death rates** of a country have changed, you can analyse what **stage** of the DTM it's in. You can then **forecast** how it may change, which helps governments decide on **policies** such as **immigration laws**. However, there are some **limitations** to the DTM:

1) The **original data** used to **create** the **DTM** was from richer countries (e.g. **European** countries). What happened in these countries might not be the **same** as what's happening in others, e.g. countries in **Africa**.

2) **Extreme poverty** and **low levels of development** may cause a **lack of population growth** and **prevent** many **less developed** countries from passing through **all** the stages.

3) It doesn't consider **migration** — **international migration** can cause significant **population change** (see p.204-205).

4) **Other factors** can also affect the population so a country **no longer fits** the DTM, e.g. **war** and **infectious disease**.

Cultural Controls Affect Natural Population Change

Birth rates and **fertility rates** are heavily influenced by **cultural controls**. For example:

- **Role of women** — female access to **education** and **employment** delays the **age** at which women **start families**, and attitudes towards women affect how much **choice** they have about **family size**. **More developed** countries tend to have **lower birth rates**, e.g. in the **UK**, **nearly half** of the labour force are women, which makes them **less likely** to have big families — the total fertility rate is **1.89**.

- **Attitudes towards marriage** — in some countries, there is a culture of women getting **married young**, which means they are more likely to have many children. For example, in **Niger**, **three quarters** of girls are married before they turn 18, and the **total fertility rate** is the highest in the world (**6.6** children per woman).

- **Religion** — **different religions** have different views on issues such as birth control and abortion. For example, the **Catholic** church **condemns contraception** — in **East Timor** in southeast Asia, **98%** of the population is Catholic and the fertility rate is around **5** children per woman.

- **Population policies** — **high** levels of **population growth or decline** have forced some governments to introduce **policies discouraging** or **encouraging** larger families. For example, population growth in **France** is very **low**, so the government has introduced things like **subsidised childcare** to encourage **larger families**. In **China**, the government tried to **reduce** birth rate using a **one-child per family policy** between 1979 and 2015.

Practice Questions

Q1 Define 'dependency ratio'.

Q2 What are the characteristics of stage 5 of the demographic transition model?

Exam Question

Q1 Assess the extent to which cultural controls account for variations in population between countries.   [9 marks]

Rabbits never seem to get much past Stage 2...

There's a lot of information on these pages, but it's crucial stuff. That DTM diagram might look a little bit daunting at first, but if you take some time to learn what's happening at each stage, you'll soon know it better than you know yourself.

Natural Population Change

Just when you thought it was safe to turn the page... there's another two pages on population change. Whoopee.

The **UK** is in **Stage Four** of the **DTM**

1) The UK is a **developed** country. It has a **low birth rate** (**12.1**/1000) and a **low death rate** (**9.4**/1000).

2) The **size** of the population isn't changing much — it's growing at about **0.5%** per year.

3) The UK has reached **stage 4** of the DTM because both **physical** and **human** factors have helped it to **develop**:

> *Low birth and death rates and a fairly stable population show that the UK is in Stage 4.*

Physical setting

- The UK has a **temperate** climate and **fertile** soils. This means that there is lots of **arable land**, which results in a **reliable food supply**. Relatively high **rainfall** means that there is enough **water**.
- Much of the UK is **low-lying** and **flat** — this makes it easier to **grow** crops, **transport** resources and **build**.
- It is rich in **natural resources**, such as coal, natural gas, oil and various minerals. These resources helped the country to industrialise and develop a diverse **economy**.
- The UK is surrounded by **sea** — this has given it easy access to marine resources, e.g. **fish**, as well as access to the **international shipping trade**.

Human setting

- **Education** is compulsory. Most people stay in education until at least the age of **18**, **regardless of gender**. Most women don't have children until they've **finished** education, so there's a **low fertility rate** (**1.9**).
- **Female participation in the workforce** is high — **70%** of working-age women have a job. This has delayed the age at which women have children — in 2015, the average age that a woman had her first child was **28.6**. Having a career may also reduce the total **number** of children that women **want** to have.
- **84%** of women aged 16-49 use **contraception** — it's easily **accessible** and most people are taught about it at **school**. This means couples have **control** over when to have children and **how many** to have.
- Access to good **health care** for the **whole** population has resulted in a **low infant mortality rate** of **4.3** deaths per thousand live births, and a **high life expectancy** of 78.5 years for men, and 83 years for women.

Uganda is in **Stage Two** of the **DTM**

1) Uganda is a **less developed** country in central Africa. It has a **high birth rate** (**43.4**/1000) and a **low death rate** (**10.4**/1000).

2) The population is **increasing** at a rate of about **3.2%** per year — this makes it the **fifth fastest growing** population in the world.

3) Uganda's **physical** and **human settings** help explain why it has only reached **stage 2** of the DTM:

> *High birth rate and low death rate mean that the population is growing fast, so Uganda is in Stage 2.*

Physical setting

- Uganda has a hot and humid climate, and receives a **moderate** amount of **rainfall**, making it suitable for crops such as bananas, coffee and sugar. However, the north has a **dry season**, which **limits** agricultural productivity.
- Much of the soil is not very **fertile**, which means **food** production is **low**.
- It has some deposits of **copper**, **gold** and other **minerals**, as well as **oil reserves**. However, these have not yet been exploited to generate **economic growth**.
- It's a **landlocked** country, which has limited its opportunities to engage in **international trade**. However, it borders **Lake Victoria**, the largest lake in Africa, which supports a large **fishing** industry.

Human setting

- The **total fertility rate** is high — **5.8** children per woman. This is partly as a result of **gender inequality**. Women generally receive **less education** and are less likely to be **employed** than men, which means they often start having children **young** — the mean age a mother first gives birth is **18.9**.
- Another reason for the high birth rate is the lack of **birth control** — in 2015, only **34.3%** of couples used contraception. There is also a **lack of government support** for family planning services.
- **Infant mortality** is still quite **high** (**57.6** deaths per 1000 births), because of **poor medical care** — parents have many children because there is a high chance that not all of their offspring will survive past infancy.
- However, the overall **death rate** has **fallen**, due to improvements to **sanitation** and **healthcare**. This has contributed to **rapid** population growth.
- Even if fertility rates fall (as Uganda enters stage 3 of the DTM), it will take **decades** for the population to **stop expanding** — as the large number of children reach **reproductive age**, the population will **continue** to grow.

Natural Population Change

Population Structure is How the Population is Made Up

1) **Population structure** is the **number** or **%** of **males** and **females** in different **age groups** within a population.

2) **Population pyramids (age-sex pyramids) show** population structure:

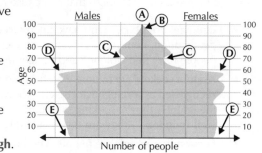

Ⓐ The **top** of a population pyramid indicates how **old** people live to be. In this pyramid, a few people are living to be **100**.

Ⓑ Comparing the two sides of the pyramid shows the **sex ratio**. This pyramid shows there are more **women** in the highest age groups than **men** — female **life expectancy** is **higher**.

Ⓒ **Narrow** points can indicate that there was a time in the past when the **birth rate** was **low**, or when people of a certain age had a high **death rate**, e.g. because of **war**.

Ⓓ **Wide** points can indicate periods when the **birth rate** was **high**.

Ⓔ The **base** of a pyramid shows how many **children** and **young people** are in a population — if the **birth rate** is **declining**, the pyramid will get **smaller** towards the bottom.

3) A country's population structure **changes** through **time** as it moves through the **stages** of the **DTM** (see p.200-201).

4) This means a **population pyramid shape** can show **which** stage of the DTM a country is in:

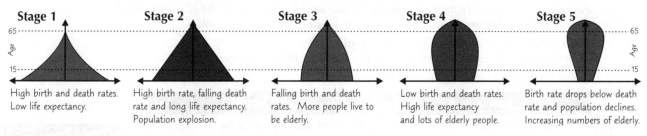

Stage 1	Stage 2	Stage 3	Stage 4	Stage 5
High birth and death rates. Low life expectancy.	High birth rate, falling death rate and long life expectancy. Population explosion.	Falling birth and death rates. More people live to be elderly.	Low birth and death rates. High life expectancy and lots of elderly people.	Birth rate drops below death rate and population declines. Increasing numbers of elderly.

Some Countries Experience the Demographic Dividend

1) A **demographic dividend** is the potential for **rapid economic growth** in a country as its **dependency ratio** (see p.200) **falls** — this normally occurs at around **stages 2 to 3** of the DTM.

2) **Death rate** starts to decrease **before birth rate** — people continue to have lots of children, but more **survive** to adulthood. This creates a **bulge of young people** in the population pyramid.

3) When these young people reach working age, there is a **large workforce** with relatively **few people dependent on it** — there are relatively few children and elderly people.

4) This can lead to **economic growth** — for example, working people pay **taxes** and can afford to **spend more**, boosting the **local economy**. **Transnational corporations** may also be attracted by the **large workforce**, leading to more **jobs** and more **investment** in the country.

5) However, to obtain the demographic dividend countries need to **invest** in **education** and **job creation** — **unemployed** and **underemployed** adults are still **dependent** on others.

Practice Questions

Q1 Describe one way that the physical setting of the UK has helped it reach stage 4 of the DTM.

Q2 What is the demographic dividend?

Exam Question

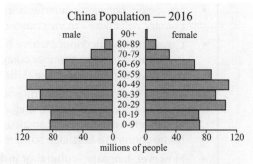

China Population — 2016

Q1 Assess the factors that might account for the shape of the population pyramid shown. [6 marks]

Um, some of these 'pyramids' don't look very pyramid-shaped...

OK, so the name 'population pyramid' kind of falls apart once you get past stage 2 of the DTM, but you've got to admit they're super-handy little diagrams. Make sure you understand what they show — you might be asked to interpret one in your exam.

International Migration

Populations don't just change because of changes to birth rates and death rates — migration can also have a major effect...

There are **Different Types** of **Migrants**

International migrants are people who move from one country to another.
There are different circumstances that can cause migration — these determine the **type** of migrant:

- **Refugees** are people who have been **forced** to **flee** their country, and are **unable to return**, because of **persecution**, **conflict** or changes to the **environment** (e.g. natural disasters). For example, over **1.8 million** people have fled violence and hunger in **South Sudan** to find safety in neighbouring African countries.

- **Asylum seekers** are people who have fled their country, but have not yet had their application to be **recognised as a refugee** accepted. They can only receive formal **assistance** and **legal protection** from the country they're seeking sanctuary in once it's been demonstrated that their fear of returning home is **well-founded** — they are then granted **refugee status**.

- **Economic migrants** are people who have moved to another country to **work**.

Migration Occurs Because of **Push** and **Pull** Factors

1) The **reasons** for migration can be divided into **push** (**negative**) and **pull** (**positive**) factors:

- **Push factors** — these are things that **make** people want to **move out** of the place they're in. They're **negative factors** about the place they're **leaving** (their **home country**).

- **Pull factors** — these **attract** people to a **new place**. They're **positive factors** about the place they're **moving to** (the **host country**).

2) These factors can be **environmental** or **socio-economic**:

	Push factors	Pull factors
Environmental	• **Natural disasters** • **Desertification** (see p.34) • Impacts of **climate change**, e.g. land flooded by **rising sea levels**	• More desirable **climate** • Better **farming** conditions • Fewer impacts of **climate change**, e.g. fewer **extreme weather** events
Socio-economic	• **Political instability**, **war** or **persecution** • Lack of **jobs** or access to **education** • Lack of **food** • **Economic decline**	• Better access to **health care** • Better **job opportunities** and **higher salaries** • Better **schools** and **universities** • Better **quality of life**

Hmm, he's got his own boat, but it's a shame about the beard. I'll give him a pull factor of 5.

3) For example, recent **large-scale** migration has taken place because of **conflict** — e.g. over **5 million** Syrian people have been forced to leave their country since **war** began in 2011. Many of these **refugees** have moved to **nearby** countries, such as **Jordan** and **Egypt**, and others have fled to **Europe**.

4) As well as push and pull factors, there are other factors that affect the **patterns** and **processes** of international migration:

- Movement between countries is influenced by **government decisions** about **how many** migrants their country will take — many countries have a **limit** on the number of immigrants they will accept per year.

- Governments can control **where** they accept immigrants **from**. **EU citizens** can freely move to other member countries to work, but migrants from other countries may have to **prove** they have skills that there are shortages of in the host country.

- There are often **obstacles** to migration. These can be **physical barriers**, such as water or difficult terrain that migrants have to cross — journeys can be **expensive** or **dangerous**. Obstacles can also be **human** factors, such as ties to family in the home country or language barriers in the host country.

  Following a referendum in 2016, the UK opted to leave the EU. This may impact on the movement of people to and from the UK.

- However, **language**, **cultural** or **historical ties** can also have a **positive** influence on migration, e.g. many **Angolan** migrants move to **Brazil** because both countries speak **Portuguese**.

- **Distance** influences migration — most migrants don't move very far, especially if they have been **forced** to move by, for example, war or a natural disaster.

- Migration takes place on a range of **timescales** — migration can be **permanent**, but many people only move on a **short-term** basis, e.g. economic migrants with seasonal jobs.

International Migration

Migration Can Have Implications for Both Host and Home Countries

Migration can have **demographic**, **economic**, **political**, **health**, **environmental** and **social** implications for both the host and the home country. These can be **positive** or **negative**. For example:

	Implications for home countries	Implications for host countries
Demographic	• Large-scale migration causes population **decline**. • Migration can lead to an **ageing population**, as elderly people tend to stay while working-age people leave. • Males are more likely to leave, leading to a **gender imbalance**.	• Large numbers of immigrants cause **population growth**. • The population **structure** can change, as most migrants are of **working age**. • The **birth rate** might rise because of the influx of people of **child-bearing age**.
Economic	• Migrant **workers** may send some of their income back **home** (remittances — see p.126). • When **highly skilled** people **leave**, there can be a shortage of people qualified for high-skilled jobs — this is known as a 'brain drain'.	• **Expansion** of the **workforce** can **fill jobs** that weren't filled by the native population, and help the economy to **grow**. • However, it can also mean there **aren't enough jobs** to go around.
Political	• In countries that are **losing** their **skilled workforce**, governments might try to **discourage** workers from **leaving**, or **encourage** migration **into** the country. • They might also introduce programmes to increase **fertility** to prevent population decline.	• Some governments introduce **policies** to **reduce immigration** when there's a concern that **too many** people are coming into the country. • There is the potential for a rise in **extremist** organisations, if local people feel threatened by changes to their society.
Health	• A country might have a **shortage** of **healthcare professionals** if many migrate to work elsewhere. • The **most vulnerable** people are often **left behind** while the healthy go to work in other countries — this puts **pressure** on local healthcare systems.	• Large numbers of migrants can put **pressure** on **healthcare** services, especially if migrants have to live in overcrowded, poor-quality housing where they're more likely to develop health problems. • Immigrants could **spread infectious diseases** from their home countries.
Environmental	• If the population declines, the environment may **improve** because of **reduced** resource exploitation and farming. • However, buildings and farmland could be abandoned, and there may be fewer resources and less funding for **environmental management**.	• More **houses**, **infrastructure** and **resources** are required to cope with the influx of people — **green spaces** may be **built on** and **resource extraction** can cause environmental damage and **pollution**. • There may be larger amounts of **waste** to dispose of, which can cause **pollution** of ground, air and water.
Social	• Sometimes **families** are **split up**. • People might be more likely to **find a job** at home if other working people have left. • There may be less pressure on **education**, but **funding** could also be cut as demand falls. • There can be a **loss of culture**, or a **change in culture** if migrants **return** with new ideas.	• The presence of people from different countries creates **cultural diversity**. • However, it can also lead to **social tensions** between local people and immigrants. • Certain **areas** might become associated with immigrants — people often move to areas where people with a **similar background** are already living.

Practice Questions

Q1 What is an asylum seeker?
Q2 What demographic consequences might migration have on the country of origin?
Q3 Describe two economic consequences of migration.

Exam Question

Q1 Assess the extent to which international migration has negative impacts on the country of origin. [9 marks]

Revision is starting to miGRATE on me...

There are lots of reasons why someone might migrate, but fleeing your A-Levels isn't a good one — get off that airline website and have another read of these pages. If you get a question on migration in the exam, adding some specific details is sure to impress.

Population and Resources

These pages are about population ecology — how populations interact with the environment.

Population Growth Dynamics Show How Populations Change

1) **Population growth dynamics** is the study of how and why population sizes and structures change over time.

2) Population growth is limited by **environmental factors**. For example, **climate**, **soil**, **geology** and **topography** affect the availability of **resources** such as food, water and energy.

> *Infectious diseases can also limit population growth, but most of these are now treatable.*

3) The **balance** between population growth and resource availability leads to three scenarios:

- **Optimum population** — the **ideal number** of people in an area — all **resources** are used to give the **highest economic return** per person and therefore the **highest standard of living**.
- **Overpopulation** — if the population of an area becomes **too high** for the available resources, the standard of living **falls** — there isn't enough food, water, energy etc.
- **Underpopulation** — if the population **declines** or is **too low**, there are too few people to use the available resources to their **full potential** and the standard of living **falls**, or is **lower** than it could be.

4) The optimum population can **increase** as **technology improves** — e.g. technology can increase crop yields, meaning there is more food available. The discovery of **new resources** can also increase the size of the optimum population.

5) The optimum population also depends on population **structure** — e.g. a low **dependency ratio** (see p.200) might mean a higher population can be supported because there is **more economic growth**.

Population Growth May Exceed the Earth's Carrying Capacity

1) The **carrying capacity** is the **largest** population that an area is capable of **supporting** in the long term.

2) Whether a population is living within the limits of an environment's carrying capacity depends on the **population size** and the amount of resources **consumed by each individual**.

3) There are two models that show how a growing population might change in **response** to the carrying capacity:

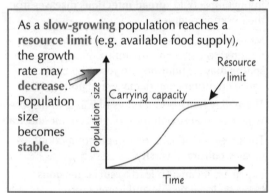

As a **slow-growing** population reaches a **resource limit** (e.g. available food supply), the growth rate may **decrease**. Population size becomes **stable**.

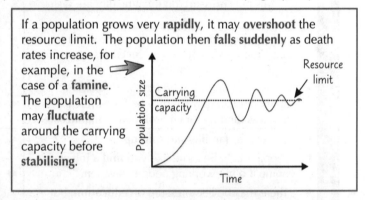

If a population grows very **rapidly**, it may **overshoot** the resource limit. The population then **falls suddenly** as death rates increase, for example, in the case of a **famine**. The population may **fluctuate** around the carrying capacity before **stabilising**.

Ecological Footprints can Measure the Impact of Population Growth

1) An **ecological footprint** is a way of measuring the environmental **impact** of human activities, by calculating the amount of **productive land** required to **produce** the **goods** and **services** that are being used.

2) Ecological footprints can be calculated on any **scale** — **individual** people have their own ecological footprints, but they can also be measured for a **group of people** of any size, or for a certain **activity**.

3) They're measured in **global hectares** (gha) — this is the amount of **land**, of **average productivity**, that is required. **Developed** countries have a **greater** ecological footprint than **developing** countries, e.g. a person living in the UK has an ecological footprint of about **5 gha**, while that of someone living in Zambia is **less than 1 gha**.

4) In general, ecological footprints are **increasing** all over the world. As the ecological footprint **increases**, the **carrying capacity decreases** — if more resources are required per person, the environment can support fewer people.

5) At **current rates** of consumption, the world's population is using the equivalent of **1.6 Earths** — in other words, it takes the Earth over a year and a half to **regenerate** the resources that humans use in one year. According to the UN, if the global population reaches **9.6 billion by 2050**, almost **three planets'** worth of natural resources would be required to sustain current lifestyles.

Mark was baffled by his ecological footprint.

Population and Resources

The **PRP Model** Shows the **Effects** of **Resource Extraction** and **Use**

1) The **population, resources and pollution** (**PRP**) **model** shows the relationships between people and the environment. Natural **resources** provide **goods** and **services** to human populations, but the **acquisition** and **use** of these resources disrupt environmental processes and produce **pollution**:

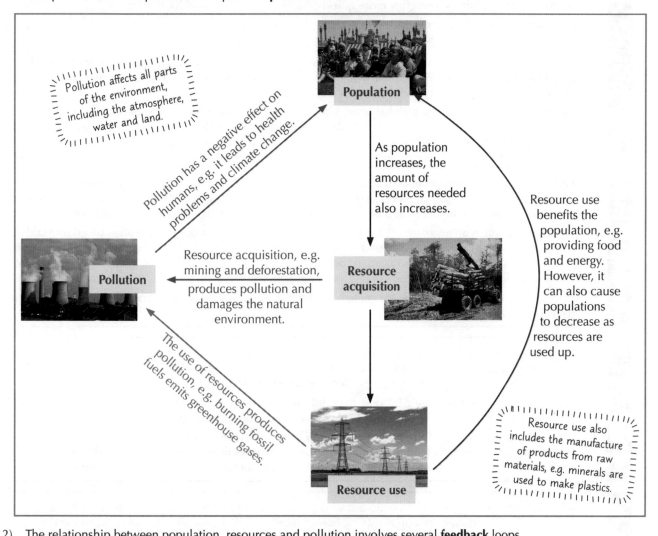

Pollution affects all parts of the environment, including the atmosphere, water and land.

Pollution has a negative effect on humans, e.g. it leads to health problems and climate change.

Population

As population increases, the amount of resources needed also increases.

Resource use benefits the population, e.g. providing food and energy. However, it can also cause populations to decrease as resources are used up.

Resource acquisition, e.g. mining and deforestation, produces pollution and damages the natural environment.

Pollution

Resource acquisition

The use of resources produces pollution, e.g. burning fossil fuels emits greenhouse gases.

Resource use also includes the manufacture of products from raw materials, e.g. minerals are used to make plastics.

Resource use

2) The relationship between population, resources and pollution involves several **feedback** loops.

3) **Positive feedback** is when a change leads to processes that **amplify** the original change. For example:

- **Population growth** leads to a need for more food, which drives an increase in **food production**. The increase in food availability allows the **population** to **increase further**, as more people can be supported when there is **more food**. This leads to a **further** drive to improve yields, which leads to **even higher** food availability, which leads to **more** population growth... and so on.

- An **increased population** results in more extraction of **fossil fuels**, so more fuel is available for **transporting** food to places where there are **shortages**. This **decreases malnutrition** and allows the population to **increase**.

4) **Negative feedback** is when a change leads to processes that have an **opposite** effect to the original change. For example:

- **Growing populations** cause **expansion** and **intensification** of **agriculture**, which leads to increased **soil erosion**. This **decreases** agricultural **yields** as the soil becomes **less fertile**. Food production is **no longer high enough** to support the population, causing it to **decline**.

- An **increased population** leads to increased **extraction** and use of **fossil fuels** for energy. Increased levels of greenhouse gases from burning fossil fuels cause **climate change**, which reduces rainfall and **crop yields** in some areas. This causes **malnutrition**, which **reduces** the population.

Population and Resources

There are **Contrasting Theories** About the **Future** of **Population Change**

There are **different ideas** about population growth and its implications:

Malthus

- **Thomas Malthus** was an economist who worked during the late 18th and 19th centuries. His **1798** theory stated that a population could grow **more quickly** than its capacity to **feed itself**, because:
  - populations can grow **exponentially** (more and more rapidly).
  - food supply can only increase **arithmetically** (at a **constant** rate).
- He thought that when a population increases to the point where there are **too many people** for the **food** available, population size will be **reduced** by events such as **famine**, **war** and **disease** — the population will **exceed** the **carrying capacity** and death rates will increase (see p.206).
- This has **not** yet happened on a **global** scale, but there have been **famines** in some areas. One **problem** with Malthus's theory is that it was based on the idea that the **rate of growth** in food production **can't increase** — but it's actually **increased rapidly** since the 18th century due to technological advances (see p.191).

Neo-Malthusians

- Rapid population growth in the 20th century led some people to believe that population growth rates were increasing faster than resource production rates. Neo-Malthusians argue that rapid population growth is an **obstacle** to **development** and should be slowed down, e.g. by reducing birth rates through contraception.
- The **Club of Rome** is an international think tank. In the 1970s, they used **computer models** based on **Malthusian** ideas to model relationships between populations and resources — the models predicted that **continued** rapid population growth would lead to a dramatic **decline** in economic growth within 100 years. They argued that humans can live indefinitely on Earth only if they **limit** population growth and use resources more sustainably.
- However, some people think there are **enough resources** to support a bigger global population — the **problem** is with how resources are **distributed**.

Boserup

- **Ester Boserup** was an economist who **challenged** the idea that there were **limits** to human population growth — in **1965** she wrote that, **however big** the world's population grew, people would always produce **sufficient food** to meet their needs.
- She believed that **farming** would become more **intensive** as the population increased, because population growth would encourage new **methods** and **technology** to be developed.
- There is **evidence** to support Boserup's theory — techniques to increase food production have been developed, such as **genetic modification** and the use of **agrochemicals**. However, it's **uncertain** whether food production will be able to **keep up** with the expanding human population in the **long term**.

People have applied these models to other resources — not just food.

Simon

- **Julian Simon** was a 20th-century economist who argued that population increase was **positive** for humanity. He wrote that the '**ultimate resource**' was the **human mind** — with a growing population, he believed the world would produce enough intelligent people to **solve** the problems that arise, so resources wouldn't run out.
- Simon's views **support** Boserup's — they suggest that human **innovation** will fix future problems.
- For example, he argued that **natural resources** have become **less scarce** as people have found new ways to obtain them, and **quality of life** has **improved** in most countries as population has increased. However, there have been **criticisms** of Simon — e.g. conditions in some countries have got **worse** as climate has changed.

Practice Questions

Q1 Define 'optimum population'.

Q2 What does 'carrying capacity' mean?

Q3 Give an example of a negative feedback mechanism relating to the population, resources and pollution model.

Exam Question

Q1 'Of the contrasting perspectives on population growth and its implications, Boserup and Simon's theories are more applicable in the 21st century than those of Malthus or the neo-Malthusians.' How far do you agree with this statement? [20 marks]

The revision section of my brain is beginning to reach its carrying capacity...

Population growth is quite a controversial topic. Some people think we're headed for catastrophe if humans carry on breeding like rabbits — others think it'll all be fine. Whatever your opinion is, you've got to learn all the viewpoints.

Global Population Futures

All this population growth is causing major environmental damage, which has some pretty serious impacts on human health. Just to add to the challenge, there's a lot of uncertainty about what might lie ahead for human populations...

Ozone Depletion *is a* Public Health Concern

1) Ozone (**O₃**) is a gas mainly found in the upper **atmosphere** — it forms a layer that **absorbs** harmful **ultraviolet** (UV) radiation from the sun.

2) Some substances cause **depletion** of the ozone layer. For example, chlorofluorocarbons (**CFCs**) were used in **aerosols** and **fridges** until the late 20th century, leading to **thinning** of the ozone layer and the formation of a **hole** over Antarctica.

3) Lower concentrations of ozone mean **more UV radiation** reaches the Earth's surface.

4) UV radiation increases the risk of **health problems**, such as:

- **skin cancer** — this is when UV rays cause **genetic mutations** in skin that has been **exposed** to the sun. In 2012, skin cancer caused about **55 000 deaths** worldwide.

- **cataracts** — this is when the **lens of the eye** gradually becomes more **opaque** (cloudy), causing **blurred** vision. About 20 million people are **blind** due to cataracts. It's thought that **20%** of cataracts are caused by overexposure to UV radiation.

5) Global actions to reduce emissions of ozone-depleting gases have meant that the ozone layer is beginning to **recover**. However, the damage is likely to **persist** for at least another 50 years.

Geoffrey just hadn't been able to get the same volume from his hairspray since the CFC ban.

Climate Change *is Also Affecting* Public Health

Some areas may experience colder winters, which increase health problems such as colds and flu.

1) Climate change is causing **temperature** in many areas to **increase**:

- **Heatwaves** may become more common and intense, and many areas will experience **warmer summers**. This is likely to result in **thermal stress**, which will increase **deaths**, especially among the **elderly** and people suffering from **cardiovascular** or **respiratory diseases**.

- However, in places where the winters are getting **milder**, cold-related disease and deaths will **decrease**.

- **Disease vectors** (see p.194) may **spread** to new regions. For example, **mosquitoes** carrying **malaria** are currently confined to **tropical** and **subtropical** areas, but the warming climate may increase their range.

2) Changing **precipitation** patterns may also mean that **vector-borne** and **water-borne diseases** emerge in areas with higher rainfall, particularly those that flood more frequently.

3) Climate change is also changing **agricultural productivity** in many parts of the world:

- **Rising temperatures** increase **evaporation** rates, causing **salinisation** of soils (see p.190), and **dry out** soils, making them vulnerable to **desertification** (see p.33). This leads to **reduced yields**.

- Dry areas are expected to get **drier**, making it harder to grow crops. **Seasonal patterns** of rainfall are also changing — e.g. in **Indonesia**, the rainy season is likely to arrive **later** and to be **shorter** and more **intense**, reducing the length of the **growing season**.

- Increases in the frequency and intensity of **extreme weather events** are damaging harvests, e.g. **storms** can cause **soil erosion** and flatten crops.

- **Rising sea levels** are causing **saltwater intrusion** into farmland, making it **hard** for some crops to survive.

- However, climate change is making some areas **more productive**, e.g. warmer temperatures mean that there's a **longer growing season** in the UK, and crops such as **melons** and **peaches** can be grown.

4) Changing patterns of food production are affecting **nutritional standards**:

- Climate change is **decreasing crop yields** most in **tropical** regions, so areas where **hunger** was already a problem are getting less food. For example, some parts of Indonesia have a '**hunger season**' before the rice harvest. A later rainy season will mean that rice has to be **planted later**, lengthening the hunger season.

- Climate change may also affect the **types** of food that people consume. If greenhouse gas emissions aren't decreased, the availability of **fruit** and **vegetables** is likely to **decrease** in some developing countries. It's estimated that changes to diet resulting from climate change will cause over **500 000 deaths** in 2050.

- Decreasing agricultural productivity is likely to increase **food prices**. Food may become **less affordable** for **poorer** countries, which will increase **hunger** and reduce dietary **diversity**, leading to **malnutrition**. In **wealthier** countries, the rise in **obesity** may continue as **unhealthy** food is often **cheaper** than a healthier diet.

Global Population Futures

The World's Population is Likely to Keep Increasing

1) In **2016**, the world population reached **7.4 billion**, and the United Nations (**UN**) predicts that by **2100** it is likely to reach **11.2 billion**.

2) However, the rate of population growth is **slowing down**. In **2005**, the population was growing by **1.24%** per year, but by **2015** it had slowed to **1.18%** per year. This trend is expected to continue.

3) There are **two** key factors driving global population change:

   - **decreasing fertility rate** — the global fertility rate fell from **4.98** in **1960** to **2.45** in **2015**. This is **slowing** the rate of population growth. However, the fertility rate is still **high** enough for the population to continue increasing overall.

   - **increasing life expectancy** — more children are **surviving beyond infancy**, and people are **living longer**, which is contributing to overall population **growth**.

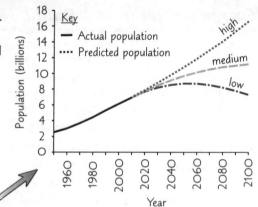

4) The graph shows projections for global population made by the **UN**. There are different **variants** of the projection — the **low**, **medium** and **high** variants are based on different predictions of how **fertility** rates will change in the future. There is a lot of **uncertainty** in population predictions — for example:

   - Population projections use **assumptions** based on **past** and **present** fertility and mortality trends. Different groups (e.g. the UN and the World Bank) base their projections on **different assumptions**, leading to different results.

   - The accuracy of projections depends on whether current trends **continue** — e.g. a major investment in **family planning** in some areas with fast-growing populations could significantly reduce birth rates.

   - Factors such as **war** and **disease** could have an effect on future population sizes, but they can't be incorporated into projections as they are **difficult to predict** very far in advance.

Population Distribution is Likely to Change

1) Population change varies around the world, as **fertility** is changing at different rates. E.g. in **Latin America** and **Asia**, fertility rates have **recently fallen rapidly**, so population growth rate is slowing. In **sub-Saharan Africa**, fertility rates are **falling slowly**, so population growth rates are still high.

2) **Developed** countries are generally experiencing quite **low** population growth, because of low birth rates. Fertility rates in some countries are **lower** than the **replacement rate** of just over **2 children per couple** — some of these are experiencing natural population decline, e.g. Japan.

Replacement rate is the fertility rate at which there is no population change.

3) **Developing** countries tend to have **more rapidly** growing populations — most of the population growth **between now and 2050** will be in **less developed** countries:

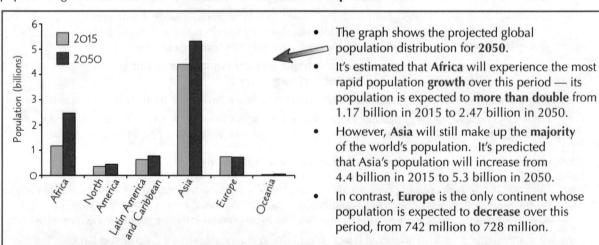

- The graph shows the projected global population distribution for **2050**.

- It's estimated that **Africa** will experience the most rapid population **growth** over this period — its population is expected to **more than double** from 1.17 billion in 2015 to 2.47 billion in 2050.

- However, **Asia** will still make up the **majority** of the world's population. It's predicted that Asia's population will increase from 4.4 billion in 2015 to 5.3 billion in 2050.

- In contrast, **Europe** is the only continent whose population is expected to **decrease** over this period, from 742 million to 728 million.

4) The relative population sizes of the **most populous** countries are also expected to change:

   - **China** and **India** are likely to remain the **two most populous** countries in the world, but India is expected to **overtake** China to become the **most** populous by **2030**.

   - The USA currently has the **third** biggest population, but the **UN** predicts that **Nigeria** will rise from the **seventh** to the **third** most populous country by about **2050**, because it has the **fastest growing** population in the world.

Global Population Futures

Increases *in* Population *and* Consumption *are* Threats *to the Environment*

1) Global population is **growing**, and **per capita resource consumption** is increasing too.

2) As countries become more **wealthy**, the amount of **land**, **energy**, **food**, **water** and **materials** consumed per person increases because people can afford higher **standards of living**. People in **developed** countries consume **up to 10 times more** natural resources than people in developing countries.

3) Many of these resources are **finite** — e.g. **fossil fuels** that have been burnt **can't be replaced**.

4) The **mass production** of goods to meet demand has an environmental impact — **manufacturing processes** use large amounts of **energy** and generate **pollution** and **waste**.

5) **Population growth** and **increased consumption** are both potential threats to the environment:

Derek thought population growth sounded good — maybe he'd be able to make some human friends.

- **Population** is expected to continue to **grow** — more people means more resources used and more environmental damage (e.g. deforestation, soil erosion). However, population growth is **slowing down** as **fertility rates** fall — this reduces the **long-term impact** of an increasing number of people.

- Increasing per capita **consumption** is likely to continue as **economic development** continues. Resource use is becoming more **efficient** due to **technological developments**, and **regulations** are being introduced that **reduce consumption**, e.g. the Paris Agreement limits greenhouse gas emissions (see p.15). However, consumption may increase **faster** than resource **efficiency**, leading to **exhaustion** of some resources.

The USA opted out of the Paris Agreement in 2017 — this may reduce its effectiveness.

Population-Environment Relationships *May* Change

1) There are **alternative possible futures** for people and the environment — these futures depend partly on the rates and patterns of **population change** and **resource consumption**.

2) They also depend on whether **relationships** between people and the environment **change**. For example:

See p.226, 236 and 241 for examples of how technological advances may change resource consumption in the future.

- **Technological advances**, e.g. in **agriculture** and **renewable energy** generation, can help reduce pollution and mitigate climate change.

- Developed countries can **share** technology with **developing countries** to help them develop in a more **sustainable** way.

- **Education** can make people think about their consumption patterns and how they impact on the environment. This can result in **behaviour changes** — e.g. buying **locally sourced** products, reducing food and water **waste**, **reusing** products instead of replacing them, and **recycling**.

- **Policy changes** can reduce a country's resource consumption — e.g. offering incentives for **renewable energy** schemes and promoting **public transport**.

Practice Questions

Q1 How does ozone depletion affect human health?

Q2 Briefly describe how global population is likely to change between now and 2100.

Q3 How will the distribution of population change over this period?

Exam Question

Q1 Using the graphs on the previous page, analyse how relationships between people and the environment are likely to change in the future. [9 marks]

My biscuit consumption is increasing as I get further through this book...

The world's population isn't going to stop growing any time soon. Population increase and resource consumption are damaging the environment in all kinds of ways, and that damage is harmful to people too. It's not a very jolly topic, but look on the bright side — there are things we can do to make our consumption and population growth a little more sustainable.

Population Change in Bangladesh — Case Study

This has been a beast of a section, but hang in there cos you're nearly through. Here's a lovely case study for you — you didn't think I'd let you get away without applying all of that theory you've learnt to the real world, did you?

Bangladesh is *Overpopulated*

1) Bangladesh has a **large** and **growing** population. It's the **8th** most populous country in the world — its population is currently **165 million**, and this is expected to rise to **202 million** by **2050**.

2) The current annual rate of population **increase** is **1.05%**. The growth rate has been **slowing down** in the last few decades, as the country moves from stage 2 to **stage 3** of the DTM.

3) The **birth rate** is **19/1000** and the **death rate** is **5.3/1000**. **Total fertility rate** is **2.2** — low for a developing country.

4) Bangladesh has a **young** population — **58%** of the population is **under the age of 30**. However, birth rates have been **falling**, which has caused the population pyramid to **narrow** slightly at the base — there are now about **1.6 million fewer** people under the age of 10 than there are in the 10-19 age group.

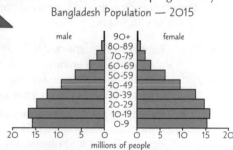
Bangladesh Population — 2015

5) Bangladesh is very **densely** populated — there are **1238 people per km²**. Population density is especially **high** in **urban** areas because of rural-urban migration. The capital city, **Dhaka**, is one of the most densely populated areas in the world, with over 40 000 people per km².

Population Change is Influenced by *Environmental Factors...*

1) Bangladesh is **small**, covering less than 150 000 km² (just over half the size of the UK). It's a **low-lying**, **flat** country with a **hot**, **wet** climate. Its many rivers **flood** regularly, making the soils **fertile**. This makes it ideal for growing **crops**, e.g. **rice**. There are hopes that **genetically modified** (GM — see p.191) varieties of **rice** and other crops will **increase yields** and make Bangladesh's growing population more **food secure** in future.

2) **Environmental stresses** are changing the population **distribution** of the country — people are moving to cities. It's estimated that **70%** of the people living in **slums** in **Dhaka** moved there because of environmental pressures, such as:

   • **Climate change** is leading to **sea level rise**, which means flooding is becoming more frequent, and some coastal areas are being lost to the sea. Sea level rise is also causing **saltwater intrusion** (see p.209).

   • There is a lot of **pressure** on the **land** because of the high population **density** — **70%** of land in Bangladesh is already used for farming, meaning there is little **capacity** for **agricultural expansion**.

... and *Social, Cultural* and *Economic Factors*

1) **Fertility rates** in Bangladesh used to be very high (e.g. 7.0 in 1970) because:

   • women became mothers at a **young age** — girls had **limited education** and there was a **cultural expectation** that they would **marry young** and have **lots of children**.

   • **infant mortality** was high — people had many children to ensure some **survived** past infancy to help the family.

2) However, the fertility rate has been **declining** — by 2017, it was 2.3 births per woman. This is for several reasons:

   • The proportion of couples using **contraception** increased from **less than 8%** in the 1970s to **over 60%** in 2014. This was achieved by **government** and **NGO** schemes, such as providing **rural** communities with **health workers**.

   • The **infant mortality rate** has fallen, mainly because of a successful **immunisation** programme. There were only **32** deaths per 1000 births in 2014, compared with **150** in 1970.

   • **Female** access to **education** has increased — the longer that girls stay in school, the **later** they are likely to be **married**. Improved education also means women are becoming more informed about **contraception**, which delays the age at which they start having **children**.

3) The population is **still growing** despite lower fertility rates, because:

   • Improvements to **healthcare** mean people are **living longer** — **life expectancy at birth** is now **73.2** years, compared to only **47.5** years in 1970, so the number of older people is growing.

   • A large proportion of the population is of **childbearing age**, so the **birth rate** is still quite **high**.

4) Bangladesh's population is also influenced by **migration** — the **net migration rate** is **-3.1 migrants per thousand**, meaning more people **leave** Bangladesh than **enter** it. Many of those leaving are **economic migrants** on short-term labour contracts — the most common destination for workers moving out of Bangladesh is the **Arab Gulf states**.

Population Change in Bangladesh — Case Study

Population Change Has Many Implications for Bangladesh

Rapid population growth has **social**, **economic** and **environmental impacts** in Bangladesh.

As the population continues to increase, these impacts are likely to increase.

Social

1) Population growth and rural-urban migration has led to large **slums** on the outskirts of cities, e.g. **Korail** is the biggest slum in Dhaka, with around **200 000** residents. Slums are made up of **poor-quality** housing and often **lack basic services** (e.g. electricity and clean water).

2) Although **sanitation** in Bangladesh has been **improving**, provision has not kept up with the rate of population growth. Only **one third** of the **urban** population has access to a **piped water supply**. The country's only **sewer system** is in **Dhaka**, and it serves just **18%** of the city. The lack of proper sanitation allows the rapid transmission of **waterborne diseases** (see p.194).

3) **Food security** is a challenge — the growing population means **more food** has to be produced or imported. However, as population growth **slows down**, it is becoming easier for food supply to **keep up** with demand. The percentage of **stunted children** (those with low heights for their age due to undernutrition) fell from **55%** in **1997** to **36%** in **2014**.

4) Changes to the population **structure** can also have impacts:
   - In **2000**, **5%** of the population was **aged over 60**, but by **2050** this is expected to increase to **19%**. This is increasing the incidence of **non-communicable diseases**, such as cancer and coronary heart disease.
   - The number of people **under the age of 15** is **stabilising**, which may make **education provision** easier, as the school system will not have to expand to provide for more children.

Economic

1) The **dependency ratio** is **falling**, which means Bangladesh could experience the **economic benefits** of a **demographic dividend** (see p.203). To ensure the dividend occurs, there needs to be **investment** in the **health** and **education** systems so that **more people** are able to **work**, especially in **skilled** jobs.

2) The high proportion of **working-age** people means there are lots of **economic migrants** to other countries — Bangladesh receives around **$1 billion** per month in **remittances** (see p.126), which helps with **development**.

3) Bangladeshi **graduates** often attempt to get a job or continue their education **abroad**, meaning there is a shortage of **highly-skilled** people in some professions, e.g. doctors, engineers and university staff. However, some migrant workers **gain skills abroad** which they then bring back to Bangladesh.

Environmental

1) **Increasing demand** for land for **agriculture**, **houses** and **industry** is causing high rates of **deforestation** — only **11%** of the country is now covered by forest. This is increasing **soil erosion**. Clearance of coastal **mangrove** forests also leads to **coastal erosion**, **flooding** and **salinisation** of soils.

2) Because there is a lack of land to **expand** agriculture into, farming has **intensified**. This is causing an increase in the use of **fertilisers**, **pesticides** etc., which increases **water pollution** from **agricultural runoff**.

3) The increasing population and economic growth have increased air **pollution** in cities, mainly because of the huge number of **motor vehicles**. In **Dhaka**, the annual mean concentration of $PM_{2.5}$ (**fine particulate matter**) is **over 8 times higher** than recommended air quality limits. It's estimated that in 2015, more than **120 000 deaths** in Bangladesh were a result of exposure to $PM_{2.5}$ in the air.

Practice Questions

Q1 Give one piece of evidence that Bangladesh is entering stage 3 of the DTM.

Q2 Outline two social factors that have reduced fertility rates in Bangladesh.

Q3 Briefly describe the reasons why the population of Bangladesh is still growing.

Exam Question

Q1 Analyse the implications of population change in a country or society you have studied. [9 marks]

The population problem is a real Bangla-mess...

Hurrah — that's the end of Population. Well, not the end of population as in the end of the world — that wouldn't be anything to cheer about. But that's the topic finished. Hopefully you've completed the five stages of the Demographic Revision Model — from pure denial that you even have an exam, right through to being able to recite the facts backwards.

Resource Development

This section is about the delicate balance between supply and demand of resources. First up though, what resources are...

Resources can be Classified as **Stock** or **Flow Resources**

1) Natural **resources** are any naturally occurring parts of the environment that can be **used** by people to meet their needs.

2) They can be physical **materials**, e.g. minerals such as iron ore, or intangible **flows of energy** such as sunlight and wind.

3) Resources can be categorised as **stock** or **flow** resources:

Stock resources are non-renewable and flow resources are renewable.

Stock Resources

- **Stock resources** can **run out** and **can't be replaced** in the **foreseeable future** (the planet has a limited 'stock', which when used up won't be replaced within human timescales).
- **Fossil fuels** (coal, oil and gas) are stock resources — they take millions of years to form, so when used up are no longer available.

Flow Resources

- **Flow resources** are resources that can be **replenished**.
- They include resources that will **never run out** and don't rely on **human input** to **manage** them, e.g. sunlight, wind.
- They also include resources that may require careful **management** by **humans** to ensure they are replenished, e.g. wood from forests. These are called **critical flow resources**.

Resource Development Follows a General **Pattern**

1) There is an **uneven** global **distribution** of resources. Countries are able to **generate** some of the resources they need from their **environment**, but other resources must be obtained through **trade**.

2) This results in **local**, **regional** and **global transfers** of resources — this enables countries to get the resources they **need**.

3) Stock resources (e.g. minerals like iron ore) can be **expensive** to extract and transport, but they can also be extremely **valuable**, so companies go through an **evaluation** to decide if a resource is **economically viable** (i.e. if it can be extracted and sold whilst still making a profit).

4) When evaluating potential new stock resources, extraction industries distinguish between the terms '**resource**' and '**reserve**'. A '**resource**' is the **entire supply** of a material (including the bits that haven't been found yet or aren't economically viable to extract). A '**reserve**' is the amount of the resource that it's **economically viable** to extract. There's an international scale that's used to **evaluate** resources:

The extraction and sale of resources is mostly controlled by TNCs.

- **Possible resources** — these are resources that are thought to exist (e.g. based on knowledge of local geology), but haven't been sampled.
- **Inferred resources** — these are resources that have been **identified** (e.g. from limited samples of local geology) but **haven't** been **measured**.
- **Indicated reserve** — the size of the reserve has been **partly measured**, and the measurements have been used to **estimate** the actual extent.
- **Measured reserve** — the size of the reserve has been **measured** and is known **accurately**.

5) Over time, resources go through several stages of **development**, from being located to being exhausted:

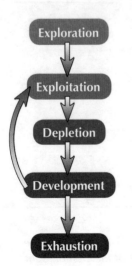

Exploration — Locating a potential new resource and evaluating (see above) whether it is viable to extract it, e.g. by sampling and surveying the local area.

Exploitation — Extracting the resource, preparing it for use and transporting it to where it will be used.

Depletion — The resource begins to run out.

Development — As yields decrease, new methods of extraction may be developed to prolong the life of the resource.

The companies developing resources are also often responsible for environmental management of sites, e.g. fixing any environmental damage resulting from resource development.

Exhaustion — Eventually, the resource becomes so limited that it is not physically possible or economically viable to extract any more.

Resource Development

Resource-rich Areas Can Become **Resource Frontiers**

1) A **resource frontier** is a place with **abundant** natural resources that are being exploited for the **first time**. Areas often haven't previously been exploited because they are geographically **remote** (e.g. the Arctic) or **hard to access** (e.g. very mountainous or sub-sea areas).

2) Resource frontiers often develop as other, more accessible, resources are **depleted**. Ongoing or increasing demand makes it necessary or economically viable to exploit areas that weren't previously **worth** exploiting.

3) As a frontier area begins to be exploited for its resources, new **facilities** and **equipment** are needed there for the extraction of the resource. New **buildings** (e.g. for housing workers) and **transport links** may also be constructed.

Example — The Arctic

1) Some areas of the Arctic contain rich resources of **oil**, **natural gas** and **minerals** (e.g. iron ore, gold).

2) Many of these resources **haven't** been exploited, for several reasons:

- They are hard to **access** — e.g. more than 80% of the Arctic's gas and oil reserves are **offshore**.
- There is **little infrastructure** (e.g. roads, pipelines) in the Arctic, which makes **extraction** and **transportation** of resources difficult.
- The environment is **challenging** — **sea ice** can make transport difficult, while **extreme cold** and winter **storms** can put equipment and workers at risk.
- There are concerns about how resource extraction will damage the **fragile environment**.

3) However, resources in some parts of the Arctic are being **exploited**, e.g. large oil reserves were discovered at Prudhoe Bay in northern **Alaska** in 1968. In the 1970s, the **Trans-Alaska pipeline** was constructed to carry oil to southern Alaska, from where it could be transported to customers.

4) In some frontier areas, exploitation has **stopped** for now. For example, in 2015, the oil and gas company Shell stopped drilling in the Chukchi Sea in Alaska because the **cost** of extracting oil was too high and reserves were **smaller** than expected, so exploitation wasn't **economically viable**.

The Trans-Alaska pipeline

The Period of **Highest Production** is Called the **Resource Peak**

1) When a **new stock resource** (e.g. a new reserve of oil or coal) is found and exploited, the **amount** extracted each day (or week, month etc.) tends to follow a similar **pattern**:

- Initially, production **increases** as investment increases (there are more workers, more money spent on equipment etc.), and the most **easily accessed** parts of the reserve are extracted.

- The graph of resource production is a **bell-shaped curve**, which shows a **normal distribution**. The **resource peak** is the point at which the **maximum** amount of the resource is being extracted each day. This tends to be when about **half** the resource has been used.

- After this, production begins to **decline**. This is because the most accessible parts of the reserve have been **exhausted**, and only the **harder-to-reach** parts remain.

- Eventually, the resource **runs out**, or what remains becomes too **difficult** or **expensive** to extract, and production **stops**.

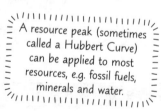

A resource peak (sometimes called a Hubbert Curve) can be applied to most resources, e.g. fossil fuels, minerals and water.

2) The resource peak can be applied at a **local** scale (e.g. a single mine or oil field) or at a **global** scale (e.g. if extraction continues, all significant reserves of coal and oil will one day be exhausted).

3) In some cases, new technology results in a **second peak** or a **slowing down** of depletion as it allows hard-to-reach reserves to be exploited. E.g. **hydraulic fracturing** has allowed exploitation of unconventional oil reserves in shale.

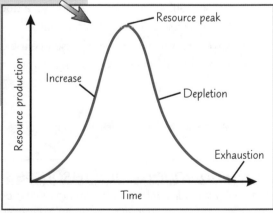

Topic Eleven — Resource Security

Resource Development

Resource Use Can Be Made **More Sustainable**

1) Making resource use more **sustainable** means ensuring that resources are not extracted so **quickly** that they leave future generations **without** sufficient supplies, or in such a way that their extraction causes large-scale **environmental damage**.

2) Use of **stock** resources can be made more sustainable in a number of ways. For example:

   - **Using less** of each resource (e.g. making cars more fuel-efficient to limit fuel consumption).
   - Increasing rates of **reuse** or **recycling** to minimise the amount of new materials that are needed.
   - Finding **new reserves** or **new ways** of extracting resources — this often happens as technology advances (e.g. fracking — see p.232).
   - Finding **alternatives** to each resource.

3) **Flow** resources can be **more sustainable** than stock resources because they can be **replenished**, so there won't be less available in the future (e.g. forests can regrow).

4) However, to be sustainable flow resources must not be used more **quickly** than they can be renewed, or in **greater quantities** than are available. For example, if more energy is **used** than can be **produced** by wind power in an area, then using wind power as the only energy source is **unsustainable** as people won't have **enough** energy to meet their needs.

[Insert your own wind power joke here...]

EIAs can Assess the **Impacts** of Resource Development Projects

1) An **Environmental Impact Assessment** (EIA) is undertaken **before** a new development is started. It's used to assess the potential **environmental** effects of the development, as well as related **social**, **economic** and **cultural** impacts. These are used to **decide** whether it can go ahead.

   Impacts can be positive or negative.

2) An EIA is used when planning a new **resource development** (e.g. a new mine, wind farm or dam). It normally involves the following steps:

   - Assessing potential **impacts**, e.g. damage to habitats, increased pollution, health impacts for people living nearby.
   - Identifying how any negative impacts can be **managed** or **reduced**.
   - Looking at **alternatives** to see whether there are **less damaging options** (e.g. a different type of development or a different location).
   - Making a **decision** about whether the project can go ahead, and under what **conditions**.
   - **Monitoring** the development to assess whether the impacts are in line with those **predicted**.

3) EIAs are widely used in **developed** countries, but are often used less strictly in **developing** countries. This can lead to resource developments in developing countries going ahead with little or no consideration of their possible impacts.

Practice Questions

Q1 Briefly outline the difference between a stock resource and a flow resource.

Q2 What is meant by an 'inferred resource'?

Q3 Give one way in which stock resource use can be made more sustainable.

Q4 Briefly outline the purpose of an Environmental Impact Assessment.

Exam Question

Q1 Assess the extent to which exploitation of resource frontier regions is likely to be necessary in future. [9 marks]

Develop your mental resources — learn these pages...

That might seem like more information than your poor, overloaded brain can handle. But don't panic — from here on in it all gets a bit more real and a bit easier to get your head around (well, hopefully). So go back over these three pages until you're sure all the definitions have stuck, then move on to the next page. Go on, stop loitering and be off with you. Skedaddle.

Water Supply and Demand

It's easy to take water for granted in the UK — turn on any tap and it flows right out. But a lot goes into making that water available to us, and not all areas of the world are as lucky as we are when it comes to water. Read on for enlightenment...

Water Comes From **Various Sources**

1) Water can be **extracted** from both **surface** and **underground** sources. The process of removing water from water sources is called **abstraction**.

2) Surface resources include **rivers**, **lakes**, **melting glaciers** and **reservoirs**.

3) Reservoirs are **man-made** lakes — they are usually made by building a **dam** across a river, which **traps** water so it can be used by people. E.g. **Haweswater** is a reservoir in Cumbria that supplies water to **large areas** of **North West England**.

4) Fresh water can also be obtained by removing the salt from **sea water** in a process called **desalination** (see p.220).

5) Underground sources include **aquifers**. These are areas of **porous rock** below the Earth's surface which are full of small holes and **saturated** with water. Water can be **pumped** out of them and up to the surface via deep **boreholes** drilled into the **rock**. Water from aquifers flows into **surface water sources** (e.g. rivers and lakes) and **recharges** them.

Water Supply is Controlled by **Physical** and **Human Factors**

The **volume** and **quality** of water available in an area depends on a range of **physical** factors:

Climate
- Most places rely on **rainfall** for their **water supply**. Areas with high rainfall generally have a more reliable water supply.
- In **hot** climates, lots of water is lost from lakes and rivers due to **evaporation**, which can cause water scarcity.
- Very high rainfall can **overwhelm sewers** and **water treatment plants** and can increase surface runoff from fields and urban areas — this can reduce water quality as more pollutants end up in water supplies.

> Climate change is altering the total amount of rainfall in places, as well as how often it rains and how heavy it is.

Geology
- When rain falls on **impermeable rock** (e.g. clay) it can't soak in, so it **flows** into **rivers** and **lakes**.
- When rain falls on **permeable rock**, e.g. sandstone, it **flows** through them and can form **aquifers** — water is harder to extract from these, but they can make **water available** in very **dry** places.
- Some types of rock contain **salts** and **minerals** that **dissolve** into the water, sometimes making it **unsuitable** for **drinking** without lots of treatment.

Drainage
- Drainage systems **move** water from one area to **another** (see p.7), changing the distribution of water.
- Large drainage basins cover more land, so are more likely to receive a lot of rainfall, increasing water supply.
- In some areas, drainage systems don't have **enough capacity** to cope with heavy rainfall — this can cause sewage systems to overflow, affecting water **quality**.

Water supply is also affected by **human** factors. For example:
- Increasing **demand** (see next page) is **reducing** supplies, e.g. extracting groundwater limits recharge of lakes and rivers.
- Human activities such as **farming** and **industry** can **pollute** water supplies, e.g. runoff from farmland can result in high concentrations of fertilisers and pesticides in water, making it **unsuitable** for many uses.
- As water supplies are reduced, the **price** of water may increase, making it **inaccessible** for some people.

People Need **Water** For Lots of **Reasons**

1) Water is **essential** to humans — people use water **directly** for things like **drinking**, **washing** and getting rid of **sewage**.

2) People also **indirectly** rely on water because of its importance in **many different industries** and for **trade**. For example:

- **Farming** — Farms use water to **irrigate crops** and **raise livestock**.
- **Electricity generation** — Water is heated in many types of power station to **generate steam** to drive **turbines** which generate electricity. It's also used to directly drive turbines in **hydro-electric plants**.
- **Manufacturing** — Factories of all kinds use water in the **production** of their products, e.g. **paper factories** use it to produce the **wood pulp** that's used to make sheets of paper. Many factories use it for **cooling** machinery.
- **Trade** — Waterways and oceans enable the **transport** of goods within and between countries.

Water Supply and Demand

Water Availability and *Demand Varies* Globally...

Total water resources **available** per person and the **demand** for water per person varies around the world:

Water Availability

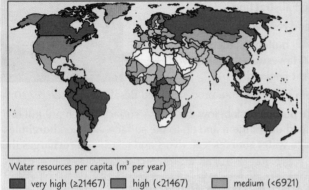

Water resources per capita (m³ per year)

- ■ very high (≥21467)
- ■ high (<21467)
- ■ medium (<6921)
- ■ low (<2879)
- □ very low (<1363)
- ■ no data

1) Some countries have **lots** of water available, e.g.:
   - Brazil, Gabon — annual rainfall is high.
   - Canada, New Zealand — annual rainfall is quite high, and low or moderate temperatures limit evaporation.
   - Australia — wealthy enough to invest in schemes to increase water supply, e.g. desalination (see p.220).

2) Water availability is much **lower** in other areas, e.g.:
   - Egypt — has an arid climate and inadequate water treatment facilities.
   - Jordan — has an arid climate. There is over-abstraction of water upstream, reducing water availability (see p.224).

Water Demand

1) Some countries have **high demand** for water, e.g.:
   - USA, Argentina — lots of farming, mining and industry, which use lots of water.
   - Australia — high domestic use (in homes and gardens), and lots of farming.

2) Other countries use much **less** water, e.g.:
   - Angola, Papua New Guinea — poor water infrastructure (e.g. broken pipes) and high prices limit access to water, so people **can't** use much.
   - Mongolia — has limited industry. Much farming is herding of nomadic livestock, which doesn't use much water.

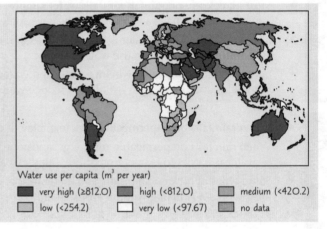

Water use per capita (m³ per year)

- ■ very high (≥812.0)
- ■ high (<812.0)
- ■ medium (<420.2)
- ■ low (<254.2)
- □ very low (<97.67)
- ■ no data

Global demand for water is rising for **two** main reasons:

1) **Population growth** — more people means more water is needed for **drinking, washing, preparing food** etc. The growing population also means that demand for **food, electricity** and other **goods** increases. Producing these uses water.

2) **Economic development** — as countries develop, **energy use** increases and **manufacturing** grows — energy production and manufacturing use a lot of **water**. As people's **wealth increases**, they can afford flushing **toilets, showers**, etc.

... Which is Causing *Water Stress* in Some Areas

1) When **demand** for water **exceeds supply**, or when water is **not** of high enough **quality** to use, places experience **water stress**.

2) Significant water stress is most likely in areas with **high population density** and **unreliable** or **low** water supplies.

3) The map shows the **level** of water stress around the **world**.

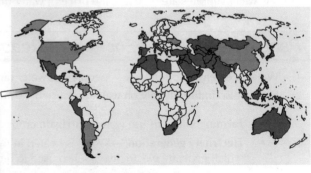

- Places with high water availability and/or low demand have **low water stress**, e.g. Brazil, Russia.
- Places with low water availability and/or high demand have **high water stress**, e.g. Mexico, India.
- Some places have low availability and low demand, which **limits** water stress — e.g. Ethiopia, Kenya.

Water use as a percentage of available supply

- ■ high (>40%)
- ■ medium (20-40%)
- □ low (<20%)

Water Supply and Demand

*Water **Trade** is Important for Ensuring **Adequate Supply***

Water can be **traded** between regions and countries to increase water availability and reduce water stress in countries where **demand** is greater than **supply**:

- This can be trade of **physical supplies** — for example, **Singapore** has very limited natural water reserves, but it ensures adequate water availability by **importing** around half of the water it needs from Malaysia.

- **Water transfer** (see p.220) is another way of **moving** water from places where there is plenty to places where there is not enough. For example, **Spain** transfers large amounts of water from the Tagus river basin to Murcia, Alicante and Almeria, in the **dry** south-east.

- **Rights** to **extract** water can also be **bought** and **sold** — for example, in the Murray-Darling Basin in southern **Australia**, individuals and organisations can buy and sell the right to **use** a **share** of the available water.

Hume Dam on the Murray River supplies water to large areas of New South Wales, Australia.

*Water Resource **Distribution** Causes **Geopolitical Issues***

Water availability and demand affects **individual countries** and the **relationships** between them. For example:

Geopolitics means the ways that geography affects relationships between countries.

1) Some countries with **rapid rates of population growth** are in areas facing **severe** water shortages — this could hinder **development** and have severe impacts on people's health and quality of life.

2) **Poorer countries** in dry areas can struggle to afford to **import** enough water or to build desalination plants (see p.220), meaning that they can't obtain enough water to meet demand.

3) Changes upstream can have a **major impact downstream** — for example, over-abstraction can result in **low flows** downstream, industry can increase **pollution**, and farming can increase soil erosion and therefore **suspended sediment concentration**. This means that countries or regions upstream must **manage** rivers carefully to avoid knock-on effects for downstream areas.

4) Many rivers cross **international boundaries** — e.g. the River Nile flows through nine countries. This can give upstream countries **power** over downstream countries, and failure to **manage** water resources properly can cause **disputes** or **conflict** between countries. For example, in 2015 a dispute between **Iran** and **Afghanistan** over water rights from the **Hari Rud River** led to the killing of Afghan villagers trying to extract water from the river.

There's more on conflict over water on p.223.

5) **Climate change** is reducing water availability in some already water-stressed countries. Countries are **working together** to try to reduce climate change, e.g. countries that are party to the 2015 Paris Agreement have agreed to reduce greenhouse gas emissions. However, there is **disagreement** over how to do this and what **role** different countries should play — in 2017, the USA pulled out of the agreement.

Practice Questions

Q1 Give three sources of water.

Q2 State two things that humans use water for.

Q3 Explain why global water demand is increasing.

Q4 Explain what is meant by the term 'water stress'.

Q5 Outline one geopolitical issue associated with water supply.

Exam Question

Q1 Study the map of water availability on the previous page.
Analyse the factors that account for the distribution of water availability shown. [9 marks]

Exams — water you so stressed about?

Wow — rivers are a water source. Who'd have thought it? Well, everyone probably... Make sure you know the sources of water that we use, and what we use water for. It's all pretty much common sense really. What's not so obvious is the physical factors that can affect water availability and quality, so make sure you go over it properly. Flip the page when you're done.

Increasing Water Security

You need to know how we can make sure that people have enough water. Luckily, that's what the next few pages are about.

There Are **Strategies** to **Increase Water Supply**

1) Water security is about a population having **reliable** and **sustainable** access to enough **good quality** water to meet **everyone's** needs — for **industry**, **agriculture**, **personal health** and to maintain the **ecosystem**.

2) There are a number of things that can be done to **increase** the **amount** of **water** available in an area and therefore **increase water security**. For example:

Water Diversion and Transfer

1) **Water diversion** involves changing the course of a river so it flows to a different area. For example, in the 1960s, rivers flowing into the Aral Sea were diverted to irrigate desert crops. As a result, the Aral Sea is now 10% of its original size.

2) **Water transfer** schemes involve **moving** water from areas of surplus to areas of shortage — this is normally done by pumping it through **pipes**, **tunnels**, **canals** and **aqueducts**. For example, most of **Birmingham's** water supply comes from the Elan valley in **mid-Wales** — a series of dams and reservoirs provide a continuous supply for the city.

3) Water transfer has the potential to **increase water security** in the **receiving** area, but it can also **increase water stress** (see p.218) for the **area** that water is **diverted from**. The infrastructure needed is **expensive** to construct and maintain, and can have environmental impacts (see p.222).

Water Catchment

1) **Water catchment** means collecting water (e.g. rainfall) for use.

2) **Rainwater harvesting** is an example of a water catchment scheme. Instead of allowing **rainwater** to **fall** on the **ground** and soak into the soil, it is **intercepted before** it hits the ground and **stored** in tanks.

3) This allows people to **quickly** access water in areas of shortage, rather than having to extract it from groundwater or surface water supplies.

4) For example, in **Bermuda** there are **no rivers** or **lakes**, and **groundwater** is **hard** to **access**. To **avoid water shortages**, every house is built with a **stepped roof** that is designed to collect enough rainwater to meet the **water needs** of the people that live in it.

5) In **Gansu Province**, **China**, a large-scale rainwater harvesting scheme collects enough water to **irrigate farmland** as well as to meet the needs of **individuals**.

Water Storage

1) Water can be **stored** during times of **surplus** — this means there's enough water during times of **deficit**.

2) For example, building a **dam** across a river valley **traps** water, creating a **reservoir**. The **reservoir** is **filled** during periods of extended rainfall, and the water is **released** during drier periods. This ensures a **consistent** flow of water in the river **all year round**. For example, the Avon Dam and Reservoir in Devon was constructed in the 1950s to ensure a **regular water supply** to South Devon.

3) Reservoirs can **increase** water security, but they can also **flood** agricultural land and **drown settlements** — their construction can therefore cause **conflict**.

Desalination

1) **Desalination** is the removal of **salt** from **seawater** so that it can be **used** as a water source. Seawater can be **heated** to **evaporate** it and then **condensed** to collect the freshwater. Alternatively, seawater can be passed through a series of **membranes** to remove the salt (this is called reverse osmosis).

2) Seawater is abundant in many areas that lack sufficient freshwater, so desalination can significantly increase water security. For example, **Dubai** is in an arid area with very limited freshwater resources, but it is on the coast of the Persian Gulf — as a result, it obtains **98.8%** of its water through desalination.

3) However, a lot of **energy** is needed to desalinate water. This means that it is an **expensive** way of increasing water supply, and as most of the energy comes from **fossil fuels**, desalination may cause **pollution** and contribute to **climate change**. Desalination is also a less viable option of increasing water security in **landlocked** countries.

Increasing Water Security

There Are Also **Strategies** to **Manage Water Consumption**

Domestic and **business** water consumption can be managed to **reduce demand** and help to conserve supplies. E.g.

- People can take **showers** instead of baths — **water-efficient shower heads** further **reduce** the amount of water used.
- The amount of water used to **flush** the **toilet** can be reduced by adding a **displacement bag** to the cistern or installing a modern **water-efficient toilet**. In **2001**, the UK government banned the installation of toilets that use **more than 6 litres** per flush. Most modern toilets use **between 4 and 6 litres** per flush.
- Modern appliances such as **water-efficient washing machines** and **dishwashers** use **less** water.
- People can have a **water meter** fitted — these **charge** users for the **exact** amount of water they use, so they **encourage** people to use **less water**. In the UK, every **new house** built since **1990** has been fitted with a water meter.
- Home-owners and water supply companies can **fix leaks** to minimise waste.

Agricultural water use can also be **reduced**. For example:

- Farmers can install **drip pipes** that direct water to **exactly** where it's **needed**, and **collect storm water** for irrigation.
- Farmers can also change their practices, e.g. by watering crops **early** in the morning to **reduce water loss** through evapotranspiration, or by **contour ploughing** (ploughing across a slope) to reduce **runoff**.

Management Can Make Water Supplies More **Sustainable**

1) Water can be **managed sustainably** to ensure the **security** of the **water supply now** and for **future generations**. If water is **not** managed **sustainably**, it can lead to shortages and water stress (see p.218).

2) **Conserving water** (see above) is one way that water supplies can be made more sustainable. Other methods include:

Recycling and 'Greywater'

1) **Recycling water** means treating **used** water to make it safe to **reuse** straight away (rather than returning it to a river or the sea).

2) Most recycled water is used for **irrigation**, **industry**, **power plants** and **toilet flushing**, though it can also be treated enough to make it safe to drink.

3) Recycling makes water supplies **more sustainable** because it helps people meet their water needs without **extracting** more water from rivers or from groundwater.

4) **'Greywater'** is a type of recycled water — it's mostly **waste water** from homes and businesses, e.g. from washing machines and showers. This water is relatively **clean**, so it can be used to water gardens, flush toilets, wash cars and irrigate farmland without being **treated** first. It's **not safe** for washing hands or drinking though.

5) Using greywater can make water supplies more **sustainable**, especially when it is used by **industries** that have high water use, such as hotels and sports centres.

6) It also means that clean water isn't **treated** unnecessarily, which helps **conserve energy**.

Virtual Water Trade

1) **Virtual water** is a term used to describe water that has been **used** in the **production** of something, e.g. the water required to grow a tonne of lemons or produce a tonne of steel.

2) When these **products** are **traded** between countries, the **virtual water** is also **traded**.

3) Sometimes, **products** that require **a lot** of water to make are **exported** from countries with **high water stress**. For example, **India** is the world's **largest exporter** of **basmati rice**, which is one of the most **water-intensive** crops in the world.

4) Being **aware** of the **virtual water value** of a product can **help** countries to think about **managing** their water **more sustainably**.

5) For example, **Middle Eastern countries** where water is scarce may choose to **import** foods with a **high virtual water value** from countries with more water. Similarly, they may choose **not** to grow crops with a high virtual water value for **export**, so **more** water is **available** for **other purposes**.

Groundwater Management

1) Groundwater can be **managed** to make sure its **quantity** and **quality** are conserved. For example:
   - The amount being **extracted** can be **monitored** to ensure it is not extracted **faster** than it is **naturally replaced**. **Laws** can be passed to prevent **over-extraction**.
   - Farmers can be encouraged to apply less **artificial fertiliser** and **pesticides** to farmland, and companies that leak or dump toxic **waste** can be **fined** — this helps to reduce **pollution** of groundwater.

2) In places where groundwater has been **overexploited**, **aquifers** can be **artificially recharged**. For example:
   - **Injection wells** allow water to be piped back into depleted aquifers.
   - **Infiltration structures** are water-filled basins, ponds or trenches, from which water **infiltrates** to the aquifer.

Increasing Water Security

Water Transfer Schemes Can Have Environmental Impacts

Water transfer (see p.220) has **impacts** on the environment in the place the water is taken **from**, the places it passes **through** and the place it's taken **to**. For example:

1) The **South-North Water Transfer Project** (SNWTP) is a $62 billion scheme intended to increase water insecurity in China.

2) It involves a network of tunnels and canals that will divert about **45 billion cubic metres** of water **every year** from the Yangtze River and its tributaries in the **south** of the country to the Yellow River in the **drier north**.

3) The project is designed to provide water to places where there isn't enough, such as the cities of **Beijing** and **Tianjin**. It will ensure there is enough drinking water, allow **industry** to continue to **develop**, and provide **water** for **irrigating farmland** so crops can be grown.

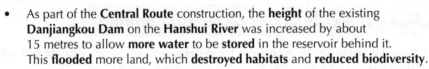

4) **Two** out of **three** planned routes have been **completed** — the **Central** and **Eastern Routes**. The **Western Route** is expected to be finished by **2050**.

5) The completed parts of the SNWTP have already had some **environmental impacts**:

- As part of the **Central Route** construction, the **height** of the existing **Danjiangkou Dam** on the **Hanshui River** was increased by about 15 metres to allow **more water** to be **stored** in the reservoir behind it. This **flooded** more land, which **destroyed habitats** and **reduced biodiversity**.

  Biodiversity is the number of different species found in the area.

- Increasing the height of the dam also **decreased the velocity** of the Hanshui River **downstream**. This contributed to an increase in **algal blooms** (thick blankets of algae on the water surface), which **prevent light** from penetrating below the surface. This causes **plants** in the river to **die**, resulting in **oxygen shortages** in the water and the **death** of organisms that **rely** on **oxygen**, such as fish and amphibians.

- The water can be **polluted** during the transfer — this can make it **toxic** to plants and animals. **Water treatment plants** require **large amounts** of **energy** to operate, much of which comes from burning **fossil fuels** — this releases **greenhouse gases** and contributes to **global warming**.

6) Scientists have also **predicted** other **environmental impacts** that are likely to occur:

1) **Decreased flow speeds** near the **Yangtze delta** may change which species **thrive** in the area, e.g. populations of **water snails** that carry the **parasite** which causes the disease **schistosomiasis** may increase. Schistosomiasis can infect and kill **other animals**, including pigs and water buffalo, leading to significant changes to the **ecosystem**.

2) **Reduced** water flow into the **Yangtze delta** could lead to **salt intrusion**, where seawater **mixes** with river water **further upstream**. This could **affect** the delta **ecosystem** by **killing freshwater species**.

3) **Wetlands** (e.g. around the Yangtze delta) could become **drier**, and **drylands** to the north could become **wetter** as water is moved. This would affect **habitats** and change the **species** that live in these ecosystems.

Practice Questions

Q1 Give two ways that individuals can reduce their water consumption.

Q2 What is meant by the term 'greywater'?

Q3 Explain what is meant by 'virtual water trade'.

Q4 Outline one environmental impact of the South-North Water Transfer Project in China.

Exam Question

Q1 'It is impossible to meet the water demands of the growing global population without damaging the natural environment.' To what extent do you agree with this statement? [20 marks]

Lock up your taps, hide away your bathtub — water security is a big issue...

The methods we use to increase water supply are pretty critical. It's not all about finding new ways to get hold of water though — reducing demand and managing supplies sustainably can also help to make sure that there's enough to go around.

Water Conflicts

Nobody likes conflict (except my brother), but unfortunately the world is full of conflicts. Water is sometimes the cause...

Water Resources Can Cause *Conflict* at *Different Scales*

1) **Conflicts** over water occur where different groups **share** the same water supply, and water **demand exceeds supply**.

2) This can occur because:
   - Water supplies **decrease**, e.g. groundwater has been **over-exploited** or rainfall in the area has **decreased**.
   - Water demand increases, e.g. the **population grows** or **industry expands**.

3) This leads to more **competition** for resources, which can cause conflict at **local**, **national** and **international** scales:

Local Conflict — PEPSI® Factory, Kerala, India

- **PEPSI**® is based in the USA, but it has factories all over the world, including one in the **Indian** state of **Kerala**. This factory has been the source of an ongoing **water conflict** between PEPSI® and **local people**.

- **Droughts** have increased **water stress** in the area, which has led to **shortages** of **drinking water**. The lack of water for **irrigation** has led to the **loss of crops**.

- **Local people** claim that the factory is worsening the problem by **over-exploiting groundwater**. PEPSI® **deny** this — they claim that an **independent study** showed that the effects of the factory were **insignificant** compared to other water users.

- **Local authorities** have tried to **stop** the factory extracting so much **groundwater** on several occasions — in 2017, PEPSI® agreed to **cut** water use by **75%** while drought conditions persisted. There have also been **protests** by local people demanding that the plant be **shut down**.

- In March 2017, an organisation **representing** many local **traders** discussed plans to **stop stocking** PEPSI® in favour of local drink brands.

National Conflict — Water Crisis in Yemen

Yemen is an **arid** country in western Asia that has **very high** levels of **water stress** (see p.218). Water is a major source of **conflict** between many **different** parties in Yemen:

- There is anger amongst people in **rural communities** about the **uneven availability** of water **between rural** and **urban** areas. This has sometimes led to **violent clashes** and **protests**.

- In 2002, the government introduced a **law** requiring landowners to get a **licence** to **drill** and **maintain wells**, and tried to introduce a **register** of wells in the country. This was met with **backlash** from **farmers** concerned that the **government** would try to **control** the **amount** of water they could **extract** from wells on their property.

- In 2009, the government tried to **restrict** the cultivation of **qat** — a leaf chewed by much of the population — because **irrigation** of qat crops uses around **30%** of Yemen's **groundwater**. **Farmers objected** to the government restrictions, arguing that they would lose their **income**. As a result, the limits were largely **ignored**.

International Conflict — The River Nile

Conflicts often arise over water sources (such as rivers or lakes) that **cross borders** between **countries**. For example:

- The **Nile river** is a source of water for **many countries** in **north east Africa**. There's **conflict** between the **downstream countries** (e.g. Egypt and Sudan) that use **most** of the water, and the **upstream countries** (including Uganda, Rwanda, Ethiopia and Tanzania) that **want** to use **more** water.

- In 2011, **Ethiopia** started to build the **Grand Ethiopian Renaissance Dam** near the border with Sudan to generate **hydroelectric power** (**HEP**) and take better **control** of the river's **flow** to prevent drought and flooding. **Egypt** is concerned that the dam will lead to the loss of **billions** of **cubic metres** of water by **evaporation** from the lake formed behind the dam, meaning that **less** water will **flow** into **Egypt**. This led to **disputes** between the two countries, but a **partial agreement** was reached in 2015.

Practice Questions

Q1 Briefly outline two changes to water supply and demand that can result in conflict.

Q2 Briefly describe one way that water is causing conflict at a national scale.

Exam Question

Q1 Assess the importance of water supply as a cause of conflict. [9 marks]

Don't argue over water — just go with the flow...

Remember that conflicts can be anything from a bit of tension to all-out war. If you're asked about water conflicts, try to get a few specific examples in your answer to show that you've got really good knowledge of the subject. Examiners love that.

Jordan Basin Water Resources — Case Study

Time for a case study — this one is about water in the Jordan Basin, but in class you might have studied a different example of water issues, or issues associated with energy or ore minerals. As long as you know one inside out, I'll be happy...

The Jordan Basin Experiences Water Insecurity

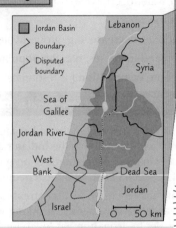

1) The Jordan Basin is in the **Middle East**. The River Jordan rises on the border of Syria and Lebanon, and flows **south** to the Dead Sea.

2) The basin has an area of about **18 000 km²** — about **40%** is in **Jordan**, with smaller proportions in **Syria**, **Israel**, **Lebanon** and the disputed territory of the **West Bank**.

3) The **physical setting** of the Jordan Basin means that water is **scarce** in many areas. For example:

- **Climate** — the area is **arid**, with an average annual precipitation of 380 mm. Rainfall **varies**, with many southern areas receiving less than 100 mm each year. Temperatures are **high** — the annual average is 18 °C, but summer temperatures are often above 30 °C. In some areas, around **70%** of rainfall is lost to **evaporation**.

- **Geology** — much of the rock in the Jordan Basin is **limestone**, which is relatively **permeable**. This means that water infiltrates fairly quickly, reducing **runoff** and river **discharge**.

Climate change is expected to increase temperature and decrease rainfall in the area.

4) **People** are also contributing to **water scarcity** in the Jordan Basin:

- Over **7 million** people live in the basin, and the population is **growing**. This is increasing **demand** for water.

- The countries in the Jordan Basin are **developing economically** — this involves increases in **industrial activity** and **wealth**. This increases **energy use**, and producing energy increases **water use**.

- River discharge in the southern part of the basin has decreased due to **damming**, **diversion** and **groundwater abstraction** further north. For example, in 1964 Israel completed a water diversion scheme called the **National Water Carrier**, which uses canals and pipes to divert water from the Sea of Galilee to **irrigate** farmland and provide water for **cities** such as Tel Aviv. This has lowered the River Jordan's **discharge** by around **25%**.

- **Civil war** in **Syria** since 2011 has caused an influx of **refugees** into Jordan, putting more pressure on water supplies. Refugees are **concentrated** in small areas, e.g. the **Zaatari Camp** — some people are concerned that inadequate water treatment in these areas may **pollute groundwater** and **rivers**, reducing water availability.

- Much water infrastructure (e.g. pipes) **leaks**, either because it is **old** and worn, or because it has been **damaged**.

Water Insecurity Affects Human Welfare in the Jordan Basin

Water stress (see p.218) in the Jordan Basin has significant **impacts** on the **people** living there:

Each person in the West Bank has access to less than 200 m³ water per year — well below the water poverty threshold of 1000 m³.

- **Water shortages** are common, e.g. in 2016, some villages in the West Bank had no water supply for **two weeks**, while more than **80%** of rural households in Jordan **run out** of water at least once a month. Water is sometimes available to **buy** from private sellers, but it is **expensive** and the **quality** isn't always high. Shortages can affect people's **health** and **wellbeing**.

- From **1998** to **2012**, the region experienced its most **severe drought** in 900 years. This caused huge reductions in **agricultural yields**, e.g. less than 1% of cereal crops in Jordan were harvested from 1998 to 2001. This threatened **farmers' livelihoods** and left around **25%** of the population vulnerable to **food insecurity**.

- Water has been a **cause** of various **conflicts** in the Jordan Basin. For example, since Israel was designated the Jewish homeland in 1949, there have been ongoing disputes between **Israelis** and **Palestinians** in the area over access to **land** and **water**, and there are hostilities between Palestinian and Israeli settlements in the **West Bank**. Lack of **cooperation** over **water management** has also resulted in conflict. For example, plans to **divert** water from the River Jordan to Syria and Jordan were one of the causes of the **Six-Day War** against Israel in 1967, which **killed** around **19 000** people.

- **Conflict** and **land disputes** have also made it hard for countries to establish **water treatment plants** — this means that waste water is often pumped directly into watercourses, **decreasing** the amount of drinking water available. Pollution of watercourses also affects **human health** — for example, in 2013, residents of Bruqin in the West Bank suffered from **respiratory illnesses** and **skin problems** when their homes were **flooded** with sewage and industrial waste after heavy rainfall.

Jordan Basin Water Resources — Case Study

There Have Been Attempts to *Increase Water Security* in the Area

1) Some of the individual countries within the Jordan Basin have come up with **strategies** to **increase** their water **supply** and **decrease demand**. For example:

- In **Jordan**, the **Jordan Water Strategy** started in 1998, and has been extended until 2025. Water supply is **intermittent**, so part of the strategy is to fit **rooftop tanks** on homes to **store** water. Another method involves using **treated wastewater** for irrigation, so more high quality water is available for domestic use. The Jordan Water Strategy has increased water security — over **90%** of Jordan's residents now have access to mains water and effective sanitation systems. However, water supply is still fairly **infrequent**, and groundwater reserves are still being **over-exploited**.

- Water is **rationed** in some areas during shortages, e.g. in 2008 the Jordanian government **halved** the amount of water available to farmers, and **restricted** water supply to houses to 3-5 hours at a time, once or twice a week.

- Many **dams** have been constructed in the basin — e.g. in 2005, construction finished on the **Wahdah Dam** on the **Yarmouk River** (a major **tributary** of the River Jordan) to supply water to **Jordan**. Dams and reservoirs supply **90 million cubic metres** of water to Jordan each year — e.g. water is transferred to **Amman** (the capital city of Jordan) and other areas by the **King Abdullah Canal**. However, water **diversion** has meant that the River Jordan has **lost 95%** of its natural water flow.

- Israel is increasing investment in **desalination** (see p.220) — about **50%** of Israel's drinking water now comes from desalination plants, and there are plans to increase this to **70%** by **2020**. However, some areas of Israel are a long way from desalination plants, so a lot of water is still taken from the **Sea of Galilee**.

- Israel is using new **agricultural technology** to reduce water use while maintaining crop yields. For example, **drip irrigation** uses up to 75% less water than flood irrigation — water is piped directly to each plant, reducing **evaporation** losses. **New varieties** of crops have also been developed that need less water, e.g. dwarf wheat.

2) There have also been **cross-boundary strategies** and **agreements** to increase water security in the region, such as:

- **Israel** and the **West Bank** formed the **Joint Water Committee** in 1995 as part of an agreement to secure peace. The committee aims to improve **water supply** and **wastewater treatment** in the West Bank, for example by improving the water network and building new storage facilities. Ongoing **disputes** between Israel and the West Bank mean that little has yet been achieved. However, in 2017 they agreed to **renew cooperation** on the project.

- The **Red Sea-Dead Sea Water Conveyance Project** is a scheme involving **Israel**, **Jordan** and the **West Bank**. The project aims to build tunnels and pipelines to **transfer** water over 100 miles from the Red Sea to the Dead Sea, at a cost of up to US $10 billion. This would provide an additional water source that could be converted to **fresh water** by **desalination**, and could also be used to generate **hydroelectric power**. However, the project could take up to **20 years** to complete, and there are concerns that it may cause **environmental damage** to **coral reefs** in the Red Sea and to **ecosystems** in the Dead Sea.

3) The area also receives **international aid** to help ensure a **sustainable** water supply. For example, in 2000 the German government funded the **Al-Bireh wastewater treatment plant** in the West Bank to reduce river and groundwater pollution.

Practice Questions

Q1 Outline what the climate of the Jordan Basin is like.

Q2 Describe two ways in which people are contributing to water insecurity in the Jordan Basin.

Q3 Give one impact of water stress on people living in the Jordan Basin.

Q4 Briefly outline two responses aimed at increasing water security in the Jordan Basin.

Exam Question

Q1 With reference to **either** water **or** energy **or** ore minerals, assess the extent to which resource management strategies are improving human welfare at a global scale or in a region you have studied. [9 marks]

Red Sea, Dead Sea, Red Sea, Dead Sea — try saying that quickly 20 times...

Who'd have thought that water could be so complicated, and cause so many problems... I for one am going to stop belly-aching about the lack of sun in the UK and start being grateful that when I turn a tap on, water actually comes out.

Resource Futures — Water

OK, last bit on water. I'll be right back with you once I've grabbed a drink — this revision malarky is pretty thirsty work.

Water Stress is Likely to Increase in the Future

1) Current water use isn't **sustainable** — **excessive withdrawal** has led to severe **depletion** of freshwater supplies, e.g. many **aquifers** have had so much freshwater removed that they have now filled with seawater.

2) **Water stress** is expected to **increase** in the future as the **availability** of water **decreases** and **demand increases**:
   - Globally, water **demand** is likely to exceed the current **supply** by **40%** by 2030.
   - It's predicted that by 2050, around **2.5 billion people** will be living in areas of water scarcity.
   - Water stress is likely to be most **severe** in the **Mediterranean**, the **Middle East**, western **USA**, eastern **Australia**, western **Asia**, northern **China** and **Chile**.

   See page 218 for more on water stress.

3) Increased water stress would lead to problems for **people**. For example:
   - Insufficient **drinking water** is a threat to human life — where water is scarce, supplies of drinking water often become polluted, e.g. by sewage. This can cause **death** or **disease**.
   - A lack of water for **irrigation** limits **food production** — this could lead to **reduced incomes** and **malnutrition**.
   - Competition over remaining water resources is likely to cause more **conflict** (see p.223).

4) Water **futures** will be affected by **technological**, **economic**, **environmental**, and **political** developments. For example:

Technological
- **Increasing water supply** — improvements to **desalination** (e.g. using graphene oxide sieves that efficiently filter salt from seawater) may mean that freshwater can be obtained from seawater more **cheaply** than at present and with minimal **energy use**.
- **Appropriate technology** — e.g. in arid countries such as Kenya, **sand dams** can be constructed on seasonal rivers to trap water, making it available **all year round**.
- **Reducing water waste** — e.g. nanotechnology could be used to **purify** polluted water, allowing more to be recycled. Smart monitoring of distribution networks could catch **leaks** early so that less water is **wasted**.

Economic
- More economically developed countries use **more water per person**. This means that as more countries become more developed, global water demand will **increase**.
- However, as more countries become more developed, they will also be able to **afford the technology** and **infrastructure to obtain** more water and **deliver** it to where it's needed, so more people will have reliable **access** to clean water.

Environmental
- **Climate change** — dry areas are likely to become **drier** and wet areas **wetter**. Water **management strategies** will need to take this into account. However, global efforts to **minimise** climate change may help to **limit** its impacts on water supply.
- **Integrated catchment management** — looking at all aspects of a river catchment (e.g. geology, ecology and land use) can help to ensure that water **supply** and **use** are **sustainable**.

Political
- **Cooperation** — countries with abundant water supplies can **help** countries with water shortages. There can also be **agreements between countries** that withdraw water from the **same source** about how much they take, so that overall withdrawal is **sustainable**.
- **Policies** — government policies can encourage people to **use less water**, e.g. water meter installation could be compulsory, so people have to pay for the water they use.

Practice Questions

Q1 Give two regions where water stress is expected to increase in the future.

Q2 Briefly outline how economic developments might affect the future of water resources.

Exam Question

Q1 Assess the extent to which meeting future global water needs will require technological developments. [9 marks]

Well, it looks like the future of water is in a deep hole...

No one knows exactly what will happen to water resources in the future but some trends, like increasing demand and the effects of climate change, are likely to be hard to reverse. Make sure you know the factors that will affect how water is used.

Energy Supply and Demand

Energy resources are unevenly distributed — a bit like my grandad's comb-over. Time to have a look at how and why...

Energy Comes From *Primary* and *Secondary Sources*

1) There are lots of different **sources** of energy, for example:

- **Fossil fuels** (**coal**, **oil** and **natural gas**) form over millions of years from organisms that die and are buried. They can be burnt in power plants to generate **electricity**, or oil can be refined to produce **petrol** for vehicles.

- **Renewable** energy comes from various sources, e.g. **wind** and **water** can be used to turn turbines and generate electricity, **solar** power can be converted to electricity using solar panels, and **geothermal** energy can be used to boil water to produce **steam** — this can be used for **heating** or to turn turbines to generate electricity.

- **Nuclear** energy is released by splitting uranium atoms — this produces **heat** that is used to generate **electricity**.

- **Biomass** includes wood, plants and animal waste. It can be burnt to produce energy or processed to make **biofuel**.

2) Energy can be classed as **primary** or **secondary**. **Primary energy** is released from a **direct source** as it naturally occurs, e.g. **burning coal** generates **heat**. When primary energy is **converted**, it becomes **secondary energy**, e.g. a **thermal power station** may use coal to generate **heat** that's then used to generate **electrical energy** (a secondary energy source).

3) Energy is used by **individuals** and by **businesses**. The **main components of demand** for energy are:

- **Residential** — people use **electricity** and **heat** in their homes, e.g. for lighting, heating and powering appliances.
- **Industrial** — energy is needed to **manufacture** goods, run machines, light and heat factories etc.
- **Agricultural** — energy is needed to **heat** greenhouses and power irrigation pumps.
- **Services** — buildings such as **shops**, **banks**, **schools**, **hotels** and **hospitals** need energy for lighting, heating etc.
- **Transport** — energy is needed to **fuel vehicles** to transport people and goods.

Global *Energy Production* and *Consumption* are *Unevenly Distributed*

The map shows the total amount of energy **produced** per country in 2012.

1) Some countries produce **lots of energy** because they have **lots of natural resources** to produce energy (e.g. coal, oil) and the **money** to **exploit** them. For example:
- Iran, Saudi Arabia — large oil reserves.
- China, Australia — large coal reserves.
- UK, Russia, Canada — large oil and gas reserves.
- USA, Indonesia — large coal, oil and gas reserves.

2) Some countries produce **little energy** because they have **few resources** or are **unable to exploit** their resources due to lack of **money** or **political instability**.
- Angola — large oil reserves, but politically unstable and lacks money.
- Spain — relatively wealthy, but small fossil fuel reserves.

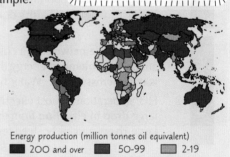

This map shows the energy produced in each country, not the total reserves of energy.

Energy production (million tonnes oil equivalent)
- ■ 200 and over
- ■ 100-199
- ■ 50-99
- ■ 20-49
- ▨ 2-19
- □ Less than 2

The map below shows the energy **consumption** per person across the world in 2014.

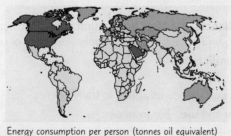

Energy consumption per person (tonnes oil equivalent)
- ■ 6.0 and over
- ▨ 4.5 – 6.0
- ▨ 3.0 – 4.5
- □ 1.5 – 3.0
- □ 0 – 1.5

There's a **strong relationship** between **GDP** and **energy consumption**:

1) **Wealthy countries** tend to **consume lots of energy** per person because they **can afford to**. Most people in these countries have **electricity** and **heating**, and use **energy-intensive devices** like cars. E.g. **Sweden**, **USA**.

2) **Poorer countries** consume **less energy** per person as they are **less able to afford it**. **Less energy** is **available** and lifestyles are less dependent on high energy consumption than in richer countries. E.g. **Ghana**, **Mongolia**.

Some countries don't consume much energy per person, but consume a lot overall because they have large populations, e.g. Brazil.

Some countries don't **produce** much **energy** but still **consume a lot**, and vice versa. This is possible because **energy** is **traded between countries** — countries that are able to produce a lot of energy **export** it to those that can't. For example, Canada, Saudi Arabia, Norway and Australia all **export large amounts** of **energy**, whereas Ireland, Italy, Spain and Japan all **import large amounts** of **energy**.

Electricity is traded between neighbouring countries, while coal, oil and natural gas can be transported around the world.

Topic Eleven — Resource Security

Energy Supply and Demand

Energy Supply is Controlled by *Physical Factors*

1) Energy supply is **unevenly distributed** around the world (see previous page) — it varies in both **volume** (how much is available) and **quality** (e.g. how pure a fossil fuel reserve is and whether the supply is constant or fluctuating).

2) Energy supply is affected by physical factors, such as **climate**, **geology** and **drainage**:

Climate

1) Climate can affect the volume and quality of **renewable** resources. For example:
   - **Wind** — wind energy can only be generated in locations with an average annual wind speed above about 5.5 m/s. However, **very high** winds can **damage** wind turbines, so most turbines stop working automatically if winds get above about 25 m/s.
   - **Hydroelectric power (HEP)** — HEP relies on **large flows** of water to generate electricity. In areas with low rainfall or frequent droughts, it cannot produce **reliable** power.
   - **Solar** — solar power is generated using sunlight, so it is most effective in places with **little cloud cover**. The amount of energy that can be produced varies with **time of year** — in many areas, days are longer in the summer, so more energy can be generated.

2) Climate also affects the production of **non-renewable** sources. For example, mines can become **flooded** and access roads impassable in areas with very high **rainfall**, and offshore oil rigs can be **damaged** by storms.

Geology

1) Geology affects **fossil fuel** supply. For example:
   - **Coal** is a sedimentary rock — it forms when plant material undergoes specific **geological processes** such as **burial** and **heating**. Coal that has undergone the most change is the **highest** quality (anthracite), while coal that has been changed least is the **lowest** quality (lignite).
   - **Oil** and **natural gas** need specific geological conditions in order to **form** and be **stored** — when organic-rich rocks are buried, they are heated and compressed, and begin to break down into oil and gas. Gas forms at **higher** temperatures, often deeper underground, than oil. Both gas and oil travel upwards through pores in rocks, until they meet a layer of **impermeable rock** and become trapped — they are found where impermeable **'cap'** rock (e.g. granite) overlies permeable **'reservoir'** rock (e.g. sandstone).
   - Oil and natural gas can also form in **shale** — shale is **impermeable**, so it is difficult to **extract** oil and gas from it. A process called **hydraulic fracturing** (**fracking**) can be used to extract the fuel (see p.232).

2) Geology is also important for **geothermal** energy production — many geothermal power stations are located in places where the Earth's crust is **thin**, so molten rock is close to the **surface**.

Drainage

1) The **drainage network** of a country (e.g. the **number** of rivers and the **size** and **shape** of drainage basins) affects the **volume** of energy that can be generated using **hydroelectric power (HEP)**. To generate HEP, a **dam** is built across a river. Water flows through tunnels in the dam, turning turbines to produce **electricity**.

2) HEP generation is most effective if there is a **large volume** of water flowing consistently down the river, and a large **drop** in **elevation** from the reservoir to the water outlet. It therefore works best in drainage basins with **large rivers** and fairly **steep** terrain. However, steep terrain can make dam construction **difficult** or **expensive**.

The *Geopolitics* of Energy *Production*, *Trade* and *Use* is a Big Issue

Energy production and use affects **relationships** between countries. For example:

1) Countries that **produce** lots of a particular type of energy might form **alliances**, e.g. the Organisation of the Petroleum Exporting Countries (**OPEC**) is a group of countries that work together to influence the **global supply** and **price** of **oil**.

2) Because energy resources are **unevenly distributed** across the world, **conflicts** can arise between countries trying to obtain the resources they need.

3) A country's **financial situation** or **existing conflicts** with other countries can reduce its ability to trade energy.

There are a number of **geopolitical issues** linked to energy **production**, **trade** and **use**. For example:

- Global **energy use** is **increasing** and **fossil fuel reserves** are **decreasing**. Many people believe we're coming to an '**energy crisis**', so governments are very concerned about how to **secure energy supplies** for the future.

- Many of the **largest reserves** of oil and gas are in areas that are **politically** or **economically unstable**, e.g. Iraq. This means that **energy supplies** to many countries are at risk of being **disrupted**.

- As energy consumption increases, so does the **impact** of energy use on the **environment** (see page 233). **International agreements**, e.g. the Kyoto Protocol, try to **address these problems**, but these can also lead to political **conflict** if environmental protection clashes with other national interests, e.g. economic growth.

Energy Supply and Demand

The *Energy Mix* Describes the *Sources* of *Energy* a *Country Uses*

1) Many countries **can't supply** all of their **energy needs** from **one source**. Others may not want to for **energy security** reasons — e.g. countries that rely on only one energy source will be affected by **disruptions** to supply of that source, and if the **price increases** they will have no option but to pay.

2) For these reasons, countries use a **variety** of energy sources instead.

3) **Energy mix** is the **composition** of different primary energy **sources** from which households and industries in an area get their energy. It's usually shown as **percentages**. For example:

Solar and wave energy were the ideal mix to satisfy Sam's energy needs.

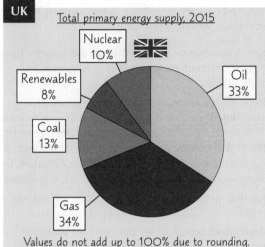

UK

Total primary energy supply, 2015

Nuclear 10%
Renewables 8%
Coal 13%
Gas 34%
Oil 33%

Values do not add up to 100% due to rounding.

The pie chart on the left shows the **UK's energy mix** in 2015.

1) **Nearly 70%** of the UK's energy supply is provided by **oil** and **gas**.

2) The UK's **consumption of oil is high** due to reserves of oil in the North Sea and the growing demand for **transport** fuel.

3) The UK also has large **onshore** and **offshore** reserves of **natural gas**, so domestic supplies are currently plentiful.

4) Coal also forms a significant proportion of the UK's energy mix. However, use of **coal** has **fallen** significantly since 1990, due to closure of mines and the move to using less polluting sources.

5) **Renewable resources** form a fairly small proportion of the energy mix, but their use is gradually **increasing** as the government aims for a more **sustainable** energy supply.

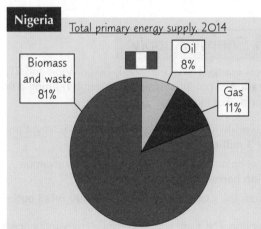

Nigeria

Total primary energy supply, 2014

Biomass and waste 81%
Oil 8%
Gas 11%

The pie chart on the left shows **Nigeria's energy mix** in 2014.

1) **Biomass** (e.g. wood) and **waste** (e.g. burning refuse) is the main energy source — this is **partially renewable**. Use of biomass and waste is high partly because, in many **rural areas**, few people have access to alternative energy sources. However, recent initiatives in Nigeria have started generating **electricity** from **waste**, increasing **sustainability** of energy supply.

2) **Fully renewable** energy sources contribute **little** to the energy mix, e.g. **hydroelectric power** provides only **0.003%** of Nigeria's energy. **Solar** and **wind** power are **not yet significant**, partly because Nigeria has not had enough **money** to develop them.

3) The rest of Nigeria's energy supply comes from **fossil fuels** — the country has **large reserves** of oil and **natural gas**.

Practice Questions

Q1 What is the difference between a primary and a secondary energy source?

Q2 Give two components of energy demand.

Q3 What is meant by a country's 'energy mix'?

Exam Question

Q1 The graph shows Finland's energy mix and CO_2 emissions from 1970 to 2010. Analyse the trends shown by the data. [6 marks]

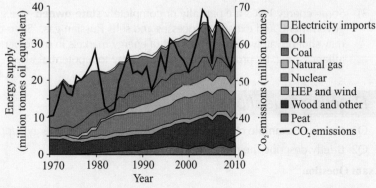

Legend:
☐ Electricity imports
■ Oil
■ Coal
☐ Natural gas
■ Nuclear
■ HEP and wind
■ Wood and other
■ Peat
— CO_2 emissions

Energy supply (million tonnes oil equivalent) vs Year (1970–2010), CO_2 emissions (million tonnes)

Mayonnaise is my primary sauce, BBQ is my secondary...

...I only have ketchup if there's nothing else. The UK and Nigeria have pretty different energy mixes, but you could also learn about somewhere that relies heavily on renewable sources — for example, nearly 70% of Iceland's total energy supply comes from geothermal sources, and the majority of domestic electricity is generated from hydroelectric power.

Energy Supply and Globalisation

Turns out that countries' economies, political systems and cultures are becoming more connected through energy. Who knew?

Globalisation *of Energy Supply Causes* Competing National Interests

1) **Energy production** and **consumption** are unevenly distributed (see p.227) — this means that energy needs to be transferred between countries, increasing **links** between them. This contributes to **globalisation**.

2) **Technological advances** mean that long-distance energy **trade** is becoming easier, e.g. with tankers and cables. For example, the Yamal-Europe Pipeline is a 4000 km-long pipe that was built to carry gas from Russia to western Europe.

3) Energy resources are **vital** to countries' **development**, so the **control** of energy resources is increasingly important. This means that different countries have different **priorities** when trading energy. What's in **one country's interests** isn't necessarily in the interests of **another** country, or of the world as a **whole**. For example:

- **Price** — the country **selling** the energy will want to charge as **much** as possible, whereas the country **buying** will want to pay as **little** as possible. This influences the potential **markets** for an energy resource and determines whether **extracting** the resource is economically **viable**.

- **Environment vs. development** — many countries **exploit** energy resources in order to increase economic development. However, exploitation can damage the **environment** (see next page). Countries may want to exploit energy resources in **another country** (e.g. China is developing oil reserves in Africa, which could cause environmental damage in some African countries) or in the **global commons** (see p.139). In some cases, the **global community** may step in to prevent large-scale damage to fragile environments, e.g. the **Antarctic Treaty** bans resource development there. However, as resources dwindle, **pressure** to exploit new areas is **increasing**.

- **Energy security** — countries with high energy consumption may **pressure** countries with large natural resources to develop and export them in order to meet their energy needs.

- **Political instability** — countries might avoid becoming **dependent** on countries that have an **unstable** government, as **conflict** can interrupt supply of energy resources.

Transnational Corporations *Are Involved in Energy Supply*

1) TNCs are companies that operate in **two or more** countries. Most energy TNCs, e.g. Shell, ExxonMobil and BP, are involved in **all stages** of oil and gas production, from **exploration** of potential reserves, through **refining** crude oil to a usable product, to **selling** it to consumers around the world. For example:

- **BP** is involved in oil and gas **exploration** and **production** worldwide, including in the USA, UK, Egypt and Russia. In 2016, its **daily** oil and gas production was over **3 million barrels** of oil equivalent.

- Crude oil is then **transported** to refineries and petrochemical plants — BP has refineries in, for example, the USA, Netherlands and Germany, and refined **1.7 million barrels** of oil every day in 2016.

- The products are then **sold** to industry and individuals across the world — e.g. BP has **18 000 retail outlets**.

2) Because of their **wealth** and their **control** of a valuable resource, energy TNCs are very **powerful** — they influence the **global economy**, **politics** and the **environment**. For example, TNCs can choose **how much** to charge for energy, and whether to **vary** their prices for different consumers. If one TNC **drops** its prices, others have to follow, starting a **'price war'**.

3) Some energy TNCs are partially or completely **state-owned** — e.g. Gazprom is partially controlled by the Russian government, and extracts, processes and sells Russian gas. State-owned TNCs can exert **global influence**, e.g. they may shut privately owned **TNCs** out of energy markets in some parts of the world, or can be used to help build political alliances (e.g. by providing low-price energy to a potential ally).

Practice Questions

Q1 Give one example of a conflicting national interest in energy supply.

Q2 Briefly describe the role of TNCs in energy supply.

Exam Question

Q1 Assess the extent to which globalisation of energy supply has led to competing national interests. [9 marks]

I rely on Cadbury and Mars for my energy supply...

This page covers some pretty complicated stuff. Basically, you need to understand how countries' energy priorities influence the production and trade of energy across the world, and the role that TNCs play. Put like that, pretty simple, right...

Energy Supply — Environmental Impacts

It's not all rainbows and candy floss in the world of energy production — there can be some pretty serious environmental impacts.

Developing Energy Resources Can Have **Environmental Impacts**

1) Alaska's **North Slope** has extensive oil deposits — the largest are at **Prudhoe Bay**.

2) Development of the North Slope oil reserves started in the 1960s, and the area now has around **20 oil fields** that cover more than 2500 km², as well as a number of **offshore** wells. At their peak in the 1980s, they produced over **720 million** barrels of crude oil each year.

3) **Infrastructure** has been constructed to **support** the oil fields — more than 800 km of **roads**, 20 **airports**, 3000 km of **pipes** and two **refineries** have been built on the North Slope. The **Trans-Alaska oil pipeline transports** oil from Prudhoe Bay to Valdez in the south of Alaska — from there, it is **shipped** to other parts of the world.

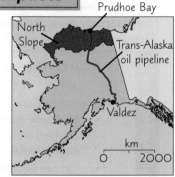

4) The North Slope oil fields have had significant **environmental impacts**, for example:

- **Fragile tundra habitats** have been **destroyed** by the development of the oil fields. **Wildlife** has been **disturbed**, e.g. surveying close to **polar bear dens** can cause females to **abandon** their young.

- Offshore exploration and drilling generate **noise** and **vibrations** that can disturb **marine creatures**, e.g. bowhead whales. Offshore platforms and embankments built to support oil drilling alter **fish migration patterns**.

- Over 60 000 tonnes of nitrogen oxides are released from the oil fields each year, **polluting** the **air**. Pollutants from Prudhoe Bay have been detected **hundreds of kilometres** away. Oil extracted at Prudhoe Bay usually comes mixed with **natural gas**, which has to be **burnt off**. This is known as **gas flaring**, and it causes the release of **greenhouse gases**, such as carbon dioxide and methane, which contribute to **climate change**.

- **Groundwater** is also **brought** to the surface by drilling — it often contains **salt**, **oil** and other **chemicals**, which can **kill vegetation**. Tundra vegetation grows **slowly**, so it takes a long time for the ecosystem to **repair** itself.

- **Freshwater** is pumped from lakes to use during oil extraction, which **reduces** the amount available for animals. If too much water is removed, a lake may become so shallow that its **entire depth freezes** during winter, damaging or destroying lake-bed ecosystems.

5) The **distribution networks** used to transport the oil to consumers also have **impacts** on the **environment**, e.g.:

- **Pipelines** transporting oil can develop **leaks** — pipes are so long and pass through such remote areas that leaks are often **not noticed** for a long time. For example, a leak discovered near Prudhoe Bay in February 2001 is thought to have started in early December 2000. By the time it was stopped, around **270 000 litres** of crude oil had been spilt, contaminating **wetlands** and **freshwater lakes**. There are concerns that the **Trans-Alaska pipeline** is becoming **corroded**, which may result in more leaks.

- Oil **spills** can also occur from **ships** transporting oil, damaging marine ecosystems. For example, in 1989 the oil tanker **Exxon Valdez** ran aground just offshore of Valdez, spilling over **50 million** litres of oil. The oil washed up on over **1600 km** of coastline and **killed** hundreds of thousands of animals, including sea otters, herring, killer whales and seabirds. The populations of some species still **haven't recovered**.

- **Standing water** collects on **road** surfaces during the summer, changing the **water cycle** in the region and creating **new habitats** for mosquitoes. **Dust** blown up from roads can **settle** on vegetation, adding **nutrients** to the ecosystem and **changing** the species that grow there. Thick dust deposits can **smother** small plants.

Practice Questions

Q1 Briefly outline the extent of oil development in North Slope, Alaska.

Q2 Give one environmental impact of oil field development on Alaska's North Slope.

Q3 Give one environmental impact of oil distribution networks in Alaska.

Exam Question

Q1 Assess whether energy distribution networks have greater environmental impacts than energy production. [9 marks]

Oi'll refrain from making a crude joke...

You may well have learnt about a different energy resource development in class, e.g. a coal or gas field. Whichever example you learn for the exam, make sure you're clear on the environmental impacts of the development and its distribution network.

Increasing Energy Security

People are trying different ways to increase energy security. Unfortunately, some of them have some pretty nasty side-effects...

There Are **Strategies** to **Increase Energy Supply**...

Energy security means having **affordable**, **reliable** access to energy. The world's population is **growing**, and energy demand is **increasing**, so there's a need to increase **energy production** to ensure security. There are various ways to do this, e.g.:

Oil and gas exploration

1) In 2014, **81%** of energy used worldwide came from **fossil fuels***. As fossil fuel reserves are depleted, their prices **rise** and it becomes more economically viable to develop **less accessible** reserves.

2) This can be done by developing ways of extracting oil or gas from **unconventional** reserves. For example:
   - **Hydraulic fracturing** ('fracking') is designed to extract natural gas from shale. High-pressure fluid is pumped into rock, causing it to crack and release gas, which can then be collected. However, fracking is **controversial** — it may cause **environmental issues** such as groundwater contamination and air pollution.
   - Oil can be extracted from **tar sands** — sediment that contains **bitumen** (low-grade oil) — by mining the sediment then separating the oil from it. It takes about **2 tonnes** of tar sand to make one barrel of oil, so mining is **large-scale** and has major **environmental impacts**.

3) As reserves run out, there may be pressure to explore reserves in **remote** or **protected** locations, e.g. Antarctica.

Nuclear power

1) A lot of nuclear energy can be generated from a very **small amount** of fuel, and nuclear power has **low** CO_2 emissions. However, **disposing** of waste can be difficult (see next page), and **accidents** (e.g. leaks of radioactive material) have devastating **impacts** on people and the environment.

2) In 2014, nuclear power provided about **5%** of the world's energy — this has **declined** slightly since 1990. Countries such as **Germany** and **Belgium** are **phasing out** nuclear power as their plants become old.

3) However, research is being conducted into how to **improve** nuclear power production. Some countries, e.g. **China** and **Russia**, are planning **new** nuclear power plants, and the International Energy Agency suggests that **doubling** global nuclear energy production by 2050 would help limit climate change.

Renewable resources

1) Developing **renewable** energy resources, such as solar, wind and biomass, decreases reliance on **fossil fuels** and increases **energy security**. For example, the **Three Gorges Dam** in **China** has a generation capacity of more than 20 000 megawatts of hydroelectric energy.

2) Renewable resources are more **sustainable** than fossil fuels or nuclear energy — they won't run out and they don't cause long-term **environmental damage**. However, they are **expensive** to develop and can be **unreliable** (e.g. wind turbines don't generate power on a still day). Some schemes caused **other problems**, e.g. the **Three Gorges Dam** project involved **flooding** 632 km^2 of land, which **displaced** over **1 million** people.

3) Use of renewable resources is being encouraged by **financial support schemes**, e.g. the **UK** government runs a **feed-in tariff** scheme, where energy suppliers **pay** small-scale renewable energy producers for electricity.

4) Global reliance on renewable energy **increased** from **12.4%** in 1973 to **14.1%** in 2014*.

...as well as **Strategies** to **Manage Energy Consumption**

1) Energy security can be increased if **individuals** and **businesses** reduce their **energy demand**. This makes energy supply more **sustainable** because it **conserves** resources and **reduces** environmental impacts.

2) **Buildings** can be **adapted** to reduce their energy consumption, for example:
   - Installing **double glazing** and **insulation** and using energy-efficient **building materials** helps **reduce heat loss**.
   - Building in features that help **absorb** and **retain** the Sun's energy (e.g. large, south-facing windows) reduces the need for **artificial light** and **heat**, and **low-carbon technologies** such as **solar panels** can help provide electricity.
   - Installing **energy-efficient boilers** and other **energy-saving appliances** reduces electricity use.

3) Manufacturing industries can also lower energy consumption by **reusing waste heat** generated during production — it can be used to **heat** buildings or water, or it can be converted into **electricity**.

4) Changes to **transport** can also reduce fuel usage. For example:
   - Governments can reduce car use by **improving public transport**, e.g. increasing bus services or building new park-and-ride schemes. They can also encourage people to **walk** or **cycle**, e.g. by building more cycle lanes or by introducing schemes to make buying a new bike cheaper (such as the Cycle to Work scheme).
   - Governments can also discourage car use by **penalising** drivers, e.g. using congestion charging or road tax.

5) Companies can install **combined heat and power** systems, which **capture usable heat** released by electricity production.

Increasing Energy Security

Energy *Production*, *Trade* and *Consumption* Cause *Sustainability Issues*

The production, trade and consumption of energy has lots of **impacts** on **people** and the **environment**. Some of these impacts threaten the ability of **future generations** to meet their needs, meaning many current practices are **not sustainable**. For example:

> Use of renewable energy sources and energy conservation strategies would help to limit issues such as acid rain and the enhanced greenhouse effect.

Acid Rain

Burning fossil fuels releases various **gases**. Some of these **dissolve** in **water vapour** in the atmosphere, which then falls as **acid rain**. Acid rain reduces sustainability by:

- **Killing fish** and other **aquatic life**, which can lead to **reduced biodiversity**.
- **Killing trees** and other **plant life**, which also **reduces biodiversity**.
- **Reducing** the **nutrient content** of **soil** so that some species of plants can't grow, or grow more slowly.
- **Corroding rocks**, e.g. limestone and sandstone, including buildings.

> New technologies, such as carbon capture and storage, can help to reduce emissions.

Enhanced Greenhouse Effect

1) The greenhouse effect is where **greenhouse gases** such as CO_2 and **methane** in the Earth's atmosphere **absorb** outgoing solar radiation, so **less** is lost to space. This keeps the Earth at a habitable temperature.

2) **Burning fossil fuels releases more** greenhouse gases into the air. This is **unsustainable**, as it **enhances** Earth's natural greenhouse effect, **increasing global temperatures** and causing other changes to **climate** (e.g. changing rainfall patterns). This could lead to:

- **Rising sea levels** and **increased flooding**.
- **More frequent** and **severe extreme weather events**, e.g. hurricanes, droughts.
- **Habitat loss** (which leads to **loss of biodiversity** and the **extinction** of species).
- Changing patterns of **agriculture** — e.g. reduced rainfall in Africa and Australia could **decrease agricultural productivity**.
- Decreases in **water availability** in some areas, which could cause **conflict**.

Kurt worried that global warming would make his commute much less fun.

Nuclear Waste

1) Producing nuclear energy generates waste, including **used fuel**, which is highly **radioactive**. This can be **processed** to recover uranium and plutonium that can be **used again** — however, most waste is **not** currently treated in this way, so it has to be **disposed of**.

2) **High-level** nuclear waste has to be **stored carefully** for **thousands of years** — if it **leaks** into the environment it can have devastating and long-lasting consequences, e.g. **contamination** of large areas of land, and **human**, **animal** and **plant deaths** and **illnesses**.

3) Many people believe that the best way to dispose of nuclear waste is to **bury** it deep **underground**. However, this is very **expensive** — some countries do not yet have enough waste to make it economically **viable** to create geological storage facilities. It also raises **objections** from environmental groups and people living near proposed sites, who are worried about the **long-term effects** (e.g. on health, the environment and tourism) of **transporting** radioactive material to the area and **storing** it there.

4) **No deep underground stores** like this are in use yet — most countries currently store used nuclear fuel in **temporary** facilities above ground, which is **not sustainable** in the long term. However, some countries have **started** building **permanent** stores, e.g. **Finland**.

Practice Questions

Q1 Outline one strategy used to increase energy supply.

Q2 Give three ways that energy consumption can be reduced.

Q3 Briefly describe how nuclear waste disposal can cause sustainability issues.

Exam Question

Q1 'The need to increase energy security outweighs potential damage to the environment.' To what extent do you agree with this view? [20 marks]

Conserve energy — take an afternoon nap...

... though only after you've read and absorbed everything on these pages, of course. In fact, maybe you'd better wait till you've taken your exams. Once it's all over, you may nap to your heart's content... Unless you've got things to do, of course.

Energy in the Netherlands — Case Study

Another case study now. Make sure you've read the other energy pages, otherwise this might all look like double Dutch...

The Netherlands Relies Mostly on Fossil Fuels

1) The Netherlands is a small country in **western Europe** that borders the North Sea. It is very **flat** and more than a **quarter** of the land lies **below sea level**.

2) The Netherlands is **highly developed** and **densely populated**, with 488 people per km². There is a **high demand** for **energy** — in 2013, annual energy usage was **4600 kg** of oil equivalent per capita.

3) Energy comes from a **mix** of sources, but **over 90%** is from **fossil fuels**.

4) Compared to other European countries, the Netherlands gets very **little** of its energy from **renewable** sources — less than **6%** is renewable, which mainly comes from **biofuels** and **wind power**.

5) In 2009, EU countries agreed to **increase** the share of their energy coming from **renewable** sources by 2020. The Netherlands' target is **14.5%** — however, it currently looks unlikely to meet that goal.

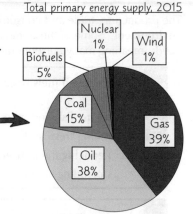

Total primary energy supply, 2015

- Nuclear 1%
- Wind 1%
- Biofuels 5%
- Coal 15%
- Gas 39%
- Oil 38%

Values do not add up to 100% due to rounding.

Energy Availability and Cost are Influenced by Physical Factors

The Netherlands has a unique **physical environment** — this has an effect on **energy supply** and **cost**, as well as the **major sources** of energy. For example:

Climate

- The prevailing **wind** blows southwesterly from the **North Sea**. **Coastal** areas are particularly windy, but the small size and high population density of the country means there is **little land** available for **onshore** wind farms.

- However, offshore wind farms have been built in the **North Sea**. E.g. in May 2017, **Gemini Offshore Wind Park** was opened — this is one of the **largest** offshore wind farms in the world. It is situated **85 km off the coast** in a location that experiences some of the **highest** and **most constant wind speeds** in the North Sea. The new wind farm has led to a significant **drop** in the price of **wind energy**.

- On average, the **sun** shines for **30-40%** of each day — this means that the Netherlands can generate **solar power**, but not as much as sunnier locations. Solar power currently contributes very little to energy supply, but it is **increasing** — e.g. in 2017, a new solar farm opened on the island of Ameland that can power **1500 homes**.

Geology

- The Netherlands has **large natural gas reserves** and over 250 onshore and offshore gas fields. E.g. the **Groningen gas field** in the north of the Netherlands is the **largest** natural gas field in Europe.

- This means gas is readily **available** — almost every household is connected to the gas grid. However, gas is relatively **expensive** (€0.75 per m³ in 2015, compared to the EU average of €0.69) — this is mostly because **taxes** on gas are high.

- The Netherlands also has onshore and offshore **oil reserves**. However, oil production **declined** by around **two-thirds** between 1986 and 2015. The **price** of oil is generally **increasing**.

- The geology of the Netherlands also allows **coal** formation — the last coal mines **closed** in 1974, but there are **measured** and **indicated reserves** in the southeast and east of the country.

Drainage

- There are lots of rivers in the Netherlands, but few of them have been **dammed** to produce **hydroelectric power** (HEP) — HEP contributes **less than 0.1%** of the energy generated.

- This is partly because the flat **topography** means rivers flow **slowly**, so they don't have much **energy**.

- **Reservoirs** created by damming rivers would flood **large amounts** of **agricultural** and **residential land**. This would **reduce income** from agriculture and require **compensation** payments to residents, which would add to the overall **cost** of the energy generated.

Energy in the Netherlands — Case Study

The **Industry** Sector **Consumes** the **Most** Energy

1) The Netherlands is in the **top 25** countries in the world for per capita energy consumption.

2) The **physical environment** affects energy **consumption** and **components of demand**. For example:

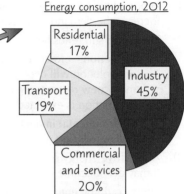

Energy consumption, 2012

Residential 17%

Industry 45%

Transport 19%

Commercial and services 20%

Values do not add up to 100% due to rounding.

- **Industry** is the largest energy consumer. There is lots of industry in the Netherlands because it is very **accessible** — it is located on the **coast**, several **major waterways** flow through the country, and the **flat** landscape is good for **transport** infrastructure. Industries that use **bulky products**, e.g. **steel** and **iron**, **oil** and **petrochemicals**, are common, as it's easy to **transport** these materials to and from the Netherlands.

- **Transport** consumes relatively little energy. The **flat terrain** makes **cycling popular** in the Netherlands — **25% of commuting** is by bicycle. All electric **trains** now run off **wind power**, and railway companies are working on ways to **reduce** energy demand.

- The **residential** sector demand is affected by **climate** and **latitude** — low temperatures and short days in winter mean that **heating** and **lighting** are necessary. However, demand is reduced by **solar power** — around **400 000 homes** have solar panels to fulfil part or all of their energy demand.

There are Plans to Make Energy Supply **More Sustainable**

1) Continuing to rely on **fossil fuels** for energy is **unsustainable** — **gas** production is declining, and there is increasing pressure from the **EU** for the Netherlands to meet its **renewable energy targets**.

2) The Netherlands aims to change its **energy mix**. This will include:

- **Reducing reliance on gas** — gas reserves will eventually **run out**, and the Netherlands is likely to be a net **importer** of gas by 2025. Since 2013, the Dutch **government** has been reducing gas production by setting caps on the amount that can be extracted — e.g. the cap was set at 24 billion m³ for 2016 for the Groningen gas field.

- **Increasing renewable energy** — as well as **increasing offshore wind power** (see previous page), the Netherlands may also increase the amount of energy it gets from other **renewable sources**. For example, the government set up the SDE+ scheme to give **grants** to organisations that **produce renewable energy**. The Netherlands could also buy surplus energy from **solar farms** in Spain or **hydropower plants** in Norway as part of the European **Emissions Trading Scheme**.

'My gas reserves will never run out. NEVER,' chuckled Brian evilly.

- **Reducing coal use** — five coal-fired power stations were **closed in 2015**, and in 2016 the Dutch parliament voted to close **all** remaining coal-fired plants.

- **Promoting energy conservation** — the Dutch government has reached agreements with industries that they will **reduce energy consumption** by using more energy-efficient **equipment** and **processes**. They are also providing **grants** and **low-interest loans** to homeowners to install **insulation** and **double glazing**.

Practice Questions

Q1 Briefly describe the Netherlands' energy mix.

Q2 Why does the Netherlands get so much energy from natural gas?

Q3 What is the biggest component of demand for energy in the Netherlands?

Exam Question

Q1 Analyse the influence of the physical environment on the availability and cost of **either** water **or** energy **or** ore minerals in a place you have studied. [9 marks]

There might not be many HEP dams, but there's plenty of Edam...

Energy in the Netherlands is pretty exciting, but if you choose a different case study I promise I won't hold it against you. Just make sure you know how its physical environment has influenced the availability, cost and use of energy there.

Resource Futures — Energy

Hope you've got enough energy left to consider what might happen in the future. Turbo-chargers on and foot down...

Energy Futures Are Uncertain

1) Energy supplies will be put under increasing pressure in the future, as **population growth** and **economic development** increase the demand for energy. The amount of energy **generated** will need to **increase**.

2) The world still relies heavily on **fossil fuels** for energy, but this is likely to **change** for two main reasons:

   - **Depletion** — fossil fuels are **finite** resources, so their reserves will be **depleted**. The rate of depletion will depend on the **rate** at which they **continue** to be exploited, and how many **new** reserves are discovered. **Oil** and **gas** have the **most depleted** reserves, so their production is expected to decline **first**, while **coal** will **continue** to be used for longer.

     Fossil fuels are still likely to make up most of the global energy mix until 2050.

   - **Environmental impact** — as **climate change**, **air pollution** and **ocean acidification** worsen, individuals and governments may take more action to **reduce** fossil fuel use.

3) **Alternative** energy sources will have to make up for the reduction in energy from fossil fuels. It may also become increasingly important to **reduce energy consumption** per capita.

4) There could be **energy shortages** if energy supply isn't increased or consumption isn't reduced to sustainable levels. This could **reduce standard of living**, **limit economic development** and lead to **conflict**.

5) The **future** of **energy** supply and use is likely to be affected by a range of technological, political, environmental and economic **developments**:

Technological
- **Improving traditional renewable energy sources** — e.g. making wind turbines more **aerodynamic** and creating **transparent** solar panels that can be used as windows would increase their **efficiency** so more energy would be generated.
- **Developing new renewable sources** — e.g. a scheme in Bihar, India uses **rice husks** (a waste product from rice production) in small, local power plants to generate electricity.
- **Improving nuclear power** — nuclear reactors are becoming **smaller**, **cheaper**, **safer** and more **efficient**.
- **Reducing energy consumption** — e.g. developing more **energy-efficient appliances** and **vehicles**.

Economic
- **Energy costs** — energy costs may **rise** as unconventional fossil fuel sources (e.g. fracking) make up more of the supply. This could lead to **fuel poverty**, where people can't afford to adequately heat their homes. Higher energy costs may also affect **industry**, hindering economic **development**.
- **Carbon markets** — countries have to **pay** for their carbon emissions. **Prices** may increase to make the use of **renewable** sources more **attractive**.

Environmental
- **Public opinion** — increasing environmental awareness may put **pressure** on governments and TNCs to develop and use more **environmentally friendly** energy sources.
- **Climate change** — the Paris Agreement (2015) is a global climate deal that aims to **reduce global carbon emissions**, e.g. by taxing carbon emissions. This may change the global **energy mix** and force companies to use **greener** energy sources and more **efficient** technologies. However, the USA's **withdrawal** from the deal in 2017 may affect its success.

Political
- **Instability and conflict** — most remaining **conventional** supplies of fossil fuels are located in the Middle East, Russia, Iran and Central Asia. These areas are politically **unstable** — conflicts could cause **rapid supply** shortages and **price shocks**.
- **The global commons** — e.g. countries bordering the Arctic and energy TNCs are **arguing** over rights to drill for **oil** in the **Arctic**, one of the **last** large conventional reserves.

Practice Questions

Q1 Give two reasons why the proportion of energy sourced from fossil fuels may decrease in the future.

Q2 How might political developments affect the future of energy resources?

Exam Question

Q1 'Technological, economic, environmental and political developments will prevent energy shortages in the future.' To what extent do you agree with this view? [20 marks]

My energy future is uncertain — blimmin' biscuit barrel's empty again...

One thing's pretty clear — energy use isn't going to slow down anytime soon. The positives are that some smart people have got some great ideas about how to generate renewable energy and that there's a global consensus that things need to change.

Ore Mineral Supply and Demand

Nope, sadly that's not <u>or</u> minerals — you've got to study them as well as water and energy. I don't make the rules.

Production and Consumption of Ore Minerals is Unevenly Distributed

1) **Ore minerals** are mined to produce **metals**. For example, **lead**, **iron**, **tin** and **gold** can be extracted from ores. These metals are used in the production of lots of **products**, e.g. gold is used in jewellery and on circuit boards, and copper is used in pipes and electrical wires (see p.239 for more on the uses of copper).

2) The **distribution** of ore minerals is **uneven** across the globe, and some are **rarer** than others.

3) **Production** of ore minerals varies globally, depending on the **size** and **accessibility** of a country's ore mineral reserves (including whether reserves have **already** been **depleted**) and whether the country can **afford** to **extract** its deposits.

4) **Consumption** also varies around the world, depending on the **wealth** of the country and its **major industries** (e.g. countries with plants for extracting iron from its ore and producing steel from it are likely to import large amounts).

> **Example — Gold**
>
> - Gold **production** is high in **China**, **Australia** and **Russia**, and **consumption** is high in **China**, **India** and the **USA**.
> - In 2015, **China** was the largest producer and consumer of gold in the world — it produced over **450 tonnes**, and demand was over **980 tonnes**. Production is high because China has large gold **reserves** and is **wealthy** enough to exploit them. High **wealth** also contributes to China's high **consumption**.
> - Some developing countries have **large reserves** of gold, but are not wealthy enough to fully exploit them. For example, **Ethiopia** has large **reserves** — the Benishangul-Gumuz state in the west of the country has reserves of around 900 tonnes — but produces relatively **little** (less than 12 tonnes in 2016).

5) Differences in **where** the largest amounts of ore minerals are **produced** and where they are **consumed** means that minerals need to be **traded** between countries. For example, in 2016 the value of **iron ore exports** worldwide was over **US $70 billion**. The biggest **exporter** of iron ore was **Australia** (over 50% of all exports by value), and the biggest **importer** was **China** (nearly 70% of all imports by value).

Yep, the people of China really hate creased clothes.

Mineral Ore Development Causes Geopolitical Issues

Supply and **demand** of mineral ores affects **countries** and influences the **relationships** between them. For example:

1) If a country is **poor**, it may **not** be able to **afford** to import enough ore minerals to meet its need. This may hinder economic **development**.

2) Some ore minerals may be obtained **illegally**, e.g. using slave labour and without permission from the state — this impacts on **human rights**, and may hinder a country's **development**. There have been international efforts to **stop** the trade of illegally obtained ore minerals, but it is probable that many of them eventually make it into **consumer goods** manufactured in **other countries**.

3) Ore mineral reserves can cause **conflict** — this can be **between countries**, or between **different groups** in the **same** country. For example, in the **Democratic Republic of Congo**, there's ongoing conflict between government forces and **armed militia** over the control of **tin**, **tantalum** and **tungsten** production.

4) Reserves in **global commons** (e.g. Antarctica) may come under **pressure** from different groups wanting to exploit them. This could cause **disputes** between countries and have global **environmental impacts**.

Practice Questions

Q1 Name a country that produces a large amount of gold.

Q2 Describe one factor that affects ore mineral consumption.

Q3 Outline one geopolitical issue associated with ore mineral use.

Exam Question

Q1 The table shows iron ore production and trade data for the USA. Analyse the patterns shown by the data.

[6 marks]

	2012	2013	2014	2015	2016
Production*	54.7	52.8	56.1	46.1	40.8
Imports*	5.2	3.2	5.1	4.6	5.2
Exports*	11.2	11.0	12.1	7.5	6.6
Value (US \$/tonne)	116.48	87.42	84.43	81.19	82.41

* All figures in million tonnes

Gold production — I have my magic goose at the ready...

This page is your whistlestop intro to the thrilling world of ore minerals. If you've enjoyed it as much as me (and let's face it, how could you not), you'll be delighted to learn that there are another four pages on ore minerals coming right up. You're welcome.

Ore Mineral Security

If you like minerals, and security's your thing, you might just find this to be the most exciting page of any book ever written. These pages are all about copper and how we get hold of it. To top it off, there's even some info about sustainability. Wow.

Copper Deposits Are Found All Over the World

1) Copper is mainly extracted from **copper ores** such as **chalcopyrite** and **bornite**, although **small amounts** are found in the ground as **pure copper**.

2) Copper ores are found all over the **world**. There are **different types** of copper deposits, which form in **different conditions**. Porphyry deposits are the most common source of copper ore, followed by **sedimentary deposits** (see below).

3) There are particularly **large concentrations** down the **west coast** of North and South America, and across **Europe** and **Asia**.

• Porphyry copper deposits   • Sedimentary copper deposits

4) In 2014, **Chile** was the biggest producer of copper in the world, accounting for **31%** of all **copper mined**. **China** had the **next biggest** global share with **9%**.

5) Global copper production has **increased** by about 3% per year since 1900. Since 1960 Latin America and Asia have seen the most growth in copper production. **Chile** and **Peru** are continuing to **invest** in mines in order to continue producing enough copper to meet the **demands** of the major industrial nations, especially **China**.

6) **Less developed** regions are becoming more important. For example, south-central **Africa** has large sedimentary deposits, and there are significant porphyry deposits in **southeast Asia**, e.g. in Indonesia and Papua New Guinea.

Physical Factors Affect Copper Ore Availability

1) Specific **geological processes** have to occur for copper ores to **form**. This means they're only found in **some areas**.

Porphyry Deposits	Sedimentary (Strata-Bound) Deposits
• Porphyry deposits are found in **igneous rocks** formed at **destructive plate margins** (see p.76), usually where a dense oceanic plate is being **forced underneath** a less dense continental plate. • The continental plate melts, forming **magma** that contains **copper**. This magma is forced **upwards** through cracks in the rock. • As the magma rises it **cools**, and copper compounds **crystallise** as porphyry rocks.	• When **water** in the Earth's crust is **heated**, it **dissolves compounds** of metals, including **copper**. • **Sedimentary** copper deposits form when this mineral-rich **water** flows through gaps in **sedimentary rocks**, e.g. shales and sandstones. **Chemical changes** cause the copper ore minerals to **solidify** in cracks and **gaps** in the rock.

2) Whether the copper reserves are **exploited** is affected by **four** factors:

• **Richness of the reserve** — the **more copper** an ore contains, the **less rock** has to be **mined** to produce the **same amount** of copper. This means that richer deposits are more **cost-efficient** to extract.

• **Extent of the reserve** — whether there is **enough** copper to pay for the **investment** required to extract it.

• **Ease of extraction** — e.g. reserves that are **close** to the surface are easier and cheaper to mine.

• **Location** — if the ore is in a **remote location**, the **cost** of **extraction** is **increased**, as people, machinery and extracted ore have to be **transported** to and from the mine. If the country is **politically unstable**, mining companies may be unwilling to **invest** in mines there.

3) The **richness** and **extent** of the reserves also influence the **type** of mining:

• **Open-pit mining** — **surface** material is **removed** before the **ore** is extracted **layer by layer**, leaving a huge **hole**. Open-pit mining is fairly **cheap** because it's easy to **mechanise** and doesn't require too much **infrastructure**.

Open-pit mining of copper is more common than deep mining.

• **Deep mining** — shafts and tunnels are dug **underground** to extract the ore. Deep mining is expensive, so it's generally only carried out when the copper deposits are too **far below** the surface for open-pit mining and contain **enough** copper to make the **extra investment** worthwhile.

4) **Rich, extensive** deposits are starting to **run out**. Mining is gradually decreasing in some extensively mined areas, e.g. Australia, and some open-pit mines are turning to deep mining beneath the original pits as the surface reserves decline. Many **new reserves** exploited contain **lower grade** copper.

Ore Mineral Security

Copper Has Lots of *Different Uses*

1) Copper is a very **versatile** metal because of its **properties** — e.g. it's a good conductor of heat and electricity, it can be precisely bent or moulded into shape and it's resistant to corrosion. Copper can be **combined** with other metals to make **alloys**, e.g. brass, bronze.

2) This means it's used in **lots** of **different products**. End uses include electrical wiring, pipes, roofing, cookware, coins and motors.

3) These products are **used** in many different areas.

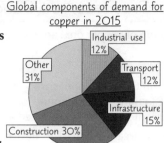
Global components of demand for copper in 2015
Industrial use 12%
Transport 12%
Infrastructure 15%
Construction 30%
Other 31%

Construction workers fitting a copper roof.

Copper Plays an Important Part in Global *Commerce* and *Industry*

Industry

1) Copper is used in almost **every industry**, e.g. construction, transport, electricity distribution — this makes it very important.

2) Copper-related industries (e.g. mining, processing and manufacturing products containing copper) can be **major contributors** to a country's **economy**. For example, in 2013, the **copper** industry accounted for **20%** of **GDP** in **Chile**.

3) Industries are **expanding** as countries **develop**, so demand for copper is **increasing**.

4) Any decrease in **availability** or disruption to **supply** would damage **industry** and countries' **development**.

Commerce

1) There is a large global trade of copper in lots of **different forms**, e.g. ores, part-refined copper, refined copper or used copper for recycling.

2) **Most** copper **traded** each year is in the form of **refined copper** — around **8 million tonnes** of **refined copper** were **exported** by copper-producing countries, including Chile, Russia and Japan, in 2015. China, Germany and the USA **imported** the **most** refined copper in 2015.

3) **Supply** and **demand** of copper affects its **price** — for example, if demand **falls** then price **decreases** too. This happened between 2011 and 2016, when an **over-supply** of copper, combined with the **global financial crisis**, caused copper prices to **halve**.

4) Because copper is so important to a range of industries, its **price** is often used to indicate how **healthy** the global economy is.

Milton was a particularly refined copper.

Copper Ore *Extraction* Has *Environmental Impacts*

Copper mines and their associated **infrastructure**, such as roads and railways, have **environmental impacts**. For example:

Example — Grasberg Mine, Papua, Indonesia

1) The **Grasberg** mine is located in the province of Papua in Indonesia. Mining began there in 1990, and it is now the **second largest** copper mine in the world — it produces around **230 000 tonnes** of copper ore **every day**.

2) The **construction** of the **mine** has had a big impact on the **environment**:

- The main mine is a 4 km-wide **open pit** — digging it resulted in **deforestation** and loss of **biodiversity**.
- Millions of tonnes of **rock** have been dumped in Lake Wanagon, causing the loss of the **aquatic ecosystem**.
- Rock is **broken up** during mining, and some types of **exposed** rock can react with oxygen and water to form **acid**. Waste rock at Grasberg is producing **strongly acidic solutions**, which are **killing vegetation**.
- **Toxic waste** from the **refining process** has been released into the Aghawagon-Otomona-Ajkwa river system, **destroying aquatic life**. Copper **accumulates** in organisms, so this has knock-on effects up the **food chain**. Waste is also draining into the Arafura Sea, destroying **coastal mangrove forests**.

3) The **distribution networks** associated with the mine also have environmental impacts:

- New infrastructure included a **port**, an **airport**, a new **town**, a 121 km **access road** and a 109 km **pipeline** that carries copper slurry from the mine to the port. This has led to **habitat destruction**.
- The **trucks**, **planes** and **ships** used to **transport** the copper and waste from the mine use **fossil fuels**, contributing to **global warming** and **acid rain**.

Ore Mineral Security

Developing Copper Ore Reserves Causes *Sustainability Issues*

Extraction, **processing** and **trade** of copper ore can lead to **sustainability** issues for people and the environment:

1 Extraction

1) As the ores that contain the **most** copper are generally **mined first**, they **run out** first too. This means that companies have to mine **larger amounts** of **ore** to extract the **same amount** of **copper**, so the **cost** of **extraction** gets **higher**, **more waste** is produced and the **environmental impact** increases.

2) Open pits take up **huge areas** of **land**. This **destroys habitats** and can **reduce biodiversity**. However, many countries require mining companies to **restore** the **landscape** once mining has finished.

3) Exposed rock continues to react with air and water to produce **acid** for **hundreds of years** — **continued management** of mines is necessary even **after** mining has finished, in order to limit environmental damage.

4) **Spills** and **leaks** of **toxic** substances can contaminate **local water supplies** (see previous page). Metals don't break down so this leads to **long-term pollution** of streams and rivers, threatening **water security** in the area.

5) The **influx** of **people** seeking **employment** at copper mines can put **pressure** on **existing local services** such as doctors and schools. Once mines **close down**, settlements can be **abandoned** and **communities broken up**.

2 Processing

1) To extract copper from its ore, the ore is **crushed**, **dissolved** in acid, **filtered** and **smelted** (heated) at over 1000 °C. This produces large amounts of contaminated **waste water**. Waste water is stored in **ponds**, but it may be **washed** into local watercourses by **heavy rainfall** — this can affect ecosystems and human health.

2) Processing copper uses **large amounts** of **energy**. Many processing plants have their own power stations — they often rely on fossil fuels, which increase **greenhouse gas** emissions. **Coal** is also becoming more **expensive**, making copper processing plants less **economical** to run.

3) Processing copper requires **lots of water**, but many plants are in dry areas. One solution is to pump **seawater** to the plants. However, the construction of pipelines to carry water can **disrupt ecosystems** in the coastal area where the pipe begins, and along its length. Water is often pumped **uphill**, which uses lots of **energy** — this is **expensive** and has **environmental** impacts. Leaks of saltwater can also be **toxic** to plants.

4) **Smelting** releases **sulfur dioxide** — this contributes to **acid rain**, which kills vegetation and aquatic life.

3 Trade

1) Countries whose **economies** rely on the **copper trade** can be hit hard by **reductions** in **copper prices**. For example, in **Zambia** copper prices **fell** by around **20%** in 2015, mostly because the **demand** for copper from **China fell**. Zambia's overall **economic growth rate** in 2015 was roughly **half** that in 2014.

2) **Price fluctuations** affect **investment** — if the price of copper **falls**, companies are unwilling to search for **new reserves** or to invest in the **infrastructure** needed to extract the copper. This could mean that there isn't enough copper extracted to meet the **demand**.

Practice Questions

Q1 Give two physical factors affecting copper availability.

Q2 Give three properties of copper that mean it can be used for a wide variety of purposes.

Q3 Give two possible environmental impacts of copper mining or processing.

Exam Question

Q1 Assess the extent to which the extraction, processing and trade of a named ore mineral is sustainable. [9 marks]

Copper — I'm totally in ore at how important it is...

You might have learned about a different type of metal ore in class. That's fine, but you'll need to make sure you know all about where it's found, what it's used for, things that affect its availability, and any environmental or sustainability issues associated with it. Luckily, there's quite a lot of overlap between different metal ores when it comes to this stuff.

Resource Futures — Ore Minerals

Just one more page. You deserve a medal after this. I'm afraid it'll have to be a virtual medal — there aren't any metals left.

Ore Mineral Reserves May be Depleted in the Future

1) The **availability** of minerals will gradually **decrease** as more reserves are used up. Meanwhile, the **demand** for minerals will **increase** as the **population grows**.

2) Rising **economic development** around the world will also put pressure on ore mineral reserves. As countries develop they use more minerals for **infrastructure**, **transport** and **consumer goods**. For example, **electricity** access will continue to become more widespread, which will increase the demand for the metals used in **wiring**.

3) A group of **17 metals** known as the **rare earth elements** is particularly important for the future — they are used in a huge number of everyday items such as **mobile phones**, **computers** and **vehicle exhaust systems**. As **modern technology** becomes more widespread, **demand** for rare earth elements is **rapidly increasing**. However, they very **rarely** occur in concentrations high enough to be **mined**.

4) There are **alternative possible futures** for mineral ores, which are related to various factors. For example:

Technological

- **Exploration** — strategies for finding minerals are improving, e.g. using **remote sensing** and **3D imaging**. However, an increase in the number of mines will have an **environmental impact**.
- **Extraction** — more efficient **machinery** and developments in **robotics** could allow minerals to be extracted more **quickly** and **effectively**, e.g. using driverless vehicles. **Phytomining** is when **plants** are grown to absorb copper compounds from the soil, then **burnt** to extract the copper. This can allow **low-grade** ores to be exploited.

Economic

- If supply **falls** or demand **increases**, price will increase — this will increase the **price** of goods, and may hinder some countries' economic **development** if they can't afford the minerals they need.
- **Recycling** of minerals is sometimes limited by economic cost, but it may become more common as ore reserves are depleted.
- Some mineral reserves have not yet been exploited for **economic** reasons. However, as more accessible reserves are **depleted**, it may be necessary to **invest** in mineral extraction at more difficult sites.

Environmental

- **Resource frontiers** — depleting resources may mean that resource frontiers (see p.215) are exploited. This could have environmental impacts, e.g. **deep sea mining** could disrupt marine ecosystems and pollute oceans.
- **Fragile environments** — **environmentally sensitive areas** are being exploited. E.g. China is investing in large-scale mining operations in the Tibetan plateau. This has led to **degradation** of the local environment, and is **negatively** affecting local people's **livelihoods** and **quality of life**.
- There may be **conflict** between TNCs and governments pushing for **economic development** and environmental groups who are concerned about the **impacts** of mining.

Political

- **Conflict** over ore minerals may increase, and the **search** for new reserves is likely to become more of a **political priority** as demand increases and reserves are depleted.
- Governments and TNCs are being forced to recognise the rights of indigenous people in the **development** of **new mines**. For example, uprisings and strikes by local people over the social and environmental impacts of the Santa Ana mine in Peru led to the **closure** of the mine. This could impact on the **supply** and **cost** of resources.

Practice Questions

Q1 What are rare earth elements?

Q2 How might technology influence the future of mineral ore extraction?

Q3 Give two economic factors that may affect the future use of mineral ores.

Q4 Outline one environmental impact that declining ore mineral reserves may have.

Exam Question

Q1 Assess the extent to which future ore mineral shortages will cause problems for people and the environment. [9 marks]

Copper — I'm totally in ore... oh sorry... seems these jokes aren't recyclable...

At last — the end of Topic Eleven. Your enthusiasm reserves might be somewhat depleted, but by now you should have a reliable knowledge supply that's sure to last you far into the future. (Well, hopefully as far as the end of the exam at least...)

Fieldwork Investigation

Ahh, it's time to don the wellies, grab a clipboard and venture out into the real world. Unfortunately it's not just for fun — once you're done investigating you've got to write up your findings. Don't panic though — these pages have lots of handy hints.

You Have to Complete a *Fieldwork Investigation*

1) You have to carry out a **fieldwork investigation** based on part of the **geographical** content of your A-Level course, then produce a **report** on it.

2) The report needs to be **3000-4000 words** long and there are **60 marks** available (20% of your A-Level).

3) Your report needs a good **structure** — to get full marks you need to present a **clear** and **well-argued case**.

You Need to Have a *Research Question* and a *Hypothesis*

1) When you're doing fieldwork and research you won't get very far without a **research question** or an **issue** to investigate, and a **hypothesis** to **test**.

2) A research question is **what you want to find out**, e.g. 'Do coastal defences at Holderness affect the rate of erosion of the coastline?'. It has to be closely related to the content you have studied for A-Level.

3) A hypothesis is a **specific testable statement**, e.g. 'Coastal defences at Holderness increase the rate of erosion downdrift of the defences'.

4) Your hypothesis should be '**developed**' — this just means that it has to be **really specific**. E.g. the hypothesis above is better than 'Coastal defences do affect erosion'.

Herman's hypothesis that large grey rabbits could play miniature pianos was very specific (and seemed to be correct).

5) Once you've decided on a research question you'll need to **read around** the topic to find out what's **already known**. **Summarise** your findings in your report to show you understand the **geographical theory** related to your hypothesis.

You Need to *Collect Data*

1) You'll **collect data** when you're doing your **fieldwork** and when **researching** your fieldwork investigation.

2) There are two types of data — **qualitative** and **quantitative**:

- **Qualitative** data is **descriptive** — it might be in words or images, so you can't easily use it in calculations, e.g. interviews with residents.
- **Quantitative** data is **numerical** — it can be measured and used in calculations, e.g. pedestrian/traffic counts.

3) You'll have to collect **primary** data, and you might also use **secondary** data:

- **Primary** data is data you **collect yourself** (i.e. the data you get from your **fieldwork**).
- **Secondary** data is data **someone else** has **collected** (i.e. the data you get from your **research**).

4) There are lots of **secondary data sources** that you could use, including:

- **Images** — e.g. historical and present-day images can help to show how an area has changed over time.
- **Factual text** — e.g. articles about a place or processes that you are investigating.
- **Creative material** — e.g. stories or songs about real places can provide information about how a place is perceived or what it was like in the past.
- **Spatial data** — information with a location, e.g. maps (see pages 250-251) and GIS.
- **Crowd-sourced data** — information that has been contributed by members of a community, e.g. online. One way it can be used is after a natural disaster, when people on the ground contribute information about who needs help, the extent of damage to infrastructure and so on.
- **Big data** — very large datasets that require powerful computers to analyse. They are often created from logs of digital actions, e.g. social media posts, transactions completed, journeys made.

5) In your report, you need to describe how you collected your data. This includes things like what type of **equipment** you used (e.g. a velocity meter), **how you did it** (e.g. you conducted a questionnaire containing 10 questions) or **what source** it came from (e.g. 2011 census data).

6) You need to **justify** the techniques you used to collect your data — e.g. why the **methods** you used were appropriate, **why** you took observations **when** you did, and **why** you chose particular **sampling techniques** (see next page).

7) You also have to **critically examine** any data you use — this means pointing out any **limitations** of the **data**, e.g. whether it could be **biased** due to the collection method, or if it might not be **representative** of the whole population.

Fieldwork Investigation

You Need to *Select* Your *Sites Carefully*

1) When you're investigating a large area, e.g. a city, river or coast, you **can't study** the **whole thing**, so you have to **select sites** to investigate instead.

2) Selecting sites can be **tricky** though — you need places that are **easy to get to** (e.g. places with **footpath access**) and **not too far** from a **parking place** (if you've got **heavy equipment** to carry you don't want to be walking for miles). But you also need sites that are a **good representation** of all the things you want to study, e.g. if you're studying how **characteristics** of a city change in different areas, it's no good selecting three sites in the **city centre** — this would be a **biased sample**. You need to select sites in **different** locations, from the **city centre** to the **rural-urban fringe**.

Don't forget to do a risk assessment — it might affect which sites you can use.

There are *Three Sampling Techniques* You Could Use to Select Sites

To make sure your sites are **representative**, you might want to use these sampling strategies:

Random Sampling — e.g. using a **random number table** to find the distance of a site from the city centre. As long as you're using a big enough sample this should **remove** any **bias** because each possible sample site has the same **probability** of being chosen. However, there is a **risk** that **large areas** of the survey area might not be chosen if the random samples **happen** to fall in such a way that a large area is not sampled.

Systematic Sampling — this involves selecting sites in a **regular, structured** way, e.g. **every 2 km** along a coastline, or **every third shop** on the high street. Doing it this way means you should be able to **cover** the **whole area** in an unbiased way.

Stratified Sampling — this is when **different parts** of the study area are **identified** and **sampled separately** in **proportion** to their size or importance in the study area as a **whole**. For example, in an urban fieldwork investigation you might identify **different neighbourhoods** and interview a **different number of people** in each in proportion to their population size. This **reduces** the likelihood that some areas could be **under-represented** in your investigation.

You Also Need to *Process* and *Analyse* Your Data...

1) Once you've collected your results, you'll need to **process** the data into a form that you can **use**, e.g. **collating** responses to questionnaires and adding them to a **spreadsheet**.

2) You'll then need to **present** your data, e.g. in a **graph** (see page 249) or on a **map** (see pages 250-251). To get top marks, you have to use a **range** of presentation techniques, so don't just stick to the same old bar graph every time.

3) You'll also need to **analyse** your data, e.g. by using **statistics** (see pages 252-254), to find any **patterns**.

4) You can then **interpret** your results to work out what they **show** in relation to your **original research question**.

...and Use it to Draw *Conclusions*

Draw Conclusions About Your Data

A conclusion is a **summary** of what you found out in relation to the **original research question**. It should include:

- A **summary** of what your results show.
- An **answer** to the question you are investigating (does your data agree with your **hypothesis**?), and an **explanation** of why that is the answer.
- An explanation of how your conclusion fits into **wider geographical knowledge**.

Evaluate Your Data and Methods

Evaluation is about **assessing** what went **well** and what could have been **improved** in your investigation.

- Identify any **problems** with any part of the investigation, e.g. problems with sampling or inability to access big data sources.
- Describe how **accurate** the results are and any problems with the **methods** used that might have affected the results.
- Comment on the **validity** of your conclusion — could any problems you encountered have **affected** your conclusion?
- Consider any **ethical issues** that your fieldwork might raise, e.g. whether people were free to opt out of the research.
- Think about how your results could be used by **other people** or in **further investigations**.

Answering Questions

No matter how much you revise, you aren't going to do well in your exams if you don't answer the questions properly. This can be trickier than it sounds, but fear not, I've included a whole page on it, because I'm nice like that...

① *Make Sure You Read the Question Properly*

> There are loads of hints about how to answer the questions in this book in the Answers section at the back.

It's dead easy to **misread** the question and spend 10 minutes writing about the **wrong thing**. **Five** simple tips can help you avoid this:

1) Figure out if it's a **case study question** — if the question wording includes 'using **named examples**' or 'with reference to **a place that you have studied**' you **need** to include a case study.

2) <u>Underline</u> the **command words** in the question (the ones that tell you **what to do**):

'Assess', 'Evaluate' and 'Discuss' all mean pretty much the **same thing**. They're all about **weighing something up**, e.g. the **success** of a coastal management scheme. You need to give a **balanced** answer — talk about all the **different viewpoints** on the subject.

Answers to questions with 'explain' in them often include the word '**because**' (or '**due to**'). E.g. for the question 'Explain where earthquakes occur', your answer would include 'Earthquakes occur at plate boundaries because of a build up of pressure...'.

Command word	Means write about...
Analyse	what the information means
Assess Evaluate Discuss	the **advantages** and **disadvantages OR** the **arguments for** and **against**
Compare	the **similarities AND differences**
Contrast Distinguish	the **differences**
Explain Suggest reasons...	why it's like that (i.e. give reasons)
Outline	the **main points**
To what extent	**both** sides of the argument **AND your opinion**

When writing about differences, '**whereas**' is a good word to use in your answers, e.g. 'Unemployment in north-east England in 2007 was 6.1%, whereas it was 4.1% in the south-west'.

In 'to what extent...' questions, you need to give a balanced discussion and a **well-reasoned** opinion, which is supported by evidence.

3) <u>Underline</u> the **key words** (the ones that tell you **what it's about**), e.g. wildfires, urban waste, social impacts etc.

4) For **essay** questions, **re-read the question** a couple of times **whilst you're answering it**, just to make sure you're still **sticking** to what the question is asking you to do.

5) For **all** questions, **re-read** the question and your answer **when you've finished**, just to check that your answer really does address **all parts** of the question being asked. A **common mistake** is to **miss a bit out** — like when questions say 'use data from the graph in your answer' or 'use evidence from the map'.

② *Figure Out Your Structure Before You Start*

For any **longer answers**, you need to think carefully about how to **structure** your answer. Jot down the **order** you're going to cover things in. **Label** your **plan** and **answer** clearly so the examiner knows which is which.

Q1 Assess whether short-term or long-term responses are more effective in reducing the impacts of seismic hazards.

PLAN
1. Intro — define the types of response
2. Short-term — e.g. rescuing people — reduces immediate danger but doesn't reduce future danger
3. Long-term — prevention, preparedness, adaptation — reduce impacts of future hazards, but can be expensive
4. Conclusion — long-term more effective
ANSWER
Responses to seismic hazards can be either short or long-term...

③ *Include Relevant Geographical Terms*

Use the **proper geography words** for things, e.g. say 'tributary' rather than 'little river', and 'migration' instead of 'movement of people'.

Don't Forget all the Usual Rules

1) Your answer should be **legible** (you won't get many marks if the examiner can't read it), use **correct grammar**, and **everything** should be **spelt correctly** (double-check jazzy geography words).

2) **Use diagrams** where they're appropriate — drawing a diagram can be way **quicker** than describing the same thing in words.

3) If you're **running out of time** at the end of the exam, **don't panic** — just write what you can as **bullet points**. You'll still get some marks for doing this.

Answering Case Study Questions

Geography examiners are even keener on case study questions than they are on tweed jackets with fetching elbow patches...

Don't Forget the **Three Tips** When Answering **Case Study Questions**

1) For **every question** you need to do the following three things:

① **Read** the **question properly**.
② **Figure out** your **structure before** you **start**.
③ **Include** relevant **geographical terms**.

2) But for case study questions you also **need to**:

Include PLENTY of RELEVANT DETAILS

3) This includes things like **place names**, **dates**, **statistics**, **names** of **organisations** or **companies**.

4) Don't forget that they need to be **relevant** though — it's no good including the exact number of people killed in a tropical storm when the question is about the causes of a storm.

5) For many case study questions, a great way to show your specific knowledge is to learn an **annotated map** and re-draw it in the exam (e.g. the Kashmir earthquake map on page 85) — but take care to only include labels relevant to the specific question being asked.

Jeremy's case study revealed very few relevant details... black, handle, smells a bit funny...

Here's an **Example Answer** to a Case Study Question

'For a coastal area beyond the UK' means you have to include a **case study**, and it must not be from the UK.

> Q1 For a coastal area beyond the UK, <u>assess</u> the extent to which people have <u>overcome</u> the <u>challenges</u> the region presents. [20 marks]
>
> <u>PLAN</u>
>
> 1. Introduce the Sundarbans region and some of the challenges (flooding, tropical cyclones, salinisation, difficult access).
> 2. Describe the responses to these challenges (storm shelters, early warning systems, salt-resistant crops, better roads), and how successful they have been.
> 3. Conclude — some success, but also some problems.
>
> <u>ANSWER</u>
>
> The Sundarbans is a flat, low-lying coastal area in southwest Bangladesh and east India. Much of it is covered by mangrove forests, but it is home to 4 million people.
>
> There are numerous challenges to living in and developing the Sundarbans. The area is low-lying and vulnerable to coastal flooding and damage from tropical cyclones. As well as endangering people and destroying buildings and infrastructure, these hazards can cause salinisation of soil, making it difficult to grow crops. In addition, access to the Sundarbans is difficult because there are few roads, and those that do exist are of poor quality. People have attempted to overcome these challenges by increasing resilience, mitigating the challenges or their impacts, and adapting behaviour to work around the challenges.
>
> For example, to mitigate the impacts of tropical cyclones, the government and NGOs are funding storm shelters and early warning systems. Early warning systems give people a chance to evacuate the area or prepare for cyclones, reducing the death toll and damage to property. However, the lack of electricity and communications infrastructure in some areas means that not everyone receives early warnings, and some people may not be able to evacuate because they do not have transport available. Therefore, this strategy has not yet helped the people living in the greatest poverty to overcome the challenges of tropical cyclones.
>
> Adaptation responses include planting salt-resistant varieties of rice to minimise the impact of soil salinisation. This allows people to grow crops for food and income, which can help to increase food security and reduce the impacts of hazards. However, this strategy causes farmers to rely on a smaller range of crops. This can reduce biodiversity, and pests or diseases that these crops are particularly vulnerable to can spread quickly and wipe out a large amount of the region's food.
>
> In conclusion, people have successfully overcome some of the challenges in the Sundarbans through increased resilience, mitigation and adaptation. However, some strategies have caused other problems, and some only benefit certain people.

Don't think 'Ah, this is about the bit of coast I've studied' and then write everything you know about a particular coastline. The key words are '**overcome**' and '**challenges**' and the command word is '**assess**', so you need to write about the challenges, responses to them and how well the responses have worked.

Use relevant **geographical terms**, e.g. salinisation, resilience, mitigation and adaptation.

Include **relevant details**, e.g. if different crops are being planted, say exactly what sort of crops are being grown.

End with a **conclusion**. You'll often want to mention **both sides** of an argument — things are rarely **totally brilliant** or **absolutely awful**.

These are just some ideas — you'd need to write more than this to get a good mark on a 20-mark question. E.g. you could include paragraphs about building new roads and bridges, and replanting mangrove forests.

Exam Skills

Answering Resource Interpretation Questions

In the exam, you're going to get some questions where you have to interpret a resource.
The next few pages show you the kind of thing that might crop up. Knock yourself out...

You Might Get a Question Based on a **Map**...

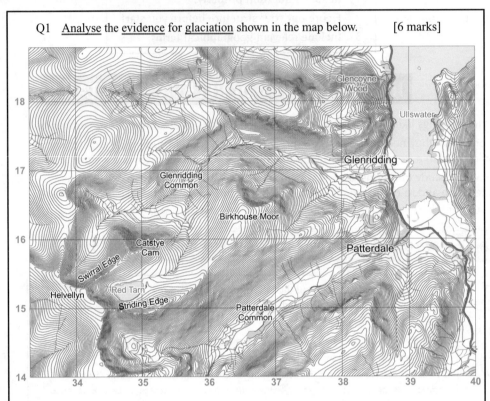

Q1 <u>Analyse</u> the <u>evidence</u> for <u>glaciation</u> shown in the map below. [6 marks]

The question asks for **evidence of glaciation**, so you shouldn't mention any non-glacial features.

<u>PLAN</u>

1. Describe area shown and mention evidence for past glaciation.
2. Give evidence from map — glacial trough, corrie, tarn, arête, truncated spur.

<u>ANSWER</u>

The map shows an upland, mountainous area. It appears not to be glaciated at present (there is no ice shown), but there are several landforms that indicate that the area has been glaciated in the past.

Patterdale Common is a glacial trough. It was probably formed when a glacier flowed northeast along the valley, eroding a V-shaped river valley. This glacial trough is a clear sign that the area in the map was glaciated in the past.

There is a corrie and a tarn (Red Tarn) at grid reference 347153. The corrie is a bowl-shaped hollow that formed at the head of a glacier through plucking and abrasion. Red Tarn formed in this corrie after the glacier retreated.

To the northwest and southeast of Red Tarn there are two arêtes, which are ridges that form when two glaciers flow in parallel valleys. One of these is Striding Edge, which formed as the corries at grid references 347153 and 347145 eroded the valley sides, forming a steep-sided ridge between.

The ridge to the north of Glenridding, at grid reference 383176, ends abruptly, so it may be a truncated spur. It could have formed by a glacier flowing in the valley in which Ullswater is now located; this glacier could have truncated ridges of land sticking into the main valley.

In conclusion, the map shows landforms that can only form through glacial processes, such as glacial troughs, corries and arêtes. This shows that the area was glaciated in the past.

Give the **grid reference** when you're talking about somewhere specific.

Include specific place names.

Answering Resource Interpretation Questions

...or a **Photo**...

It's a good idea to put key geographical terms in your plan, to remind you to use them in your answer.

The command word in the question is 'suggest' so you need to use evidence from the photo to come up with possible ways in which flood risk might be affected.

Q1 Suggest how human activities might affect flood risk in the area shown in the photograph.   [6 marks]

Scour the photo to make sure you've got everything — it'd be really easy to miss the tree stumps if you hadn't looked properly.

PLAN
1. Deforestation — reduced interception, evapotranspiration and infiltration — increased runoff
2. Cattle — trampling decreases infiltration — increased runoff

ANSWER

There is evidence of two human activities likely to be affecting flood risk in the area shown in the photo: deforestation and agriculture.

Trees have been felled to create the clearing shown in the photo. This reduces the amount of precipitation that is intercepted and the amount that is taken up by tree roots and returned to the atmosphere by evapotranspiration. This means that more rainwater reaches the ground surface. Deforestation also reduces the amount of leaf litter on the ground; leaf litter can help to hold water, giving it time to infiltrate, so removing it decreases infiltration. These factors are likely to increase surface runoff, which will increase the likelihood of flooding.

The other human activity shown in the photo is the use of the land for livestock grazing. This will increase flood risk further, because trampling by cattle compacts the soil, which decreases infiltration and therefore increases surface runoff.

...or a **Graph**...

Q1 Study the graph, which shows changes in the percentage of people living in urban areas in Ireland (a developed country) and Botswana (a developing country) from 1960 to 2015.

The command word is 'analyse' so you need to look carefully at the graph and describe the trends shown. Then you need to give reasons for them.

Analyse the differences in rate of urban population change between the two countries.   [6 marks]

PLAN
1. Describe trends in Ireland.
2. Suggest reasons for the trends.
3. Describe trends in Botswana.
4. Suggest reasons for the trends.

Use evidence from the graph to back up your points. To get accurate figures from a graph it often helps to draw lines on with a ruler.

ANSWER

In 1960, a fairly high proportion (45%) of the population of Ireland lived in urban areas. It grew to 54% in 1975, after which the rate of increase slowed. Since 1995, the rate of increase has been slightly faster, and by 2015 63% of people in Ireland lived in urban areas.

Ireland is a developed country, so urbanisation happened before 1960 (the earliest date on the graph). Counter-urbanisation may have been responsible for the slowing down of urban population growth in the 1980s, and there may have been some urban resurgence since 1995, explaining the slight increase in rate of growth since this time.

As well as describing general trends, describe specific details, e.g. the percentage of people living in urban areas in Botswana increased in the period shown, but you also need to say it increased rapidly between 1965 and 1990.

In 1960, the percentage of the population living in urban areas in Botswana was very low (<5%). This increased rapidly from 1965 until 1990, when the rate of increase slowed down. By 2015 about 58% if people in Botswana lived in urban areas, nearly the same percentage as Ireland.

Botswana is a developing country; as a country develops, there is usually a big migration of people from rural areas to towns and cities. This could explain the very rapid increase in urban population from 1965 until 1990. In addition, a lot of the people moving to cities are young adults, so they often start families, which increases the number of people in the city even more. The rate of increase slowed down in 1990, and by 2015 it was increasing at roughly the same rate as Ireland. This may be due to Botswana becoming more developed so having slower rate of urbanisation.

Answering Resource Interpretation Questions

Q1 The table below shows information about two areas of Bristol.

Using the data in the table, <u>assess the extent</u> to which there are <u>economic and social inequalities</u> between Hartcliffe and Clifton. [6 marks]

*This question is asking about how far the **information** in the table shows social and economic inequalities, **not** about the causes or effects of these inequalities.*

Measure	Area of Bristol	
	Fulford Rd North, Hartcliffe	**Clifton Village, Clifton**
Total population (2011)	1515	1449
Average weekly household income (2008)	£480	£800
% Unemployed (2011)	8.1	1.8
% 'not good' general health (2011)	23.6	7.8
% not born in the UK (2011)	5.7	15.7
Police recorded burglaries (2016)	21	16
% people aged 16 or over with no qualifications (2011)	41.7	2.7
% households with >1 person per bedroom (2011)	35.0	19.0

The question asks you to 'assess the extent' so you need to describe the information in the table and explain how far the information does or doesn't show economic and social differences.

PLAN

1. Define economic and social inequalities.
2. Describe and explain data that shows economic and social inequalities.
3. Describe and explain data that doesn't show economic and social inequalities.

Quote data from the table to back up your points.

ANSWER

Economic inequalities are related to the uneven distribution of money. Social inequalities are related to differences in people's quality of life, for example their access to good education, healthcare and open space.

There is some evidence for economic and social inequalities in the areas shown. For example, the average weekly household income in 2008 was £320 higher in Clifton than in Hartcliffe, meaning that households in Hartcliffe earned less than two-thirds of the amount earned by households in Clifton. This is a significant economic inequality, and may be related to the much higher unemployment figures — in Hartcliffe in 2011, unemployment was 8.1% but in Clifton it was only 1.8%. Together, these data show that Clifton is wealthier than Hartcliffe.

Manipulate data from the table where appropriate, e.g. instead of giving the average weekly income for each place, give the difference between them.

There are also significant social inequalities shown in the table. The percentage of people aged 16 or over with no qualifications is much higher (41.7%) in Hartcliffe than in Clifton (2.7%) and the proportion of the population with 'not good' general health is around three times as high. Hartcliffe also has nearly twice the proportion of households with more than one person per bedroom, indicating that overcrowding may be an issue in this area. These data suggest that Hartcliffe has more social issues than Clifton.

Not all rows of the table show inequalities. There were more burglaries in Hartcliffe than Clifton in 2016, but the difference is only five, so it's difficult to know if this is significant or not. The areas have similar populations, so the number of burglaries per person is broadly similar.

Overall, the table shows that there are large economic and social inequalities between Hartcliffe and Clifton.

Graph and Map Skills

As sure as death and taxes, there'll be graphs and maps in your exam. So make sure you know all the different types...

There are Loads of **Different Types** of **Graphs** and **Maps**

1) There are some types of graphs and maps that you'll have come across lots of times before. These include **line graphs**, **bar charts**, **pie charts**, **scatter graphs**, **atlas maps** and **sketch maps**.

2) Some graphs and maps are trickier than others — the next three pages will help you interpret the tougher ones.

3) When you're **interpreting** graphs and maps you need to remember to **read** the **scale** or **key really carefully**.

4) If you have to read from a graph, **draw working lines on** to help you get an accurate figure.

Triangular Graphs Show *Percentages* Split into *Three Categories*

1) To read a triangular graph, start by **finding the point** you want on the graph.

2) **Follow** the **line** that goes **down** from the **point** to the **lowest end** of the **scale** and record the percentage.

3) Then **turn the graph around** so that the next axis is at **the bottom, follow** the **line** down to the lower end of the scale and record that percentage.

4) Do the same for the **third axis**.

5) The three readings should **add up** to **100%**.

6) The graph on the right shows the age distribution of three populations. There are **three age groups** so a triangular graph can be used. **Each point** represents **one population**.

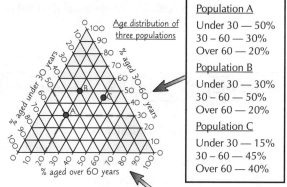

Population A	
Under 30 — 50%	
30 – 60 — 30%	
Over 60 — 20%	
Population B	
Under 30 — 30%	
30 – 60 — 50%	
Over 60 — 20%	
Population C	
Under 30 — 15%	
30 – 60 — 45%	
Over 60 — 40%	

On this scale the lowest end is on the **left**, so to find the percentage you follow the line down and towards the left of the scale.

Dispersion Diagrams Show the *Frequency* of *Data*

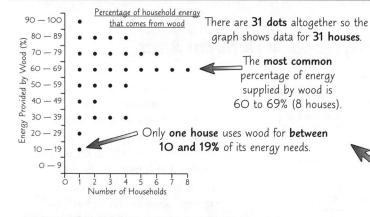

There are **31 dots** altogether so the graph shows data for **31 houses**.

The **most common** percentage of energy supplied by wood is 60 to 69% (8 houses).

Only **one house** uses wood for **between 10 and 19%** of its energy needs.

1) Dispersion diagrams are a bit like a cross between a **tally chart** and a **bar chart**.

2) The **range of data that's measured** goes on one axis. **Frequency** goes on the other axis.

3) **Each dot** represents **one piece of information** — the **more dots** there are in a particular category, the **more frequently** that event has happened.

4) The dispersion diagram on the left shows the **percentage** of **household energy** that comes from **wood** for **houses** in a **particular village**.

Logarithmic Scales are Used When the *Data Range* is *Large*

1) The **intervals** on logarithmic scales are **not fixed amounts** (e.g. they don't go up by 5 every time).

2) Instead, the **intervals** get **increasingly larger** at the top end of the scale (e.g. 10, 20, 40, 80).

3) This lets you fit a **very wide range** of **data** onto one **axis** without having to draw an enormous graph.

4) The graph on the right uses a **logarithmic scale** on the **vertical axis** to show how the world's population changed between 1950 and 2000.

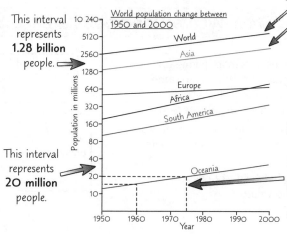

This interval represents **1.28 billion people.**

This interval represents **20 million people.**

Be careful, it looks like the world's population isn't much bigger than Asia's but that's only because there are **big jumps** at this end of the scale.

Graphs with log scales are **really tricky** to **read**. It's OK if your working line hits a label on the log axis (e.g. there were 20 million people in Oceania in 1975), but if it doesn't it's easiest to **give a range** (e.g. it was between 10 and 20 million in 1960).

Exam Skills

Graph and Map Skills

Choropleth Maps Show *Information* Using *Colours* and *Patterns*

1) Choropleth maps show how something **varies** between **different areas** using **colours** or **patterns**.

2) The maps in exams often use **cross-hatched lines** and **dots**.

3) They're straightforward to read but it's **easy to make mistakes** with them as the patterns can be very similar.

4) If you're asked to talk about all the parts of the map with a **certain type of hatching**, look at the map carefully and put a **big tick** on each part with that hatching, to make them all **stand out**.

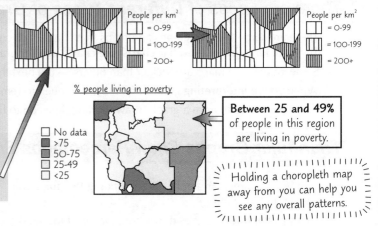

People per km²
☐ = 0-99
▥ = 100-199
▦ = 200+

% people living in poverty
☐ No data
■ >75
▨ 50-75
▨ 25-49
☐ <25

Between 25 and 49% of people in this region are living in poverty.

Holding a choropleth map away from you can help you see any overall patterns.

Dot Maps Show *Distribution* and *Quantity* Using *Identical Symbols*...

1) Dot maps use **identical dots** to show how something is **distributed** across an **area**.

2) Use the **key** to find out what **quantity** each dot represents

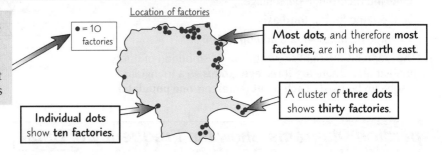

Location of factories
● = 10 factories

Most dots, and therefore **most factories**, are in the **north east**.

A cluster of **three dots** shows **thirty factories**.

Individual dots show **ten factories**.

...*Proportional Symbol Maps* Use *Symbols* of *Different Sizes*

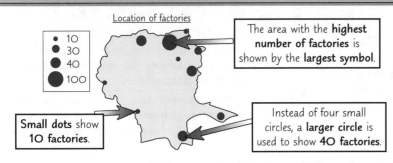

Location of factories
● 10
● 30
● 40
● 100

The area with the **highest number of factories** is shown by the **largest symbol**.

Small dots show **10 factories**.

Instead of four small circles, a **larger circle** is used to show **40 factories**.

1) **Proportional symbol maps** use symbols of **different sizes** to represent **different quantities**.

2) A **key** shows the quantity each symbol represents. The **bigger** the **symbol**, the **larger** the **amount**.

3) The symbols might be **circles**, **squares**, **semi-circles** or **bars**, but they're always read the **same way**.

Isoline Maps Show Where *Conditions* are the *Same*

1) **Isolines** are lines on a map **linking** up all the **places** where something's the **same**, e.g. on **weather maps** isolines show places that have the **same air pressure**.

2) If the place you're being asked about lies **on** an isoline you can just **read** the value off the line.

3) If the place is **between** isolines you have to **estimate** the value.

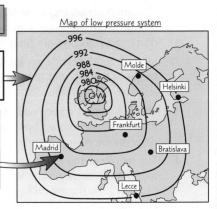

Map of low pressure system

Helsinki and Lecce both lie **on** this line so both have a pressure of **996 mb**.

Madrid lies **between** the lines for **988** and **992**. It's pretty much in the middle of the lines, so has a pressure of roughly **990 mb**.

Graph and Map Skills

Flow Lines and Trip Lines Show Movement...

1) **Trip line maps** have straight lines showing the **origin**, **destination** and **direction** of movements, but they **don't** show the **volume** of movement.

2) **Flow line maps** have **arrows** on, which can be **different sizes** to show how many things **move** (or are moved) from **one place to another**.

3) The flow line map on the right shows the movement of people **into** and **out of** a region. The sizes of the arrows show **how many** people are moving.

The **largest flows** of people are **to Region A**, as these are the **largest arrows**.

Roughly the same number of people are **immigrating to Region A from Regions B and C**. This is shown by the arrows, which are the **same size**.

Some of the flows of people to and from Region A

Region B   Region A

Key
- Urban area
- Rural area
- Emigration
- Immigration

Region C

The **smallest flows** of people are **out of Region A**, as these are the **smallest arrows**.

...and so do Desire Lines

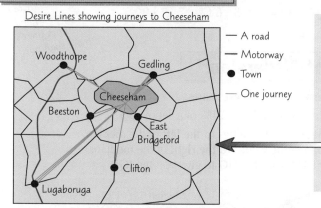

Desire Lines showing journeys to Cheeseham

Woodthorpe
Gedling
Cheeseham
Beeston
East Bridgeford
Clifton
Lugaboruga

— A road
— Motorway
● Town
— One journey

1) **Desire line maps** have **straight lines** that show **journeys** between two locations, but they **don't follow roads** or railway lines.

2) They're used to show **how far** a population has **travelled** to get to a **place**, e.g. a shop or a town centre, and **where** it's **come from**.

3) In the map on the left, the **number of lines** represents the number of **journeys**.

4) The **width** of the lines can also be changed to show the **volume** of the movements.

Ordnance Survey Maps Show Detailed Information of All Areas

1) Ordnance Survey® (OS®) maps use lots of **symbols**. It's a good idea to **learn** the most common ones.

2) You can find places on OS maps using **grid references**.

3) **Four-figure grid references** direct you to a 1 km × 1 km **square** on the map, e.g. for **1534** go **across** to the number **15** (the **eastings** value) and then **up** to the number **34** (the **northings** value). This grid reference refers to the **square above** and to the **right** of the point 1534.

4) **Six-figure grid references** are more precise and can direct you to a more **exact spot** (a 100 m × 100 m square). E.g. for 15**5**341 the eastings value is 155, so go across to 15 again and then a further **5 "tenths"** across the square. For the northings value of 341 go up to 34 and a further **1 "tenth"** of that square. The spot you're looking for is where the easting and northing values **cross**.

5) Every map has a **scale** so that you can work out the **distance between points**. If the scale is **1:25 000**, it means that every **1 cm** on the map represents **25 000 cm** (250 m) in real life.

6) **Altitude** (height above sea level) is shown on OS maps using a type of isoline called **contour lines**. The **closer together** the contour lines are, the **steeper the gradient** is. Sometimes, the altitude of specific **spot heights** is also given.

Common OS Map Symbols
- Motorway
- Main (A) road
- Secondary (B) road
- Railway
- Building
- Place of worship
- Place of worship, with a tower
- Place of worship with a spire, minaret or dome
- Bus station
- PO Post office
- PH Pub
- County boundary
- National Park boundaries
- Footpaths

Grid reference: 1534

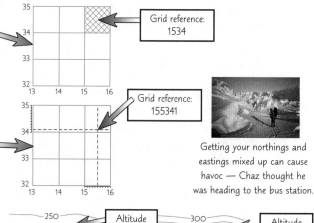

Grid reference: 155341

Getting your northings and eastings mixed up can cause havoc — Chaz thought he was heading to the bus station.

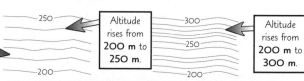

Altitude rises from **200 m to 250 m**.

Altitude rises from **200 m to 300 m**.

The contour lines on the right are closer together and show a **steeper slope** (there's a **greater increase in height** over the **same distance**).

Exam Skills

Statistical Skills

As if knowing about loads of weird graphs and maps wasn't enough, you also need to be pretty familiar with statistics. These next three pages cover the ones you need to know.

There are **Different Ways** of Finding the **Average** Value of a Set of Data

1) The **mean**, **median** and **mode** are different ways of finding the **average** value of a set of data.

2) You find the **mean** by **adding up** all the numbers in a set of data, then **dividing** by the number of **sample points**, **n**.

Take a look at the data in this table:

Location	1	2	3	4	5	6	7	8	9	10	11
Temperature in °C	3	7	4	3	7	9	9	5	5	7	6

n = 11, so the mean temperature is: $\dfrac{3+7+4+3+7+9+9+5+5+7+6}{11} = \mathbf{5.9\,°C}$.

3) The **median** is the **middle value** in an ordered set of data. So you need to **sort the numbers into order**, then work out which one is in the middle. So for the data above the median is **6 °C**.

If there are an even number of sample points the median is the mean of the middle two numbers.

3 3 4 5 5 (6) 7 7 7 9 9

4) The **mode** is the **most common value** in a set of data. So for the data above the mode is **7 °C**.

3 3 4 5 5 6 (7 7 7) 9 9

Sometimes there isn't a mode, and sometimes there's more than one.

The **Interquartile Range** is a **Measure of Dispersion**...

1) The **range** of a dataset is the **difference** between the **highest** and the **lowest** values.

2) The **interquartile range** (**IQR**) is the range of values covered by the **middle 50%** of a set of data.

3) To find the interquartile range you first need to find the median of the values **to the left** of the median. This is called the **lower quartile** (**LQ**). Next find the median of the values **to the right** of the median. This is the **upper quartile** (**UQ**). Then you just **subtract** the **LQ from the UQ** to give you the **IQR**.

4) So, for the data above, the **LQ** is **4** and the **UQ** is **7**, and the interquartile range is UQ − LQ = 7 − 4 = **3 °C**.

5) The interquartile range tells you about the **spread** of data **around** the **median**. If it's a **big** number, it shows that the numbers are pretty **spread out**. And yep, you've guessed it — a **small** number means that a lot of the data is pretty **close** to the **median**.

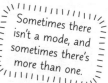

3 3 (4) 5 5 (6) 7 7 (7) 9 9 — LQ, Median, UQ, IQR

...and so is **Standard Deviation**

1) The **standard deviation** is a bit trickier to calculate than the IQR, but it's often a **more reliable** measure of dispersion (spread). The symbol for it is **σ**.

The formula is $\sigma = \sqrt{\dfrac{\sum(x - \bar{x})^2}{n}}$

Σ just means 'sum of', and $\bar{x}$ is just a way of writing 'mean'.

2) To calculate it, it's easiest to **work out** the **individual bits** in the formula **first**, e.g. the mean. It's a good idea to **draw** a **table** to help you. Below is a simple example for the set: 5, 9, 10, 11, 14.

- For these numbers, the **mean** is (5 + 9 + 10 + 11 + 14) ÷ 5 = **9.8**. This is shown in the 2nd column in the table.
- For each number, **calculate** $x - \bar{x}$ (3rd column in the table).
- Then **square** each of those values (4th column) — remember that the square of a **negative number** is always **positive**.
- Then **add up** all the squared numbers you've just worked out — this will give you $\sum(x - \bar{x})^2$.
- Now just **divide** your total by **n**, then take the **square root**.
- In this example, n = 5, so $\sigma = \sqrt{\dfrac{42.8}{5}} = \mathbf{2.93}$ (2 d.p.)

x	$\bar{x}$	$x - \bar{x}$	$(x - \bar{x})^2$
5	9.8	−4.8	23.04
9	9.8	−0.8	0.64
10	9.8	0.2	0.04
11	9.8	1.2	1.44
14	9.8	4.2	17.64
		Σ	42.8

3) If the standard deviation is **large**, the numbers in the set of data are **spread out** around the **mean**. If it's **small**, the numbers are **bunched** closely around the mean.

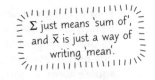

Standard deviation can be represented by σ or s.

Statistical Skills

Make Sure You Know How to Find **Spearman's Rank Correlation Coefficient**

The Spearman's Rank correlation coefficient is a test to find out whether two sets of numbers are **correlated** (there's a **relationship** between them). The example below uses the test to see if **GDP per capita** ($) and **life expectancy** (in years) are correlated.

1) The bad news is that it's a bit of a pain to calculate. The first step is to give a **rank** to each number in both sets of data. The **highest** number is given rank **1**, the second highest is given rank 2... you get the idea.

2) Then you **calculate 'd'**, the **difference** between the ranks for each item, e.g. if the ranks for Country F are 4 and 6, the difference is 2.

3) Next you **square 'd'** and **add up** the **d²** values to give $\sum d^2$, which you use in the formula below.

4) Finally you need to work out the **Spearman's Rank Correlation Coefficient** (known as **r_s**).

The formula is: $r_s = 1 - \dfrac{6\sum d^2}{n^3 - n}$

Country	GDP per capita ($)	GDP rank	Life expectancy	Life expec. rank	d	d²
A	14 000	5	72	5	0	0
B	19 000	4	71	6	2	4
C	9000	9	67	8	1	1
D	6000	11	61	11	0	0
E	21 000	3	75	3	0	0
F	13 000	6	74	4	2	4
G	22 000	2	76	2	0	0
H	35 000	1	78	1	0	0
I	5000	12	60	12	0	0
J	7000	10	65	9	1	1
K	11 000	8	64	10	2	4
L	12 000	7	69	7	0	0
					$\sum d^2$	14

5) So for the example above, $\sum d^2 = 14$ and n = 12. So $r_s = 1 - \dfrac{6\times 14}{12^3 - 12} = 1 - \dfrac{84}{1716} = 1 - 0.05 = \mathbf{0.95}$

6) The number you get is always **between –1** and **+1**.

7) A **positive number** means the variables are **positively correlated** — as one variable **increases** so does the **other**. The **closer** the number is to 1 the **stronger** the correlation.

8) A **negative number** means that the two sets of variables are **negatively correlated** — as one variable **increases** the other **decreases**. The **closer** the number is to –1 the **stronger** the correlation.

9) If the coefficient is **0**, or near 0, there probably isn't much of a relationship between the figures.

10) The value of r_s in the example above was **0.95**, which is **close to 1**, so there's a **strong positive correlation** between the **data** for GDP per capita and life expectancy.

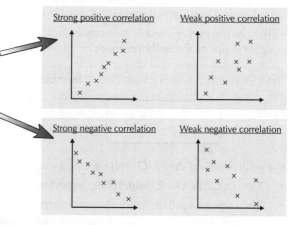

Strong positive correlation | Weak positive correlation

Strong negative correlation | Weak negative correlation

You Have to **Check** the **Correlation is Significant** Though

1) A **Spearman's Rank correlation coefficient** might tell you that **two sets of numbers** are **correlated**. But you need to check whether this is evidence for a **genuine link** between the two quantities you're looking at. (You sometimes get correlations between sets of data **by chance**, even if there's no underlying relationship. For example, there **is** a correlation between GDP per capita and life expectancy **for the data shown above**, but this might have been a fluke and there might be **no real relationship** between the two things.)

2) You can check whether it's evidence for a genuine link by looking at the **probability** that a correlation would happen by chance. If there's a 5% (or higher) probability that a correlation is because of chance then it's **not significant** evidence for a link. If there's a **0.1% or less** chance, then it's **very significant** evidence for a link. (This is what's meant by the **significance level** of a statistical test — it's a kind of 'cut-off' probability.)

3) To test whether the value of r_s is evidence for a relationship between GDP per capita and life expectancy, you'll need a **graph** like the one on the right, or a **table** of critical values. You'll also need to know the **degrees of freedom** (in the example above this is just n – 2, so 12 – 2 = **10**). Since r_s = **0.95**, you can use the graph to find that this correlation has a **less than 0.1%** probability of being due to chance. This means you have **very significant** evidence for a **relationship** between GDP per capita and life expectancy.

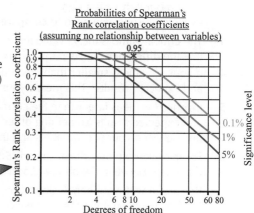

Probabilities of Spearman's Rank correlation coefficients (assuming no relationship between variables)

Statistical Skills

The Chi-Squared (χ²) Test tells you whether Two Variables are Linked

1) There's no better way of explaining the chi-squared test than by showing you an example. So, here we go...

> A student is interested in finding out whether the **number of wells** in three areas of Africa is related to how much **rainfall** the areas receive each year.

2) In this case the two variables are the **number of wells** and the **amount of rainfall**.

3) You always start by making a **hypothesis** and a **null hypothesis**. The hypothesis is your theory about the link between the variables. In this example the student thinks the variables are linked, so the **hypothesis** is:

> **There is a link between the number of wells and the amount of rainfall the area receives.**

4) The **null hypothesis** is **always** that the two variables are **independent** (i.e. there isn't a link between them). E.g.:

> **There is no link between the number of wells and the amount of rainfall the area receives.**

5) First, use the null hypothesis to **predict** a **result** — this is called the **expected result**. In this example, there are 144 wells in total. If there was **no link** between rainfall and number of wells you'd **expect** that there would be an equal number of wells in each area, i.e. **48** (144 ÷ 3 = 48).

6) Next, the experiment is carried out and the **actual result** is recorded — this is called the **observed result**. The **observed** result in this case is the actual number of wells in each area.

7) The chi-squared (χ²) **test** is then carried out and the **outcome** either supports the **null hypothesis** or allows you to **reject** it.

	Area A (lower rainfall)	Area B (medium rainfall)	Area C (higher rainfall)	
Expected	48	48	48	
Observed	64	49	31	
O – E	16	1	–17	
(O – E)²	256	1	289	
$\frac{(O - E)^2}{E}$	5.33	0.02	6.02	**11.37**

The χ² test uses a complicated looking **formula**:

$$\chi^2 = \Sigma \frac{(O - E)^2}{E}$$

Put your observed values (**O**) and expected values (**E**) into this **equation** to work out chi squared (χ²) one step at a time:

- First calculate **O – E** (**subtract** the **expected** result from the **observed** result) for each area, e.g. 64 – 48 = 16.
- Then **square** each of the resulting numbers, e.g. 16^2 = 256.
- Next, **divide** each of these figures by the **expected result**, e.g. 256 ÷ 48 = 5.33.
- Finally, **add** the numbers for Areas A, B and C together to get χ². 5.33 + 0.02 + 6.02 = 11.37, so χ² = **11.37**.

Compare Your Result to the Critical Value

1) The χ² value shows whether there is a **significant difference** between your observed and expected results. If there **is** a significant difference, this suggests your two variables are **linked** (and you can **reject** the null hypothesis).

2) To find out if there is a significant difference between your observed and expected results, you need to **compare** your χ² **value** to a **critical value**.

If you're not given the critical value, you might have to look it up in a table.

3) The critical value is the χ² value that corresponds to a 0.05 (**5%**) level of **probability** that the **difference** between the observed and expected results is **due to chance**.

4) If your χ² value is **smaller** than the critical value then there is **no significant difference** between the observed and expected results. This means your variables are **independent** and you accept your **null hypothesis**.

5) If your χ² value is **larger** than the critical value then there is a **significant difference** between the observed and expected results (something **other than chance** is causing the difference). This suggests that there is a link between your two variables and the **null hypothesis** is **rejected**.

6) For this example the critical value is **5.99**. The χ² value of 11.37 is bigger than 5.99, so there is a significant difference between the observed and expected results and the **null hypothesis** is **rejected**.

7) Be careful with your conclusions though — your χ² value is **evidence supporting** your hypothesis that there is a link between the number of wells and the amount of rainfall. However, it **doesn't prove** this link — there could be **other factors** involved that you haven't considered in your investigation.

Answers

Topic One — Water and Carbon Cycles

Page 3 — Natural Systems

1   One mark for each valid point, up to a maximum of 4 marks.
    E.g.: Both energy and matter can enter and leave an open
    system *[1 mark]*. In closed systems, matter can't enter or
    leave and can only cycle between stores *[1 mark]*. The
    amount of matter in an open system can change, whereas in a
    closed system it always stays the same *[1 mark]*. Energy can
    enter and leave a closed system *[1 mark]*.

2   One mark for each valid point, up to a maximum of 4 marks.
    E.g.: Positive feedback mechanisms amplify a change in inputs
    or outputs *[1 mark]*. This means that the system responds
    by increasing the effects of the change *[1 mark]*. The system
    moves even further from its previous state *[1 mark]*. For
    example, higher temperatures cause more ice to melt, so less
    solar energy is reflected and more is absorbed, leading to
    even higher temperatures *[1 mark]*.

Page 5 — The Water Cycle

1   One mark for each valid point, up to a maximum of 4 marks.
    E.g.: Higher temperatures cause the rate of evaporation to
    increase *[1 mark]*. This means that more water is transferred
    from stores on the ground surface to the atmosphere *[1 mark]*.
    As a result, more water is available for condensation and
    precipitation *[1 mark]*. During periods of higher global
    temperatures, transfers between stores are therefore generally
    faster *[1 mark]*.
    You could also mention that during periods of lower global
    temperatures, more water is locked in cryospheric stores as ice, so less is
    available for transfer between stores in the water cycle.

Page 7 — Drainage Basins

1   One mark for each valid point, up to a maximum of 4 marks.
    E.g.: In wet seasons (e.g. winter in the UK), precipitation is
    higher than evapotranspiration *[1 mark]*. This creates a water
    surplus *[1 mark]*. In dry seasons (e.g. summer in the UK),
    precipitation is lower than evapotranspiration *[1 mark]* and
    water in the ground store is depleted *[1 mark]*. This leads to a
    water deficit *[1 mark]*.

Page 9 — Variations in Runoff and the Water Cycle

1   Maximum of 6 marks available. This question is level marked.
    HINTS:
    • You need to describe the differences between the lines on the
      hydrograph for the two rivers and suggest reasons for them.
    • Take your time to study the hydrograph and pick out the differences.
      Think about what might have caused each one — you could consider
      the effect of differences in drainage basin characteristics, land use and
      farming practices.
    • Once you've done that, write about each difference individually — say
      what the difference is and give possible explanations for each one. E.g.
      'River A has a higher peak discharge than River B. This could be
      because River A has a larger drainage basin than River B, which can
      catch more precipitation, so more water ends up in the river'.

2   Maximum of 20 marks available. This question is level marked.
    HINTS:
    • Begin by introducing the idea that both physical changes and
      human activities can cause variations in the drainage basin-scale
      water cycle.
    • Then describe some of the physical causes of variation. For example,
      'Seasonal variations in plant growth can affect the drainage
      basin-scale water cycle. Vegetation intercepts precipitation, which
      increases the amount of water being returned to the atmosphere
      through transpiration and evaporation from the vegetation rather
      than making it to the river channel. Interception is highest when
      there's lots of vegetation and deciduous trees have their leaves.'
    • Next, describe some of the human causes of variation — for
      example, you could write about the effect of land use change,
      farming practices and water abstraction on the water cycle.
    • The question asks you to evaluate the relative importance of physical
      and human factors, so you need to say which you think causes
      greater changes and explain your opinion. For example, 'Physical
      changes such as storm events and seasonal changes can have a
      large impact on the water cycle in the short term (e.g. over hours
      to months). In contrast, human activities such as deforestation and
      farming may have a smaller immediate impact, but tend to continue
      for years and may therefore cause larger changes in the longer term.
      Human activities may also become more intensive over time, further
      increasing their impact on the water cycle.'
    • Finish with a conclusion — it should briefly sum up how physical
      and human factors affect the drainage basin-scale water cycle, and
      state which you think has a greater impact.

Page 11 — The Carbon Cycle

1   One mark for each valid point, up to a maximum of 4 marks.
    E.g.: Plants transfer carbon stored in the atmosphere to the
    biomass store through photosynthesis *[1 mark]*. Animals
    and plants transfer carbon from biomass to the atmosphere
    through respiration *[1 mark]*. When plants and animals
    die they are decomposed by bacteria and fungi *[1 mark]*,
    transferring carbon back to the soil and the atmosphere
    [1 mark].
    You could also mention uptake of carbon by marine organisms, which
    then becomes sequestered in rocks.

Page 13 — The Carbon Cycle

1   One mark for each valid point, up to a maximum of 4 marks.
    E.g.: Increased levels of CO_2 in the atmosphere can increase
    the acidity of the oceans, which can affect marine life
    [1 mark]. Increased levels of carbon in the atmosphere
    can also cause global warming, which may increase the
    temperature of the oceans *[1 mark]*. This may mean that
    organisms that are sensitive to temperature change may
    decrease in number *[1 mark]*. Warmer water is less able
    to absorb CO_2, decreasing the amount of CO_2 that could
    potentially be dissolved in the oceans *[1 mark]*.

Answers

Page 15 — Water, Carbon and Climate

1 Maximum of 20 marks available. This question is level marked.
   <u>HINTS:</u>
   - Begin by briefly outlining the carbon cycle and water cycle and explaining what positive and negative feedbacks are.
   - Describe some of the feedbacks in the carbon cycle and how they can affect life on Earth — you could consider positive and negative feedbacks. For example, 'If temperatures rise, the respiration rate of plants will increase. This means they will release more carbon dioxide, so the amount of carbon dioxide in the atmosphere will increase. This increases the greenhouse effect, which causes temperatures to increase more. This will cause plants to grow faster because their respiration rate is higher. This is a positive feedback.'
   - Then do the same for some of the feedbacks in the water cycle and their effect on life on Earth.
   - The question asks you to 'Assess the extent...', so you could mention some of the other factors (apart from feedbacks) that affect life on Earth, and discuss their importance. For example, you could write about interactions between the water and carbon cycles, such as increases in water availability driving plant growth, which removes more carbon from the atmosphere.
   - Finish with a conclusion — it should briefly sum up the feedbacks and their effects on life on Earth, as well as coming to a clear conclusion about the extent to which these feedbacks may affect life on Earth.

Page 17 — The Amazon Rainforest — Case Study

1 Maximum of 20 marks available. This question is level marked.
   <u>HINTS:</u>
   - Start by briefly outlining the natural water cycle and carbon cycle, with reference to tropical rainforests.
   - Give some examples of human activities that take place in rainforests and examine the effect of each on the water cycle in the rainforest. For example, 'Many human activities cause deforestation of the rainforest. This can affect the water cycle in several ways, for example the lack of a canopy means that less rainfall is intercepted by vegetation, so more water reaches the surface. This causes runoff to increase...'.
   - Next, do the same for some human activities that affect the carbon cycle in tropical rainforests — you could mention the impacts of deforestation and climate change.
   - The questions asks 'To what extent...', so you could also describe some ways in which people are trying to limit their impact on the water cycle and the carbon cycle. For example, you could talk about limiting deforestation and replanting trees that have been cut down.
   - You could use examples from your case study in your answer.
   - Finish with a conclusion that sums up the points you have made and comes to an overall conclusion about the extent to which human activity is affecting the water cycle and the carbon cycle in tropical rainforests.

Page 19 — The Eden Basin — Case Study

1 Maximum of 20 marks available. This question is level marked.
   <u>HINTS:</u>
   - Begin by briefly describing the location you have studied — where it is, what the landscape is like etc. You could use the Eden Basin case study to answer this question.
   - Briefly describe the issues the area faces with flooding or sustainable water supply. You could relate this to the physical setting of the drainage basin, e.g. its geology and topography.
   - Then describe some changes in the water cycle in the drainage basin and how they have affected sustainable water supply or the risk of flooding. For example, 'Parts of the Eden Basin have been deforested. This means that there is less interception and infiltration during heavy rainfall than there would be if the area was still forested, so water reaches the Eden more quickly, meaning there is a greater risk of flooding.'
   - The question asks you to 'Assess the extent...', so you could also consider ways in which changes haven't affected flood risk or sustainable water supply — for example, the basin may be prone to flooding because of its physical characteristics, rather than any human changes. You could also mention changes that have helped reduce flood risk or increase sustainable water supply, such as the building of flood defences.
   - Finish up with a conclusion that sums up the ways in which changes in the water cycle have affected the risk of flooding or sustainable water supply, and come to an overall conclusion that answers the question.

Topic Two — Hot Desert Systems and Landscapes

Page 21 — Desert Systems

1 One mark for each valid point, up to a maximum of 4 marks. E.g.: Positive feedbacks occur when there is a change to the desert system that triggers further changes with a similar effect *[1 mark]*. This can result in the formation of desert landforms *[1 mark]*. For example, sand dunes form when the deposition of sediment causes the wind to slow down and drop more sand *[1 mark]*. Negative feedbacks restore the balance when there is a change to the system *[1 mark]*. This helps to maintain the landscape in its existing form *[1 mark]*.

Page 24 — Deserts — Distribution and Characteristics

1 Maximum of 6 marks available. This question is level marked.
   <u>HINTS:</u>
   - First, say that if Riyadh is 25° north of the equator it's located in an area of circulating air known as a Hadley cell.
   - Then you need to explain how the circulating air leads to low precipitation, e.g. 'As air rises at the equator, the moisture that it holds condenses and falls as rain. The dry air descends over Riyadh, creating an area of high pressure. Winds blow outwards from this area, meaning no moisture can be brought in, so there's very little precipitation'.
   - You also need to explain the temperature patterns shown by the graph, e.g. 'Riyadh is at a relatively low latitude, so insolation is powerful, which increases temperature. High pressure in the area also prevents clouds from forming. This means there is nothing blocking insolation, further increasing temperatures.'
   - You might also write that the summer has higher temperatures and very low precipitation because Riyadh is far enough from the equator to have distinct seasons.

Answers

Page 27 — Processes in Hot Desert Environments

1 One mark for each valid point, up to a maximum of 4 marks. E.g.: Very small particles are transported by suspension *[1 mark]*, which means they are picked up and carried by the wind *[1 mark]*. Small particles are transported by saltation *[1 mark]*, which is when they are temporarily lifted up from the ground and bounce along *[1 mark]*. Larger particles are transported by surface creep *[1 mark]*. This means they are hit by the particles being moved by saltation, and pushed along the ground *[1 mark]*.

You could also have written about transport by water — small particles (e.g. sand and pebbles) can be transported by suspension and saltation during sheet floods and channel flash floods, and larger pieces of rock can be transported by traction during channel flash floods.

Page 30 — Landforms in Hot Desert Environments

1 Maximum of 6 marks available. This question is level marked.
HINTS:
- You need to identify the fluvial landforms in the photograph and describe how they formed.
- You could start with the wadis, e.g. 'There are at least two wadis visible in the photograph. These are gullies formed by water erosion. They could be the result of seasonal rivers that form after rainstorms, or rivers that flowed in the past when the climate was different, but have now dried up.'
- Then move on to the bahada, e.g. 'Alluvial fans have formed at the mouths of the wadis. Alluvial fans form when the water in a wadi spreads out and slows down, causing it to drop the sediment load it was carrying. Because the wadi mouths are close together, the alluvial fans have spread out and joined together, forming a bahada.'

Page 32 — Hot Desert Environment — Case Study

1 Maximum of 20 marks available. This question is level marked.
HINTS:
- Start by summarising the influence that climate has on hot desert processes, e.g. stating that temperature affects weathering, and precipitation brings water into hot desert systems, which affects weathering, erosion, transport and deposition. Climate also determines the amount of vegetation cover, which further affects desert processes.
- Then give some specific examples of how processes in hot deserts are affected by climate, e.g. 'Low rainfall and high temperatures mean that the ground surface is dry and sparsely vegetated. This means that it is easily eroded and transported by wind, so aeolian processes are more dominant in desert environments than in other climate zones.'
- The question doesn't specifically ask for a case study, but you can still use one, e.g. you could bring in details about how the Qattara Depression in the Sahara may have been initiated by fluvial processes during a wetter period, then enlarged by deflation during drier conditions.
- The question asks you to 'Assess the extent...' so you should also consider factors other than climate that may influence desert processes. For example, you could mention that rock type affects type and extent of weathering, and particle size affects processes of erosion and transport.
- Finish with a conclusion — it should summarise your points and come to a clear decision about the extent to which the climate affects the processes that operate in hot deserts.

Page 35 — Desertification

1 Maximum of 20 marks available. This question is level marked.
HINTS:
- Begin by outlining some of the ways that desertification already affects local populations — you could mention declining agricultural productivity, migration and health problems.
- Next, summarise why these impacts might become worse, e.g. 'Some would argue that the impacts of desertification on local populations can only worsen because, as climate change progresses and the human population grows, desertification will speed up. This would increase the impacts on local populations. For example, the loss of fertile land could lead to malnutrition and famine, and people who make their living on farms may have to migrate to urban areas for alternative work.'
- Then, summarise the alternative possible futures for local populations. You could write about how further desertification could be prevented, e.g. through climate change mitigation and crop rotation, or how people could adapt to the impacts of desertification, e.g. farmers could diversify their produce.
- The question asks you the extent to which you agree, so you should explain how likely you think each possible future is.
- The question doesn't specifically ask for a case study, but you could still use one to back up your points, e.g. you could discuss strategies being used to manage desertification in southern Spain.
- Finish off with a conclusion that sums up your points and clearly states the extent to which you agree that the impacts of desertification on local populations can only worsen over time.

Page 37 — Desertification — Case Study

1 Maximum of 20 marks available. This question is level marked.
HINTS:
- Start by stating that human activities such as agriculture and development are a major cause of desertification.
- Then go into a bit of detail about some of the ways that human activities are responsible, e.g. 'Unsustainable irrigation is causing desertification in many areas, because it can deplete aquifers, which means eventually there's not enough water left for plants. This reduces vegetation cover, which increases the risk of soil erosion.'
- The question doesn't specifically ask for a case study, but you can still use one to back up your points, e.g. you could follow a point about irrigation with the example of crops being grown in Andalusia that are not adapted for the dry climate, so they need intensive irrigation, which is lowering groundwater levels and increasing desertification risk.
- The question asks you to 'Assess the extent...', so you should write about how far human activities are responsible, e.g. you could discuss the fact that climate change is also a major cause of desertification, and that it can occur naturally (although it can also be a result of human activities).
- Finish with a conclusion — you should sum up your points and clearly state the extent to which human activities are responsible for desertification.

Answers

Topic Three — Coastal Systems and Landscapes

Page 39 — The Coastal System

1 One mark for each valid point, up to a maximum of 4 marks.
E.g.: Constructive waves are flat and gentle *[1 mark]*. They
have a low frequency *[1 mark]* of about 6-8 waves per minute
[1 mark]. Their swash is greater than their backwash *[1 mark]*
which carries material up the beach and deposits it *[1 mark]*.

2 One mark for each valid point, up to a maximum of 4 marks.
E.g.: Wind can bring energy into the coastal system as air
moves from areas of high pressure to areas of low pressure
[1 mark]. If the pressure gradient is high, winds can have
a lot of energy *[1 mark]*. Energy can also be brought into
the system by water, in the form of waves, tides and currents
[1 mark]. The amount of energy brought into the system by
movement of water is affected by fetch *[1 mark]*.

Page 41 — Coastal Processes

1 One mark for each valid point, up to a maximum of 4 marks.
E.g.: Freeze-thaw weathering and salt weathering occur when
seawater enters cracks and pores in coastal rocks *[1 mark]*.
Crystals of ice or salt form and expand when water freezes or
evaporates *[1 mark]*. This exerts pressure on the rock, causing
small pieces to fall off *[1 mark]*. Rocks that contain clay
may be weathered by wetting and drying *[1 mark]*. As they
become wet, the clay expands, breaking pieces off the rock
[1 mark].
You could also have written about other types of weathering, such as
biological or chemical weathering.

Page 44 — Coastal Landforms

1 One mark for each valid point, up to a maximum of 4 marks.
E.g.: Headlands and bays form where there are bands of
alternating hard rock and soft rock *[1 mark]* at right angles
to the shoreline *[1 mark]*. The soft rock is eroded quickly,
forming a bay *[1 mark]*. The harder rock is eroded less and
sticks out as a headland *[1 mark]*.

2 One mark for each valid point, up to a maximum of 4 marks.
E.g.: Spits form where the coastline suddenly changes
direction, e.g. at a river mouth *[1 mark]*. Longshore drift
deposits material across the break in the coastline *[1 mark]*.
This leaves a ridge of sand and shingle sticking out into the
sea *[1 mark]*. If the dominant wind and wave direction
changes, the spit may change direction and develop a
recurved end *[1 mark]*. Repeated changes in wind and wave
direction may result in multiple recurved ends *[1 mark]*.

Page 47 — Sea Level Changes

1 One mark for each valid point, up to a maximum of 4 marks.
E.g.: Coastal submergence happens when the sea level
rises relative to the land *[1 mark]*. This creates a range of
landforms, e.g. rias are formed when the sea drowns river
valleys *[1 mark]*. Similarly, fjords are formed when sea level
rise floods glacial valleys *[1 mark]*. In areas where valleys
lie parallel to the coast, an increase in sea level can form
Dalmatian coastlines *[1 mark]*. These occur when valleys are
flooded, leaving islands parallel to the coast *[1 mark]*.

2 Maximum of 20 marks available. This question is level marked.
HINTS:
- Start off by briefly describing how climate is likely to change in the
future, e.g. 'Climate change is likely to cause global temperatures to
rise in the future, and may cause increased storminess in some areas.'
- Describe some of the physical impacts that this could have on
coastal areas, e.g. 'Increased global temperatures are likely to result
in sea level rise. This would cause more frequent and more severe
flooding of coastal areas, and the submergence of some low-lying
areas. For example, sea level rise of 0.5 m would submerge most of
the Maldives.'
- You could discuss the possible environmental impacts of climate
change on coastal areas, such as damage to ecosystems caused by
increased storminess and flooding.
- You could also mention the possible impacts on people, such as
salinisation of water bodies and soil, leading to a lack of fresh water
for people to use and difficulty growing crops.
- You could also mention factors that might mitigate the impacts of
climate change, such as increased investment in coastal defences to
protect vulnerable areas from flooding and storm damage.
- Finish with a conclusion that sums up the probable impacts of
climate change in coastal areas.

Page 49 — Coastal Management

1 One mark for each valid point, up to a maximum of 4 marks.
E.g.: Hard engineering schemes involve built structures,
e.g. sea walls and gabions *[1 mark]*. They are normally
designed to hinder natural processes, e.g. erosion *[1 mark]*.
Soft engineering schemes try to work with natural processes
[1 mark], e.g. beach nourishment involves adding sand and
shingle to beaches to reduce erosion of the cliffs behind
[1 mark].

Page 51 — Coastal Environment — Case Study

1 Maximum of 20 marks available. This question is level marked.
HINTS:
- Start by outlining the reasons for coastal management, and some of
the different options (e.g. hold the line, managed retreat).
- Next, explain how coastal management can be made sustainable
— you could outline different strategies (e.g. Integrated Coastal
Zone Management) and soft engineering techniques (e.g. beach
stabilisation and dune regeneration).
- You should also consider some of the challenges to sustainability, e.g.
'It is socially unsustainable to allow homes and businesses to flood,
but it may be economically and environmentally unsustainable to
build and maintain defences for the area.'
- The question doesn't specifically ask for a case study, but you can still
use one, e.g. you could bring in details about management strategies
on the Holderness coast.
- Finish with a conclusion — it should summarise your discussion
and come to a clear decision about the extent to which sustainable
management of coastal areas is achievable.

Page 53 — Humans at the Coast — Case Study

1 Maximum of 20 marks available. This question is level marked.
HINTS:
- You could start by outlining some of the challenges that people
living in coastal areas face, such as sea level rise, coastal flooding and
salinisation of soils.
- You could then go on to explain some of the ways that people
have responded to these challenges — this could include attempts
to mitigate them (e.g. building flood defences), adapt to them (e.g.
designing houses to withstand sea level rise) and increase resilience
(e.g. training people to use the environment sustainably).

Answers

- For each response you talk about, you need to evaluate how successful it has been or is likely to be, e.g. 'Hard engineering strategies such as groynes can reduce coastal erosion and flooding in the area where they're located. However, groynes may also starve downdrift areas of sediment, increasing the challenges for people living there.'
- You could also bring in details from your case studies, e.g. 'Coastal flooding in the Sundarbans region causes salinisation of soils, which makes it difficult to grow crops. In some areas, people are growing salt-resistant varieties of rice; this helps to prevent loss of crops during floods. Salt-resistant crops could help to increase food security for people in the region, which would have positive effects on health and quality of life. However, growing a smaller range of crops could reduce biodiversity in the region and increase vulnerability to pests and diseases that affect those particular crops.'
- Finish off with a conclusion — it should briefly summarise human responses to challenges in coastal areas, and come to an overall conclusion about how far you agree with the statement in the question.

Topic Four — Glacial Systems and Landscapes

Page 55 — Cold Environments

1 Maximum of 6 marks available. This question is level marked. HINTS:
- Begin by outlining briefly where polar, alpine and periglacial environments are found today.
- Then outline briefly where polar, alpine and periglacial environments were found 21 000 years before present.
- Finally, describe the differences in the distribution of these areas. You could describe the overall trend, e.g. 'The extent of cold environments has reduced and they have moved polewards between 21 000 years before present and today.' Then give some specific examples, e.g. 'Most of Europe was polar or periglacial 21 000 years before present, whereas today there are only small patches of alpine areas.'

Page 57 — Glacial Systems

1 One mark for each valid point, up to a maximum of 4 marks. E.g.: A glacial budget is the balance between accumulation (the input of snow and ice into a glacier) and ablation (the output of water from a glacier) over a year [1 mark]. If accumulation exceeds ablation the glacial budget is positive [1 mark]. If ablation exceeds accumulation, the glacial budget is negative [1 mark]. The glacial budget shows whether the mass of ice in the glacial system has increased or decreased [1 mark]. This determines whether the snout of the glacier advances or retreats [1 mark].

Page 59 — Glacial Processes

1 One mark for each valid point, up to a maximum of 4 marks. E.g.: Cold-based glaciers have bases that are below the melting point of ice, so there is very little melting [1 mark]. This means that the glacier is frozen to the valley floor, so it moves very little [1 mark]. As a result, cold-based glaciers cause very little erosion [1 mark]. Warm-based glaciers have bases that are warmer than the melting point of ice, so their bases melt [1 mark]. The water acts as a lubricant, making it easier for the glacier to move downhill [1 mark]. Warm-based glaciers therefore move quite a lot and cause a lot of erosion [1 mark].

Page 61 — Glacial Landforms

1 Maximum of 6 marks available. This question is level marked. HINTS:
- You could start by stating that the landscape shown appears to have been formed largely from glacial erosion.
- Go on to name the main landforms present in the photograph and explain how glacial processes contributed to the formation and development of each one.
- You could start with the arête, e.g. 'There is an arête in the centre-right of the photograph. It was formed by two glaciers flowing in parallel valleys. These glaciers eroded the sides of the valleys, creating a sharp mountain ridge between them.'
- Then move on to the corrie on the left of the photo and the tarn in the corrie. You could also mention the glacial trough in the background of the photo.

2 One mark for each valid point, up to a maximum of 4 marks. E.g.: Moraine is unsorted till left behind by glaciers [1 mark]. Lateral moraine forms where the sides of a glacier were as it retreats [1 mark]. Medial moraine is deposited in the centre of the valley where two glaciers converge (the two lateral moraines join together) [1 mark]. Terminal moraine builds up at the end of the glacier, and is deposited as semicircular hillocks of till [1 mark].

Page 63 — Fluvioglacial Processes and Landforms

1 One mark for each valid point, up to a maximum of 4 marks. E.g.: Kames are mounds of sand and gravel found on the valley floor [1 mark]. Meltwater streams on top of glaciers collect in depressions and deposit layers of debris [1 mark]. When the ice melts, the debris in the depressions is dumped onto the valley floor [1 mark]. Kame terraces are piles of sand and gravel deposited against the valley wall [1 mark]. They are laid down by meltwater streams that flow between the glacier and the valley side [1 mark]. The meltwater streams deposit their heaviest loads first, so kame terraces are sorted into layers [1 mark].

2 One mark for each valid point, up to a maximum of 4 marks. E.g.: An outwash plain forms as meltwater flows out of a glacier, depositing sediment in front of the snout [1 mark]. The sediment is sorted into layers according to weight [1 mark]. Gravel gets dropped first because it's heavier than sand and clay, so it forms the bottom layer of the outwash plain [1 mark]. Clay is dropped last and gets carried furthest away from the snout because it's the lightest sediment — it forms the top layer of the outwash plain [1 mark].

Page 65 — Periglacial Processes and Landforms

1 One mark for each valid point, up to a maximum of 4 marks. E.g.: Very low temperatures in winter cause the ground to contract and cracks to form in the permafrost [1 mark]. In spring, the active layer thaws and meltwater seeps into the cracks [1 mark]. The permafrost layer is still frozen, so the water freezes in the cracks, forming ice wedges [1 mark]. Ice wedges can grow each year as frost contraction re-opens existing cracks, which fill with water and freeze again, causing further expansion of the ice wedge [1 mark].

Answers

Page 67 — Glacial Landscape — Case Study

1   Maximum of 20 marks available. This question is level marked.
    HINTS:
    • Start by briefly outlining the differences between glacial and fluvioglacial processes, and the landforms that they create.
    • You could go on to outline the different conditions needed for glacial or fluvioglacial processes to operate, and how this might affect their importance, e.g. 'Glacial processes occur where temperatures are cold enough for ice to be present year round. Glacial processes are therefore likely to be more important in landscape formation during cold periods, e.g. glacials. Fluvioglacial processes occur as ice melts, so they are likely to be more important during warmer periods, e.g. interglacials.'
    • You could also discuss the likely lifespan of landforms produced by glacial and fluvioglacial processes, e.g. 'Glaciers cause large-scale erosion of rock as they flow, for example creating glacial troughs and arêtes that endure for thousands of years. In contrast, fluvioglacial processes result in depositional landforms such as kames and eskers, which may be eroded by later processes. Fluvioglacial processes may therefore not have such a long-lived effect on the landscape'.
    • Details from your case study could be relevant too — you could write about the different landforms found in a glaciated landscape you have studied, how they were formed, and whether the landscape is dominated by glacial or fluvioglacial features.
    • Finish off with a conclusion that summarises your points and comes to a clear conclusion about the relative importance of glacial and fluvioglacial processes in forming glacial landscapes.

Page 69 — Human Impacts on Cold Environments

1   Maximum of 6 marks available. This question is level marked.
    HINTS:
    • There are several details you could pick out from the photo to discuss how people might have affected this environment, such as the buildings themselves and the infrastructure needed to support it (e.g. powerlines).
    • For each one, explain the impact it could have on the area. For example, 'The coal mine consists of several large buildings, which are likely to have a higher temperature than the surrounding ground surface. This could lead to melting of the permafrost.'
    • The question also asks you to use your own knowledge, so you could infer details about the likely impact of the mine, for example 'Mining produces waste that has to be disposed of. If any of this waste is released into the environment, it could damage the fragile ecosystem.'

Page 71 — Humans in Glacial Landscapes — Case Study

1   One mark for each valid point, up to a maximum of 4 marks. Your answer will vary according to which case study you have learnt. E.g.: There are very large oil and gas reserves in the north of Alaska, which could be extracted *[1 mark]*. Large amounts of mineral resources in the Tintina belt towards the centre of the state also offer opportunities for mining *[1 mark]*. There are rich stocks of salmon, crab and pollock in the waters around Alaska, which offer opportunities for fishing *[1 mark]*. Around 2 million tourists visit Alaska each year, creating job opportunities and bringing money in to the area *[1 mark]*.

2   Maximum of 20 marks available. This question is level marked.
    HINTS:
    • You could begin by briefly outlining some of the opportunities for development in cold environments.
    • Next, outline some of the challenges to development in cold environments, e.g. 'It's difficult to construct buildings to support development in cold environments as such areas are often difficult to access. In addition, buildings may melt the permafrost, which would cause them to collapse.'
    • Then suggest ways in which the challenges you outlined can be overcome, including responses of resilience, mitigation and adaptation, e.g. 'Humans can respond to challenges by mitigating risks. For example, buildings can be constructed on stilts to prevent them from melting the permafrost, so that they don't collapse.'
    • For each challenge you write about, you should mention the pros and cons of overcoming it, e.g. 'Limiting permafrost melting helps to minimise damage to the environment. However, it also adds to the cost of construction and may not be possible for all buildings and infrastructure.'
    • You might refer to examples from a cold environment you have studied, e.g. Alaska.
    • Finish off with a conclusion that summarises the points you made and comes to a clear, balanced view about the extent to which you agree that challenges to development can and should be overcome.

Topic Five — Hazards

Page 73 — Natural Hazards

1   Maximum of 9 marks available. This question is level marked.
    HINTS:
    • Start by outlining some of the different perceptions of hazards, such as acceptance and dismissal of risk.
    • Next, outline some of the ways that people's perceptions of hazards might affect their responses to them — e.g. 'If people perceive a hazard as unavoidable and beyond their control, they are less likely to attempt to prevent it or reduce its magnitude. They may instead choose to adapt to the risk, e.g. by buying insurance in case their home or livelihood is affected.'
    • The question asks you to 'Assess the extent...', so you should also discuss some of the factors other than perception that may affect people's responses to hazards. This could include factors such as wealth of individuals (e.g. poorer people may not be able to respond in certain ways) and education (e.g. people with less education may not be aware of some response options).
    • Finish with a conclusion that sums up your main points and comes to a clear view about how far people's perception of hazards affects their responses to them.

Page 75 — Plate Tectonics

1   Maximum of 6 marks available. This question is level marked.
    HINTS:
    • Start by using the map to work out what sort of plate margin Iceland is located on, e.g. 'Iceland is located on a constructive margin, so the two plates are moving apart.'
    • Next, suggest what large-scale tectonic changes are likely to be happening, e.g. 'As the plates move apart, magma rises up to fill the gap, then cools and hardens, creating new crust. Over time, the land surface is widening.'
    • The question asks you to refer to the photo too, so you need to look for evidence of tectonic activity and suggest how it relates to the tectonic development of the area, e.g. 'The rope-like surface of the rock in the bottom right of the photograph suggests that this is viscous lava that has cooled and hardened. This suggests that the rocky outcrop shown could have formed as lava rose between the two spreading plates.'

Answers

Page 77 — Types of Plate Margin

1 Maximum of 6 marks available. This question is level marked.
   HINTS:
   - Start your answer by briefly describing what a magma plume is and what causes it, e.g. 'A magma plume is a vertical column of magma that rises up from the mantle, causing an area of volcanic activity away from a plate margin (a hot spot).'
   - Describe the distribution of the Hawaiian islands, making sure that you include plenty of relevant details from the map. E.g. 'The oldest island is Kauai, at 6 million years old, and the islands become younger in age as you move towards the south-east'.
   - Next, give reasons why the islands are distributed in this way. State that the chain of volcanic islands has formed due to the magma plume staying still, whereas the plate has moved over it in a north-westerly direction.

Page 79 — Volcanic Hazards

1 Maximum of 9 marks available. This question is level marked.
   HINTS:
   - Start by outlining the different types of plate margin, and stating whether or not volcanic hazards occur there — e.g. you could mention that most volcanoes occur at constructive and destructive margins.
   - Next, you could discuss the type of lava found at one type of plate margin and its effect on the characteristics of volcanic hazards there. E.g. 'At constructive margins, basaltic lava is formed. It has a low viscosity, which means that eruptions tend to be frequent and long-lived, but not very violent. This may mean that lava flows are relatively rapid and travel a long way, but pyroclastic and ash fallout is likely to be restricted to a smaller area.'
   - Make sure you explain the effect of the likely volcanic hazard on people, e.g. 'Rapid lava flows at constructive margins give people less time to evacuate the area, so they may cause more deaths than slower flows. The large distance that the lava travels is likely to increase the amount of destruction. However, the risk to people from pyroclastic and ash fallout is likely to be more limited.'
   - Go on to do the same thing for destructive plate margins.
   - Finish with a conclusion that sums up the risks associated with different types of plate margin and comes to a judgement about the role of plate margin type in determining level of risk.

Page 81 — Volcanic Hazards — Impacts and Responses

1 Maximum of 20 marks available. This question is level marked.
   HINTS:
   - Start by briefly outlining some of the impacts of volcanic eruptions — you could mention social, environmental, economic and political impacts.
   - Next, outline some of the ways that these impacts can be managed, including responses of mitigation, preparedness and adaptation.
   - For each response to mention, you could suggest how successful it is likely to be at managing the impacts of the eruption, e.g. 'Evacuating people before an eruption could help to save lives. However, it won't help to protect buildings and infrastructure, so the economic impacts of the eruption would remain high.'
   - You should also discuss whether or not the impacts of an eruption can be prevented, e.g. 'It is not possible to prevent volcanic eruptions, but some of their impacts could be prevented. For example, authorities could prevent the land around a volcano from being developed, so that an eruption would pose less threat to people. However, this would not reduce the environmental impacts of an eruption, or the impacts of widespread hazards such as ash clouds.'
   - You could bring in the impacts of and responses to a specific eruption, such as the Soufrière Hills eruption in 1997.
   - Finish with a conclusion that sums up your points and clearly states how far you agree with the statement in the question.

Page 83 — Seismic Hazards

1 Maximum of 6 marks available. This question is level marked.
   HINTS:
   - Start by briefly outlining the distribution of highest tsunami risk from the map, in relation to plate boundaries, e.g. 'Areas of high tsunami risk are concentrated around the destructive plate margins to the south and west of the Pacific plate. Risk is also high along the destructive margin on the eastern coast of Central and South America, and along the conservative plate margin on the east coast of North America.'
   - Go on to briefly explain what tsunamis are and how they're generated.
   - Then explain why tsunami risk might be concentrated along destructive (and to a lesser extent conservative) plate margins, e.g. 'The highest magnitude earthquakes tend to occur at destructive margins, but large earthquakes can also occur along conservative margins. When high magnitude earthquakes occur underwater, they can trigger tsunamis.'
   - You could mention that tsunamis are most powerful when they start close to land, so plate margins along coasts pose the greatest risk.

Page 85 — Seismic Hazards — Impacts and Responses

1 Maximum of 9 marks available. This question is level marked.
   HINTS:
   - Start by outlining the different forms of seismic hazard and distinguishing between primary and secondary impacts.
   - Next, outline some of the primary impacts of seismic hazards, e.g. 'People can be drowned if a coast is hit by a tsunami, and may be buried by landslides or avalanches.'
   - Then, outline some of the secondary impacts of seismic hazards, e.g. 'Earthquakes can damage gas pipes — if gas is ignited, the resulting fire can kill many people. Damage to water supplies and sanitation could lead to the spread of disease, potentially affecting many people.'
   - You could bring in impacts from a specific case study, e.g. the Kashmir earthquake in 2005.
   - Finally, sum up your points and come to a clear conclusion about whether you think the primary or secondary impacts of seismic hazards are more dangerous.

Page 87 — Storm Hazards

1 Maximum of 9 marks available. This question is level marked.
   HINTS:
   - Start by outlining some of the possible impacts of storm hazards — you could include social, political, environmental and economic impacts.
   - Next, explain what is meant by adaptation and how it might help to reduce the impacts of storm hazards, e.g. 'Adaptation involves people changing their behaviour or surroundings to minimise the risks of a hazard. For example, buildings can be strengthened using reinforced concrete to prevent storm damage.'
   - The question asks you to evaluate the role of adaptation, so comment on how effective it is. E.g. 'Adaptation can help to reduce the social and economic impacts of a storm, such as deaths and damage to buildings. However, people may be lulled into a false sense of security by adaptation measures — this could mean that they remain in the area instead of evacuating, which may increase the death toll.'
   - You could also mention other responses, such as preparedness and prevention, and comment on whether they play a greater role than adaptation in reducing the impacts of storms.
   - Finish with a conclusion that sums up how important a role you think adaptation plays in reducing the impacts of storm hazards.

Answers

Page 89 — Storm Hazards — Case Studies

1 Maximum of 20 marks available. This question is level marked.
   HINTS:
   - Start by outlining some of the forms of storm hazards, such as high winds, heavy rain and storm surges. Describe some of the impacts that these hazards can have.
   - Next, you could outline some of the ways in which storm hazards are likely to have a greater impact in less developed countries, e.g. 'Less developed countries may not have the warning and communication systems needed to predict tropical storms and urge people to evacuate vulnerable areas. This means that the death toll of a tropical storm in a less developed country is likely to be higher than in a more developed country.'
   - Back up your points using examples from the case studies you have learned. E.g. 'Hurricane Katrina, which hit the south-east USA in 2005, killed around 1800 people. In contrast, Cyclone Nargis, which hit Myanmar in 2008, killed more than 140 000 people. This supports the view that the social impacts of tropical storms are greater in less developed countries.'
   - Make any points that contradict the view that tropical storms always have greater impacts in less developed countries. For example, you could discuss the economic impacts of tropical storms, which are likely to be higher in more developed countries.
   - Finish by summing up your points and coming to a clear conclusion about how far you agree with the statement in the question.

Page 91 — Wildfires

1 Maximum of 9 marks available. This question is level marked.
   HINTS:
   - Start by introducing the wildfire event you are going to write about — give a brief overview of where and when the wildfires occurred and what caused them. You could use the wildfires in south-east Australia in 2009.
   - Next, describe the impacts of the wildfire event — you could include the number of people killed, injured or made homeless, the total cost and the impacts on habitats and animals.
   - Then outline the responses to the wildfire event — this could include short-term responses, such as evacuation and fire-fighting, and long-term responses, such as rebuilding houses to be more fire-resistant.
   - The question asks you to evaluate the impacts and responses, so you need to discuss how successful the responses were at reducing the impacts — think about ways in which they were successful and ways in which they were not.
   - Finish with a brief conclusion that sums up the impacts of and responses to the wildfire event, and outlines how successful the responses were.

Page 92 — Multi-Hazard Environment — Case Study

1 Maximum of 9 marks available. This question is level marked.
   HINTS:
   - Start by briefly outlining some of the hazards that people in multi-hazard environments have to cope with. You could mention the hazards of a specific geographical area.
   - Next, outline how humans have responded to these hazards — this could include changes in people's perception of hazards, e.g. accepting them as a natural and unavoidable part of life. It could also include attempts to manage hazards and mitigate their impacts.
   - You should also discuss how successful these responses are — think about ways in which they work, and ways in which they don't work.

   - You could refer to the Philippines, which experiences volcanic and seismic hazards and tropical storms. Individuals have responded by trying to increase their own resilience to disasters, e.g. by stockpiling food. Authorities have responded by attempting to increase large-scale resilience, e.g. adapting buildings to cope with earthquakes. Such responses can help people to manage the impacts of hazards, but cannot prevent hazards or eliminate their impacts.
   - Finish with a conclusion that sums up your points and outlines how successful human responses to multi-hazard environments are.

Page 93 — Hazardous Setting — Case Study

1 Maximum of 9 marks available. This question is level marked.
   HINTS:
   - Start by outlining the area you are going to write about — give a brief overview of where it is and the hazard(s) it experiences.
   - Describe how the character of the location has been affected by its hazardous setting. You could write about social, economic and political character.
   - You could use L'Aquila in central Italy as an example, e.g. 'The social character of L'Aquila has changed as a result of past earthquakes and the threat of future earthquakes. For example, much of the city centre was destroyed by the 2009 earthquake, and people were rehoused in suburban areas and new towns. As a result, the city centre is much less populated and much quieter.'
   - Finish with a conclusion that sums up how the character of the study area has changed as a result of its setting.

Topic Six — Ecosystems Under Stress

Page 96 — Ecosystems

1 Maximum of 6 marks available. This question is level marked.
   HINTS:
   - Discuss the diagram in order of the web's hierarchy. Start with the autotroph and move up through the trophic levels to herbivores, carnivores/omnivores and top carnivores.
   - Refer specifically to the diagram, using the names of the consumers shown rather than talking about food webs and chains in general.
   - Show that you know which consumer belongs to which trophic level, e.g. 'Greenfly is a primary consumer (herbivore) while a sparrow is a primary and secondary consumer because it is an omnivore.'
   - Explain how energy is lost in the process of consuming as well as from the consumer themselves, e.g. 'The sparrow loses some energy through respiration and waste, and the sparrowhawk loses further energy in eating the sparrow, as it cannot digest the bones or the feathers.'

Page 98 — Biodiversity

1 Maximum of 9 marks available. This question is level marked.
   HINTS:
   - Begin by stating that declining biodiversity can impact both the physical environment and human wellbeing.
   - Next, analyse a few examples of physical impacts, e.g. 'Declining biodiversity could cause the extinction of species that relied on those lost, e.g. those which fed on them or had symbiotic relationships with them. This is a positive feedback loop because a reduction in biodiversity causes biodiversity to decline further.'
   - Then do the same for the human impacts of biodiversity decline, e.g. 'Some species could have medicinal qualities that have not yet been discovered. Humans will not be able to benefit from these if those species are lost.'

Answers

- You could discuss how the impacts vary around the globe, e.g. 'Lower biodiversity could reduce the amount of food available for humans, because of a reduction in the number of pollinators for crops. This is likely to have the greatest effect on people living in countries where hunger is already a problem.'
- Finish with a conclusion that briefly summarises your points and comes to a general decision about the global impact of biodiversity loss.

Page 99 — Biomes

1   Maximum of 6 marks available. This question is level marked.
    HINTS:
    - Begin by describing the distribution of tropical rainforests using the map.
    - Next, explain how the distribution of the tropical rainforest biome relates to one aspect of its location, e.g. 'Tropical rainforests are located close to the equator because the Sun is overhead all year round, which means that temperatures are high. This allows the growth of species adapted to warm temperatures.'
    - Do the same for other aspects of the environment, such as high levels of precipitation and the consistency of the climate.

Page 102 — Tropical Rainforests

1   Maximum of 9 marks available. This question is level marked.
    HINTS:
    - Start by briefly describing the characteristics of the climate and soil moisture budget in tropical rainforests, e.g. 'Tropical rainforests are hot all year round, and it rains every day throughout the year. The soil moisture budget is high, because precipitation is higher than potential evaporation.'
    - Then, give a few examples of how plants have adapted to these conditions, e.g. 'Some plants have evolved drip-tips in response to the high rainfall. These channel rainwater off the leaves, so that the weight of the water doesn't damage the plant or form pools on them where fungi and bacteria could grow.'
    - Next, give some examples of ecological responses by animals to the hot, wet conditions. E.g. 'There is a high soil moisture budget, so heavy precipitation can cause flooding of the forest floor. Many animals are adapted to this by having the ability to swim.'
    - Finish with a conclusion — it should briefly sum up your points and clearly state that animals and plants in the tropical rainforest have adapted to cope with the climate and soil moisture budget.

Page 105 — Savanna Grasslands

1   Maximum of 20 marks available. This question is level marked.
    HINTS:
    - Begin with a brief summary of the ecology of savanna grasslands and how it is changing. Briefly outline the types of development issues that affect savanna grasslands — you could mention population change, economic development, and agricultural extension and intensification.
    - Then explain in detail how population change is causing ecological change, e.g. 'Because of the increasing amount of land now being used for agriculture, settlements and other developments associated with the growing human population, the amount of land available for nomadic communities to graze their livestock is decreasing. This means the vegetation doesn't have time to recover before it is grazed again, so soil is more exposed and can be eroded. The impact of this is likely to increase in the future, as indigenous people are forced to occupy smaller areas, instead of pursuing the traditional nomadic lifestyle.'

- Then explain some other causes of ecological change in savannas. For each one, consider how important it is as a driver of ecological change, compared to population change. For example, 'Tourism is also increasing the amount of habitat loss in savanna grasslands. Construction of roads and buildings for tourists causes habitat loss, and the increase in vehicle use, e.g. for safari holidays, increases pollution. However, money from tourism is often used towards conservation of habitats, so its impact is arguably not as great as that of population change.'
- The question doesn't specifically ask for a case study, but you can still use one, e.g. you could bring in details about development in the Serengeti.
- Finish with a conclusion that sums up your points and comes to a clear conclusion about the extent to which you agree that population change is the most important driver of ecological change in savanna grasslands.

Page 107 — Ecological Change — Case Study

1   Maximum of 9 marks available. This question is level marked.
    HINTS:
    - Start by introducing the region you have studied, briefly describing its main characteristics, the local community and how the ecology of the area has been changing.
    - Then describe some of the community responses to the ecological changes. For example, for the Serengeti, you could write 'Wildlife Management Areas (WMAs) have been set up, where the local community works together to manage the wildlife and only uses resources within sustainable limits.'
    - The question asks you to 'Evaluate', so you should describe positive and negative outcomes of the community responses. E.g. 'WMAs are successful to some extent, because they allow local people to continue to obtain food and income from the ecosystem with minimal damage, but some people have refused to stop farming and hunting within them.'
    - Finish with a conclusion — it should briefly sum up the ways that the community has responded to ecological change in your case study region, and how successful these responses are.

Page 109 — Coral Reefs

1   Maximum of 6 marks available. This question is level marked.
    HINTS:
    - Begin by studying the table and the map carefully, and working out whether coral is likely to form at the site described.
    - Choose one piece of information and explain whether it is likely to allow or prevent coral formation. For example, 'The area in the table is located 26 °N of the equator. The map shows that tropical coral reefs most commonly form between 23.5° north and south of the equator, but some are at slightly higher latitudes, up to about 30° north or south. This shows that it's possible for coral reefs to form at this latitude.'
    - Do the same for the other pieces of information given in the table and on the map.
    - Finish with an overall conclusion summing up how likely it is that a coral reef would form at this location.

Answers

Page 111 — Great Barrier Reef — Case Study

1   Maximum of 9 marks available. This question is level marked.
    HINTS:
    • You could start by outlining the coral reef you have studied and stating that human activity has generally damaged its health.
    • Then describe some of the ways that human activity is having a negative impact on the reef's health. For example, 'Human use of fossil fuels is changing the climate, causing global temperatures to rise. High sea temperatures kill the symbiotic algae in the Great Barrier Reef, which is causing large parts of the reef to become bleached. The extent of the annual bleaching is getting worse.'
    • You should also mention that not all human impacts have been negative, e.g. money from tourism to the reef can be put into conservation.
    • Finish off with a conclusion, briefly summarising how the coral reef you studied has been influenced by human activity.

Page 113 — Succession

1   Maximum of 9 marks available. This question is level marked.
    HINTS:
    • Begin by briefly describing what decomposers are and stating that they play an important role in succession.
    • Then describe their role in the early stages of primary succession. E.g. 'Decomposers form the initial basic soil in an ecosystem by breaking down pioneer species when they die. This organic matter can then support new organisms.'
    • Next, describe their role in the later stages of succession, or in secondary succession. E.g. 'When soil is present, decomposers break down dead plant material to form humus. This makes the soil deeper, so that larger plants are able to grow there. Eventually, a climax community forms, e.g. a temperate woodland containing species such as oak and beech. Decomposers maintain this community by recycling nutrients.'
    • You could give a specific example of the role of decomposers in certain conditions, e.g. 'In a hydrosere, decomposers turn the leaf litter of marsh plants such as reeds and rushes into a wet soil. They gradually build up the soil depth until the body of water is no longer present.'
    • Finish with a brief conclusion that summarises your points.

Page 115 — Succession in the British Isles

1   Maximum of 9 marks available. This question is level marked.
    HINTS:
    • Start by briefly describing the plagioclimax you have studied, and how it differs from the climatic climax.
    • Then explain each stage of how human activity created the plagioclimax. E.g. for the North York Moors heather moorland, you could write 'From about 5000-2000 years ago, humans cut down the woodland that covered the area, to clear land for crops and livestock. Deforestation reduced the nutrients entering the soil, so soil quality became poor. When crops could no longer be grown, people abandoned their fields and moved on.'
    • Next, you could explain how the plagioclimax has since been maintained by human activity, e.g. for the North York Moors heather moorland you could talk about grazing and controlled burning.
    • Finish with a brief conclusion that sums up the main ways that human activity resulted in the plagioclimax you have written about.

Page 118 — Local Ecosystems

1   Maximum of 9 marks available. This question is level marked.
    HINTS:
    • Start by introducing the local ecosystem you studied — state its location, what type of ecosystem it is, and a brief description of the conservation issues it is facing.
    • Then describe a conservation strategy and explain how it helps to conserve the ecosystem, e.g. 'Trees and scrub on the sand dunes at Ainsdale are cut regularly, and marram grass is planted. These actions help to maintain the sand dune ecosystem by stopping the woodland from encroaching onto it, and the marram grass binds the sand so dune erosion is reduced.'
    • You need to consider how successful the strategy has been. E.g. 'Cutting scrub and planting marram grass helps to preserve the dunes and ensures that there is an adequate amount of habitat for the rare species that are adapted to live there. However, as visitor numbers to the area increase, trampling may damage marram grass and increase erosion, despite conservation efforts.'
    • Do this for one or two more conservation strategies.
    • Finish with a conclusion that summarises the conservation strategies you have discussed and weighs up their success.

Page 121 — Local Ecosystems — Case Study

1   Maximum of 9 marks available. This question is level marked.
    HINTS:
    • Begin by introducing the ecosystem you have studied. You should mention its location and the type of ecosystem it is.
    • Then describe an opportunity for its sustainable development. For example, if you're writing about the Broads, you could say 'The wildlife and navigable waterways in the Broads present the opportunity to develop the local tourism industry, as people are attracted to the area for holidays where they can go boating and enjoy the scenery. This can only be sustainable if the area is managed so that visitor damage to the ecosystem is minimised, as the quality of the environment is part of the attraction for tourists.'
    • Next, describe any challenges this might present, and how they are being addressed, e.g. 'However, boating on the broads can cause problems, such as the introduction of invasive species and water pollution. Therefore, efforts have been made to raise awareness of how people can make their boating more environmentally friendly.'
    • Do this for one or two more opportunities and challenges in your chosen ecosystem.
    • Finish with a conclusion that sums up your points and clearly states both the opportunities for sustainable development in the ecosystem, and the challenges it presents.

Topic Seven — Global Systems and Global Governance

Page 123 — Globalisation

1   One mark for each valid point, up to a maximum of 4 marks. E.g.: Lower labour costs in less developed countries have caused many companies from more developed countries to locate the production side of their business overseas *[1 mark]*. The products are then imported to more developed countries where they are sold *[1 mark]*. This is increasing international trade in manufactured goods, making the world more interconnected *[1 mark]*. The financial investment in the factories needed to produce the goods also increases flows of capital between countries, promoting globalisation *[1 mark]*. The movement of factories abroad can also increase the flows of people between the home and host countries *[1 mark]*.

Answers

Page 125 — Factors Affecting Globalisation

1 One mark for each valid point, up to a maximum of 4 marks.
E.g.: Improvements in information technology, e.g. the development of the Internet, has meant that people can access information from all over the world *[1 mark]*. Investors can easily access company information, allowing them to make an informed decision when they invest *[1 mark]*. This has contributed to globalisation by allowing people to invest more easily in foreign companies, increasing the flow of capital between countries *[1 mark]*. Improvements in communication technology have meant that people can contact each other from all over the world from their mobile phone or personal computer *[1 mark]*. Cheap satellite technology, optic fibre cables and software make contacting others easy and efficient, even for people in remote areas *[1 mark]*. This increases globalisation by allowing anyone to communicate with anybody else in the world whenever they want to *[1 mark]*.

Page 128 — Global Systems

1 One mark for each valid point, up to a maximum of 4 marks.
E.g.: Most migration is from less developed countries to more developed countries *[1 mark]*. Many skilled people leave less developed countries to seek better-paid work, which can lead to a 'brain drain' in their home country *[1 mark]*. Skilled people help the more developed country to grow at the expense of the less developed country, which widens inequalities between the two countries *[1 mark]*. Working migrants can bring more wealth to developed countries by contributing taxes, further increasing inequalities *[1 mark]*. Low-skilled migrants may be happier to work for lower wages than low-skilled locals, depressing wages and increasing inequalities within countries *[1 mark]*.

Page 131 — International Trade

1 Maximum of 6 marks available. This question is level marked.
HINTS:
- Begin by studying the table carefully, looking for any patterns and any countries that don't fit the trends.
- Outline the trade patterns of developed countries using evidence from the table to support your answer, e.g. 'Developed countries tend to export high-value manufactured goods, such as machinery, cars and chemicals, to other developed countries. This is supported by the data in the table, which shows that both Germany and the USA's main export is machinery. Germany's main export destination is the USA, whilst the USA's is Canada.'
- Point out any anomalies, giving reasons why they might be different to expected, e.g. 'Australia mainly exports to China rather than to other developed countries. This could be because China has a very large economy and Australia has regional links with Asia.'
- Do the same for emerging economies and less developed economies.
- Finish with a summary of your main points and a conclusion stating how far the data in the table reflects patterns of international trade.

Page 133 — The Global Coffee Trade

1 Maximum of 6 marks available. This question is level marked.
HINTS:
- Begin by studying the map and graph carefully.
- Describe the patterns shown on the map, e.g. 'The map shows that the countries with the highest coffee production are less developed countries or emerging economies in Africa, South America and Asia, while the largest importers are mainly developed countries in North America and Europe.'
- Explain the ways in which this reflects patterns of international trade, e.g. 'This reflects the pattern of international trade because less developed countries tend to export raw materials, such as agricultural products, which are imported by developed countries, processed and sold for a profit.'
- Explain any ways in which the graph reflects patterns of international trade, e.g. 'The graph shows that the price paid to growers and the retail price follow roughly the same pattern, so as the retail price increases, the price paid to growers also increases. Products sold internationally tend to fluctuate in price according to supply and demand — when the demand is high, prices rise because there is more competition for a limited supply. The graph also shows that the price paid to coffee growers in Guatemala is always much less than the retail price in the UK. This reflects the pattern in international trade because less developed countries often sell unprocessed products at low prices, whereas retailers have to pay a higher price to purchase the product once it has been processed, so they charge consumers more.'

Page 136 — Transnational Corporations (TNCs)

1 Maximum of 20 marks available. This question is level marked.
HINTS:
- Begin with a brief summary of what TNCs are and how their operations are usually distributed around the world.
- Then explain how TNCs create opportunities for the home country, e.g. 'Most of the profits that TNCs make are returned to the home country. Also, by taking advantage of lower labour costs in host countries, the TNC will be able to sell its products to consumers in its home country at a lower price.'
- Then explain why host countries may not benefit from TNCs, e.g. 'As most of the profits return to the home country, the host country's economy may not benefit significantly. Also, local companies may not be able to compete with TNCs and may be forced to close.'
- Then give examples of any ways that TNCs do benefit their host country, e.g. 'TNCs create a lot of new jobs in their host country. These workers can gain new skills at the TNC, and can then use these skills at other companies in the host country, helping to drive economic development.'
- You could also point out that TNCs can have negative impacts on their home countries too, such as the loss of local businesses and unemployment due to the movement of factories abroad.
- You could bring in specific examples from your case study, e.g. you could include details about poor working conditions at Wal-Mart® in both developed and less developed countries.
- Finish with a summary of your main points and a clear conclusion about the extent to which you agree that the opportunities TNCs create in their home countries don't benefit their host countries.

Page 138 — Global Governance

1 One mark for each valid point, up to a maximum of 4 marks.
E.g.: Global institutions pass laws that countries have to abide by *[1 mark]*. This means that countries act more predictably, making conflict less likely and increasing stability *[1 mark]*. Some global institutions have an active role in reducing conflict, e.g. the United Nations undertakes peacekeeping missions in many countries *[1 mark]*. Global stability can increase economic growth because countries and companies are more confident in investing abroad *[1 mark]*. Global institutions such as the World Trade Organisation also promote economic growth, e.g. by facilitating trade deals that increase the volume of trade *[1 mark]*. Other global institutions promote social stability, e.g. the World Health Organisation helps to combat outbreaks of disease *[1 mark]*.

Answers

Page 139 — The Global Commons

1   One mark for each valid point, up to a maximum of 4 marks. E.g.: The high seas are facing pressure from overfishing, pollution and acidification *[1 mark]*. International trade has increased the potential markets for fish, so there is a greater global demand for it *[1 mark]*. Globalisation has also allowed for the development and spread of better transport technology *[1 mark]*. This means areas of the high seas which were once inaccessible can now be fished, so more fish are being taken than is sustainable *[1 mark]*. Globalisation has led to an increase in industry, including in countries with few environmental regulations *[1 mark]*. This has led to more chemical waste being discharged into watercourses and, ultimately, the oceans *[1 mark]*. Increased carbon dioxide emissions from factories are causing acidification of the oceans, damaging marine organisms *[1 mark]*.

Page 142 — Global Commons — Antarctica

1   Maximum of 20 marks available. This question is level marked.
    HINTS:
    • Begin with a brief summary of the threats Antarctica faces, including climate change, fishing and whaling, mineral extraction, tourism and research. Briefly introduce some of the international laws, norms and institutions that currently protect Antarctica from environmental threats such as these.
    • Then explain some of the ways in which international governance protects Antarctica from environmental threats, e.g. 'The Protocol on Environmental Protection to the Antarctic Treaty (1991) bans all mining in Antarctica, protecting it from oil, gas and mineral extraction. The 1991 protocol also ensures an Environmental Impact Assessment (EIA) is carried out every time a new activity in Antarctica is planned, which means countries can only undertake scientific or commercial activity in Antarctica if it has a minimal effect on the environment.'
    • Then explain the ways in which international governance does not protect Antarctica from environmental threats, e.g. 'While the IWC Whaling Moratorium (1982) banned all commercial whaling in Antarctica, some countries believe the ban is not properly monitored because the IWC does not register or inspect whaling boats. The fact that NGOs such as ASOC are fighting to protect the Southern Ocean Whale Sanctuary from being re-opened to commercial whalers suggests that the IWC is limited in its effectiveness. Countries like Japan can also kill whales in Antarctica for scientific purposes, which raises the question of whether the ban should extend to whales killed for scientific purposes.'
    • You could also discuss threats that cannot be dealt with by the governance of Antarctica alone, such as climate change.
    • Finish with a summary of your main points and come to a clear conclusion about the extent to which existing international governance is sufficient to protect Antarctica from the threats to its environment.

Page 143 — Impacts of Globalisation

1   Maximum of 20 marks available. This question is level marked.
    HINTS:
    • Begin with a brief summary of what globalisation is and state that it has created both costs and benefits.
    • Then explain in detail the ways in which globalisation has created benefits, e.g. 'Globalisation has created economic growth. By trading globally, countries can profit from their natural resources while ensuring they have access to all of the products and services they require. For example, participating in global trade has meant that China has become the largest exporter of goods in the world and has a rapidly growing economy.'
    • Then explain in detail the ways in which globalisation has created costs, e.g. 'Globalisation has created inequality within and between countries. Low-skilled workers in developed countries may lose relatively well-paid jobs as factories are moved to less developed countries to take advantage of lower labour costs. Equally, developed countries have greater amounts of technology, creating a technology gap which gives them an advantage over less developed countries. This means the gap between richer and poorer countries widens, as does the gap between richer and poorer people.'
    • You could use specific details from your case studies to support your answer, for example the benefits and costs caused by the global coffee trade.
    • Finish with a summary of your main points and come to a clear conclusion about the extent to which globalisation has created more costs than benefits.

Topic Eight — Changing Places

Page 145 — The Concept of Place

1   One mark for each valid point, up to a maximum of 4 marks. E.g.: The concept of 'place' involves looking at places as more than locations — geographers look at all the things that come together to make a place what it is *[1 mark]*. This includes all the physical and human characteristics of places *[1 mark]* plus all the things that flow in and out of that place, such as people, money, resources and ideas *[1 mark]*. It also includes people's 'sense of place' — the emotional meanings places have to groups or individuals *[1 mark]*.

Page 147 — The Character of Places

1   One mark for each valid point, up to a maximum of 4 marks. E.g.: The physical geography of a place refers to the environmental features of a place, such as altitude, aspect, soil type and rock type *[1 mark]*. It can have a direct influence on the character of a place, e.g. rock type may affect the type of landscape that forms *[1 mark]*. It can also affect other factors that influence character, e.g. abundant natural resources in an area may cause it to become characterised by mining *[1 mark]*. This could change the economic and demographic characteristics of the place, e.g. by increasing jobs and attracting migrants *[1 mark]*.

Page 149 — Changing Places — Shifting Flows

1   Maximum of 20 marks available. This question is level marked.
    HINTS:
    • Start by briefly introducing the place you have studied. You should mention its name and location as well as a short summary of either its demographic and cultural characteristics or its economic characteristics and social inequalities, and how these have changed over time.
    • You should also introduce some of the flows that have affected the place you've studied, such as flows of people, money, resources and ideas.
    • Next, explain in detail the flows that have affected one set of characteristics of the place you've studied and the effect they had, e.g. if you're writing about demographic characteristics, you might say 'Flows of people in and out of places can alter their demographic characteristics, such as the age and gender structure of the population as well as the overall population size. For example, flows of younger people out of the town of Uckfield in East Sussex have been caused by high house prices in the area. As a result of these flows, the population now has a high proportion of older people.'

Answers

- Do the same for the flows that have affected the other type of characteristics (e.g. cultural).
- Finish with a conclusion that sums up your points and clearly states how the characteristics of the place you've studied have been affected by shifting flows.

Page 151 — Changing Places

1   Maximum of 20 marks available. This question is level marked.
HINTS:
- Start by briefly outlining how the decisions of governments, MNCs and global institutions can affect the demographic, cultural, economic and social characteristics of places.
- Next, you should outline some of the decisions of governments, MNCs and global institutions and write in detail about how they have affected the characteristics of the place(s) you have studied, e.g. 'In 1992 the UK government helped to fund the Hulme City Challenge Partnership, a scheme that was aimed at regenerating this run-down part of the city. The Partnership rebuilt houses, created a park, refurbished shopping areas, built an arts venue and a business park. This altered the demographic characteristics of the area as the population increased. It also affected the economic and social characteristics of Hulme, as new jobs were created, unemployment was reduced and quality of life increased for some residents.'
- The question asks how far you agree with the statement, so you need to discuss ways in which you don't agree with it. You could write about other important controls on the characteristics of places, such as past and present connections with other places, and endogenous factors such as physical geography and land use.
- Finish by summing up your points in a brief conclusion. You need to clearly state how far you agree with the statement in the question for the place(s) you have studied.

Page 153 — Meanings and Representations of Place

1   Maximum of 6 marks available. This question is level marked.
HINTS:
- Start by explaining how the painting could aid understanding of the character of Venice, e.g. you could mention what is shown in the painting, what it tells you about the character of the place (e.g. its architecture, physical features) and the sense of place the painting creates.
- You should also comment on the problems of using this painting to understand the character of Venice, e.g. 'The painting shows a romanticised view of Venice, which may not be true to life. It shows the view of the painter, which is subjective and may not be shared by other people.'
- You could also mention that the painting tells you very little about the demographic, social or economic characteristics of the place, so other sources would need to be used to provide a more accurate impression.
- You should also write more generally about how effective qualitative sources are in illustrating the character of places. For example, you could refer to photographs, poetry, articles or stories you used to study your local or distant place, and analyse how helpful they were.

Page 157 — Place Studies

1   Maximum of 20 marks available. This question is level marked.
HINTS:
- Start by introducing the place you have studied, e.g. 'Central Liverpool is located on the River Mersey estuary in north west England, and is the centre of one of the UK's major cities.'
- Next, you should give details of the past development of the place you've studied, e.g. 'Liverpool was a major port for trading and a centre of manufacturing between the 18th and mid-20th centuries. During this time, the area grew and attracted immigrants from around the world. The docks and factories declined during the 1960s, which led to large scale deprivation. More recently though, Liverpool has attracted a lot of investment for redevelopment and was chosen as the European Capital of Culture in 2008.'
- Next, you need to use examples to show the extent to which people's lived experience of the place today is affected by its past development, e.g. 'In 2007 a poem called the Liverpool Saga was created to celebrate the 800th birthday of the city. This poem was written by a broad range of people living in the city today, so it reflects a mix of the different lived experiences of Liverpool. One of the lines, "Eight hundred different cultures, eight hundred different tongues" reveals that today Liverpool is a place of many different cultures where many different languages are spoken. This is a result of the large scale immigration to the city from its industrial past, and shows a direct link between the lived experience of the city today, and its past development.'
- You need to make sure you draw on a mix of quantitative and qualitative sources to show people's lived experience of your place.
- Finish with a conclusion that sums up your points and clearly states the extent to which people's lived experience of the place you have studied is affected by the past development of that place.

Topic Nine — Contemporary Urban Environments

Page 159 — Urbanisation

1   Maximum of 9 marks available. This question is level marked.
HINTS:
- Start by briefly defining a megacity, then describing the distribution of megacities shown on the map, e.g. 'Megacities are cities with more than 10 million residents. The map shows that they are concentrated in emerging economies (e.g. Brazil) and developing countries (e.g. Nigeria); relatively few are located in developed countries.'
- Next, suggest reasons why most megacities might be located in developing countries and emerging economies, e.g. 'Large population centres develop due to rural-urban migration; in emerging economies and developing countries, migrants are drawn to cities by easier access to schools and healthcare. There is also higher availability of jobs as more businesses choose to locate there.'
- You could also mention that companies are attracted to cities by the large number of workers, which creates more jobs and therefore attracts more migrants. Many migrants are young adults who then have children, so population increases further by natural increase. This could cause large cities to grow into megacities.

Answers

Page 161 — Urban Change

1   Maximum of 9 marks available. This question is level marked.
    HINTS:
    - Start by briefly defining urbanisation, and outlining some of the ways in which the character of a city may be affected by urban growth (e.g. changing demographic, social and economic characteristics).
    - For each element of character, discuss how it may be affected by urbanisation, e.g. 'Migrants may form their own communities, leading to concentrations of people from the same ethnic background in particular areas, e.g. Chinatown in New York City. Migrants tend to be of working age, which may decrease the average age of the population. Young migrants may also start families, further decreasing the average age.'
    - The question ask you to 'Assess the extent...', so you need to discuss ways in which urbanisation has not affected the character of cities — e.g. you could mention historic city centres where some architecture has remained unchanged for hundreds of years. You could also mention factors other than urbanisation that could affect the characteristics of cities, e.g. processes such as suburbanisation and counter-urbanisation.
    - Finish with a conclusion that sums up your points and states how far urbanisation affects the character of cities.

Page 163 — Urban Forms

1   Maximum of 9 marks available. This question is level marked.
    HINTS:
    - Start by briefly describing traditional land-use patterns of cities in the developed world, including patterns of residential and commercial use.
    - Next, give some examples of new urban forms, such as town centre mixed developments, cultural and heritage quarters and fortress developments.
    - For each one, explain how it may replace or alter traditional urban forms, e.g. 'Town centre mixed developments are areas where land use is mixed, so residential, commercial and leisure uses are combined. This challenges traditional urban forms, where different land uses are generally kept more separate.'
    - You could also explain some of the ways in which the urban form of cities has not changed, e.g. 'Although many cities have some elements of these new forms, they are generally restricted to certain areas, for example there may be only a few fortress developments on the outskirts of a city. This means that the majority of the city retains a relatively traditional form.'
    - Finish with a conclusion that sums up your points and clearly states the extent to which traditional urban forms are being challenged by new urban forms.

Page 165 — Urban Issues

1   Maximum of 9 marks available. This question is level marked.
    HINTS:
    - Start by briefly describing some of the social and economic issues that can influence the character of cities, such as economic inequalities, cultural diversity and social segregation.
    - For each issue, explain how it might affect a city's character, e.g. 'Economic inequalities within a city can have a range of impacts on the character of a city, for example, the quality of housing and types of businesses will differ between different areas. In addition, people with little or no money may resent those with plenty, possibly leading to tension and even violence between different groups. This can lead to some areas of a city feeling unsafe for residents and visitors.'
    - You could bring in examples from specific places you have studied, e.g. 'Some parts of London, such as Notting Hill, have been gentrified by wealthier people. This has forced poorer people out of these areas, changing their character entirely.'
    - Finish off with a conclusion, briefly summarising the different ways in which social and economic issues can affect the character of cities.

Page 167 — Urban Climate

1   Maximum of 6 marks available. This question is level marked.
    HINTS:
    - You need to describe the differences and suggest reasons for them.
    - Take your time to study the table and pick out the differences.
    - Once you've done that, write about each climate characteristic individually — say what each difference is and explain why the two cities might be different. E.g. 'Annual average rainfall is 100 mm higher in City B than in City A. This could be because City B has more pollution that City A, so there are more condensation nuclei in the air to encourage cloud formation'.
    - Include data from the table to support your points. Try to manipulate the data if you can, e.g. 'The average number of days without cloud cover is 50% higher in City A than City B'.

Page 169 — Urban Air Quality

1   Maximum of 9 marks available. This question is level marked.
    HINTS:
    - Start by briefly outlining why air pollution is common in urban areas.
    - Then describe some of the ways pollution can be reduced — you could write about schemes aimed at reducing traffic and larger scale solutions such as legislation and the use of alternative fuels.
    - You need to discuss how far air pollution can be managed, so you need to evaluate each of the strategies you discuss. Outline the ways in which it will reduce pollution, and any ways in which it won't help. For example, 'Some city centres, such as London, have introduced congestion charges to discourage people from driving. This helps to reduce pollution in these areas. However, drivers may choose to go round the congestion zone instead of through it, which could increase pollution in less central areas.'
    - You could also mention other factors that might make it difficult to manage pollution, such as population growth and economic development, which tend to create more pollution.
    - Finish with a conclusion that sums up your points and comes to a clear view about the extent to which air pollution in urban areas can be managed.

Page 171 — Urban Drainage

1   Maximum of 9 marks available. This question is level marked.
    HINTS:
    - Start by briefly describing some of the drainage issues faced in cities, such as flooding, water pollution and drought.
    - Next, explain briefly what river restoration and conservation are, and some of the methods they use, e.g. replanting of vegetation, creation of wetland areas.
    - Explain how river restoration and conservation can help to reduce urban drainage issues, e.g. 'Creating wetlands means that surface runoff from roads enters wetlands rather than being channelled straight to rivers. This increases lag time, which can help to decrease flood risk. Wetlands also help to filter pollutants from water before it enters rivers, so water quality is improved.'
    - Outline any reasons why river restoration and conservation may not be successful in reducing urban drainage issues, e.g. 'In some areas, returning a river to its natural state might involve removing structures such as floodwalls. This could significantly increase the risk of flooding in that area.'
    - You could use specific examples in your answer, e.g. Enfield in London.
    - Finish with a conclusion that sums up your points and clearly states how far you think river restoration and conservation can reduce urban drainage issues.

Answers

Page 173 — Urban Waste

1 Maximum of 9 marks available. This question is level marked.
HINTS:
- Start by outlining the different approaches to waste disposal, and stating that each has positive and/or negative environmental impacts.
- Next, discuss the environmental impacts of some of these approaches — focus on both positive and negative impacts. E.g. 'Producing items from recycled material generally uses less energy than creating them from scratch, so it results in lower emissions of greenhouse gases such as CO_2 and has less of an impact on climate. However, recycling also requires separate processing facilities and collections, which can increase emissions. This means that, although recycling still has a lower environmental impact than many other methods of waste disposal, its impacts are not entirely positive.'
- Finish with a brief conclusion, summarising the environmental impacts of each approach you have discussed.

Page 175 — Urban Environmental Issues

1 Maximum of 9 marks available. This question is level marked.
HINTS:
- Start by outlining the environmental problems likely to affect urban areas, e.g. air pollution, water pollution and dereliction.
- Next, outline some of the strategies that can be used to tackle one of these issues, e.g. for water pollution you could mention regulations on wastewater discharge, SUDS and improved sewage systems. The question asks you to evaluate, so you could comment on the possible pros and cons of different strategies — think about their likely success, cost and any problems they could cause.
- The question asks about strategies in 'contrasting urban areas', so you need to include examples of strategies from at least two cities with different approaches. For example, 'Manchester in the UK is investing in Sustainable Urban Drainage Systems (SUDS), such as increasing green spaces, to absorb runoff and prevent pollution entering water courses. However, these can be quite expensive; cities such as Bangkok in Thailand lack funding to improve drainage systems, so water pollution remains a major issue.'
- Then go on to do the same for the other issues you identified.
- Finish with a conclusion that recaps the strategies you have mentioned and briefly sums up their overall success.

Page 177 — Sustainable Urban Development

1 Maximum of 9 marks available. This question is level marked.
HINTS:
- Start by defining urban sustainability and briefly describing some of the characteristics of a sustainable city.
- Next, outline the opportunities cities offer for sustainable development, e.g. 'People are more densely concentrated in cities, so providing services such as clean water, sanitation and public transport is easier and cheaper. This can help to increase social sustainability, because people have a better quality of life, and natural sustainability, because air and water pollution is reduced.'
- Outline some of the challenges to urban sustainability, such as lack of investment, unsuitable infrastructure and rapid population growth.
- You could mention that making cities sustainable is likely to be more difficult in developing countries, because rapid and unplanned growth makes it difficult to provide services or manage environmental impacts.
- You could also bring in examples from your case studies of sustainability strategies that have been used in cities, and how well they have worked.
- Finally, sum up your points and come to a clear conclusion about the extent to which cities can be made sustainable.

Page 179 — Mumbai — Case Study

1 Maximum of 20 marks available. This question is level marked.
HINTS:
- Begin by defining urbanisation and briefly outlining some of the problems that it can cause, such as air pollution, water pollution and social and economic inequalities.
- Next, outline some of the solutions to these problems, e.g. 'Many cities have attempted to reduce the number of vehicles on the road, for example by improving public transport systems and building cycle lanes.'
- For each solution you mention, discuss how effective it has been — make sure you write about ways in which it may help to solve the problem, and ways in which it won't. E.g. 'Reliable, cheap public transport encourages people to drive less, while cycle lanes encourage them to cycle rather than drive. This helps to reduce traffic congestion and air pollution. However, the cost of implementing new public transport systems may make it difficult to achieve, whilst cycle lanes are not easy to build in cities with narrow roads.'
- You should bring in some specific examples from your case studies of problems that urbanisation has caused, ways that people have tried to resolve these problems, and how effective these solutions have been. For example, you could mention plans to upgrade public transport systems in Mumbai.
- Finish by summing up your points and coming to a clear and balanced conclusion about how far you agree with the statement in the question.

Page 181 — Birmingham — Case Study

1 Maximum of 20 marks available. This question is level marked.
HINTS:
- Start by briefly outlining some of the issues that can affect urban areas — you could mention social, environmental and economic issues.
- Next, discuss some of the ways in which urban issues affect poorer communities more than richer communities. E.g. 'Some people in poorer communities may find it hard to access healthcare facilities, especially if they live in a country with limited free healthcare or if they don't have transport. This would tend to mean that health was poorer and life expectancy lower in poorer areas compared to richer ones.'
- Make any points that contradict the view that poorer communities are more affected by urban issues than richer communities. E.g. 'Some issues, such as flooding, could affect any area of a city. In richer areas, the overall economic impacts of a flood may be greater than in poorer areas.'
- Back up your points with examples from your case studies — you could write about Birmingham, Mumbai or both, e.g. 'In Birmingham, for example, average life expectancy is eight years lower for men living in the poorest communities than in the richest ones, possibly due in part to reduced access to healthcare.'
- Finish with a conclusion that summarises your points and comes to a clear, balanced view about the extent to which you agree that urban issues affect poorer communities more than richer communities.

Answers

Topic Ten — Population and the Environment

Page 183 — People and the Environment

1 Maximum of 9 marks available. This question is level marked.
   HINTS:
   - Start with an introduction that outlines the main physical controls on population, e.g. climate, soils and natural resource distribution.
   - Next, explain how one physical factor affects population, e.g. 'Climate affects how easy it is to produce food in an area, which influences population distribution. For example, few people live in arid climates, where crops are difficult to grow, whereas temperate areas are more densely populated.' You could also mention that climate change affects population distribution, e.g. people are migrating inland in places where the sea level is rising.
   - Then do the same for the ways that soils, natural resource distribution, or any other physical controls you mentioned in your introduction affect population size, distribution and density.
   - The question asks you to 'Assess the extent...' so you should mention that there are other factors that affect population, such as development. You could also comment on the fact that the physical environment doesn't affect populations as much as it used to, because technological advances have made it easier to survive in challenging environments.
   - Finish by summarising your points and coming to a clear conclusion about how far you think physical factors affect population.

Page 185 — Food Production and Consumption

1 Maximum of 6 marks available. This question is level marked.
   HINTS:
   - Start your answer by stating that both food production and consumption are unevenly distributed around the globe.
   - Then outline some of the main patterns shown on the map of cereal production and suggest reasons for the patterns, e.g. 'Cereal production is low throughout Africa, which could be because the soils and climate are unsuitable for crops, and there is a lack of money to invest in improvements to agriculture.'
   - Next, do the same for the map of calorie intake. You could write about how the wealthiest countries consume a lot of calories, emerging countries consume fewer, and the least developed countries consume the least. Suggest reasons for this.
   - You could point out similarities and differences between the two maps, e.g. 'Some places produce a lot of food and consume a lot, such as the USA. However, some countries, such as India and Indonesia, produce large amounts of cereals but still have low calorie intakes. This might be because these countries are large, so there is enough space to produce lots of food, but the populations are so big that the food produced cannot adequately feed everyone.'

Page 187 — People and Climate

1 Maximum of 9 marks available. This question is level marked.
   HINTS:
   - Start by briefly introducing the climatic type you are going to write about — give a brief overview of where it's found and the main characteristics of the climate.
   - Then explain how the climate impacts humans — think about agriculture, lifestyles and development, and how they affect the number of people that the climate type can support. For example, for polar climates, one point you could make is, 'The low temperatures mean that arable farming isn't possible, as the ground is often frozen solid and there are few crops that can survive. The lack of productive land contributes to the low population density in polar areas.'

- Next, explain how humans have adapted to these impacts. E.g. 'Because they can't grow crops, people living in the Arctic rely on animal products instead of plants for food. This can come from the wild, such as through fishing, trapping and hunting, or some populations keep herds of reindeer for their meat and milk.'
- Finish with a brief conclusion summing up the main relationships between the climate and human numbers and activities in your chosen climate type.

Page 190 — People and Soils

1 Maximum of 20 marks available. This question is level marked.
   HINTS:
   - Begin by stating that agriculture can cause soil problems, such as erosion, waterlogging and salinisation, but that these problems can be managed.
   - Then write about why the worsening of soil problems might be inevitable, e.g. for soil erosion, you could write, 'Large amounts of natural vegetation are likely to be cleared for agricultural expansion. The presence of permanent vegetation with deep roots protects the soil from wind and water, and binds it together. If it is replaced with shallow-rooted crops, the soil is more vulnerable, especially when it is left exposed after ploughing. This will lead to more soil erosion.'
   - Next, write about the reasons why soil problems may not worsen in future, such as factors that might mitigate problems. E.g. 'Although agriculture is expanding, new methods and technologies could be developed to improve soil health. Many farmers already use management strategies; if these become more widespread, they could considerably reduce soil issues.' Then you could write about one or two specific examples of management strategies, such as crop rotation and windbreaks, and how they maintain or improve soil quality.
   - Finish by summing up your points and coming to a clear and balanced conclusion about how far you agree with the statement in the question.

Page 191 — Increasing Food Security

1 Maximum of 9 marks available. This question is level marked.
   HINTS:
   - Start with an introduction defining food security and briefly outlining some of the ways that it can be increased, such as increasing food production, increasing access to food and reducing waste.
   - Next, go on to explain some of the ways that climate change could affect attempts to increase food production, e.g. 'Rainfall is likely to decrease in some areas, including Africa and Australia. This will make it harder to grow crops in these areas, which may mean that meat and dairy farming expand at the expense of arable farming. As meat and dairy produce less food per unit area than arable, this will make it harder to increase food security.' You could also mention some of the possible positive impacts of climate change on food production, such as increased agricultural productivity in the USA and Europe.
   - You could go on to discuss the possible impacts of climate change on food access and food waste — for example, for food waste you could write about the changing distribution of agricultural pests and diseases, and explain that this may make it harder for farmers to protect crops and therefore to increase food security.
   - Finish off by summing up your points, and come to a clear conclusion about how climate change is likely to affect food security.

Answers

Page 193 — Global Patterns of Health, Disease and Death

1 Maximum of 6 marks available. This question is level marked.
HINTS:
- Begin by describing the expected global distribution for non-communicable disease morbidity. E.g. 'Non-communicable disease morbidity is usually higher in developed countries than in less developed countries.'
- Then describe any ways in which the global distribution of male obesity shown by the map follows the same pattern. E.g. 'The map shows that many developed countries, such as the USA, Canada and many European countries, have high levels of male obesity, whereas many developing countries, such as those in sub-Saharan Africa, have low levels of obesity.'
- Then comment on any areas of the map that don't follow the general pattern of non-communicable disease morbidity. E.g. 'However, male obesity is high in some parts of South America, e.g. Chile and Argentina, as well as in some countries in north Africa and the Middle East. As these are developing countries and emerging economies, non-communicable disease morbidity is likely to be relatively low.'

Page 195 — The Geography of Disease

1 Maximum of 9 marks available. This question is level marked.
HINTS:
- Begin by stating that some environmental factors, such as climate, topography, and air and water quality, can increase the risk of infectious diseases.
- Then explain some of the ways that each of these factors can increase the risk of disease. E.g. 'Temperature affects infectious disease incidence because many disease vectors can only survive above a certain temperature. Heavy rainfall can increase breeding grounds for disease vectors such as mosquitoes, which increases the incidence of disease.'
- The question asks you to 'Assess the extent...', so you should also discuss factors other than the environment that may affect infectious disease morbidity. E.g. 'Socio-economic factors may also increase the risk of infectious diseases. For example, over-crowded housing and poor sanitation make it easier for infectious diseases, such as cholera, to spread.'
- Finish with a summary of your main points and a clear conclusion about the extent to which infectious disease morbidity is influenced by environmental factors.

Page 197 — The Geography of Disease

1 Maximum of 9 marks available. This question is level marked.
HINTS:
- Begin by stating that the incidence of non-communicable diseases is related to both socio-economic and environmental factors.
- Outline some of the socio-economic factors that can increase the risk of non-communicable diseases, and explain their effect — you could write about the effect of age and lifestyle choices including diet, exercise and smoking. E.g. 'The risk of developing coronary heart disease (CHD) is closely linked to socio-economic factors. For example, smoking, drinking an excessive amount of alcohol and eating a diet high in saturated fat greatly increases the chance of a person developing CHD.'
- You need to assess how far socio-economic factors are responsible for the incidence of non-communicable disease — to do this, you could explain some of the other factors that increase risk. E.g. 'Environmental conditions can also affect non-communicable disease incidence. For example, air pollution can lead to respiratory problems, cardiovascular diseases and some types of cancer.'

- You could include details from the non-communicable disease that you have studied to support your argument.
- Finish by summing up your main points and reaching a clear conclusion about the extent to which socio-economic factors influence the incidence of non-communicable diseases.

Page 199 — Health in Knowsley — Case Study

1 Maximum of 9 marks available. This question is level marked.
HINTS:
- Begin by outlining the socio-economic characteristics of the place you have chosen — e.g. where it is and an overview of health there.
- Describe the influence of socio-economic factors, such as employment, education and income, on the health of the place that you have chosen. E.g. 'Unemployment can contribute to depression and encourage poor health habits, such as smoking. In Knowsley, 7.7% of people are out of work, which is significantly higher than the national average. This may have contributed to the higher than average rates of depression and unhealthy lifestyles in Knowsley. Around 30% of people in Knowsley smoke, and mortality rates from smoking-related illnesses are high. This suggests that unemployment may have a major impact on health in the area.'
- You need to comment on how far health is influenced by socio-economic factors — to do this, you could mention some of the other influences on health in the place you have studied, for example, the effect of the physical environment.
- Finish with a summary of your main points and come to a clear conclusion about the extent to which socio-economic factors have an influence on health in your chosen place.

Page 201 — Natural Population Change

1 Maximum of 9 marks available. This question is level marked.
HINTS:
- Start by briefly outlining some of the ways in which population varies between countries — e.g. size, distribution and structure.
- Go on to outline some of the cultural controls that affect population. For each one, explain its effect on population, and give specific examples where possible, e.g. 'The role of women is an important cultural control on population. For example, in countries where women have good access to education and employment, they are more likely to have a career; they will therefore start to have children later and have fewer. In the UK, for instance, women make up nearly half of the labour force and have, on average, 1.89 children each.'
- The question asks you to 'Assess the extent...', so you also need to comment on some other factors that are likely to affect population — for example, you could mention socio-economic factors such as availability of health care and education, and their likely effect.
- Finish off by summing up your points and coming to a clear conclusion about how far you think population is affected by cultural controls.

Answers

Page 203 — Natural Population Change

1 Maximum of 6 marks available. This question is level marked.
   HINTS:
   - Begin by studying the population pyramid and picking out two or three aspects of it to discuss in detail — for example, you could write about the relatively high number of older people, e.g. 'A significant number of people live to be over 60. This suggests that there is good health care available, which has reduced death rates and increased life expectancy.'
   - Then choose another aspect to write about — describe it and then suggest a reason for it. E.g. 'A very high proportion of people are aged 20-49. This could be because, even after infant mortality rates were reduced by improvements to health care, a cultural expectation that people would have many children persisted for some time.'
   - You could then go on to discuss the fact that the pyramid narrows at its base, suggesting that birth rates have decreased in the last 20 years. You could link this to population control measures introduced by the government (the one-child policy).

Page 205 — International Migration

1 Maximum of 9 marks available. This question is level marked.
   HINTS:
   - Start by defining international migration and briefly outlining some aspects of a country it can impact on, e.g. demography, society and economy.
   - Go on to discuss the negative impacts of each aspect in detail — make sure you focus on the country of origin. E.g. 'Migration can have negative effects on the demographic characteristics of the country of origin. For example, it is likely to be working-age people who leave, which can result in a high proportion of dependent people (older people and children). This may increase strain on public services, such as health care and education systems.'
   - You need to assess how far the impacts of migration are negative, so you should also comment on some of the positive impacts for the country of origin. E.g. 'Although working-age people may leave their home country, they often send part of their income back in the form of remittances. This can boost the economy of the country of origin and aid development there.'
   - Finish with a conclusion that sums up your points and comes to a clear, balanced view about how far the impacts of migration on the home country are negative.

Page 208 — Population and Resources

1 Maximum of 20 marks available. This question is level marked.
   HINTS:
   - Start by summarising the contrasting theories on population growth and its implications.
   - Then discuss the ways in which Boserup and Simon's theories are more applicable than Malthus's in the 21st century, e.g. 'Boserup and Simon's theories both take into account the development of technological solutions that have increased resource supply. The 21st century has seen innovations in food production methods, such as improvements in hydroponics and genetic modification, that can lead to large increases in food supply. In contrast, Malthus believed that food supply could only increase at a steady rate; this has been proven to be incorrect.'
   - Next, discuss the ways in which Boserup and Simon's theories may not be applicable, or ways in which Malthusian and neo-Malthusian theories are applicable. E.g. 'Malthus's view that population growth would outstrip food supply could be argued to have occurred in some areas; for example, famines have occurred in parts of Africa in the 21st century. This could give weight to neo-Malthusian views that, even with technological developments, resource supply cannot keep pace with population growth.'
   - You could also discuss climate change and environmental degradation caused by increasing populations, and their likely impacts on food production in vulnerable parts of the world.
   - Finish by summing up your points and coming to a clear and balanced conclusion about how far you agree with the statement in the question.

Page 211 — Global Population Futures

1 Maximum of 9 marks available. This question is level marked.
   HINTS:
   - Begin by summarising what the graphs show, e.g. 'The graphs show that the global population is expected to continue to increase, with most of the population growth occurring in Africa and Asia, whilst Europe will have fewer people by 2050.'
   - Then write about the likely impacts of these changes, such as increasing pressure on the environment and some finite resources being depleted.
   - Go on to discuss how these impacts might affect human-environment relationships, e.g. 'If people's relationship with the environment doesn't change, environmental degradation and resource scarcity could result in deaths from, e.g. famine and disease. However, people may respond to resource scarcity by making technological advances that will help them to use the environment more sustainably. For example, improvements to renewable energy technology would reduce the need for fossil fuel extraction and decrease the amount of greenhouse gases being emitted.'
   - You could also discuss some other ways that human-environment relationships may alter as the population grows, such as through policy changes and improved education to encourage sustainable use of the environment.
   - Finish with a conclusion that summarises your points and outlines a view about the most likely changes to human-environment relationships.

Page 213 — Population Change in Bangladesh — Case Study

1 Maximum of 9 marks available. This question is level marked.
   HINTS:
   - Begin by introducing the country or society you have studied. You should say where it is, and describe the main ways in which the population is changing. E.g. 'Bangladesh has a growing population. However, its population growth has slowed down significantly in the last few decades, because of a drop in fertility rates, which means there are a lot of people aged 10-39, but the proportion of the population aged under 10 has been declining. There is also a large amount of economic migration out of Bangladesh.'
   - You could split the implications of population change into social, economic and environmental implications, and write a paragraph on one or two examples of each.
   - For example, for Bangladesh you could write a paragraph on the economic implications of the changing age structure and the loss of workers to other countries, e.g. 'Falling birth rates have resulted in a large working-age population and a decreasing dependency ratio. This could lead to a demographic dividend, if enough of the working-age population are adequately employed, which would mean there is more money to go towards economic development. However, many workers are choosing to go abroad to work, which is leading to a lack of skilled professionals within the country. Bangladesh still benefits from economic migrants working elsewhere, however, because they send around $1 billion in remittances per month back to their home country.'
   - Finish with a summary of the main implications of population change for the country or society you have studied.

Answers

Topic Eleven — Resource Security

Page 216 — Resource Development

1 Maximum of 9 marks available. This question is level marked.
HINTS:
- Start by briefly outlining what resource frontiers are.
- Go on to explain why it may be necessary to exploit resource frontiers in future, e.g. 'As demand for resources grows and existing reserves are depleted, we may begin to rely on exploiting new reserves that are harder to access. For example, exploiting oil and gas reserves in the Arctic may be necessary to meet our future energy needs.'
- Then give reasons why resource frontiers may not need to be exploited in the future — you could bring in knowledge of resource futures and ways of increasing resource security. For example, 'Technological advances may mean that more resources can be extracted from existing reserves, or they may increase our ability to recycle resources (e.g. mineral ores). This would decrease the necessity for exploiting resource frontiers. In addition, increasing environmental awareness may mean that there is pressure on countries not to exploit some resource frontiers, but instead to focus on alternative means of meeting resource demand, e.g. renewable energy sources.'
- Finish with a conclusion that sums up your points and comes to a balanced opinion about how likely it is that it will be necessary to exploit resource frontiers in future.

Page 219 — Water Supply and Demand

1 Maximum of 9 marks available. This question is level marked.
HINTS:
- Begin by studying the map carefully and briefly outlining any patterns you notice.
- Go on to explain some of the physical factors that cause variations in water availability, such as climate, geology and drainage. Link these factors to the patterns you identified on the map. E.g. 'Climate is an important control on water availability: areas with high rainfall are likely to have more water available, whereas areas with low rainfall or where high temperatures drive rapid evaporation will experience low water availability. For example, Egypt and Libya have very low water availability because they have low rainfall and high temperatures.'
- Next, explain some of the human factors that affect water availability, and link them to the patterns shown by the map, e.g. 'Over-exploitation of water can result in low water availability, for example, if too much groundwater is extracted, lakes and rivers will not be recharged. For instance, over-exploitation of the River Jordan in upstream countries has decreased water availability in Jordan.'
- Finish with a brief conclusion that sums up the factors responsible for the distribution of water resources.

Page 222 — Increasing Water Security

1 Maximum of 20 marks available. This question is level marked.
HINTS:
- Start by briefly outlining how and why water demand is likely to increase as population grows.
- Go on to explain some of the impacts that increasing water demand is likely to have on the environment. You should consider specific strategies for increasing water supply to meet demand (e.g. water transfer, desalination) and their impacts. E.g. 'Removal of salt from seawater by desalination may be an important strategy in meeting future water demand. However, desalination requires a lot of energy; if it comes from fossil fuels, this can cause air pollution and contribute to climate change.'

- You could also bring in some information about the impacts of the specific water supply scheme that you have studied (e.g. algal blooms caused by increasing the height of the Danjiangkou dam in China).
- Next, discuss some reasons why increasing water demand may not damage the environment — you could mention ways of making existing supplies more sustainable, such as groundwater management and 'greywater' use. E.g. "Greywater', which has already been used in e.g. showers, sinks and washing machines, can be reused for purposes such as irrigating crops and flushing toilets. This helps to conserve groundwater and surface water supplies, so if its use becomes more widespread it will help to limit environmental damage caused by over-exploitation of water sources.'
- Finish by summing up your points and coming to a clear conclusion about the extent to which you agree with the statement in the question.

Page 223 — Water Conflicts

1 Maximum of 9 marks available. This question is level marked.
HINTS:
- Start with a brief introduction that outlines how water supply can cause conflict — you could mention that conflict tends to occur where different groups share the same water supply and demand exceeds supply.
- Next, explain the role that water has played in some conflicts that you have studied, e.g. 'The River Nile is a major source of conflict in Africa, because it flows through nine countries, causing disputes over who should have access to its water. For example, Ethiopia started constructing the Grand Ethiopian Renaissance Dam in 2011, leading to disagreements with Egypt, who were concerned that this would limit water flow.'
- Go on to discuss ways in which water is not a source of conflict — you could mention that countries are often able to reach agreements over what water each will extract from a shared resource. For example, Egypt and Ethiopia reached a partial agreement over the Nile in 2015.
- The question asks you to 'Assess the importance...', so you could mention some things other than water that can cause conflict, e.g. 'Although water can be a major cause of conflict, access to other resources (e.g. energy) can also result in conflict within and between countries. In addition, many major wars have been caused by disputes over land and conflicting beliefs.'
- Finish with a conclusion that summarises your points and reaches a clear view about how important water is as a cause of conflict.

Page 225 — Jordan Basin Water Resources — Case Study

1 Maximum of 9 marks available. This question is level marked.
HINTS:
- Start by briefly outlining the resource you have studied and the issues associated with its use in a specified region, or at a global scale. This answer relates to water in the Jordan Basin, but you could use a similar structure if you've learned a different case study.
- Next, explain some of the strategies that are being used to manage this resource, e.g. as one example for the Jordan Basin, you could write, 'Water supply in Jordan is intermittent, so as part of its national water strategy, Jordan has fitted storage tanks on roofs to help ensure a reliable water supply for residents.'
- For each strategy you discuss, you should assess how effective it has been at improving human welfare, e.g. 'Water security in Jordan has improved as a result of the strategy: 94% of residents now have access to mains water. However, water is still only delivered to houses once or twice a week, so people have to be careful not to use up the stores they have before another water delivery is due.'
- Finish by summarising the strategies you discussed and how far they have improved human welfare in the region you have studied.

Answers

Page 226 — Resource Futures — Water

1   Maximum of 9 marks available. This question is level marked.
HINTS:
- Start by outlining how global water needs are likely to change in the future — you could mention that as population increases and countries become more developed, water demand is likely to increase.
- Go on to explain why technological developments might be necessary to meet this increasing demand, and give some examples of possible developments. For example, 'Technological developments could increase water supply, which could help to ensure that there is enough to meet everyone's needs. For example, graphene oxide sieves are being developed to filter salt from seawater efficiently. This could decrease the cost of desalination, making it a viable way of increasing water supply in many countries. As most of Earth's water is in the oceans, this could provide a more or less unlimited supply of freshwater to cope with a rising global population.'
- The question asks you to assess the extent to which technological developments will be necessary to meet future water needs, so you need to discuss some of the ways in which they may not be necessary, e.g. 'Strategies such as reducing water consumption and recycling more water could help to meet increasing demand without the need for technological developments.'
- You could also outline some other possible developments (e.g. environmental, political and economic) and explain how they could help meet water needs without relying on technological developments.
- Finish with a conclusion that sums up your points and comes to a clear view about how far you think technological developments will be necessary to meet future water needs.

Page 229 — Energy Supply and Demand

1   Maximum of 6 marks available. This question is level marked.
HINTS:
- You need to look closely at the graph to work out what patterns it shows, then analyse the trends and any links between them. Support your points with figures from the graph.
- You could start by describing the overall pattern of energy supply and CO_2 emissions, e.g. 'Overall energy supply roughly doubled between 1970 and 2006, before dipping slightly to around 32 million tonnes oil equivalent in 2009. CO_2 emissions also generally increased over this period, but they increased less steeply and more erratically than energy supply, showing periods of significant decrease, such as in the early 1980s.'
- Go on to discuss some of the trends shown by individual energy sources and make links between them. E.g. 'Nuclear power showed significant change between 1970 and 2010, increasing from nothing to providing around 6 million tonnes oil equivalent of Finland's energy supply each year. In contrast, the amount of some other sources, such as HEP/wind remained fairly constant over this timescale, while use of oil actually declined slightly.'
- You should also make links between the two datasets, e.g. 'Oil use showed several periods of decline, for example in the early 1980s, early 1990s and mid-2000s. Each decline corresponds to a drop in CO_2 emissions, suggesting that oil use causes significant emissions. Nuclear power began to form a larger proportion of the energy mix from 1980 onwards, suggesting that some suppliers switched from oil to nuclear power around this time.'

Page 230 — Energy Supply and Globalisation

1   Maximum of 9 marks available. This question is level marked.
HINTS:
- Start by briefly outlining how energy supply has become globalised — you could mention trade of energy between countries, which increases links between them.
- Next, discuss some of the ways in which globalisation of energy supply has resulted in competing national interests, e.g. 'Many developing countries and emerging economies have large fossil fuel reserves; exploiting these could result in economic growth for these countries and help them to develop. However, as developed countries are the biggest consumers of energy, they are also likely to be the biggest market for imported fossil fuels. This creates a competing interest between the country producing the fossil fuel, which needs to derive as much profit from its sale as possible in order to drive development, and the country buying the fossil fuel, which wants to pay as little as possible for it in order to protect national income and ensure energy security.'
- The question asks you to 'Assess the extent...', so you need to look at ways in which globalisation of energy supply does not cause competing national interests, e.g. 'Many countries have common national interests around energy supply, such as working together to preserve the natural environment. For example, the Antarctic Treaty is an international agreement that bans resource development there.'
- Finish with a conclusion that summarises your points and comes to a clear view about how far globalisation of energy supply has led to competing national interests.

Page 231 — Energy Supply — Environmental Impacts

1   Maximum of 9 marks available. This question is level marked.
HINTS:
- Begin by briefly distinguishing between production and distribution of energy — you could mention mines and oil fields as means of production, and pipes and cables as means of distribution.
- Next, discuss some of the environmental impacts of energy production — you could bring in details from the example you have studied. E.g. 'Mines, oil fields and gas fields can destroy large areas of natural habitat. For example, the oil fields on the North Slope of Alaska have destroyed fragile tundra habitats. They also impact on local wildlife. For example, surveying for oil reserves on the North Slope has caused female polar bears to abandon their young.'
- Go on to discuss some of the environmental impacts of energy distribution networks — again, you could bring in specific details from the example you have studied. E.g. 'Pipes used to transport oil and gas can develop leaks, releasing fuel into the environment. For example, a leak in an oil pipeline near Prudhoe Bay in Alaska in 2001 released 270 000 litres of crude oil, which contaminated wetlands and lakes, harming wildlife and ecosystems.'
- You need to discuss the comparative scale of environmental impacts caused by production and distribution — you could consider the overall impact, the geographical extent of the area affected and how long the impacts are likely to last.
- Finish with a conclusion that sums up your points and comes to a clear view about whether production or distribution of energy has greater environmental impacts.

Answers

Page 233 — *Increasing Energy Security*

1 Maximum of 20 marks available. This question is level marked.
HINTS:
- You could start by briefly defining energy security and explaining why it is necessary to increase it, e.g. 'Energy security involves having reliable access to affordable energy. People rely on energy to meet many needs. For example, it is used to heat and light homes, to manufacture goods, to fuel vehicles and to help grow sufficient food. Without energy security, none of these needs can be consistently met; this has a significant impact on people's quality of life, health and livelihoods, as well as on economic development.'
- Go on to outline some of the ways in which energy security could be increased, and the environmental impacts these methods could have. E.g. 'One method of increasing energy security is to increase fossil fuel supplies; this can be achieved by exploiting new reserves or developing new ways of extracting fuel. For example, hydraulic fracturing can be used to extract previously inaccessible natural gas reserves from shale. However, this can contaminate groundwater in the extraction area; if groundwater then enters lakes and rivers, it may harm organisms and damage ecosystems.' You could then explain some of the environmental impacts of burning fossil fuels, such as acid rain and the enhanced greenhouse effect.
- You need to present reasons why environmental protection may be more important than energy security — for example, you could discuss the fact that environmental damage may hinder our ability to meet other needs, such as sufficient food and clean water. You could also discuss some of the ways in which energy security could be increased with fewer environmental impacts, e.g. by increasing use of renewable resources such as wind power and HEP.
- Finish your answer by summarising your argument and coming to a clear view on how far you agree with the statement in the question.

Page 235 — *Energy in the Netherlands — Case Study*

1 Maximum of 9 marks available. This question is level marked.
HINTS:
- Begin by briefly introducing the area and the resource you have studied. This answer is for energy resources in the Netherlands, but you could use a similar structure for a different place and resource.
- Next, outline one aspect of the physical environment and explain how it affects the availability and cost of the resource you have studied. E.g. 'Climate has a significant effect on energy supply in the Netherlands. For example, the coast and areas offshore have relatively consistent winds and high wind speeds, making them suitable for generation of wind power. A new offshore wind farm, Gemini Offshore Wind Park, was opened in 2017 — this has increased the availability of wind energy and reduced its cost, which may result in it forming a greater proportion of the Netherlands' energy mix in the future.'
- Go on to discuss other aspects of the physical environment and their impact on resource availability and cost. For example, you could write about the effects of geology and drainage.
- Finish off by summing up the main ways that the physical environment affects energy availability and cost in the place you have studied.

Page 236 — *Resource Futures — Energy*

1 Maximum of 20 marks available. This question is level marked.
HINTS:
- Start by outlining some of the possible reasons why energy shortages might occur in the future — you could mention depletion of fossil fuels, increasing population sizes and increased energy demand caused by economic development.
- Then discuss some of the technological advances that could help prevent energy shortages, e.g. 'Increased investment in renewable energy could lead to technological advances in this area. Existing renewable energy sources could be improved, for example by making wind turbines more aerodynamic or by developing solar panels that also function as windows, so their use could become more widespread. This would increase the amount of energy generated from these sources and help to prevent shortages. New sources of renewable energy may also be developed, for example, local power plants in Bihar, India are using waste rice husks to generate electricity. Further development of new sources would increase energy supply.' You could also discuss other technological advances, such as improvements to nuclear power and ways of reducing energy consumption.
- Next, present some arguments as to why technological developments may not help to prevent energy shortages, e.g. 'For many countries, renewable energy forms a relatively small component of their energy mix. Even with improvements to renewable energy technology, it will be necessary for countries to fundamentally alter their approach to energy supply and use; this may take years and require significant political changes, potentially resulting in energy shortages in the meantime. Other factors may also reduce the impact of technological advances; for example, despite improvements to nuclear technology, there are still concerns over the impact of nuclear reactors on people and the environment, and their use is being phased out in countries such as Germany and Belgium.'
- Then cover some of the ways that economic, environmental and political developments may help to reduce any shortages in future, and reasons why these developments may not help to reduce energy shortages.
- You could bring in details from your case study and other examples you have learned to back up your points — e.g. you could discuss the Netherlands' energy mix and plans for the future.
- Finish with a conclusion that sums up your points and comes to a clear view about how far you agree with the statement in the question.

Answers

Page 237 — Ore Mineral Supply and Demand

1 Maximum of 6 marks available. This question is level marked.
HINTS:
- You need to look closely at the data in the table to work out what patterns it shows, then analyse the patterns and any links between them. Support your points with figures from the table.
- You could start by describing the patterns of iron ore production, imports, exports and value, e.g. 'Iron ore production in the USA fluctuated between about 41 and 56 million tonnes between 2012 and 2016, but generally showed a decrease. Over the same period, imports remained fairly consistent. However, exports almost halved between 2014 and 2016, and iron ore value dropped by about 25% from 2012 to 2013, then continued to fall fairly steadily.'
- You need to make links between data, e.g. 'The decrease in iron ore production, exports and value are linked. It is likely that the fall in production was driven by the decrease in value: as value decreased, it was no longer economically viable to keep extracting iron ore. A decrease in production would normally result in an increase in value as remaining stocks became more sought after; this may be the reason for the slight increase in value in 2016. The decreased production and value of iron ore were probably responsible for the decrease in exports: as production fell, a greater proportion of the extracted ore was needed to satisfy domestic demand, so there was less available for export. The decrease in value also meant that there was less economic reason to export the ore.'

Page 240 — Ore Mineral Security

1 Maximum of 9 marks available. This question is level marked.
HINTS:
- Start by introducing the ore mineral you are going to write about — you could briefly outline where it's found and how it is extracted and processed, e.g. for copper you might write 'Copper ore is found all over the world. It generally occurs below the ground surface, so it is extracted by open pit mining or deep mining, before being treated with acid and heat to extract the copper from its ore.'
- Then discuss some of the sustainability issues associated with the extraction of the ore mineral, e.g. 'Copper extraction has numerous environmental impacts, which reduce its sustainability. For example, open pits take up huge areas of land, destroying habitats and reducing biodiversity in the region. As copper reserves become depleted, lower grade copper may have to be extracted to meet demand. This involves mining a larger volume of ore, so the environmental impacts of extraction will increase.'
- Next, give some ways in which extraction is sustainable, or can be made more so, e.g. 'Although the environmental impacts of copper mining are significant, many countries require that landscapes are restored to their original state once mining has finished. This reduces long-term impact and increases sustainability.'
- Go on to do the same for processing and trade of your chosen ore mineral — e.g. you could discuss recycling and new technologies that may make supply more sustainable.
- Finish by summing up your points and coming to a clear conclusion about how sustainable the extraction, processing and trade of your chosen ore mineral is.

Page 241 — Resource Futures — Ore Minerals

1 Maximum of 9 marks available. This question is level marked.
HINTS:
- Start by outlining why shortages of ore minerals may occur in the future — you could refer to depletion of existing reserves, increasing population and rising economic development.
- Next, discuss some of the problems that ore mineral shortages could cause for people, e.g. 'Ore minerals are used in many goods and industries, including construction and transport, so shortages could have a negative effect on people's standard of living and on economic development. Shortages may also result in conflict, leading to deaths, damage to buildings and infrastructure, and causing people to flee their homes. For example, there is conflict between government forces and militia in the Democratic Republic of Congo over limited reserves of tin and tantalum.'
- Go on to discuss some of the problems that ore mineral shortages could cause for the environment — you could discuss exploitation of resource frontiers and fragile environments, and the potential impacts of having to mine large quantities of low-grade ore as reserves are depleted.
- The question asks you to 'Assess the extent...', so you need to cover some of the factors that might mitigate shortages or their impacts — for example, you could discuss technological developments that may help to increase the amount of ore extracted, and recycling of ores.
- Finish with a conclusion that sums up your points and comes to a clear view about how far you think that ore mineral shortages will cause problems for people and the environment.

Acknowledgements

Photograph of Dune landscape in Rub al-Khali, Africa on cover: KARIM SAHIB/AFP/Getty Images.

Map of Eden basin on page 18: contains OS data © Crown copyright and database right 2016.

Rainfall data for hydrograph on page 19; map of polar climate zone on p.186 and map of arid climate zone on p.187 © Crown Copyright, the Met Office 2017; river level data for hydrograph on page 19. Contains public sector information licensed under the Open Government Licence v3.0

Data used to construct the Riyadh climate graph on p.24 from: http://www.climate-charts.com/Locations/s/SD40438.php © Climate-Charts.com

Image of desert pavement in Mojave Desert on p.28 by Leaflet, Wikimedia Commons

Image of alluvial fans in Mojave Desert on p.30 © DAN SUZIO/SCIENCE PHOTO LIBRARY

Aerial photographs on p.32 © NASA/JSC

Map of early Holocene hot desert distribution on p.33 from Adams J.M. (1997). Global land environments since the last interglacial. Oak Ridge National Laboratory, TN, USA. http://www.esd.ornl.gov/ern/qen/nerc.html

Maps of desertification risk on pages 34 and 36 © USDA-NRCS, Soil Science Division, World Soil Resources, Washington, D.C.

Data on forest cover in Spain on p.37 and in Bangladesh on p.213, source: Food and Agriculture Organization, electronic files and web site.

Photographs on *p.42* (Lannacombe Bay) © Philip Halling/ *p.42* (Loch Bracadale) © Richard Dorrell/ *p.43* (Slapton Sands) © Derek Harper/ *p.43* (St Ninian's Isle) © Colin Smith/ *p.50* (wave-cut platforms) © David Pickersgill/ *p.50* (beach near Bridlington) © Christine Johnstone/ *p.50* (sand dunes near Spurn Head) © Hugh Venables/ *p.50* (slumps at Atwick Sands) © Ian S./ *p.50* (aerial photo of Spurn Head) © Chris/ *p.51* (riprap at Withernsea) © Peter Church/ *p.61* (erratic) © Val Vannet/ *p.61* (Striding Edge) © Alan O'Dowd/ *p.62* (Glen Bhaltois) © Marc Calhoun/ *p.65* (terracettes below Morgan's Hill) © Mick Garratt/ *p.66* (Nant Ffrancon) © Meirion/ *p.66* (Devil's Kitchen from Llyn Idwal) © Dudley Smith/ *p.67* (Llyn Ogwen) © John Smith/ *p.67* (Llyn Idwal from below the Devil's Kitchen) © Kenneth Yarham/ *p.67* (cliff erosion) © Eric Jones/ *p.67* (Snowdon Horseshoe, Castell y Gwynt and Glyder Fawr) © Ivan Hall/ *p.115* (Fylingdales Moor in bloom) © Oliver Dixon / *p.116* (Dunes at the top of Ainsdale Sands) © Mike Pennington / *p.119* (images of Reeds in Fleet Dike and of Cattle in Church Marsh Nature Reserve) © Evelyn Simak / *p.119* (Swallowtail Butterfly RSPB Strumpshaw Fen Norfolk) © Janet Richardson / *p.119* (Damp Woodland) © Hugh Venables / *p.120* (Waxham New Cut and Brograce drainage mill) © Evelyn Simak / *p.120* (Eutrophic broad) © N Chadwick / *p.120* (Hickling Staithe) © Roger Jones / *p.159* (London skyline) © Christine Matthews/ *p.174* (Wolfson Research Institute) © Andy Waddington / *p.189* (Poplar windbreak) © Hugh Venables / *p.217* (Valve Tower, Haweswater Reservoir © James T M Towill / p.220 (Avon Dam and Reservoir) © Brian. Licensed for re-use under the Creative Commons Attribution-Share Alike 2.0 Generic Licence. https://creativecommons.org/licenses/by-sa/2.0/

Landsat imagery on pages 44 and 65 courtesy USGS/NASA Landsat.

Data for graph of global temperature change on page 46: NASA's Goddard Institute for Space Studies (GISS). © NASA/GISS.

Graph of sea level changes on page 46: Figure SPM.9 from IPCC, 2013: Summary for Policymakers. In: Climate Change 2013: The Physical Science Basis. Working Group I Contribution to the Fifth Assessment Report of the Intergovernmental Panel on Climate Change [Stocker,T.F., D.Qin, G.-K. Plattner, M.Tignor, S.K.Allen, J.Boschung, A.Nauels, Y.Xia, V.Bex and P.M. Midgley (eds.)]. Cambridge University Press, Cambridge, UK and New York, USA.

Diagram of Antarctic isotherm on page 55 reproduced from 'Fundamentals of the Physical Environment' by Peter Smithson, Ken Addison and Ken Atkinson, Third Edition, June 2002, Chapter 24, Polar Environments, Fig. 24.2. © 2007, Routledge, member of the Taylor & Francis Group

Map showing global distribution of cold environments at the last glacial maximum on page 55; data used in graphs showing changes in glacier length on page 57 © Leclercq, P. W., Oerlemans, J., Basagic, H. J., Bushueva, I., Cook, A. J., and Le Bris, R.: A data set of worldwide glacier length fluctuations, The Cryosphere, 8, 659-672, doi:10.5194/tc-8-659-2014, 2014. Licensed for re-use under the Creative Commons Attribution-Share Alike 3.0 Generic Licence. https://creativecommons.org/licenses/by-sa/3.0/

Image on page 64 (melting pingo and ice wedge): Wikimedia Commons by Emma Pike.

Photograph of solifluction lobes on p.64: © National Oceanic and Atmospheric Administration/Department of Commerce, photographer Dr. John Cloud, NOAA Central Library, Historian.

Maps of Nant Ffrancon and NW Snowdonia on page 66: contain OS data © Crown copyright and database right 2017

Photograph of rollagons on page 71 by Alaska DOT&PF. Licensed for re-use under the Creative Commons Attribution-Share Alike 2.0 Generic Licence. https://creativecommons.org/licenses/by/2.0/

Park Model on page 73: © Chris Park

LPI data on p.97 © WWF, used with permission

Image of sand lizards on p.117 © Alasdair James/Getty Images

Data used to construct map on p.126 from The World Bank

Export statistics on p.131 from A.J.G. Simoes, C.A. Hidalgo. The Economic Complexity Observatory: An Analytical Tool for Understanding the Dynamics of Economic Development. Workshops at the Twenty-Fifth AAAI Conference on Artificial Intelligence. (2011). Licensed for re-use under the Creative Commons https://creativecommons.org/licenses/by-sa/3.0/

Information on p.133 reproduced with permission from the Fairtrade Foundation.

Coffee data on pages 132 and 133, including that used to construct map and graph, from the International Coffee Organization (ICO)

Waste statistics on page 172 contain data from Hoornweg, Daniel; Bhada-Tata, Perinaz. 2012. What a Waste: A Global Review of Solid Waste Management. Urban development series; knowledge papers no. 15. World Bank, Washington, DC. © World Bank. https://openknowledge.worldbank.org/handle/10986/17388 License: CC BY 3.0 IGO.

Data relating to waste in Singapore on page 173 contains information from Waste Management accessed March 2017 from http://www.nea.gov.sg/energy-waste/waste-management/waste-management which is made available under the terms of the Singapore Open Data Licence version 1.0. https://data.gov.sg/open-data-licence

Data on pages 147, 155, 156, 174, 180 contains ONS data. www.ons.gov.uk licensed under the Open Government Licence v3.0.

Population pyramid and total population of Lerwick on page 155: © Crown copyright. Data supplied by National Records of Scotland licensed under the Open Government Licence v3.0.

Crime rate in Shetland on page 156: Police Scotland.

Population density data on p.182, including that used to draw map of global population density; population data for Niger, UK, Uganda and China on pages 201, 202 and 203; population data for Bangladesh on p.212 from The World Factbook: Washington DC, Central Intelligence Agency, 2017

Graphs of global population on p.182 and p.210 from World Population Prospects: The 2015 Revision, Volume I: Comprehensive Tables, by United National Department of Economic and Social Affairs/Population Division, © 2015 United Nations. Reprinted with the permission of the United Nations.

Cereal production map on p.184 © FAO 2015 Cereal production quantities by country 2012-2014 (http://faostat3.fao.org/browse/Q/QC/E 11.3.2016).

Calorie intake map on p.184 © FAO 2015 World food supply 2011-2013 (http://faostat3.fao.org/browse/FB/FBS/E 11.3.2016)

Meat consumption data on p.184 based on data from OECD (2016), "Meat", in OECD-FAO Agricultural Outlook 2016-2025, OECD Publishing, Paris. DOI: http://dx.doi.org/10.1787/agr_outlook-2016-10-en

Acknowledgements

Map of podzol distribution on p.188 © FAO/UNESCO Soil Map of the World.
http://www.fao.org/soils-portal/soil-survey/soil-maps-and-databases/faounesco-soil-map-of-the-world/en/ Accessed July 2017

Map of healthy life expectancy on p.192 based on WHO Healthy life expectancy (HALE) data by country.
Available from http://apps.who.int/gho/data/node.main.HALE?lang=en. Accessed July 2017.

Map of tuberculosis morbidity on p.192 based on WHO Global Tuberculosis Report 2016.
Available from http://gamapserver.who.int/mapLibrary/Files/Maps/Global_TBincidence_2015.png. Accessed July 2017.

Map of breast cancer morbidity on p.192 and map of global incidence and mortality rates of all forms of cancer on p.193 (accessed July 4, 2017); data on deaths from skin cancer on p.209 (accessed December 2013) from Cancer Research UK. Reproduced with permission from Ferlay J., Soerjomataram I., Ervik M., Dikshit R., Eser S., Mathers C., Rebelo M., Parkin D.M., Forman D., Bray, F. GLOBOCAN 2012 v1.0, Cancer Incidence and Mortality Worldwide: IARC CancerBase No. 11 [Internet]. Lyon, France: International Agency for Research on Cancer; 2013. Available from: http://globocan.iarc.fr

Data on pages 193, 210 and 212 from World Bank data. Life expectancy at birth, total (years) Source: (1) United Nations Population Division. World Population Prospects, (2) Census reports and other statistical publications from national statistical offices, (3) Eurostat: Demographic Statistics, (4) United Nations Statistical Division. Population and Vital Statistics Report (various years), (5) U.S. Census Bureau: International Database, and (6) Secretariat of the Pacific Community: Statistics and Demography Programme.

Map of male obesity on p.193 based on WHO Prevalence of obesity, ages 18+, 2014 (age standardized estimate) Male.
Available from: http://gamapserver.who.int/mapLibrary/Files/Maps/Global_Obesity_2014_Male.png. Accessed July 2017.

Data on malaria on p.196 reprinted from WHO World Malaria Report 2016, Chapter 6. Impact, page 40.
Available from www.who.int/malaria/publications/world-malaria-report-2016/report/en/. Accessed July 2017.

Data on coronary heart disease on p.197 from WHO Factsheet Cardiovascular Diseases (CVDs).
Available from http://www.who.int/mediacentre/factsheets/fs317/en/. Accessed July 2017.

Knowsley population, income and qualifications data on p.198 and 199 adapted from data from the Office for National Statistics licensed under the Open Government Licence v.3.0.

Knowsley data (life expectancy, unemployment, premature death, outdoor use, obesity, respiratory disease, depression rates, smoking-related illnesses, perceptions of health) on p.198 and 199 contains public sector information licensed under the Open Government Licence v3.0.

Data on lifestyles in Knowsley from NHS Merseyside Lifestyle Survey 2012/13 Knowsley

UN data on p.206 from UN Sustainable Development Goals: 17 Goals to Transform Our World, © United Nations.
Reprinted with the permission of the United Nations.

UN data on p.210 from World Population Prospects: The 2015 Revision, Key Findings & Advance Tables, by United National Department of Economic and Social Affairs/Population Division, © 2015 United Nations. Reprinted with the permission of the United Nations.

Data on cataracts on p.209 from WHO Ultraviolet radiation (UV). Available from http://www.who.int/uv/faq/uvhealtfac/en/index3.html. Accessed July 2017.

Data on mortality rates from dietary changes on p.209 from Global Panel on Agriculture and Food Systems for Nutrition. 2016.
Food systems and diets: Facing the challenges of the 21st century. London, UK

Bangladesh population data on p.212 from World Population Prospects 2017, United Nations DESA/Population Division, © 2017 United Nations.
Reprinted with the permission of the United Nations.

Data on stunting in children on p.213 from 'World Food Programme, 2016'

Map of water availability on p.218. Source: Food and Agriculture Organization of the United Nations, aquastat.
Available from http://www.fao.org/nr/water/aquastat/maps/World-Map.TRWR.cap_eng.htm. Reproduced with permission.

Map of water demand on p.218. Source: Food and Agriculture Organization of the United Nations, aquastat.
Available from http://www.fao.org/nr/water/aquastat/maps/World-Map.ww.cap_eng.htm. Reproduced with permission.

Map of global water scarcity on page 218 © 2014 World Resources Institute. This work is licensed under the Creative Commons Attribution 3.0 License.
To view a copy of the license, visit http://creativecommons.org/licenses/by/3.0/1

Photograph of desalination plant on p.220 © Octal. Licensed under the Creative Commons Attribution 2.0 Generic license.
https://creativecommons.org/licenses/by/2.0/deed.en

Data on rainfall in the Jordan Basin on p.224. Source: Food and Agriculture Organization of the United Nations, 2009.
Available from http://www.fao.org/nr/water/aquastat/basins/jordan/index.stm. Reproduced with permission.

Data on food security in the Jordan Basin on p.224 reprinted from 'A Review of Drought Occurrence and Monitoring and Planning Activities in the Near East Region.' Source: Food and Agriculture Organization of the United Nations and National Drought Mitigation Center, 2008.
Available from http://www.ais.unwater.org/pro/. Reproduced with permission.

Data on water supply and demand in 2030 on p.226 from 'The United Nations World Water Development Report' © 2015 United Nations.
Reprinted with the permission of the United Nations

Data used to construct energy production map on p.227, source: U.S. Energy Information Administration (July 2017).

Map of energy consumption on p.227 © BP Statistical Review of World Energy 2016.

Pie charts of energy mix in the UK on p.229 and in the Netherlands on p.234 based on IEA data from the IEA Energy Balances © OECD/IEA 2017; pie chart of energy mix in Nigeria on p.229 based on IEA data from the IEA Balances for 2014 © OECD/IEA 2017; energy data on p.232 based on IEA data from the Key World Energy Statistics © OECD/IEA 2016; pie chart of energy consumption in the Netherlands on p.235 based on IEA data from Energy Policies of IEA Countries: The Netherlands 2014 Review © OECD/IEA 2014. All from www.iea.org/statistics. Licence: www.iea.org/t&c; as modified by CGP Books.

Graph of energy mix in Finland on p.229 is based on data of 'Electricity supply 1970-2008'. Statistics Finland. Accessed July 14 2017.

Graph of CO_2 emissions on p.229 from World Bank data. CO2 emissions (kt) Source: Carbon Dioxide Information Analysis Center, Environmental Sciences Division, Oak Ridge National Laboratory, Tennessee, United States.

Data on per capita energy use on p.234 from World Development Indicators, Energy production and use. The World Bank

Data on iron production and trade on p.237 and copper deposits map on p.238: by permission of USGS

Map of Helvellyn and Glenridding on page 246: contains OS data © Crown copyright and database right 2017.

Photograph of cattle grazing in Costa Rica on page 247: WILLIAM ERVIN/SCIENCE PHOTO LIBRARY.

Data used to construct graph of urbanisation in Ireland and Botswana on page 247 from The World Bank: World Development Indicators.

Statistics on Hartcliffe and Clifton on page 248: Source: Office for National Statistics licensed under the Open Government Licence v3.0.

Data used to construct graph of world population on page 249 from World Population Prospects: 2008 Population Database © United Nations, 2009.

Acknowledgements

Index

A

abiotic factors 94
ablation 56, 59, 60
abrasion 26, 27, 29, 40, 59
accumulation 60
acidification 139
acid rain 11, 79, 233
acquisitions 134
afforestation 114
agriculture
        12, 36, 102, 105, 118, 183,
        185-191
agricultural productivity
        34, 185, 187, 209
agricultural systems 185
Ainsdale Sand Dunes 116–118
air pollution 166, 168, 169, 194
Alaska 70, 231
albedo 166
alluvial fans 28
alpine environments 54, 55
alternative fuels 169
Amazon rainforest 16
andesitic lava 78
animal adaptations 100, 103, 117
Antarctica 140–142
Antarctic and Southern Ocean
        Coalition (ASOC) 142
Antarctic Treaty 141
anticyclones 166
aquifers 6, 217, 221
arches 42
Arctic 215
arêtes 60, 67
arid climates 187
aridity index 22
asthenosphere 74
asylum seekers 204
atmosphere 3
atolls 109
attrition 26, 40
Australian wildfires 91
avalanches 56, 82
averages 252

B

backwash 40
bahadas 28
Bangkok 175
Bangladesh 212
barchan dunes 29
barrier islands 44
barrier reefs 109
bars 43
basal sliding 58
basaltic lava 78
bays 42
beaches 43
beach nourishment 49
beach stabilisation 49
berms 43
big data 242
biodiversity 97, 98, 102, 105
biofuels 169, 227
biomass 94, 227
biomes 99
biosphere 3
biotic factors 94
Birmingham 180
birth control 148
birth rate 200
block disintegration 25
blockfields 65
boreal forests 99
Boserup, Ester 208
breakwaters 48
Broads, the 119–121

C

cacti 23
Cancer Research 195
canyon effect 167
carbonation 25
carbon budget 12
carbon cycle 10
  in the Amazon 16
carr woodland 119
carrying capacity 206
cascading system 3
catchment management 170
caves 42
cavitation 40
Central Business District (CBD) 162
channel flash floods 26
chemical weathering 25, 41

chi-squared test 254
choropleth maps 250
cirques 60
City Challenge 161
cliffs 42
climate change
  and desertification 33, 35, 36
  and health 209
  and power relations 128
  and sea level rise 46
  impacts 15, 17, 96, 187, 219
  in Antarctica 140
  in the Broads 120
  in the Serengeti 106
climatic climax 113, 114
climax communities 112
cloud formation 5
Club of Rome 208
coal 228
coastal management 48
coastal realignment 49
coffee 132, 133
cold-based glaciers 58
cold environments (management of) 69
combustion 11
command words 244
commercial farming 185
communications systems 125
compressional flow 58
condensation 5, 56
conflict 35, 126, 127, 143, 204, 219,
        223, 224, 236, 237
congestion charging 168
conservative plate margins 77
constructive plate margins 76
constructive waves 38
consumers 94
convection 5
convectional rainfall 167
convection currents 75
copper 238–240
  commerce 239
  environmental impacts 239, 240
  extraction 240
  industry 239
  processing 240
  trade 240
  uses 239
coral bleaching 110, 111
coral reefs 108-111
core (of the Earth) 74
Coriolis effect 86

Index

coronary heart disease (CHD) 197
corrasion 40
corries 60, 66
corrosion 40
counter-urbanisation 158
crop rotation 35
crowd-sourced data 242
crust (of the Earth) 74
cryosphere 3–5
cultural quarters 163
cumecs 8
currents 39
cusps 43
Cyclone Nargis 89
cyclones 86, 89

D

dalmatian coastlines 47
dams 220, 225
death rate 200
debris flows 27
decentralisation 160
decomposers 94
decomposition 11
deep mining 238
deep sea trenches 76
deflation 26, 28
deflation hollows 28, 31
deforestation
        12, 16, 34, 101, 102, 114
deindustrialisation 149, 151, 160
deltas 63
demographic dividend 203
demographic transition model (DTM)
        200, 201
dependency ratio 200
deposition
  coasts 40, 43, 44
  deserts 27
  glaciers 59, 61
dereliction 174
desalination 37, 220, 225
desertification 33–37
deserts 20–37, 99
  climate 23, 24
  landforms 30
  margins 22, 23
  pavements 28, 31
  soils 23, 24
  vegetation 23, 24

desire line maps 251
destructive plate margins 76
destructive waves 38
Dharavi 179
disease
  environmental factors 194
  morbidity 192
  mortality 193
  physical factors 198
  socio-economic factors 198, 199
dispersion diagrams 249
dot maps 250
drainage basins 6, 8, 18, 19
drip irrigation 37, 225
droughts 224
drumlins 61
dune regeneration 49
dynamic equilibrium 2, 20, 38, 56

E

earth banks 48
earthquakes 76, 82–85, 92, 93
Earth's structure 74
ecological footprint 176, 206
economic inequalities 164
economic migrants 204
economies of scale 125
ecosystems 94–96
ecotourism 102
Eden Basin 18
edge cities 163
endogenous factors 146, 147
endoreic rivers 26
energy 227-236
  consumption 227, 232, 235
  environmental impacts 231, 233
  mix 229, 234
  production 227
  security 232
  trade 227
Enfield (river restoration) 171
englacial material 59
enhanced greenhouse effect 96, 233
Enterprise Zones (EZs) 161
Environmental Impact Assessments (EIAs)
        216
environmental laws 17, 141
ephemeral rivers 26
epidemiological transition model 193

erosion
  coasts 40, 42
  deserts 26, 28, 29
  glaciers 59
erratics 61
eskers 63
ethical investment 129
eustatic sea level change 45
eutrophication 110
evaporation 4, 7
evapotranspiration 7, 166
exams 1
exfoliation 25
exogenous factors 146, 147
exogenous rivers 26
experienced places 145
extensive farming 185

F

fair trade 129
Fairtrade Foundation 133
farming methods 185
feedbacks 2, 38, 57
fens 119
fertility rates 200
fetch 38
fieldwork investigation 1, 242
financial systems 124, 128
fires 104, 105, 107, 114
fishing 68, 110
fjords 47
flooding 19, 87
  coastal areas 46, 48, 120
  deserts 26
  Eden Basin 19
  storms 87–89
  urban areas 170, 178, 180
flow line maps 251
flow resources 214
flows
  of ideas 127
  of information 122
  of labour 123
  of money 122, 127
  of people 126
  of products 122
  of services 123
  of technology 127
fold mountains 76

Index

food
  access 191
  chains 94
  consumption 184
  production 184, 191, 209
  security 35, 191
  trade 191
  waste 191
  webs 94
foreign direct investment (FDI) 127, 129, 134
fortress developments 163
fossil fuels 12, 214, 227, 228, 232
fragmentation 102, 105
freeze-thaw weathering 41, 59
fringing reefs 109
frost action 59
frost contraction 64
frost heave 64
frost shattering 25

G

gabions 48
gentrification 149, 163
geopolitics 219, 228, 237
geothermal energy 228
glacial budgets 56, 57
glacial troughs 66
glaciers 54–71
  identifying glacial landforms 66
global commons 139, 140, 236, 237
global governance 137, 138
global institutions 128
globalisation 122, 124–126, 145, 230
  benefits 143
  costs 143
global trade system 124
global warming 13, 46
gold 237
granular disintegration 25
grazing 114
Great Barrier Reef 110, 111
Great Sand Sea 32
greenhouse gases 13, 14, 46, 233
'Green Sahara' 33
greywater 221
grid references 251
gross primary production 94
groundwater 4, 6, 7
  management 221
groynes 48, 51

H

habitat loss 102
Hadley cells 22
hanging valleys 60
hard engineering
  coastal management 48, 51
  in river catchments 170
hard pans 188
hazard management cycle 73
headlands 42, 50
health 192–199
healthy life expectancy (HALE) 192
Holderness 50
horizontal integration 134
hot spots 77
hunting 104
Hurricane Katrina 88
hurricanes 86
hydration 25
hydraulic action 40
hydraulic fracturing (fracking) 228, 232
hydroelectric power 68, 228, 234
hydrographs 8
hydrological cycle 4
hydroseres 113
hydrosphere 3
hypotheses 242

I

icebergs 56
ice wedges 64
identity 144
incineration 173
indicated reserves 214
Industrial Revolution 183
infant mortality rate 200
infectious diseases 192, 196
inferred resources 214
infiltration 7
  and farming 9
  in urban areas 170
inputs (systems) 20, 56, 95
inselbergs 28
insiders 144
insolation 20
Integrated Coastal Zone Management (ICZM) 49
intensive agriculture 105, 185
interception 6
interflow 7
interglacials 55

Intergovernmental Panel on Climate Change (IPCC) 15
internal deformation 58
international institutions 137
International Monetary Fund (IMF) 128
International Whaling Commission (IWC) 141
interquartile range 252
intra-firm trading 135
invasive plant species 106
investment 129
investment banks 124
iron ore 237
irrigation 34, 36, 105
island arcs 76
isoline maps 250
isostatic sea level change 45
Italy (hazards) 93

J

joints 7
Jordan Basin 224, 225

K

kames 63
kame terraces 63
Kashmir earthquake 85
key words 244
Knowsley 198
Kyoto Protocol 15

L

lagoons 43, 44
lahars 79
landfill 173
landslides 41, 82, 87
L'Aquila earthquake 93
lateral moraine 61
laterite horizons 189
latosols 100, 189
lava 78
Lerwick 154–157
lithoseres 112
lithosphere 3, 74
littoral cells 39
Liverpool 154–157
Living Planet Index (LPI) 97
lobe formations 64
lodgement till 59

Index

logarithmic scales 249
London 165
longshore drift 40

M

malaria 196, 209
Malthus, Thomas 208
Manchester 175
mantle 74
market access 130, 131
marketing 123, 135, 152
mass balance 56
mass movement 27, 41
measured reserves 214
mechanical weathering 25
Médecins Sans Frontiers (Doctors
        Without Borders) 195
medial moraine 61
media places 145
megacities 159, 178
meltwater 58
meltwater streams 62
Mercalli scale 82
mergers 134
migration 123, 204, 205, 212
  impacts 147–149, 205
  pull factors 204
  push factors 204
mining 68, 141, 238
moment magnitude scale (MMS) 82
Montserrat 81
moraine 67
mortality rate 193
mudflats 44
mudflows 41, 79
multinational corporations (MNCs)
        133–136, 150, 230
multiplier effect 135
Mumbai 178

N

natural gas 228, 232, 234
natural systems 2, 20, 56
negative feedback
        2, 14, 20, 38, 57, 207
neo-liberalism 127
Neolithic Revolution 183
neo-Malthusianism 208
Netherlands 234
net primary production 94
nivation 58

nomadic farming 104, 185
non-communicable diseases 192
non-governmental organisations (NGOs)
        138, 142, 195
non-renewable resources 214
non-tariff barriers 124, 129
North Atlantic Treaty Organisation
        (NATO) 125
North York Moors 115
nuclear power 227, 232, 236
nuclear waste 233

O

ocean ridges 75, 76
offshore bars 43
oil 228, 231, 232, 234
oil spills 68
open-pit mining 238
open systems 2, 20, 95, 185
optimum population 206
Ordnance Survey® (OS®) maps 251
ore minerals 237-241
  consumption 237
  production 237
Organisation of the Petroleum Exporting
        Countries (OPEC) 130
outputs (systems) 20, 56, 95
outsiders 144
outsourcing 125
outwash plains 62, 67
overcultivation 34, 36
overfishing 68, 139, 140
overgrazing 34, 36, 104, 105
overpopulation 206
oxidation 25
ozone layer 209

P

Paris Agreement 15, 211
Park model 73
particulate pollution 168
partnership schemes 161
patterned ground 64
pedestrianisation 168
pediments 28
percolation 7
periglacial environments 54, 55
permafrost 54–57, 64, 69
Philippines (hazards) 92
photochemical smog 168
photosynthesis 11, 94, 95

pingoes 65
pioneer species 112, 113
place 144
  marketing 152
  studies 154–157
placelessness 145
plagioclimax 113–115
plant adaptations 96, 100, 103, 116
plate margins 74–77
playas 28
Pleistocene 55
plucking 59
poaching 104, 106
podzols 188
polar climates 186
polar environments 54, 55, 99
pollution 111
  air 166, 168, 169, 194
  urban 168, 174, 175
  water 194
population 182
  and climate 183, 185–187
  and resources 183
  and soils 183, 185, 188–190
  density 182
  distribution 182, 210
  ecology 206
  growth 206, 210, 211
  human factors 202
  physical factors 202
  policies 201
  projections 210
  pyramids 203
  structure 203
population change 208
  Bangladesh 212
  cultural controls 201
  Uganda 202
  UK 202
population, resources and pollution
        model 207
porphyry copper 238
positive feedback 2, 14, 20, 38, 207
possible resources 214
post-modern western cities 163
potential evapotranspiration 22
power relations 128
precipitation 5, 6, 8, 56
  urban areas 167, 170
prevailing winds 38
primary consumers 94
primary data 242
primary succession 112
producers 94

Index

proportional symbol maps 250
protectionism 129
Protocol on Environmental Protection
    to the Antarctic Treaty 141
public transport 169
pyramidal peaks 60
pyroclastic fallout 79
pyroclastic flows 78

Q

Qattara Depression 31
qualitative data 242
quantitative data 242

R

rainfall 21
rain shadow effect 22
rainwater harvesting 220
random sampling 243
rare earth elements 241
rebranding (places) 152
recycling 241
  water 221
refugees 204
reimaging (places) 152
remittances 126
renewable resources
        214, 227, 232, 236
replacement rate 210
replanting 17
research 141
research questions 242
reservoirs 217, 220
resource frontiers 215, 241
resource peak 215
respiration 11, 95
revetments 48
rhyolitic lava 78
rias 47
Richter scale 82
ridge push 75
rift valleys 76
riprap 48
river discharge 7
River Eden 18
river restoration 171
roches moutonnées 60
rockfalls 27, 41
runnels 43
runoff 8, 21, 26

S

Saffir-Simpson Scale 86
Sahara Desert 31, 33
salination 37, 190
saltation 26, 27, 40
saltmarshes 44
salt weathering 25, 41
sampling strategies 243
sand dunes 29, 32, 44, 116
São Paulo 165
savanna grasslands 99, 103–107
  development 104
sea floor spreading 75
sea level rise 69, 96, 120
sea levels 45–47
sea walls 48
secondary consumers 94
secondary data 242
secondary succession 112
sediment
  budget 21, 39
  cells 39
  sources 21, 39
sedimentary copper 238
seif dunes 29, 32
selective logging 17
sequestration 11
Serengeti 106, 107
sheet floods 27
Sheffield 151
Shoreline Management Plans (SMPs)
        49, 51
Simon, Julian 208
slab pull 75
'slash and burn' 101, 105, 189
slumping 41, 50
slums 149, 164, 165, 178, 213
Snowdonia 66
social inequalities 149, 156
social segregation 164
soft engineering 49
  coastal management 49
  in river catchments 170
soil 188–190
  creep 41
  erosion 189
  horizons 188
  liquefaction 82
  moisture budget 100, 103

solar power 228, 234
solution 40
southern Spain 36
South-North Water Transfer Project 222
Spearman's Rank correlation coefficient
        253
special and differential treatment (SDT)
        agreements 131
Special Economic Zones (SEZs) 130
species richness 97
spits 43, 50
stacks 42
standard deviation 252
stemflow 7
stock resources 214
stores (systems) 20, 56, 95
Storm Desmond 19
storms 19, 46, 86–89, 92
stratified sampling 243
structural deterioration (of soil) 190
sub-climax community 113
subglacial material 59
subsistence farming 185
suburbanisation 158
succession 112
  human activity 115
Sundarbans 52
supply chains 125, 134, 135
surface creep 26
surface storage 6
suspension 26, 27, 40
sustainability 49, 98, 102, 105, 121,
        216, 221, 233, 235, 240
sustainable cities 176–177, 179-181
Sustainable Urban Drainage Systems
        (SUDS) 170
swash 40
systematic sampling 243
systems
  agricultural 185
  coastal 38, 39
  desert 20, 21
  financial 124
  glacial 56, 57
  management and information 125

Index

T

tariffs 124, 129
tarns 66
tar sands 232
tectonic plates 74, 75
temperate deciduous forest 99
temperate grassland 99
terminal moraine 61
terracettes 65
tertiary consumers 94
thermal fracture 25
thermokarst 65
throughflow 7
tidal barrages 48
tidal barriers 48
tides 39
till 61
tombolos 43
total fertility rate 200
tourism
  in Antarctica 141
  in cold environments 68, 70
  in deserts 36
  in the Broads 120
  in the Great Barrier Reef 110
  in the Serengeti 107
town centre mixed developments 163
traction 26, 40
trade 129, 130
  agreements 124, 125
  energy 227
  ore minerals 237
  rules 129
  water 37, 219
trading blocs 130
trans-Alaska oil pipeline 70, 231
transnational corporations (TNCs)
      133–136, 150, 230
transpiration 7
transport
  coasts 40
  deserts 26
  glaciers 59
transport systems 125
triangular graphs 249
trip line maps 251
trophic levels 94
tropical rainforests 17, 99, 100–102
  development 101
truncated spurs 60, 67
tsunamis 82
tundra 99, 231

U

underpopulation 206
United Nations Environment Programme
      (UNEP) 141
United Nations (UN) 138, 195
Urban Development Corporations
      (UDCs) 161
urban heat island effect 166, 167
urbanisation 158–160
urban resurgence 158
U-shaped valleys 66

V

vegetation storage 6
ventifacts 29
vertical integration 134
virtual water trade 221
volcanic gases 78
volcanoes 12, 76–81, 92

W

wadis 28, 32
Wal-Mart® 135, 136
warm-based glaciers 58
waste streams 172
water 217-226
  abstraction 9, 217, 219
  availability 218
  balance 7, 22
  catchment 220
  conflicts 223, 224
  consumption 221
  cycle 4, 16, 18
  demand 218
  diversion 220
  management 221
  quality 194
  security 220
  storage 220
  stress 218, 226
  table 6
  trade 37, 219
  transfer 219, 220, 222

water-borne diseases 194
waterfalls 60
waterlogging 188, 190
watershed 6
wave-cut platforms 42, 50
wave quarrying 40
waves 38
weathering 11, 25, 41
wetting and drying 41
whaling 140
Whaling Moratorium 142
wildfires 12, 90–91
Wildlife Management Areas (WMAs)
      107
wind 21, 38
  power 228, 234
  transport 26
windbreaks 35
World Bank 128, 137, 150, 195
world cities 159
World Food Programme (WFP) 150
World Health Organisation (WHO)
      137, 195
World Trade Organisation (WTO)
      124, 128, 129, 137

Y

yardangs 29, 32

Z

zeugen 29
zonal soils 188